With All Best Wishes.

Sincerely.

Peter Dunn

Contents of the Appendices on the Disc

Foreword

Volume 2 of Peter Amos's magnum opus picks up from the end of the first Volume in 1939 and takes us through the six turbulent years of World War 2. The company - Philips & Powis at the beginning and Miles Aircraft at the end - grew from a producer of light racing, sport, and general aviation to become a major supplier of military trainers. Not only that, but a source of some of the most innovative aeroplanes of not just that era but of all time. Whilst Miles may have been regarded as a producer of light aircraft, in reality over 70% of the aircraft produced had engines of over 700 hp.

In the 1930s the Government hoped and believed that the First World War was the war to end all wars and that we lived in a peaceful world. It was wrong. At the same time, the United States, and thus much of the world, had suffered the 1929 Wall Street crash and the recession which followed.

But there were people who were not blinded to the looming threat of war. The Government, to its credit, supported flying schools. The directors of Vickers Supermarine, Hawker, Avro, Rolls-Royce and Philips & Powis could see war clouds looming. They were aware of the developments in Germany and of the inferiority of the fighters and bombers in service with the RAF at the time.

The Air Ministry had a number of philosophies which led to the specification of aeroplanes, which were really quite unsuited to modern war. There was a belief that "the bomber will always get through" and thus that the need for fighters was limited. It was believed that the complexity of modern aeroplanes was such that a single pilot could not manage all the tasks and that two-seaters were needed.

The private development of the Spitfire, the Hurricane and - later - the Lancaster are well known. Less well-known is the development of the Miles Master advanced trainer.

F G Miles, an experienced designer, manufacturer, instructor and test pilot, reckoned that the transition from a bi-plane trainer with fixed undercarriage and fixed-pitch propeller to a Spitfire or a Hurricane was a step too far for a trainee pilots of average ability. He therefore produced an outline design for an advanced trainer with performance, handling and complexity comparable to the fighters. That was to become the Master.

The RAF already had numbers of Magister monoplane elementary trainers and the Master was designed to be the final step in the training syllabus.

But the Air Ministry was not interested.

Rolls-Royce, however, took a different view. They had the 745 hp Kestrel engine in quantity production and considered that the proposed Miles trainer would be the ideal airframe, mated with the Kestrel, to make the missing advanced trainer. In all 3,250 Masters and 1,724 Martinets (the target tower) were produced, 900 Masters with the Kestrel engine and the remainder with the more powerful Bristol Mercury (870 hp) and Pratt & Witney Twin Wasp Junior (825 hp).

My own conversion from the 600 hp Harvard to the 1,850 hp Griffon engined Seafire –- there were no 2-seaters –- illustrated for me the step from advanced trainer to fighter. The Battle of Britain pilots went from 715 hp Rolls-Royce Kestrel Master to the 1,050 hp Hurricane or Spitfire in challengingly few hours, but time was more pressing then.

In 1936 Miles's youngest brother George joined the company at Woodley and, in 1941, became Technical Director and Chief designer, releasing Miles to concentrate on the fast growing business. George's talent for thinking "outside the box" led him to continue the company's record of innovative designs.

Beyond the production of Magisters and Masters was a succession of experimental aeroplanes designed and built at the factory. The M.20 8/12-gun fighter was designed and built in 65 days as a stop-gap during the Battle of Britain in case the Spitfire and Hurricane factories were destroyed.

The tandem wing M.35 Libellula was designed as a naval aircraft with a wide weapon fit capability and able to go into the flight deck lift without folding its wings. The M.38 artillery support aircraft used by General Montgomery, and a naval version to be rocket-launched from a merchant ship and recovered into a net with a gap for the diameter of the propeller, intended for anti-submarine duties when there were no carriers available.

In preparation for peace, substantial work was done on an innovative trans-Atlantic airliner project with its wing faired into the fuselage, the 'X' design.

And most exciting of all was the M.52 supersonic project, which was to be capable of 1,000 mph at a time when no other aircraft had even broken the sound barrier.

The company was, however, even more versatile than that. It developed and produced an auto-pilot, a range of electric actuators, chipboard - to use up the wood chips from the manufacture of wooden airframes - and the original photocopier.

These were challenging but exciting and rewarding times.

Jeremy J Miles

The well-known Danish newspaper illustrator Otto Christensen drew George Miles when he visited Denmark in October 1945. It was said that Otto's principal purpose as a portrait artist was to capture the distinctive character of his models – in this he certainly did with George.

George Herbert Miles - a Biography

By 1940, at the age of 29, George Miles was an experienced test pilot, with 2,000 hrs on some 88 types, had designed his first aeroplane, the M.17 Monarch and was also the Manager of the Repair & Service Department, where his patience had been tested almost to the limit by Ministerial interference. This elicited one of the first of his pithy, sharply-expressed reports and may well have been the trigger for what subsequently proved to be a life-long battle with senseless or irrational bureaucracy, a habit that got him into hot water on a number of occasions.

In April 1941, following the purchase by F G Miles, Blossom Miles and George of the shares from Rolls-Royce's investment in 1937, George became Technical Director and Chief Designer.

Beneath this frenetic life George was a courteous man of compassion (especially for animals), reticence, humility and just plain good manners. Yet he was intolerant of unfairness and impatient of delay. These characteristics showed themselves in his concern for the lives of seamen, and led him towards the revolutionary idea of the Mariner, a maritime version of the Messenger, for use on merchant ships for convoy protection which, regretfully, was not taken up.

George also had revolutionary ideas for a tandem wing carrier-based fighter, which gave the pilot an excellent forward view and did away with the necessity for folding wings for carrier operations. Determined to put his idea into practice but not being prepared to wait for wind-tunnel tests or other refinements he had, within weeks, designed and built a flying test-bed, namely the 'nearly catastrophically unstable' (George's own words!) M.35 Libellula, which, true to form, he flight-tested himself. But Peter Amos tells that story much better than I can.

During one month in the spring of 1942, George Miles's pocket diaries reveal that he spent 10 hrs at the controls of six different aircraft including two prototypes; the M.35 Libellula (maiden flight) and the M.25 Martinet. During this same period he had meetings at the National Physical Laboratory and the Ministry of Aircraft Production; he met with two RAF and two Army officers and, amongst others, Prince Bernhard of the Netherlands. Whilst all this was going on, he was engaged in the design of a number of new aircraft, for which he had design responsibility.

George was a practical and experienced aviator who designed aeroplanes. He had a passion for flight, and for the shape and performance of things that fly - in particular, aircraft. He wanted his aeroplanes to look right, to use a power source that was in harmony with the design and thus to be aerodynamically sound. Later in life, as engine power increased exponentially, he was critical of designs which relied more on brute power than on good aerodynamics. He also wanted his aircraft to be light and instinctive to fly, aeroplanes which were responsive and manoeuvrable and yet stable so that they could be flown with accuracy and precision.

Many of the aircraft he designed make up the subject of this book (and the next volume), and are described in great detail in the following pages. Suffice it to say here that he was still engaged on designing new types or modifying the existing M.100 Student well into the 1980s and 90s.

I only knew George during the last 17 years of his life, following my marriage to Karen, his daughter and only child. That he was held in high regard by his peers was not in doubt. But why? He attracted no honours, never paraded his achievements, and only once did he refer to the supersonic M.52, for whose design and manufacture he had overall responsibility.

It was only after he died and it fell to me to sort his papers (50 boxes, 1200 file entries) that I began to get an idea of his varied and significant contribution to his profession, over more than 60 years of practice. His was an eager mind supported by a razor-sharp intellect and an insatiable appetite for solving problems: from prosthetic hands to supersonic aircraft, he used logic and common sense, and a wealth of practical experience, strengthened by an unshakable trust in string and plasticine.

Personally, I remember a man, short of stature, whose stance was balanced with feet set apart and arms akimbo. For me, this characteristic was exemplified in a fragment of colour film of the maiden flight of the M.39B Libellula, on July 22nd 1943: George landed, taxied the aircraft up to his colleagues waiting by the airstrip, emerged from the cockpit and unassumingly moved to the rear of the group and took up his accustomed stance as others crooned over his creation. George's ideas were fresh, innovative and unexpected; but also logical, and well thought-out. In a 1990s review of his and his brother's work, they were described as Mavericks, a term I imagined he would disapprove of, instead, it tickled him pink. He was perhaps the perfect foil for his older brother F G, the man who created Miles Aircraft, and whose naturally expansive and creative character thrived on discussion and argument, on publicity and (when needed) on controversy. George, however, was the antithesis; he was the quiet master of detail and of fact, the restrained logician at the back of the hall.

George believed that, if F G had been at the factory when the M.52 was cancelled, in February 1946, the imprudent Government decision might have been reversed. In contrast, George felt that his own contribution to the future of the company could have been decisive on September 17th 1947 in refuting the infamous Hogg report, which destroyed the company, if he hadn't been in the USA leading a sales drive. However, by the time he got home, the damage was done.

George's persistent and dogged single-mindedness, in the defence of his family or his ideals, is perhaps well illustrated in the case of Blue Steel. With his colleague and one time Personal Assistant, Don Brown, George took out a joint patent in 1956 to cover their development of the Tandem Wing, only to discover, when the first pictures of Blue Steel were released in 1960 that it embodied a design feature which they felt infringed their patent. Their case started as a simple claim for infringement, based on the rather abstruse notion that the missile was more aerodynamic than ballistic. This was Britain's main nuclear deterrent, and the Ministry was not prepared to make any concessions as to revealing its origin. Thereafter, the case followed increasingly tortuous, narrow tributaries including "unconscious plagiarism" and finally frittered to an end in the 1970s without resolution.

My wife, Karen, describes him with affection, as a kind and thoughtful father and a private family man who whistled between his teeth when his brain was onto a problem and whose favourite aphorism was:

> *Henry Ford was a grand old man*
> *Took four wheels and an old tin can*
> *Put it all together and the darned thing ran*
> *Henry Ford was a grand old man.*

Jim Pratt

Introduction

Miles Aircraft - The Early Years told the story of Miles aircraft up to the outbreak of war on 3rd September 1939. However, the Miles M.9B Master Mk.I and the Miles M.14A Magister were still in production, so their story continues here. The full story of Miles Aircraft will be told as follows:

Miles Aircraft - The Early Years - 1925-1939 (Published in 2009).

Miles Aircraft - The Wartime Years - 1939-1945 (This volume).

Miles Aircraft - The Post War Years (To follow)

Miles Aircraft - The Wartime Years - 1939-1945 follows the wartime trials and tribulations of Miles Aircraft, its large-scale production of training aircraft and target towers, early problems with Repair & Servicing, projected designs and innovative ideas, etc. It also details the most interesting range of light aeroplane prototypes and experimental aircraft prototypes produced during the war, up to and including the first part of the M.52 story.

Mention must be made of a remarkable series of small booklets on all of the Miles wartime aircraft projects produced by Phillips & Powis Aircraft Ltd and, subsequent to the 5th October 1943, by Miles Aircraft Ltd. Their pages were printed on card and their covers were made of an early black plastic material and I have chosen to call each a prospectus in their respective chapter, as they were neither a tender document nor a brochure, but they told the full story of each project, 'from the horse's mouth'. It was the almost chance discovery of a great collection of these with Jeremy Miles (the son of F G), followed by two further collections, one with Jim Pratt and the other which once belonged to Don Brown, that these full histories can now be told for the first time.

Those of us who are old enough to remember the Battle of Britain, have, in September 2010, just witnessed its 70th anniversary, and this, quite rightly, received much coverage on BBC TV. In the appropriate chapter on the Miles Master Mk.I are full details of this aircraft in service with the RAF where it is confirmed that, due to the foresight of F G Miles (and very little thanks to the Air Ministry), the RAF finally had the advanced monoplane trainer on which to train its future fighter pilots that it so badly needed, but only just in time.

Inevitably perhaps, the BBC stated in their programme that the pilots who fought in the Battle had received their advanced training on the North American Harvard - this was simply not true.

The truth of the matter is that only 200 Harvards had been delivered to the RAF prior to October 1939, with a further 200 being delivered by June 1940. Prior to September 1940, the Harvard was used mainly for training pilots who were going on to receive training on twin-engined aircraft not on to single-engined fighters.

It was indeed fortunate that 500 Master Mk.I's had been delivered to the RAF between July 1939 and September 1940.

An advertisement for the Miles Master, in *The Aeroplane* for 8th October 1943 (and undoubtedly in earlier issues), stated: . . . *'Without it, the steady flow of pilots to our fighter squadrons could never be maintained.'*

No history of Miles Aircraft would be complete without reference to the now-famous Miles Master but the BBC lost a marvellous opportunity to finally recognise its achievements in the Battle of Britain.

The aircraft and projects covered in this volume continue the story of Miles Aircraft from the Miles Magister and Miles Master Mk.I, both of which were by then in service with the RAF and foreign air forces, and the Miles M.19 Master Mk.II and Master Mk.III of late 1939, through to the first part of the story of the Miles M.52 High Speed Aircraft. This story will be concluded in the next volume.

Although the designs for many of the Miles aircraft that were to be produced in 1946 and 1947 were commenced during the latter stages of the war, their full histories will be detailed in the next volume.

Likewise, all the other post-war projects, together with full details of the post-war civil aircraft production, the full story of the so-called 'Financial Crisis of late 1947 and the Collapse of Miles Aircraft', and the formation of F G Miles Ltd at Redhill Aerodrome, Surrey, on 4th December 1948, which later developed into the large Miles Group of Companies based at Shoreham, will be told in the next volumes.

As it has proved impossible to include the Appendices and full production details for all the Miles aircraft manufactured during the war within the pages of this volume, these will be found on the CD included inside the back cover, and also in the separate booklet available on request.

Peter Amos

Additional Acknowledgements

In addition to my many friends who helped with the preparation of Volume 1, to whom I would also like to extend my thanks for their continuing help with Volume 2, I would now like to thank the following, who have added still further to our knowledge of Miles Aircraft since Volume 1 was published:

Jeremy Miles, for very kindly giving me access to so much material from his collection of George Miles' archives, including the large number of the invaluable 'booklets', as without these the story of Miles Aircraft would never have been as complete, or as near definitive, as I could ever have hoped to make it.

Karen and Jim Pratt (George Miles' daughter and son-in-law), for their support and encouragement and for kindly scanning all the 'booklets', which they had in their collection of George Miles'

archives. Also for continually sharing their finds of such wonderful 'gems' as they came across them. These included the full story of the so-called 'financial collapse' of Miles Aircraft Ltd in late 1947, as so thoroughly researched by George Miles soon after, full details of which will appear in the next volume.

Mike Hirst, for his continual support and encouragement and for very kindly scanning yet more of his collection of the 'booklets' for me.

Phil Butler, once again, this time for his unstinting help by so very kindly copying details from the record cards of the 3,250 Miles Masters of all marks and 1,742 Miles Martinets and all the other small production runs of Miles aircraft for the Services. Nothing was too much trouble, and I will forever be in his debt.

Josh Spoor, for his invaluable help in tracking down probably every surviving document on the Miles M.52, and many more documents of great interest to this story in the National Archive, and to his interest in the activities of Miles Aircraft in general.

Ken Smy, for kindly researching the South African Air Force archives for me to not only correlate the RAF s/n's with those of the South African Air Force, but to finally bring to light all the problems surrounding the introduction of the Miles M.19 Master Mk.II into service with the South African Air Force, for the Joint Air Training Scheme.

Tony Wingfield, once again, for kindly proof reading the final draft and for meticulously checking the individual aircraft histories of the Miles Master and Miles Martinet, all 4,992 of them - a true labour of love. I would also like to thank him for re-drawing the Woodley aerodrome maps, as at the end of the war, from some very poor quality prints. Mick Burrow and Douglas Rough, for their most valuable help with Miles aircraft used by the Fleet Air Arm. This was a most difficult area to research but with their help it is now as complete as I feel that it ever will be. Mike Draper and Douglas Rough (again) for their help with the Miles M.50 Queen Martinet, another problem aircraft, about which much more is now known, thanks to their diligence.

Terry Judge for finally providing the most plausible solution to the origin of the 50 Cirrus engines, which were acquired by Phillips & Powis for use in the early Miles M.2 Hawks, and for further additions and corrections to Volume 1. Denis Corley, for his help in kindly going through all the copies of ATA pilot's log books in possession of the Royal Air Force Museum and listing all the movements of Miles aircraft and to Mick Burrow (again) for going through all the copies of ATA pilot's log books in his possession for Miles aircraft entries for me.

Professor Brian Brinkworth, for sharing his refreshingly contemporary approach to the design of the Miles M.52 and for kindly checking my chapter on this project. I would also like to thank him for giving me his view on the merits of the M.35 Libellula design and also for explaining why it would not take-off and fly successfully on its first attempts at flight.

Dennis and Elizabeth Bancroft and Derek Ruben, for yet more help with the background to the design of the M.52.

Luis Tavares in Portugal for kindly checking my chapters on Miles aircraft in Portugal and for supplying yet more information and photographs on them. Luis says that the source of the other photographs is always "B.A.1, Sintra, via Luis Tavares", from where he took these copies. The only exception is the one of Master 417 (taken in the Azores) that someone from the Azores offered to him but he didn't remember his name, so this is credited to "Unknown via Luis Tavares". Thanks also to Eng Mario Canongia Lopes, who told the story of the Portuguese fighter squadrons in 'Air Enthusiast - Thirteen' August-November 1980 in his article entitled 'Fighters of the Cross of Christ'. The page of photographs was reproduced from the Portuguese aeronautical magazine *Revista do Ar*.

John Havers (once again) for kindly sharing his knowledge of Miles aircraft in the Middle East, and for giving me the date of the formation of the ARB. Graham Skillen, for his help with Miles aircraft in service with the Irish Air Corps and to JJ Masterson for his help with Irish Aviation. Ole Nikolajsen for kindly checking, offering suggestions and amendments, and also supplying extremely rare photographs of Miles aircraft in Turkey.

Barry Ketley, for kindly allowing me to reproduce details of two of the winches used in the Miles M.25 Martinet, from the book 'A Long Drag' by Don Evans. Gordon Kinsey and his book 'Martlesham Heath', for details of Miles aircraft tested at the A&AEE Martlesham Heath. Tim Mason and Rod Smith for details of Miles aircraft tested and used by the A&AEE Boscombe Down. Mark Hale, for his enthusiasm and help with his researches into the Miles M.33 Monitor. The late Lt Alan Peter Goodfellow RNVR (a recently qualified EPTS Test Pilot, seconded to Miles Aircraft as a production test pilot), for sharing his reminiscences of his time at Woodley and in particular his experience of flying the Miles Monitor.

Tony Buttler for finding the RAE Reports on the trials of the M.39B Libellula at Farnborough and for copying them to me. Vic Smith, once again, for his untiring efforts on my behalf in the Newspaper Archives. Gerald Hackemer, for his kind introduction to the GAPAN in London, and to Peter Bugge and Dacre Watson for kindly showing me the archival material held by the GAPAN and the surviving flying log books of Ken Waller, the last Chief Test Pilot of Miles Aircraft Ltd.

ASM Wedderburn, Des Keating, and Wiltshire Newspapers. The last for kindly publishing my plea for information on South Marston in December 1984. To all who responded for their invaluable help with the background to the manufacturing of not only Miles aircraft at the new shadow factory at South Marston but also of the Short Stirlings which were assembled there. The overwhelming response brought replies, with much valuable information on the construction of the site and etc, from Ron B Maxfield, Charles Smith, A L Jefferies, George Simpson, G H Hardiman, Doug Richards and Howard Ladd-Thomas. Ron Maxfield later kindly showed Julian Temple around what remained of the airfield and factory. Without all their help and later that of Rod Priddle, the full story of South Marston could never have been told.

To Jean and Ken Fostekew of The Museum of Berkshire Aviation, Woodley, for sharing the gems of information which they continually receive in the museum appertaining to Woodley and Miles aircraft, and for very kindly hosting the book launch of Volume 1 at the museum in 2009 and this volume in 2012.

The late Derek Collier Webb for allowing me to use excerpts from his book 'UK Flight Testing Accidents 1940-71' and the details of accidents to Miles aircraft during that period contained therein. Andrew Pentland for his most valuable and epic work in detailing the individual histories for all production Spitfires and Seafires on his website 'Spitfire-Main'. This, with its search facility, enabled me to select all the aircraft which had been handled by Phillips & Powis Aircraft Ltd at Woodley and South Marston. To Peter Arnold for his help with Spitfires.

The late Graham Philip and all his colleagues at the Montrose Heritage Centre for kindly sharing their Miles aircraft related archives from 8 FTS/8SFTS/2FIS Montrose with me.

To Tony Adderley for very kindly allowing me to share the wartime experiences of his father, Sqdn Ldr M C Adderley, of the Pilotless Aircraft Unit, Manorbier, through the medium of his flying log books. These gave an insight into the development of the Miles M.50 Queen Martinet and have also brought to light little known facets of the work of the three prototype aircraft involved in the tests.

Bill Harrison, for discovering, literally in the nick of time just before the completion of Volume 2, the two brochures prepared in 1940 by Guy Morgan and Partners, Architects, for Phillips & Powis, for the proposed 'Scheme for Underground Bombproof Workshop' in the Reading locality, and for the construction of the 'Shadow Factory and Aerodrome' at South Marston.

Finally, to all members of The Miles Aircraft Collection and my many friends around the world for their help, support and patience during the long gestation period leading up to the final completion of this volume, and to all who have kindly taken the trouble to contact me with additions, photographs and yet more stories to add to Volume 1, to this and the forthcoming volume - a very big vote of thanks. All un-credited photographs are mostly Phillips & Powis Aircraft Ltd via The Miles Aircraft Collection.

Peter Amos

THE MILES MASTER

*Fastest and most advanced training aircraft
in the world.*

In quantity production for the Royal Air Force.

MILES AIRCRAFT

MANUFACTURED BY PHILLIPS & POWIS AIRCRAFT LTD., READING AERODROME, BERKSHIRE.   TELE.: SONNING 2211

Advertisement from The Aeroplane *September 7th 1939.*

Pilot Officer D J C (Colin) Pinckney prepares to climb aboard a Master Mk.I while a member of the ground crew looks on. P/O Pinckney was ex Eton and Cambridge and began flying with the Cambridge University Air Squadron. He was called up in October 1939 and presumably went straight on to advanced training on Masters. He completed his training in 1940 and was posted to 603 Sqdn on 6th July, where he was credited with 3 enemy aircraft destroyed, 3 probables and 1 damaged, during the Battle of Britain. In early 1941 he was posted to Singapore to join 243 Sqdn before moving to 67 Sqdn with whom he became a Flight Commander. He moved with them to Burma for the defence of Rangoon. Squadron records were lost in the retreat but it is thought that he claimed 2 victories. Verbal reports from ground crew (J Helsdon Thomas) in a book based on diaries, say that on his last sortie, on 23rd January 1942, he shot down 3 Ki 27 Nate fighters before being overwhelmed and killed. His final score would therefore have been 7 destroyed, 3 probables and 3 damaged. He thus became a fighter ace and his DFC was promulgated on 8th May 1942. Photograph probably taken at 5 FTS Sealand, who received their Masters from August 1939.
[Photograph Photopress, dated 30th November 1939. 'Passed by Censor'. Biographical detail courtesy of Andy Thomas]

Chapter 1
Reading – September 1939 to 1945

With the outbreak of the Second World War in September 1939, Phillips & Powis Aircraft Ltd became heavily involved with the continuing production of the Magister and Master for the RAF and now the story continues with the subsequent events at Woodley being outlined in approximately chronological order. However, having due regard to the size of this volume it has been necessary to carry over some later aircraft types, which were designed during the war to the next volume.

In 1940, Phillips & Powis were instructed by the Ministry to build a 'shadow factory' at South Marston, near Swindon in Wiltshire. This site was chosen as being the most suitable as a ready pool of skilled labour already existed in the nearby GWR workshops. A recently discovered but undated brochure, entitled 'Phillips & Powis Aircraft Limited - Shadow Factory and Aerodrome', gave full details of a proposal by Guy Morgan & Partners, Chartered Architects and in it was a drawing of Swindon Aerodrome and factory, dated 14th December 1939. This proposal is reproduced in Appendix 1.

South Marston was 'in answer to the Air Ministry's request for a plan to produce 200 Master aircraft per month, including the 60 per month already scheduled to the Reading Factory, and the 80 sets of Major Components per month ordered on the Austin Motor Company at the direction of the Air Ministry'.

By the end of 1940 the new factory had been built and this also incorporated a moving aircraft assembly line similar to that first installed at Woodley. The first Master to be produced at South Marston, a Mk.II, was delivered to the RAF on 13th March 1941 and the factory ultimately produced 488 Master Mk.II and 602 Master Mk.III aircraft before changing to modification work on Spitfires.

Omitted from *Volume 1 Miles Aircraft - The Early Years 1925 to 1939*, due to late notification, I would like to thank Joe Cherrie of the National Museums of Scotland for bringing to my attention a rather unusual project known as the Miles 'Rammer'.

Details of this 'project', which had been discovered by Michael J F Bowyer, was one of the *'least known of the exotic ideas'* put forward to the British Government before and during the war. My thanks to Michael for kindly agreeing to me reproducing his article in Appendix 7.

With Miles Aircraft preparing for full scale production of Miles Master advanced trainers and continuing production of their successful Miles Magister, a new pilot joined the firm as a production test pilot on 11th January 1940; his name was Kenneth Herbert Fraser 'Ken' Waller, the famous pre-war record breaking pilot.

An oblique view across Woodley Aerodrome, from the South East, probably taken in 1941, showing the painted 'hedges'; the part completed second Bellman hangar at Repair & Service and some 44 Magisters of 8 EFTS dispersed around the airfield.

Training Past and Present.

Kenneth Herbert Fraser Waller

Ken Waller, as he was more popularly known, was born on 7th April 1908 and learnt to fly with the Cinque Ports Flying Club at Lympne in 1930. He gained his Private Pilot's Licence, No.2557, dated 25th April 1930 and his Royal Aero Club Aviator's Certificate, No.9047, in May 1930. Ken Waller later became well known as a long distance and air race pilot, and with Owen Cathcart Jones they entered the 1934 MacRobertson England to Australia Air Race in a de Havilland DH.88 Comet, built especially for the race, finishing in fourth place. The same aeroplane was then used by Ken Waller and Maurice Franchomme to fly from Belgium to the Belgian Congo and return in record time, in order to prove that an airmail route was possible and in 1934, Waller was awarded the Segrave Trophy for this feat.

By 1938 he was instructing on DH Tiger Moths with the Brooklands Flying Club but on the 5th September 1939, following the declaration of war with Germany on the 3rd, he flew to RAF Sywell, starting an instructors course there on the 11th. Upon reflection, it seems strange that a man of his experience should have needed to have gone on an instructor's course as, since learning to fly in 1930, he had amassed some 5,500 flying hours, much of it on teaching pupils to fly, but presumably he had to be taught to do it the RAF way!

He began instructing at Sywell on 2nd October 1939 but then, just prior to an entry on 11th January 1940, he wrote in capital letters across the page in his log book: PHILLIPS & POWIS. On 11th January 1940, he flew his first two Miles aircraft, a Miles M.18 and a Mentor from Woodley, both on 'H (Handling) Tests', 'Local'. On 12th he flew a Falcon on the same flight regime and from then on, apart from the occasional Falcon, Sparrowhawk and M.18 flight, he became a production test pilot, flying new build Masters and Magisters and test flying other aircraft and prototypes as required. On 29th April 1940, he flew the M.18 'U2' to 'Swindon and Return' which was only the second recorded flight into the new aerodrome, which Phillips & Powis were building there to manufacture the Miles Master.

This most interesting log book ended on the 7th December 1940 but, unfortunately, his next wartime log books are missing. It is possible that Ken Waller went to South Marston to test fly the Master Mk.II and Mk.III aircraft, but it has since been confirmed by South African Air Force records (courtesy of Ken Smy) that he was in South Africa by late 1941 as part of a small team sent out by Phillips & Powis to help the SAAF overcome the many problems that were being experienced by them with the introduction of the Master Mk.II into service. His next log book starts at Woodley on 13th May 1947 but it is known that he took over the position of chief test pilot in January 1946 after Tommy Rose retired. Details from this last log book will be published in the next volume.

At Woodley on the outbreak of war, the M.14A Magister elementary trainer was still in full scale production, as was the M.9B Master Mk.I advanced trainer, although the latter was replaced on the assembly line by the M.9C Master Mk.IA advanced trainer in April 1940. The chief test pilot, Flt Lt Tommy Rose, had become CO of the firm's Home Guard unit early in the war, and was given the rank of Major. However, this didn't stop him from proudly wearing his RAF wings on his army battledress tunic!

F G Miles addressed the Phillips & Powis workers on 23rd May 1940 and they cheered him when he announced that, as with all other aircraft factories, they were now being asked to work 7 days per week and 24 hours per day. He also stated in his address that:

"We are now as one regiment, fighting for our lives, and in asking you to work like this I want you to believe that we are all of us here, working alike..."

On 14th June 1940, George Miles, who was manager of the Repair & Service Department at that time, was told, in an interview with the Directors, that a decision had been made to place Capt ED 'Don' Ayre in charge of the Service Department and all outside liaison with the RAF. It was made very clear by Col Darby that this move was purely political and in no way connected with any inefficiency or error on George's part. Col Darby also stated that the Directors were completely satisfied with the way in which the Service Department had been run during the past months and for full details of why this move took place see Appendix 3.

Captain Edward Dundonald 'Don' Ayre already had a very full and varied aeronautical career, starting at a very early age as an apprentice with a firm of machine tool engineers in Coventry. He left them in 1917 to take a commission in the RFC but by the time he had passed his Instructor's Course, acted as test pilot and been posted to 25 Squadron, the Armistice had been signed. On demobilisation in 1918, he joined forces with a friend and acquired an obsolete war-time aircraft and started a joy-riding and taxi-trips business. This venture, however, ended in less than four weeks when a "friend" and mis-named pilot wrote off the aeroplane. He then worked on Rolls-Royce engines at their works at Derby and subsequently joined Armstrong Siddeley, where he gained considerable experience of the early Jaguar engines, of metal airframes and of production of the AW Siskin Ill.

In April, 1923, he joined AW's Reserve School at Whitley and that marked the recommencement of his flying career. Two years later he joined Imperial Airways at Croydon and after working on

An unusual sight - Tommy Rose in Home Guard battledress with RAF pilot's wings! Tommy had been a Major in the RFC in the First World War and later a Flt Lt in the RAF and it is believed that he reverted to his RFC rank when he joined the Home Guard.

Capt ED 'Don' Ayre in the rear cockpit of a Miles Magister.
[First published in the 'Miles Magazine' for November 1938]

overhauls, repairs and maintenance, he graduated from Flight Engineer to First Officer and in eighteen months, did some 1,600 hours flying on Continental routes.

Then, in 1928, after nearly a year's instructing at Colonel G L P Henderson's flying school at Brooklands, he joined Lancashire School of Aviation at Lytham, and in two seasons, with three Avro 548's (Renault-engined Avro 504K's), nearly 28,000 passengers were carried on joy-rides. With the advent of National Flying Services he left to be appointed their Manager and Pilot at Hull and on the termination of this contract, in June 1931, he joined Capt C D Barnard's Air Circus, touring the country as a leading pilot and stunt pilot.

In October, he and others from C D Barnard joined John Tranum and Oscar Garden's air circus which toured South Africa, travelling 14,850 miles and flying 210 hours, in two-and-a-half months' working. In March 1932, he returned to National Flying Services, this time at Hanworth, in the capacity of Chief Engineer and Test Pilot. He later secured the appointment of Airport Manager with Airwork at Barton, Manchester and then Sales Manager and aeronautical adviser to a company manufacturing aircraft and wireless equipment.

In February 1936, Capt Ayre joined Phillips & Powis Aircraft at Woodley, as Manager of the Service Department and, in October 1938, was appointed Assistant Works Manager, to co-ordinate with their various sub-contractors. During 21 years in aviation (by November 1938), Don Ayre had achieved 4,500 flying hours, flown 87 different types of aircraft and carried over 40,000 passengers. He still held a valid GE's Licence, which he obtained in May 1924.

The thorny problem of the relations that existed between the firm and the Ministry of Aircraft Production (MAP) in the early stages of the war now need to be elaborated upon for posterity. An internal

A view of Woodley, probably taken in 1941, looking across the 'Falcon' towards the main factory, with the Repair & Service Department at right centre. The painted 'hedges' across the aerodrome can be clearly seen, as can the part-completed second Bellman hangar at Repair & Service and the aircraft parked between Repair & Service and the main factory.

Phillips & Powis report, written in July 1940 (not signed but probably written by either F G Miles or someone very close to him), gave details of the problems which Miles had been having, and was still experiencing, with both the MAP (in general), and Mr Frederick Handley Page (in particular).

In early 1940, Lord Beaverbrook, who had been appointed Minister of Aircraft Production by Winston Churchill, 'persuaded' (in retrospect, a strange choice of word) Frederick Handley Page to take charge of training aircraft production, though just why and how he came to be appointed to that position, when he knew absolutely nothing about training aircraft and had his own aircraft manufacturing company to run anyway, is beyond my comprehension. Handley Page then seems to have singled out Phillips & Powis and made it very clear from the outset that he was determined to remove both Lt Col Darby and F G Miles from their positions as joint Managing Directors of the company. He visited Phillips & Powis in his new capacity on 12th July 1940 and then the trouble really started!

Shortly after he took up his appointment, Handley Page announced to Lt Col Darby and F G Miles that he wished to take control of Phillips & Powis Aircraft from them. However, both Darby and Miles made it quite clear in an interview with Lord Beaverbrook, that in their considered opinion the Company was an acknowledged success from every point of view, especially from that of production, and consequently they did not intend to take such flagrant injustice lying down. Mr A F Sidgreaves, the Rolls-Royce Director on the Board, also saw Lord Beaverbrook and made it very clear that Handley Page had exceeded his power.

Mr Handley Page then resigned his position.

This report, reproduced below, clearly shows just how petty minded certain people in positions of high authority could be - even though the country was, at that time, fighting for its very existence:

The History of the Chaotic Relations between Phillips & Powis Aircraft Ltd and the Air Ministry

Phillips & Powis started as a Public Company in 1937 and at that date it had a staff, inclusive of Work's Personnel of about 500 persons and in the three years since then has built itself up large enough to employ over .... persons. (this figure is blank in the report but by the outbreak of war in September 1939 the company was employing over 1,000 people - PA).

The aeroplane the Company was then building, and is still doing so, is the Magister ab initio trainer. The orders for these aircraft were placed up to January 1938 in the following lots - 90, 214, 200, 54, 100 and 100 (these figures are slightly at variance with the actual figures of 90, 25, 214, 204, 50 with the 100 and 100 not ordered until after January 1938, plus 2 replacements - PA). *With such small orders and with such complete lack of planning or foresight by the Ministry it is obvious that at no time was the Company given an inducement, from a business aspect, to really adequately tool up for large scale production with the result that the cost of production of the last batch of 100 was substantially the same as the cost of the first 100.*

The output of trainers aimed at the end of the Great War was 1,200 a month and in a report of the 11th January 1938 Mr Miles wrote that even greater numbers would be required in a new major war and that if an order were placed for say 1,000 aeroplanes the Company could plan production on an entirely new basis with a very material saving in man-hours and at the same time train up a wide circle of sub-contractors. Nothing was ever done to tackle this problem in a businesslike way with the result that production, now that we want large numbers, is far less than is required.

Magister Bombers

When Lord Beaverbrook was appointed Minister of Aircraft Production, Mr Miles was told that he wanted to see him and he did so on a number of occasions; apparently the reason for this was

misunderstood, he felt that, subsequent to the attacks on Norway and its capitulation and the over-running of Holland and Belgium, something more than an increase of production of standard aircraft was required to stop the rot, that the intention was to give energy, enthusiasm and inventive capacity free reign so that, freed from the foolish and short-sighted policy of the past, they might provide something more than an increased percentage of production.

Mr Miles had for some time past been trying to get the Ministry to consider and at least try out ideas which the Company had regarding the use of training aircraft for fighting and bombing. After the interviews with Lord Beaverbrook, it was taken that the Company might approach the Air Force and get their reactions and instructions, this was done.

An aeroplane was fitted with bomb racks and the Director of Operational Requirements and the Assistant Chief of Air Staff both came to the aerodrome to discuss the idea and see it in operation. They were genuinely and definitely enthusiastic and within a day or so bomb racks were supplied to the Company and orders given to the appropriate Officers whereby arrangements were to be made to have all the aeroplanes in the country fitted ready for use.

Then suddenly through Mr Handley Page and Lord Beaverbrook came an order that the factory is subject to the Ministry of Aircraft Production and that all orders given by the Air Force were cancelled and all work on the Magisters was to cease. No explanation was given and all appeals have failed to find one. Lord Beaverbrook after promising to visit the factory and have a Conference with the Directors, at the eleventh hour cancelled this and for over a week nothing has been heard of him.

On the 11th June (1940) the telegram cancelling the order was received and on the 1st July the Aeronautical Inspection Directorate notified the Company that the work on the Magisters was to be suspended until it had been reconsidered on August the 1st next; this statement is made at a time when England herself is daily expecting attack.

When it is borne in mind that the purpose of the modification was to have available an effective and highly approved weapon against parachute troops or flotillas of landing forces the action of the Ministry in delaying a final decision, leaving aside the over-ruling of orders placed by active Air Force Personnel is as nearly a criminally actionable act as can be. Nearly the whole 1,000 aircraft could have been completed by now.

Master Fighter

The Master Training aeroplane of which there are over 370 in service is also the subject of a policy which, if not intentional, is also muddleheaded enough to call for some drastic action against the persons responsible.

From the planning of the first order with the Company it has not been left alone for a moment; the conditions of production and the numbers to be produced and the method of production, the place of production has chopped and changed continuously with the result that the Company is now completely at a loss as to how many will be wanted or whether there will be engines for them.

When at last the Ministry decided to back the Master with a big order, the Company was told to start a new shadow factory; immediately steps were taken by the Directorate and with the enthusiastic support of the staff, plans of the factory site and buildings and sub-contracting arrangements drawn up. This was in November of last year (1939) - we are now in July and except for a few buildings practically nothing has been done. Evidence of the actual facts proving the Ministry's responsibility can be produced if required.

At one stage when it became fairly evident that certain engines would no longer be available after a number of the aircraft had been produced, at the request of the Air Ministry the Company redesigned the aircraft to take another engine specified by them. The results were perfect and the new aircraft was a great success. Notwithstanding the fact that this was so and that a lot of money had been spent and literally months wasted the Company was informed recently that there was a change of plans and it could not expect delivery of these engines and could the machine take one from a foreign country, thereby entailing the repetition of wastage in time, money and energy.

While all this was going on, we tried to persuade the Ministry that owing to the tragic shortage of fighter aircraft the Master could well be fitted with six guns and armour. Thus fitted it would at least be useful for home defence and each training school could probably look after itself to some extent. All schools have first-class pilots handy who could help disorganise dive bombing attacks. We know that Mr Jones of Hawkers has recommended it.

After the events which have been set out above, the Air Force was approached and the scheme met with their enthusiastic support and an order was placed with the Company to convert 25 of these machines. The work was actually started. The first machine was tested by the Air Force and was satisfactory, this was also knocked on the head by the Air Ministry.

Some years ago the Company had enquiries made about supplies of timber in Canada and it was felt that as a result of these and because of the danger of bombing here the Company would be in a better position to keep production at a peak if a factory were started in Canada. The source of timber used in the Company's aircraft is Canada. Lord Beaverbrook would not listen to us and has indicated that he does not think much of the idea, this in spite of the enthusiastic support from the Canadian Trades Commissioner and numerous concrete offers from Canada of capital and sites, this boiled down means that despite everything he will not allow six or seven experts to leave England to train and exploit an immense new source of supply.

Mr Miles the designer of the Master and Magister and other famous aircraft writes:-

"Because war must cause a shortage of light alloys, steel tube and extrusions of all descriptions, I have held the opinion very strongly that a wooden fighter should (and could) be designed to provide a further source of fighter supply. This suggestion has been put up to the Air Ministry again and again.

Immediately after Munich I felt the situation to be so desperate that I took the specification to Sir Kingsley Wood, the Air Minister.

In addition to the proposed aircraft being designed in wood there were many other suggestions for simplification and the cutting out of unnecessary requirements. An example of the latter is the elimination of removable wings. By making the wings and the centre-section as one component, labour, complication and principal sources of weakness are cut out.

Lord Beaverbrook said he would like me to see A.M.D.P. on these subjects and I subsequently repeated them to Craven as well. A.M.D.P. was not particularly enthusiastic - he had, in fact, heard a good deal of these ideas from me before - but later he said get ahead with 25 Master conversions to fighters. He turned down the Magister idea entirely but upon my pressing told me to take it up with D.O.R. if I liked.

The wooden fighter was also waived by Lord Beaverbrook. He explained that he could think of nothing further ahead than six weeks or two months. As far as the suggestions outlined above were concerned this covered the first phase.

I made a point of discussing at various meetings my old ideas concerning Canada and my feeling that production was delayed there by exactly the same muddle and inefficiency as prevented this country from obtaining any real progress before and since the war began. These were not accepted." *

All that was asked was to be allowed, at no expense to the Government, to build one machine and pave the way for its production in Canada if it turned out to be the success anticipated, without in any way interfering with the present production of machines urgently wanted. Could anything be more designed to kill initiative and drive? It is well known that orders are placed for aircraft by the Ministry and the Forces themselves have no other say other than about types and performance of the machines. Even in the Dominions the Ministry has the final say, hence the state of affairs in Canada, Australia and elsewhere.

A certain secret article was approved by the Authority concerned but it was with the greatest difficulty that the Air Ministry could be induced to place an order for its manufacture. In fact, it was not received until after the Company had, at its own expense set up a factory and was prepared to carry the cost itself if the order did not come.

The newspaper, long before war broke out, called for extensive ARP work and the organisation of the dispersal of factories in order to minimise the risk of loss through bombing attacks. On the 24th of May 1940 we received our first communication from the Ministry and on the 4th of July we received another letter asking us to please report on a certain method of factory dispersal.

In our reply to the first letter we intimated that we had a scheme in preparation and asked the Air Ministry to kindly support us and to take over the premises which we required. It has, therefore, taken two months for the Air Ministry to take the matter up and now we shall have to wait a considerable time before the red tape is overcome and the wheels working. This is a matter which should have been dealt with months ago and which would have placed us in a practically invulnerable position.

A final example of the state of affairs which points at a deliberate intention to thwart the efforts of the leaders of the industry is set out in the next paragraph.

Mr Handley Page, who was appointed by the Ministry to be Director of Aircraft Production, thereby being responsible for his actions, immediately on his appointment set about to do his utmost to disorganise the productive capacity of the Company by interfering in every possible way, culminating in calling the two Managing Directors to London and asking for their resignations from the Company in which action he was supported by Lord Beaverbrook. He also ordered the cessation of all experimental work in the factory thereby creating a state of affairs which can, at a minimum, be described as crass stupidity and at the worst, pro-enemy activity. What could be better for Hitler than the sterilisation of all inventive activity in England?

Mr Handley Page appears to have acted too hastily as he has resigned but experimental work is still stopped and no order has been received to re-start it, nor have any steps been taken to end the chaos that still exists. Should these actions be the result of personal dislike of the heads of the Company then all that is required is to prove the fact of the amazing results of this concern as compared with those of others, in particular the Nuffield works, and persons who can harbour malice at a time like this and use their positions to satisfy it should be removed from office and in their stead should be persons who are bigger than to take these advantages, particularly in view of the achievements of the parties concerned.

* These notes were taken from Paragraph (3) of an untitled summary, written in July 1940. This summary, although duplicating some of the points raised in the above report, is well worth reproducing here in full:

For the record, I will attempt a summary of the happenings of the last few weeks which led to Mr Handley Page's announcement to Colonel Darby and myself that he wished to take control of Phillips & Powis Aircraft Ltd from us.

When Lord Beaverbrook was appointed Minister of Aircraft Supply I was told he wished to see me and I did see him on a number of occasions. Apparently I misunderstood his reason. I felt, subsequent to the capitulation of Norway and the attacks on Holland and Belgium, that something more than an increase in the production of standard aircraft was required to stop the rot.

I felt that energy, enthusiasm and inventive capacity should be given a free run so that, freed from the extremely restrictive and conservative procedure of Government departments, they might provide something more than an increased percentage of production. It seemed obvious that time - no longer on our side - precluded any long-winded development of new ideas and that the best hope lay in the improvisation of new methods and purposes applied to existing apparatus.

Ideas had occurred to us in the past for the use of training aircraft for fighting and bombing. These ideas, with many others, had been submitted to the correct departments at the Air Ministry with no result whatsoever; yet later, when Air Staff considered them they were received with enthusiasm.

I thought Lord Beaverbrook would be interested in these suggestions and described three to him.

These were:-

(1)   That owing to the tragic shortage of fighter aircraft the Master could well be fitted with six Browning guns and armour. Thus fitted it would at least be useful for home defence and each training school could probably look after itself to some extent. All schools have first-class pilots handy who could help to disorganise dive bombing attacks. We had suggested this many times in the past and had received a good deal of support. (Mr Jones, of Hawkers, said that he too had recommended it). At one time we nearly had an order placed for special wings to accommodate guns but this never came to anything.

(2)   That there were over a thousand Magister ab-initio training aircraft in the country and that these could be used for aggressive or defensive purposes as well as for training. They could easily be fitted with racks to take eight to twelve twenty-pound bombs of the Cooper type. Such an adapted aircraft could create havoc among infantry or more especially among landing boats; parachutists and transport aeroplanes on the ground; machine gun nests established in this country by parachutists and even against light armoured vehicles.

The beauty of the suggestion lay in the fact that up to eight hundred extra light bombing planes could have been made available by now. I told Lord Beaverbrook I thought it possible that we could make adaptors and obtain enough bomb racks to convert at least 200 Magisters in from a fortnight to three weeks. These machines could be piloted by ATA personnel or advanced pupil pilots after a minimum training course.

(3)   Note: This paragraph is reproduced in full in 'The History of the Chaotic Relations between Phillips and Powis Aircraft Ltd and the Air Ministry', reproduced above.

On returning to Reading, we rang DOR and fixed an appointment. DOR (Mansell) and ACAS (Saundby) both came to Reading to discuss the Magister Bomber. They were genuinely and definitely enthusiastic. Among other things they confirmed that de Havillands were doing the same thing to Tiger Moths (of which there must be thousands) as a private venture. We discussed various purposes to which they could be put and promised that we would convert existing Service Magisters as quickly as they could be sent here.

Saundby told us that it had been arranged to send us a thousand or more practice type mechanical release light bomb racks, most of them damaged and unserviceable. I undertook to have these serviced and repaired at our female training school at Liverpool Road (Reading - PA). The job was a perfect one to introduce trainees to simple fitters' work. Also there could be no possible

complaint as to loss of production in the main factory. Apropos of this latter, all the bomb rack adaptors were sub-contracted out to firms who were begging for work and consequently we used more of our own capacity or labour; all we had to do was to fit up the Magisters. This operation took about three man-hours.

Meantime we had received a telegram from Harrogate saying "Approximately Qty 280 serviceable and 1270 repairable light series bomb carriers mechanical type being despatched to you immediately for installation in Magisters. Also approximately 550 release controls 11A/291. Effect any necessary conditioning. Request you make your own arrangements to provide control wires and shackles. AIRMINDEV HARROGATE."

And a note from the resident AID confirming a telegram received by him as follows:-

"Z.A.695. This message addressed to HQ No. 41 Group and repeated you for information. MU Z.A.563 29/5. Twenty-five, repeat twenty-five Magisters only are to be issued to Phillips & Powis from ASU's for Modifications. These aircraft M are to form a pool to exchange with Magisters in Training Command in order that all the aircraft in Training Units are modified. Request you arrange issue of twenty-five aircraft from store to Phillips & Powis by Friday 31/5 or as soon after as possible. Airmindev, Harrogate."

It seemed possible that the war had advanced to a stage where the infinite delays involved in waiting for a clear instructional contract from the Air Ministry should be avoided. Consequently I gave instructions for the work to go ahead on the basis of these two telegrams and my interviews since from these the intentions were quite clear.

The work went on like a house on fire supported by the utmost enthusiasm on the part of those responsible. (This enthusiasm has since been more than a little damped.) Within a fortnight the development had been completed, the bomb racks and adaptors for 200 machines ready and the work had started on fitting out Magisters sent here by the Air Ministry. During that time however, we received the following telegram:

"No further bomb racks are to be fitted Magister, nor are wings to be fitted to take guns" and the work has stopped. We now understand the position will be reviewed on August 1st. **Will Germany wait?**

The Master fighter was also started on verbal consent from AMDP who said we could carry on with 25. I promised to do our best and to have these completed in a fortnight and again the job was attacked with the utmost energy by the shops who, stirred by the danger of the German invasion of the low countries and of France, were grateful for a chance to put their backs into a special programme, especially because this and the Magister project were of an aggressive and novel character in contradistinction to the general policy. This work was also stopped by the telegram quoted above. In between times I had various interviews with the Minister and AMDP which I describe in a note, but at which I was in effect informed that I should not have interviewed Air Staff as this was going behind backs.

Very unfortunately just as all this special work started, two Masters crashed for unexplained reasons. I started an enquiry into the rear end of the fuselage because previous trouble had given rise to suspicions of tailplane failure. In the course of examining the rear structure I became very worried about certain rather frail details and made some urgent decisions for the strengthening of the tailplane and rear end fuselage. These I instructed the shops to put into effect on all Masters in course of manufacture. At the same time a Master was sent over to Farnborough for a physical test of the rear end.

This test confirmed that one of the points of which I was suspicious was very much under-strength and was almost certainly the cause of the failures. The modifications already issued to the shops were *approved and one or two others were introduced as further safeguards. These modifications were far reaching. The reason that they were necessary is dealt with in an addendum to this record. In spite of the number of operations and their difficulty the factory dealt with them most expeditiously and production stopped for <u>one week only</u>. The greater part of the modification had been carried out on more than 90 aircraft within a fortnight. The week after production was lost we delivered 4 Masters and the following two weeks 19 Masters and 10 Magisters and 21 Masters and 10 Magisters respectively were delivered this retrieving the position. This was incidentally a demonstration of one of the advantages of wooden aeroplanes; similar drastic modifications to metal aircraft would take many times as long.*

At the same time as this trouble arose, Mr Handley Page was appointed by the Minister to take charge of training aircraft production. Mr Handley Page took up an attitude which made it very clear he had determined upon the removal of Colonel Darby and myself from our positions. I cannot pretend to know his real reasons but an extract from a letter written for my Chairman gives some of my opinion. Colonel Darby felt also that an experience of his with Mr Handley Page some twenty years ago, when he had been compelled to take over control of ADC and put a manager into the Handley Page works was at least lending influence to this decision.

In any case we had a very unpleasant interview and Darby and I made it quite clear we were convinced that, far from having failed, Phillips & Powis was an acknowledged success from almost every point of view, especially from that of production; consequently we were not going to take an action of such flagrant injustice lying down, especially as we considered the motive strongly flavoured by personal bias. Colonel Darby put this point of view to Lord Beaverbrook immediately. We went away to prepare our case and to demand an enquiry.

Before this could take place, however, Mr Sidgreaves saw Lord Beaverbrook, who made it clear that Mr Handley Page had exceeded his power. It was left that Mr Sidgreaves should see what he thought of the whole matter.

Mr Handley Page has resigned.

However, unbeknown to F G Miles at the time the original report was written, there were to be five long hard years of war ahead and even he could not have imagined then that very little was to change in his dealings with the Ministry throughout that time.

From the notes written by F G Miles, it would appear that the antagonism between Handley Page and Phillips & Powis almost certainly went back to the days when Lieut Col Maurice Ormonde Darby OBE was Managing Director of the Aircraft Disposal Co Ltd (ADC), which had been formed at Croydon by Mr Frederick Handley Page and Mr Godfrey Isaacs after the end of the first world war. C G Grey wrote a Vivatuary upon Colonel Darby's retirement from Rolls-Royce Ltd (whom Darby had joined in 1934 as Aero Sales manager) in *The Aeroplane* for 3rd October 1947 and extracts from it, relevant to this story, are reproduced below:

I first met him when he was running, most efficiently as usual, a department on the supply side of that lunatic establishment which had been the Hotel Cecil and ultimately became the Air Ministry. It became known as the Hotel Bolo, after a recently shot French-Egyptian spy, Bolo Pasha, because everybody in it was alleged to be either doing nothing to win the War or was actively preventing our winning it. But it had its bright spots, and Darby's was one of the brightest.

Consequently, when the fighting stopped, and Mr (now Sir Frederick) Handley Page and Mr (now deceased) Godfrey Isaacs, brother of the first Lord Reading, formed the Aircraft Disposal Co., Ltd., to buy up all the RAF's surplus stock, from big bombers to tin-tacks, Colonel Darby, who was also a sound engineer and understood thoroughly the 'innards of his engines', was made

Managing Director. Those were exciting and amusing days. I wouldn't mind betting that Darby looks back on them as about the best of his business life.

After the ADC was shut down, because there was nothing but real scrap left to sell, Col. Darby joined Rolls-Royce in 1934. At that moment the terms of reference had not been fixed so, when asked what his new job was to be, Darby said so. Whereupon George Woods-Humphery, with whom he was having lunch at the RAF Club, brightly remarked: "Oh! Don't you know? He's the hyphen between the Rolls and the Royce."

Lieut. Col. Darby was, in fact, appointed Aero Sales Manager in 1934 and it was from this position that he retired in 1947. In 1936, when Rolls-Royce had acquired an interest in Phillips & Powis Ltd, Darby became a director of the firm. However, after Miles acquired the Rolls-Royce shares on 12th March 1941, Lieut. Col. Darby was lent to the Ministry of Aircraft Production as Controller of the South Marston 'Shadow Factory', where Miles Masters were built (and later where work on Spitfires was carried out). While there he also commanded a battalion of the 11th Wiltshire (Home Guard) Regt. (for details of the South Marston Shadow Factory see the appropriate chapter - PA).

Meanwhile, following the capitulation of Norway and the attacks on Holland and Belgium, Miles felt that something more than an increase in the production of training aircraft was required to 'stop the rot'. As stated above, he had suggested to Lord Beaverbrook that the Magister be adapted to take 8/12 twenty pound bombs and the Master be modified to take six Browning machine guns. In early July 1940, 8 EFTS Woodley was notified that their Tiger Moth and Magister aircraft were to be equipped with bomb racks (light series bomb carriers) to enable a load of 8 x 20lb bombs to be carried by each aircraft for use against enemy troops only as a last resort (the Banquet Light Scheme). For the purpose of putting this scheme into operation the Unit was affiliated to 26 Army Co-operation Squadron stationed at Gatwick and the scheme entailed the provision of two flights of five aircraft each with four aircraft being held in reserve. An unspecified number of Masters had also actually been fitted with machine guns when the company received the telegram stating that: *No further bomb racks are to be fitted to the Magister nor are wings to be fitted to take guns* and the work stopped immediately.

In the early days of the war, 8 FTS Montrose became one of the largest users of the Master Mk.I and in May 1940, Phillips & Powis set up a Civilian Repair Unit in a large mill on the outskirts of Montrose to keep its aircraft in serviceable condition and save the necessity of having to transport them to the Repair & Service Department at Woodley. This CRU ultimately undertook the repair of all marks of Master as well as Magisters, Martinets and Airspeed Oxfords. Upon completion, the aircraft were transported to Montrose for assembly and test flying. The resident test pilot at Montrose was Squadron Leader S G 'John' Betty who had joined the RAF as a 'Boy Mechanic' on 12th September 1921 and went on to serve thirty-three years in the RAF before becoming Administration Officer for Aberdeen and the North East Wing of the Air Training Corps. He finally retired on 24th April 1972, after a total of 51 years and 40 days in the RAF/RAFVR - which was believed to have been the longest period of service by anyone in the RAF.

Shortly after the outbreak of war in September 1939, a building in Liverpool Road, in the suburbs of Reading, previously owned by Messrs Serpells, a manufacturer of biscuit tins for Huntley & Palmers, was requisitioned by the Ministry for Phillips & Powis, in order that their Experimental Department could be dispersed. They soon built a Robin type hangar on the side of the building and 'Liverpool Road', as it was widely known, became the first of a number of outstations to be used by Phillips & Powis and a female training school was also set-up at there. In fact, this 'very secret place' was to become quite famous (some may even say 'notorious'!), due to the somewhat unofficial 'goings-on' that went on there from time to time!

Above: This very appropriate advertisement appeared in Aeronautics *for May 1940. Right: This equally very appropriate advertisement appeared in* Aeronautics *for January 1941.*

On 10th July 1940, an article in *The Sydney Morning Herald*, (Australia), reported that Phillips & Powis representatives were proposing to build Miles Master and Magister aircraft in Sydney, with the full backing of the parent company and suggested the conversion of part of the Clyde Engineering Co. workshops at Granville for this purpose. However, when Phillips & Powis officials took these plans to the Federal Government of Australia, apparently on three separate occasions, the proposals were rejected. There were also proposals to build Oxfords in Australia as well but these also came to nought.

The following month, the installation of a new 'Track Assembly Line' for Miles Master production in the new assembly building at Woodley made headlines in the newspapers. This was also fully described by F G Miles in *Flight* for 22nd August 1940 and such was its interest that it also received a mention in the *Evening Standard* and the *Ottawa Citizen* (Canada) on 23rd August 1940.

Prior to the Munich crisis of September 1938, Miles had designed and built a mock-up of an all-wooden monoplane single-seater fighter, later to be known as the 'Munich Fighter', but no interest was shown in it at the time.

Miles M.9B Master Mk.I fuselages in production.
[Photograph Monty Cook, via Bert Clarke]

However, by August 1940, just before the 'Battle of Britain', Miles felt that a further source of supply of fighter aircraft was urgently needed, so he resurrected the original design, which was then designated M.20/1, and produced it as the M.20/2. This incredible machine was designed and flown in the remarkably short time of nine weeks and two days from the time Miles first approached Lord Beaverbrook, the Minister of Aircraft Production, for authority to proceed with his proposal.

This all-wooden fighter utilised standard Master parts wherever possible and had a fixed undercarriage with no hydraulics and was first flown, by Tommy Rose, on 15th September 1940. Its per-

formance was superior to that of the Hurricane and only marginally slower than the Spitfire, but by then the crisis had passed and only one further example was built to meet a Naval requirement. Although the M.20 fighter was not ordered into production as the supply of Hurricanes and Spitfires managed to just keep pace with the attrition, it could well have been a very useful machine with its remarkable performance should the need have arisen.

Miles M.9B Masters Mk.I on the 'Track Assembly Line' in the new assembly building.

Miles M.9B Master Mk.I tailwheels in the track at the end of the final assembly line.

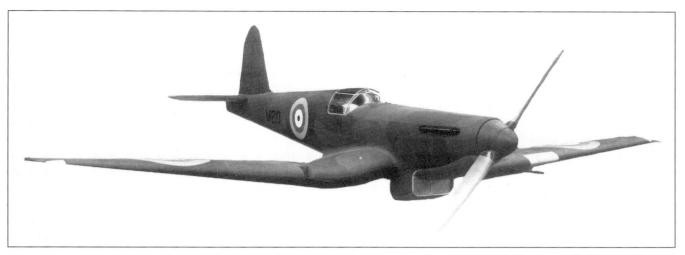

Above: The mock-up of the Munich Fighter, later designated Miles M.20/1. Below: The Miles M.20/2 Fighter in primer with 'B' mark U9.

The factory at Woodley was fortunate in that it did not receive much attention from the Luftwaffe during the war, with the first attack not coming until 16th August 1940, when one stick of four bombs was dropped on the south-west boundary of the aerodrome. Magister T9688 of the resident 8 EFTS, was set on fire by a bomb and was completely destroyed and the next day orders were received that all aircraft were to be fully dispersed.

Eric Sibbick, who was working on the design of the M.20 at the time later recalled:

During this time the battle line had moved, via Dunkirk, across the English Channel and we were stimulated by some intrusions by the opposition. One afternoon, with a misty haze off the local rivers, our star spotter alerted the design team, which was housed in a wooden hut on the fringe of Woodley aerodrome, by announcing the approach of what he described as 'a new type Blenheim'. With derisive shouts of "Is it hell!" from the team ringing in my ears, I saw the Heinkel 111 shed eight black sticks which dropped within a few yards of us. A tattoo from the Lewis gun outside the hut added to the excitement, but without any immediate result. However no damage was done and we concluded that owing to the poor visibility the bomb aimer had neglected to fuse his charges in the surprise of chancing on the works. The disposal squad dealt with the bombs next morning. (Note: This attack was probably that which occurred on 16th September 1940 but there seems to be a slight discrepancy over the number of bombs dropped - PA).

On another occasion incendiaries were dropped near some Magisters by Junkers 88s flying in daylight formation.

The next attack came at 15.45 hrs on 16th September 1940, when ten bombs were dropped across the aerodrome, all of which fortunately failed to explode.

A further attack was made on 3rd October 1940 when six bombs were dropped across the centre of Woodley from east to west, three of which were delayed action. On 6th October, two bombs were dropped in an allotment 50 yards north of the aerodrome and this time windows and hangar walls were damaged, as were three Magisters which were slightly damaged by bomb splinters. However, no major damage was ever inflicted to the factory as a result of enemy action.

Possibly as a result of these air-raids, or even because of forward thinking by Miles, Guy Morgan & Partners, chartered architects of Reading and London (who had designed many of the buildings on the aerodrome), were asked to prepare a 'Scheme for An Underground Bomb-proof Workshop for Messrs Phillips & Powis Aircraft Ltd'. A brochure, dated 26th September 1940 (reproduced in Appendix 2), was issued and this gave full details of how the workshop was to be constructed and operated. Various locations were suggested for its construction and pros and cons of each site were discussed in some detail. Drawings of the layout of factory and method of construction of the tunnels were also included but in the end the project was not proceeded with.

During the early part of the war, Sir Ian Fraser suggested to Miles that it would be a good idea to employ a small number of blind persons, as an experiment of adapting such handicapped people to industrial work had already proved successful in the introduction of industrial machinery into the workshops at St. Dunstan's. The range of semi-skilled operations performed by these sightless workers, of both sexes, at Woodley was surprisingly wide, including machining, and processing such assemblies as fuel tanks. Braille characters were used extensively to convey works instructions to the blind operatives, in a similar manner to that used by blind stenographers on a typewriter, and the 'sixth sense' developed by them was of particular application.

An oblique view across Woodley Aerodrome, from the North-West, taken at 2.30 pm on 13th June 1941. Note the 'hedges' painted across the airfield in an attempt at camouflage; the camouflaged factory buildings in the right centre and the camouflage netting hanging from the roof of the main office building to the right of the two chimneys of the boiler house in the centre. [Photograph P H T Green Collection]

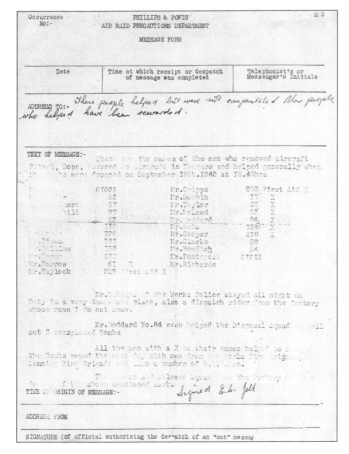

At 8 EFTS Woodley, the OC, Sqdn Ldr J F Moir, was promoted to Wing Commander w.e.f. 23rd September 1940.

It was in March 1941 that certain fundamental changes occurred within the Company. Amongst the few surviving documents from Phillips & Powis Aircraft Ltd are the minutes from the Report presented at the Company's Fifth AGM, which was held at Woodley on Wednesday 12th March 1941. These give a good account of the financial state of the company up to March 1941. The meeting was presided over by the Chairman, Mr A F Sidgreaves OBE and he reported:

The result of the year's trading, we are able to report has resulted in a profit of £77,916, after making the necessary provision for Excess Profits Tax and National Defence Contribution. This has the effect of creating a credit at Profit and Loss Account of £59,425, after writing off the debit balance brought forward. This I think can be regarded as very satisfactory. I propose to return to the Profit and Loss Account after dealing with the main items in the Balance Sheet, which, for comparison purposes, shows the previous year's figures.

The Balance Sheet, I think you will agree, is extremely clean. Goodwill remains the same as in previous years at £15,000. Land, Buildings, Plant, Machinery etc stand at £124,603, as against £131,292 in the former year. Certain extensions have been made to

Left: Phillips & Powis Air Raid Precautions Department. Message Form. Address to: These people helped but were not compensated, other people who helped have been rewarded. (These are the names of the men who removed aircraft, petrol, dope, covered up aircraft in hangars and helped generally when the bombs were dropped on September 16th 1940 at 15.45 hrs: Unfortunately, the names of some of these men have been lost in the copying.)

the Company's properties in 1939 and ample depreciation has been written off. The main extensions were, however, carried out at the Government's expense and are the property of the Government.

No value has been placed on the Shares in the subsidiary Company, which is of course Reading Aero Club Limited. The loan to this Company has been reduced. I shall at a later stage refer to this subsidiary. Investments is a new item in the Balance Sheet and is represented by Shares in a Company which carries out a considerable amount of work for us. A dividend has been received in respect of these Shares and used to write down their cost.

Stock in Hand and Work-in-Progress total £263,913, which shows an increase of £35,408 over the previous year's figure and is, of course, an indication of the increased volume of work in hand. Sundry Debtors - the increase of £117,274 in this figure is accounted for by additional sales to the Ministry of Aircraft Production.

We now come to the liability side of the Balance Sheet. The Nominal Share Capital in the year 1939 has been modified as Rolls-Royce Limited exercised their option to convert the Preference Shares into Ordinary Shares. The Issued Share Capital has been increased during the year by the allotment of a further 5,000 Ordinary Shares. 4% Second Debentures, as in the 1938 Balance Sheet, remain at £15,000. The Bank Overdraft is less that that shown in the 1938 Accounts by some £67,067. This must be considered gratifying when the increased investment in our Floating Assets is taken into account. Bills payable at £875 is self-explanatory. Sundry creditors - owing to the increased turnover and the necessity for the creation of reserves to meet Excess Profits Tax and National Defence Contribution, this figure is naturally increased over that of the previous year.

The recommendations of the Directors have been taken into account in the Balance Sheet, and therefore there are two new items shown in respect of Dividend and Reserve, both of which I will refer to again later. The remaining item on this side of the Balance Sheet is the balance of Profit and Loss carried forward after allowing for the Director's recommendations.

I now return to the year's trading result, and here I must explain the reason why the accounts are so long delayed. Practically the whole of the output of the Company is being taken by the Ministry, and owing to the large amount of sub-contract work, difficulty has been experienced in settling prices. You will realise, I am sure, the necessity of settling all prices for 1939 before the accounts could be finalised. The trading result of £77,916 is, as I have already said, arrived at after making provision for the Company's estimated liability for Excess Profits Tax and National Defence Contribution. In 1939 these taxes were on a basis of 60 per cent Excess Profits Tax for three-quarters of the year, and 5 per cent National Defence Contribution for one-quarter. I would remind you that in 1940, Excess Profits Tax will be on a basis of 100 per cent and in this respect your Company is in a very unfortunate position as the standard years; namely 1935, 1936 and 1937, were years in which development work was carried out, the benefit of which we are now reaping, but they were years in which the Company made losses.

The increase of Excess Profits Tax to 100 per cent is particularly unfair to a Company such as yours, as it does not allow it to build up those reserves which are so necessary to tide over the difficult years with which your Company will be faced after the war. The rate of profit we are allowed to make is strictly controlled, and what we are allowed to retain is so small that it is quite impossible to forecast the future possible returns whilst the Act governing

A later photograph looking over the 'Falcon' towards the main factory with the Repair & Service Department at right centre, shows the extensive hut encampment to the rear of the 'Falcon' to house the personnel of 8 EFTS and lecture rooms and two Blister hangars to the right of the 'Falcon' also for their use. The ground works for the even larger assembly building can just be seen in the background in front of the pre-war assembly building to the east of the main factory.

Excess Profits Tax remains as at present. We are applying for our case to be reviewed before the Referees, to whom application may be made in such cases as ours, where there is unfortunately no reasonable profit standard.

Dealing now with the Director's recommendations, it will be remembered that Rolls-Royce Limited gave up their rights to the accrued Preference Dividend from the time that they invested their money in the Company in 1936 to the end of June 1938, which amounted to no inconsiderable sum. Out of the Profit, therefore, of £59,425 the Directors recommend the payment of Dividend on those Preference Shares for the half-year ended 31st December 1938, which amounts to £2,187 10s 0d. They also recommend a Dividend of 5 per cent on the paid-up capital of the Company as at 7th March 1941, which will absorb the sum of £14,663 5s 0d, and after transferring £30,000 to the reserve for Income Tax, and creating a reserve of £10,000, there is a balance of £2,575 2s 7d which it is proposed to carry forward. The £10,000 recommended to be placed to reserve is considered necessary to enable the Company to build up reserves so that development work can be carried on for the future benefit of the Company. The transfer to Income Tax Reserve no doubt appears to be a large sum, but provision has to be made for a rate of 8s 6d in the £.

You will realise, I feel sure, that under the existing War conditions it is not permissible for me to tell you very much about your Company's activities during the year 1939. I can state, however, quite definitely that the amount of development work carried out in previous years has been well rewarded. On the outbreak of war we ceased to manufacture all civil types of machines, and I am revealing no secret in stating that we have been solely employed on the manufacture of aircraft for the Royal Air Force since then. Your Company has also been entrusted with the management of a Shadow Factory for the manufacture of the Company's products.

Reading Aero Club - This subsidiary company made a profit in the year 1939 which was sufficient to write off the debit standing at the Profit and Loss Account and to carry forward in the books of that company a credit balance. The Air Ministry has also requisitioned the aircraft, the property of this company, and when this transaction is agreed the result will be that the loan from the parent company will be liquidated. The assets of that company will then be represented wholly by cash.

Relations with all branches of the Air Ministry and Ministry of Aircraft Production continue to be on a most satisfactory basis. The war, naturally, has thrown an additional strain on the Directors, Administrative Staff and Employees of the Company, but this, and the sacrifices required from everyone who has been requested to work longer hours that usual without the customary relaxation of week-ends and holidays, have been shouldered with cheerfulness and a resolution which is praiseworthy.

A new name appears in the list of Directors, that of Mr E W Hives, MBE, who is Works Director of Rolls-Royce Limited, and your Company is fortunate in being able to call on his extensive experience. Our thanks are due to the two Managing Directors, Mr F G Miles and Lt Colonel Darby, for the unceasing efforts they have put into the management of the Company and to the Staff and Workers for their efficient and loyal service throughout the year

Immediately following this AGM, A F Sidgreaves, E W Hives and Lt Col Darby, who together represented Rolls-Royce on the Board of Directors, all resigned. The 500,000 Cumulative Convertible Preference Shares previously held by Rolls Royce were converted into Ordinary Shares and were purchased by F G Miles in April 1941 for the sum of £60,000. It was agreed that Rolls-Royce would take over control of the shadow factory at South Marston and that Lt Col Darby was to be lent to the MAP as its Controller. A new board was then formed comprising F G Miles as Chairman and Managing Director, with Blossom Miles, George Miles and W H Gatty Saunt as co-directors.

The mystery surrounding the question of where Miles had obtained the £60,000 to purchase the shares from Rolls-Royce can now be answered, as it has recently been found that he borrowed it from the Amalgamated Roadstone Corporation of which W H Gatty Saunt was Chairman! This then also resolved the mystery of just who Gatty Saunt was and how he had become involved with the company!

However, unbeknown to anyone at the time, or for a long time after for that matter, there was to be a major consequence to Gatty Saunt joining the board. In agreeing to become a co-director, Gatty Saunt had stipulated that his accountants, Hogg Bullimore & Co be appointed to join the existing auditors, Messrs. Kemp, Chatteris, Nicholls Sendell & Co, to audit the accounts and for Samuel R Hogg of Hogg Bullimore & Co to look after his financial interests and act as Financial Advisor to the firm.

Thus began an association between Samuel R Hogg and Phillips & Powis Aircraft Ltd (and later Miles Aircraft Ltd, after the name of the firm was changed on 5th October 1943) which was, in late 1947, to have far reaching and catastrophic consequences for the Company.

Prior to the Board changes, Miles had concerned himself mainly with technical matters, since the financial and business side had been controlled initially by Charles Powis, and later by Lt Colonel Darby, but now that the Company had virtually passed into the hands of the Miles family, F G Miles had to turn his attention to administration, while George Miles took over the duties of Technical Director and Chief Designer.

The new directors made a happy combination; the practical but impetuous Miles, with his tremendous energy, enthusiasm, force of character and drive; George, with his clear, logical and incisive mind, while also sharing his brother's flair for design and mechanical ingenuity, and Blossom, clear-thinking, calm and well-balanced - a perfect counterpart to her impulsive husband and shy brother-in-law.

In about May/June 1941, the company was instructed to take over the former Westland 'shadow factory' at Doncaster Airport for the further production of the Miles Master Mk.II. Westland Aircraft Ltd of Yeovil had previously established a production line of Lysanders in a large purpose built hangar there, which had been erected by the Ministry of Aircraft Production. These were assembled from components made by Cravens of Sheffield and other local companies but after only 17 had been completed, the contract was cancelled. Very little is known about its transfer to Phillips & Powis, except that Capt Don Ayre, the Manager of the Repair & Service Department at Woodley, and one other person from the same department, were sent there to supervise its setting up.

Components for the Master were also made by other sub-contractors in the locality, including Austin Motors, who ultimately produced 1,100 Master wings and centre sections. The first Master to be completed at Doncaster was collected by Phillips & Powis' assistant test pilot, Hugh Kennedy, and ferried to Woodley, on its first flight, on 30th October 1941. However, after only 10 Masters had been assembled at Doncaster, the Ministry changed its mind yet again and decided to release the factory for the repair and service of Wellington bombers. The remainder of the contract for 190 Master Mk.IIs was then transferred to South Marston, while the last 100 aircraft were cancelled.

As the war progressed, Phillips & Powis ultimately acquired over twenty dispersed sites in Berkshire and the surrounding counties for the production and storage of components and materials etc, and for details of these and their locations see Appendix 4.

On 18th November 1941, George Miles flew a Master Mk.III to the A&AEE at Boscombe Down to collect Don Brown and take him to Woodley. Don was then working for the MAP in London, but while he was at Woodley he flew the tricycle undercarriage M.18, U-0222.

Miles' home, 'Lands End House'; note the caricature of Adolf Hitler standing on the steps and the camouflage painting on the walls!

Don's log book shows that, although he was officially employed by the MAP on the compilation of Pilot's Notes, he also flew the new prototypes at Woodley as they appeared! However, from 10th March 1942, Don began to fly the first two M.18s from Woodley on a regular basis and it must have been at about this time that he obtained his release from the MAP to join Phillips & Powis Aircraft Ltd. He was also soon flying most of the contemporary Miles aircraft types in his capacity as an MAP approved test pilot.

In *Flight* for 20th November 1941 it was announced that, whereas most aircraft firms had employed women tracers almost since flying started: *it remained for Phillips & Powis to take the logical step and institute a school for women draughtsmen. The courses, which are under the direction of the chief draughtsman, last 14 weeks* (and were held at Liverpool Road, Reading - PA). *At the end of the drawing course the pupils spend two months in the works, and after that they begin in the drawing office in real earnest. Those with mathematical knowledge can graduate to the technical department, and some will become designers. It was logical that P&P should start this scheme, for Mrs Miles is herself a mathematician and for some years did as much of the designing as her husband, and all the stress work.*

Then, during mid-1941, Miles 'discovered' the new art of electronics and decided, in typical Miles fashion, that a completely new and lightweight electric auto-pilot would be a great advantage over the 'mechanical' types then in service. Taking 24-year old C R Peter out of the drawing office and 16-year old William Allan 'Bill' Chapman, who had joined the firm from Reading Technical College as a trainee aeronautical engineer, Miles installed them both in a hut in the garden of his home, 'Lands End House', at Lands End, near Twyford, just off the aerodrome.

Their brief was to produce, within two years, a better automatic pilot than any which already existed and they were allowed any books and tools deemed necessary to study the problem. They could also make any experiments deemed necessary but at the end of the two years they had to deliver the goods. Miles told them that he had complete confidence in their ability to undertake the task and, if the completed auto-pilot displayed some unorthodox or revolutionary idea, then so much the better.

The two youngsters soon discovered that electronics could be employed, not only in the elimination of certain awkward mechanical linkages but to also provide that element of novelty so dear to Miles' heart. Following many hours of laboratory experiments and bench testing, the prototype, which had been constructed largely from ex-German parts 'borrowed' from the RAE at Farnborough, was ready for flight testing. The new auto-pilot was installed in the firm's hybrid Nighthawk, U-0225 and this was first flown, by Hugh Kennedy, in July 1942. Chapman recalled, before his death in July 2000, that he used to badger the test pilots to tell him what he wanted to know and during the following months the auto-pilot was flown extensively in the Nighthawk. It was later installed in the company's hack Oxford to gain experience in twin-engined aircraft over longer distances.

The auto-pilot was then fitted to other Miles aircraft, including the M.57 Aerovan and M.60 Marathon, and flight testing continued until mid 1947, when it was considered ready for production. However, with plans for its full-scale production in preparation, the so-called 'financial crisis', which had apparently manifested itself in late 1947, caused the Miles Lightweight auto-pilot, by then named The Miles Co-pilot, to be abandoned.

The two-man team, which had designed and developed the Co-pilot, later developed into the Research Department and moved into a separate building, where there they also designed and produced a range of electric actuators. These developed into the Miles Electric Actuator which was used to operate the trimmers on the Monitor, the flaps on the Aerovan and the undercarriage on the Gemini. They were also later used by other companies, including Canadair to operate the radiator shutters on the Canadair Four, de Havilland on their Hornet and Fairey for use on the Firefly.

Meanwhile in 1942, the Repair & Service Department at Woodley, who undertook installation of modifications, repairs, servicing, major inspections and 'Repairs in Works' to all types of Miles aircraft and also light aircraft of other manufacture, also started to clean and service Spitfires in two large Bellman hangars which had been erected alongside the existing Repair & Service Department at Woodley to provide additional accommodation. It is not known how they became involved in this work but by 1944 it had progressed to complete overhauls, repairs, rebuilds of severely damaged aircraft, the incorporation of modifications and conversion for other roles. By the end of the war, over 300 Spitfires of various marks had been worked on by Phillips & Powis/Miles Aircraft at Woodley and South Marston, see Appendix 38 for details of these.

It was also in 1942 that George Miles, who had been interested in aero-engines for many years, set up a team of four draughtsmen in the dispersed drawing office at Binfield Manor to design and build a six-cylinder, horizontally-opposed, air-cooled engine to give approximately 1,740 hp. This engine was intended to give a better power/weight ratio than existing types of engines and was also planned to be used to provide the power for the Miles 'X' Transport aircraft.

One of the team of designers, Michael S Wooding, recalled that the team was led by Arthur Ham who had previously been an expert on the design of ticket machines. One of the other draughtsmen was Sid Porter, who had been an illustrator for *Autocar* magazine before the war and whose artist's impressions of Miles aircraft were to later appear in many of the firm's brochures and publications. Michael was responsible for the camshaft, tappets and valve gear and each of the team had a portion of the engine to produce. The first engine was built by the Experimental Department at Woodley and Michael recalls that he was responsible for installing the completed engine in what was laughingly called a 'test house' which was in reality a small shed on the south-west side of the aerodrome, adjacent to the gravel pits.

The engine was actually tested on a dynamometer up to about 70% full power 'on the bench' but further development had to be abandoned due to all resources, of necessity, having to be directed to the war effort. Michael remembers that, while the installation of the engine in the test house was in progress, he had a grandstand view of George Miles attempting to test fly the M.35 Libellula, which helps to date the bench-test running of the Miles engine to about May 1942. About this time, George was also involved in the design of a range of variable pitch propellers but apart from a few photographs of drawings of these, little else is known of this work.

An interesting document on the problems with the Experimental Department, entitled: 'Notes made by George H Miles, was dated 24th July 1942 and this was presumably an internal memorandum addressed to Stuart White, the then Manager of the Experimental Department.

This shows that things did not always run smoothly at Woodley all the time!:

My impressions of yesterday's discussion on the work of the Experimental Department in general and upon the details of the M.38/28 in particular were generally unfavourable. Firstly it was most unfortunate that a meeting of this sort should be called on the spur of the moment and in a moment of heat instead of being held in an atmosphere of calm and logical investigation. It was still more unfortunate that, under these circumstances, a number of juniors should have been brought into the discussion.

Secondly it is patently obvious to an impartial observer exactly what the fundamental cause of the trouble is. And, whatever it might be, yesterday's methods could do no possible good in that they made no attempt to ascertain their cause. Now it seems quite clear to me that the basic causes of the present state of affairs are these:-

a)   The present capacity of Experimental Department both as regards space, staff and machine tools is totally inadequate to deal in a reasonable time with anything like the number of jobs now in hand.

b)   Notwithstanding this fact additional jobs are gaily undertaken without a thought as to how they are to be accomplished.

c)   Worse still, promises are given regarding completion, promises which a moment's thought would show to be quite impossible of attainment.

d)   The situation would at least have been alleviated if some action had been taken towards the expansion of Experimental Department, as advanced by us 3 months ago: but no action was

taken and since then both the Halifax bomb doors (for more details of these see Appendix 39 - PA) and the M.38/28 have been added to an already badly overloaded Department.

e)   There is no clear policy of priority closely correlated to a programme of production. If this were done the whole situation would immediately be clarified and the futility of the promised dates of completion would become obvious.

The whole of the forgoing may be summarised by saying that there is no programme of work in which full cognisance is taken of capacity, work in hand and possible dates of completion.

The above, however, is by no means the whole cause of the trouble, for the policy of administration is also far from satisfactory and yesterday's discussion was an illustration of the worst features of this policy. It really boils down to this. If you are to be responsible for the efficient running of the Department it is essential for a more rigid system of control to be exercised by you than is the case at present.

In other words it is necessary for you to say definitely (and in the light of the present programme) exactly what jobs are to be pushed ahead and such instruction must emanate from you and from you only. It is, I am convinced, most undesirable for matters to be taken out of your hands, as they were yesterday and an investigation held into a job which is being performed by your Department. If it is felt that you are in some way at fault, the matter should be taken up with you and dealt with properly - that is by investigating it from the source of the trouble.

It should not be dealt with in a hasty manner and by attention to details only, while ignoring the basic reasons for the state of affairs. I stress this point because I feel, and my opinion is based on similar experience, that it is impossible for you to control the Department under such conditions. There is only one further detail to which I would draw attention, although it is covered in . . .

Unfortunately, the last page of this document is missing but it seems that all was not well with the Department and that things would have to change, to change fast, and for the better!

Among the plethora of projects and new types designed during the war was the M.30 'X' Minor, a flying scale model of the proposed 1936 'X' airliner series, which was so dear to Miles' heart. Other projects also included a series of twin-engined, multi-purpose aircrew trainer studies; a large wooden glider capable of transporting tanks; four and six-engined large transport project studies; an advanced trainer based on the Master Mk.II, where the instructor sat in a raised seat above and to the rear of the pilot (which was later developed into the M.37 Advanced Trainer, in turn adapted from the Martinet target tower) and details of all these design studies may be found in subsequent chapters.

Production of the Master Mk.I and Mk.II continued apace at Woodley with a total of 900 Mk.I and 1,250 Mk.II being completed before its place on the assembly line was taken by the M.25 Martinet target-tower. A total of 1,724 Martinets and 69 M.50 Queen Martinets were produced with the final Martinets sharing the assembly line with the new twin-engined M.33 Monitor high speed target-tower.

On 23rd September 1942, Phillips & Powis Aircraft Ltd transferred from Associate Constructor to Ordinary Member of the SBAC and F G Miles was co-opted on to the SBAC Council.

In January 1943, Phillips & Powis produced a brochure entitled *Miles Specialised Aircraft for Specialised Purposes*. This contained a summary of a selection of 14 Miles aircraft which had either been built or proposed up to then. Brief details of each listed on the next page were given and these have been used in the compilation of this story, appearing in their appropriate chapter.

CONTENTS

Introduction

In the days of peace Miles aeroplanes established for themselves an unrivalled reputation in the field of sporting flying and of privately owned aircraft. That this is no idle boast is proved by the fact that in 1935 Miles aeroplanes gained 1st, 2nd, 3rd, 5th and 6th places in the classic King's Cup Race - an achievement never before approached by any firm in the industry. In 1936 a development of these sporting types - the Magister - was adopted as the RAF's first ab initio trainer of the low wing monoplane type.

About the same time, despite official apathy, the firm foresaw the need for a specialised high performance advanced trainer to train pilots for the new monoplane types then coming into Service. Accordingly, entirely of its own initiative, the firm produced the

Kestrel trainer which was the fastest trainer in the world - a distinction which its development, the Master holds to this day. The Kestrel was some 40 mph faster than the contemporary Battle, 20 mph faster than the Blenheim and only 20 mph slower than the Hurricanes then coming into Service. The success of this machine was shown by the placing of the largest contract ever placed for a training aeroplane.

With the advent of war the firm realised that the need for specialised aircraft was greater than ever and in the following pages is a brief description of some of the designs which have been put forward to the Ministry to meet the multifarious needs of the Service. It should be added that the designs quoted are by no means all those which have been submitted. Among those omitted are a diminutive radio controlled aeroplane carrying a 1,000 lb bomb: a troop carrying glider which was readily convertible at short notice into a low powered aeroplane: a proposal for a large six engined freighter designed for quick mass production: a twin engined intermediate trainer and a recent suggestion for a power assisted troop carrying glider.

Sufficient is shown, however, in the following pages to indicate that the firm has spared no pains in their endeavours to cater for the Nations needs and that those types which they have been allowed to produce have, without exception, been outstandingly successful.

The sheer diversity of types and operational roles catered for in this selection up to January 1943 is really quite astounding and details of all the types mentioned in the brochure and many others not mentioned, will be found in this volume.

A new, large assembly building was constructed alongside the pre-war building in late 1942 and photographs of this under construction are shown here.

Above: A partially completed Miles M.25 Martinet, possibly the first prototype, standing outside the original assembly building in 1942. Note the ground-works and the steel framework for the new building at far right. Below: These photographs, together with those on the next page, show the new assembly building taking shape.

Four views of the new assembly building at Woodley taking shape in late 1942.

It was also in 1943 that Miles proposed, as a basis for discussion, that a post war airport for London should be built at Cliffe on the Hoo Peninsular, north of Rochester, Kent, near the Thames Estuary, and if only the powers-to-be had listened to him then this could well have formed the basis for London's post war airport. Choosing a site such as this, well away from habitation, would have provided none of the subsequent chaos that surrounded the construction of Heathrow, the government of the day's chosen site, which ultimately became London's Airport in 1946.

However, it took successive governments until 2002 to finally identify the same site at Cliffe as the leading contender among all the subsequent potential sites for a new airport for London, although it is now 2012 and still nothing has been done about it! Miles' thoughts on the subject were published in *Flight* for 3rd June 1943, under the heading:

Mr F G Miles on Our Bombing and Civil Policies:

At a gathering in London last week Mr Miles pleaded for a realisation that we have passed into a new era, which demands new ideas and, above all, up-to-date thinking and action. Following are extracts from his talk.

A well-known aeronautical engineer told me, in the bar of the Royal Aero Club, that I was talking nonsense when I forecast two years ago 100 and 200 seater aircraft in the not too distant future. The engineer who said that was chief adviser to a well-known airway company, but I still say that there will be, not only 100 and 200 seaters, but 500 and 600 seaters. There is a lot of talk now about post-war planning, but I would like to make it clear that none can have the direction and purpose without an attempt at a world-wide picture of events.

I say this: we are passing from the 40 mile-per-hour age to the 400 mile-an-hour age. We have reached the 300 mile-an-hour stage, and it will not be long before we get the 400. We are passing from the age of steam to the air age.

Thinking at 40 mph

England is already behind the United States in that change. I suggest the action which we ought to take now to be in the vanguard of progress. If we don't the stream of change and time will carry us away to wreckage. It is not a matter of inventing a new order; something has happened, and is still happening, but you will not see much at 400 mph with 40 mph reactions.

I would like to say a word about bombs and bombing. So far we have only played with aircraft in war. No one can say that Germany is not a fighting nation, but we are shaking them to the foundations under the blows of less than a thousand aircraft. Last week we read about some of those things, of large numbers of people who have been flooded and driven from their industrial cities, their factories and homes, like ants from a crushed ant hill.

I know that it is possible to make bombers capable of carrying 25, 28 and 30 tons of bombs and carry them at faster speeds, and I know that it could have been done five years ago if we had believed in the air sufficiently. With thousands of machines, said the C-in-C Bomber Command, we could end the war in a few weeks. I believe that that is absolutely factual and that so many aircraft are not an impossible conception.

As soon as you admit the uncomfortable premise that a great modern war could be ended in a few weeks by bombing on a sufficient scale, you see the world no longer as a number of isolated units.

You will also see that one-sided development of industry, of invention, of political ideas, of faith, like Nazi-ism, allowed to grow in one country for ten years, can only lead to greater and greater man-made catastrophes. Not the sort of vision I want to hold for our children's future.

But since the world will certainly not wake up to this changed picture of things overnight, we who believe in our way of life must see that we do not drop behind; we must be consistent and active in our planning until there is agreement among nations. We could rely upon no one in 1939 except ourselves.

We surely must not omit nor avoid those steps necessary to secure our place as an air power for the next ten years, while we hope and pray for the accomplishment of a better world understanding. It is our job to be leaders if we have any faith in ourselves at all.

Quite apart from security and, for that matter, from air power, there is this question of national vitality. If we permit negative and conditioned thinking to justify inaction while we wait for some possible thing to happen, and if we try to make our future a path of return to yesterday (and I am not talking politically) we shall be lost.

There are symptoms of this kind of thinking observable. To take one instance only, this question of converted bombers. It may be a useful and permissible thing to do if it is not made an excuse for real progress on the scale necessary. I don't object to using converted bombers temporarily but I do object to saying that we have some converted bombers, therefore, the whole problem is solved.

The problems of today are new and need vision. For instance, do not consider air transport as a third-rate architect considers fitting a bathroom to a tumble-down Victorian mansion, as a very regrettable necessity, but as a cornerstone of a new England. Plan the future around optimum and optimistic chances and not around the maximum of past difficulties. We may well consider the only rational thing to do after the war is to get together in an amicable way with the Allied nations round the council table and make logical arrangements about world air transport.

Especially must we avoid official planning on bureaucratic lines. The job of the Civil Service is not to criticise and filter ideas but to clear the channels of action. The roots of Britain's future are in the present. It is the action and not the talking we do now which will determine our position in the world in ten years' time.

Education and Research

We must extend education and research both in a centralised and decentralised manner on the scale which is now blazingly necessary.

Replying to questions, Mr Miles said that sites suitable for London's terminal airport had been viewed along the Thames. "My idea," he said, "is that aeronautical universities should be built very close to this airport. So many experts never see any flying. The landing ground would have runways at least three miles long. "I do not think that the question of the fog belt will make any difference in five years' time. Thames barges I do not think would interfere with the landing of flying boats, for a special lagoon could be constructed for the aircraft. If jet propulsion becomes successful the speed of aircraft will go up at no extra cost by about 100 miles an hour. I think that it is essential that bases should be marked out now and the red lines drawn on the map, and we should be prepared to operate with British aircraft. Five years ahead I envisage aircraft with an economic cruising speed of 320 miles an hour operating between London and New York. These aircraft I visualise as 100 seaters."

Thus spoke a man of true vision, for whom I have nothing but the greatest of admiration and respect - if only they'd listened, then perhaps we wouldn't be in the mess we are in today, having to rely on other people and countries, not only for aeroplanes but for just about for everything else - PA.

Taking the idea of a Thames-side airport one stage further, Miles had already commissioned his architects, Guy Morgan & Partners, to draw up a proposal for a site suitable for both flying boats and landplanes not only within easy reach of London but far enough

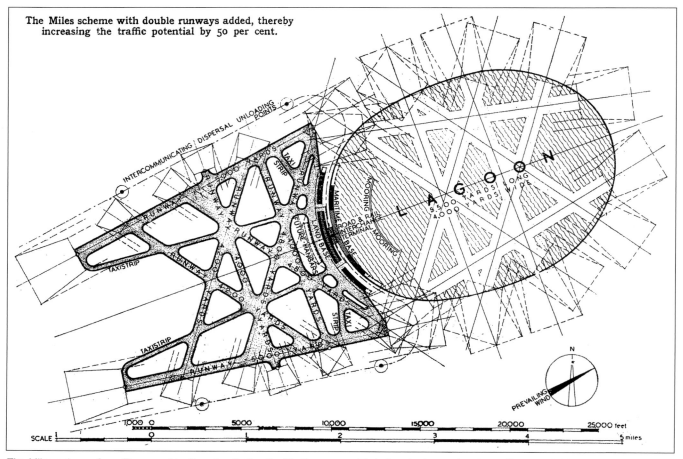

The Miles scheme with double runways added, thereby increasing the traffic potential by 50 per cent.

The Miles scheme for a Thames-side Airport, with the Double Runways added, thereby increasing the traffic potential by 50 per cent.
[Drawing from Flight *for 27th April 1944]*

away from it so as not to cause the chaos that we now see today around Heathrow, the chosen site. This proposal was published in *Flight* for 29th July 1943 under the title:

Thinking of the Future

F G Miles suggests £20 Million Airport on the Thames:

Past experience has shown that, in aviation, however large one builds, however one tries to anticipate future requirements, that which seemed lavish yesterday becomes inadequate tomorrow. Mr F G Miles, chairman of Phillips & Powis Ltd, was doubtless very sensible of this fact when he began to think of the sort of airport which London will want after the war. Taking as his basis the sort of aircraft that can be foreseen for the next ten or fifteen years, he began with the assumption that runways some 2½-3 miles long will be required. In view of the still unsettled question as to whether landplanes or flying boats, or both, will be used for long-distance air routes in the years to come, he included in his scheme an artificial lagoon large enough to serve for the taking off and alighting of any flying boat that can be foreseen at present.

Site on the Thames

Gradually the general scheme was evolved, and Mr Guy Morgan, of Guy Morgan and Partners, architects and engineers, undertook the detailed design. Not because the particular site is the only possible one, but because there is a certain air of unreality about a scheme based upon generalities, the layout was based upon a part of the Kentish coast, opposite Canvey Island, and lying roughly between Cliffe and Allhallows, the flat nature of which lends itself admirably to the project. It should be made clear that no authorities have been approached and no attempt made to ascertain the actual value of the land in question. This, however, is not expected to be excessively high in view of the nature of the land.

Our photographs show a scale model of the suggested airport. The longest runway (2½ miles) lies in the direction of the prevailing winds, running from south-west to north-east. The main airport buildings are situated between the airfield and the artificial lagoon. This arrangement would have the advantage of single control, economy of structure and rapid transport. On the banks of the lagoon are hangars into which the flying boats could be towed for loading and unloading, and the landplanes would have their corresponding hangars on the edge of the airfield.

The three main transport services - air, rail and road - have been catered for in the main buildings. They are on three levels, vertically superimposed. This arrangement reduces the lateral movement of passengers and freight to about 100 yards. Confusion between passenger road traffic is eliminated by elevated road level which serves the passenger terminal above the railway station. Car and road transport parking is provided under cover between the road and rail levels. Ramped approaches lead direct from the main perimeter.

Existing road and rail services in the locality would form links with London, which could be reached in about half an hour by fast train. Near the site is in existing cement works which would reduce transport during the construction of runways and buildings. The layout has been so planned that construction could, if deemed necessary in the interests of caution, be done in stages. This applies not only to the airfield but to the lagoon. If it were deemed doubtful that the latter would be necessary, use could be made to begin with of a tidal basin, the actual take-offs and landings being on the estuary itself.

It is estimated that the cost of the complete scheme would be in the neighbourhood of £20 million. In these days of war expenditure that represents roughly the cost of the war for a day! But even on a peace time basis, Mr Miles points out that up to the beginning of the war we had spent about £15 million on commercial aviation.

If the lagoon were omitted, the cost would be reduced by something like £4 million. It is estimated that the airport would handle eight million passengers a year, plus a large volume of freight.

Meanwhile, with the rapid expansion of the company and the increase in scope of the experimental work given to the firm by the RAE Farnborough, it was felt by 1943 that a wind-tunnel would be a great asset. Prior to this, the 'aerodynamics department' had consisted of just two men and a lady assistant, 'who could work a slide rule and was apparently very good at doing what was asked of her'! The Chief Aerodynamicist was Dennis S Bancroft, who had graduated from Northampton Polytechnic just before the war and who had joined the company from Handley Page in 1939, and he was later ably assisted by Derek Ruben.

In the early days, full-scale flight tests were undertaken by means of quickly constructed flying mock-ups and this sufficed for many years but in 1942 it was felt that the services of another qualified aerodynamicist would be useful and at that time Derek Ruben, who had just graduated, was looking for employment in the aircraft industry.

He had written to the Bristol Engine Co, Taylorcraft Aeroplanes (England) Ltd and Phillips & Powis and had been offered jobs by all three, but he chose Phillips & Powis because he liked what they were doing and therefore, soon settled in! However, as all the company's work (officially at least!) had, since the outbreak of war, been the subject of 'official' contracts, the need for a wind tunnel became apparent and the Ministry was approached for aid in constructing it.

Characteristically, this was refused, but there were a couple of old barns standing together at Davis Farm, just off the eastern edge of Woodley aerodrome so, with the help of a local builder these were converted into a useful 36ft long with a 4ft working section, closed-circuit wind-tunnel. The company manufactured the smoothing vanes and provided the instrumentation, while the power was provided by the Rolls-Royce Kestrel engine from the prototype M.9 Kestrel. This engine was fitted with an appropriate fan and the tunnel proved an immediate success. The Ministry were then invited to see it to prove that it was possible to manufacture such a useful tool, even without their assistance.

In 1943, Miles had an idea for an aeroplane which could be converted very simply into a motor-car. Two photographs have survived to show the general idea but nothing came of the project. In 1946, a Texas airman produced a "Revolutionary flying automobile" which was described as a "Roadable airplane," and this was later completed and flown. Was this another first for Miles?

It was also during 1943, that Miles and Blossom were considering the foundation of a special school, as they were convinced that the average youngster did not have the opportunity to develop and use his or her latent talent. Miles' own case was a good example of this, and although he was by no means average, had it not been for his father's generosity in allowing him to develop his own latent talents, it is unlikely that he would ever have achieved what he did.

At about this time Miles and Blossom met Tigor Csato, a Hungarian doctor and psychologist who also shared their views and, on 24th March 1943, together they founded the Miles Aeronautical Technical School for boys and girls of 16-21 years of age. Walter Evans was appointed to be its manager of training, and the remaining buildings at Davis Farm were taken over for use as classrooms (see photograph on page 32).

Equal opportunity for all was to be the keynote, regardless of age, sex or nationality, and The Miles Technical School provided courses in engineering, draughtsmanship, aircraft design and production engineering.

On the technical side, the students were expected to attend eight or ten lectures a week on mathematics and engineering subjects, the better students on this side to reach AMIMechE standard. Lectures on non-engineering subjects were arranged frequently and a full social programme was also organised by the students.

Formal instruction was to be kept to a minimum and one feature of the school was that nothing should be drawn or made unless it was actually going to be used. The students were encouraged to see a job through from its initial design and manufacture to its installation on the actual job.

In August 1943, Miles asked the students to design an aeroplane specifically for use as a test bed for a new automatic pilot, which was then under development. A specification was laid down for a high-wing monoplane powered by two DH Gipsy Six motors, with a nose-wheel undercarriage and a low landing speed. Accommodation was to be provided for a crew of four, including two flight-test observers with a work bench.

Girl students at that time were the only members with drawing training and 12 of them drew up designs and a general arrangement drawing. The name 'Venture' was appropriately selected for the aircraft, which became the centre around which the theoretical and practical work was correlated. Students designed, drew, stressed and made every part of the Venture, with the obvious exception of the engines.

By the end of 1943, many drawings had been completed, including the detailed drawings of the wings, the line drawings of the fuselage and many components. The wing spar had been built and the wing details were in process of being assembled. The fuselage mock-up had been completed and was used for design checks and, in addition, work had begun on metal fittings. In addition to this a smoke tunnel 20ft long and 7ft high had been designed and almost constructed, and much work done on the fabric of the school buildings.

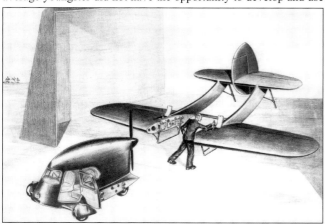

An artist's impression showing the rear portion of the Miles Convertible Aeroplane being easily detached, leaving the cabin and engine for use as a motor car.

An artist's impression of the Miles Convertible Aeroplane in flight.

Davis Farm, just off the north-eastern edge of the aerodrome. This was the site of The Miles Technical School and comprised a collection of wooden huts in which the class-rooms were situated and two Robin hangars. The Miles Wind Tunnel was also constructed there in an old barn just out of picture but to the right of the hangars.   *[Photograph P H T Green Collection]*

A short film showing students at work on the Venture and carrying out other activities in the school has recently been released by *Pathe News* and this interesting film is available on CD for the payment of an appropriate fee. Unfortunately, however, due to the so-called 'financial crisis' of late 1947, the Venture was not completed and the school itself did not survive long enough to assess the degree to which the founders' aims would have been achieved, see Appendix 6 for further details of the Miles Technical School and the Venture.

On 26th March 1943, the *First Reunion Dinner of the Pioneer Employees of Phillips & Powis Aircraft Ltd* was held and a small booklet was given to each of the diners to commemorate the occasion. This booklet gave the names of all the 'Pioneers' together with the date each joined the firm and in it was "A Message from F G Miles":

As a tree is rooted in the ground, or as a house must rest upon foundations, so must all progress, art, science, politics, or industry begin with a small group of people - the pioneers in their field. The roots of the now enormous organisation of Phillips & Powis Aircraft Ltd are composed of the employees of the Company who worked cheerfully (and almost continuously) during those early days between 1930 and 1936. It was then that the ideas and designs, many of them revolutionary in aeronautics, were being worked out. All of us remember the tension and excitement which arose when a new type was ready to fly, or when a racing machine reached the testing stage, or some fresh gadget was mocked up and flown. There was a spirit of mutual attainment and of family pride to be felt in the atmosphere which is especial and peculiar to a small concern growing through the effort of all its members. And

the fact that a certain amount of romance was attached to the flying business helped quite a lot.

What was that worth to those of us who were working in those now far-off days? Certainly the hope of wages or profit was not the preponderant feeling; the reward of working in a team towards a mutual and well understood purpose seemed to me to provide a satisfaction and sense of achievement not easily measured or replaced.

It may be that the happiness of working with a common and exciting end is not replaceable and no amount of better or richer living can make up for the joy of working too hard, too long and too cheaply on a job we all shared. It often seems that way to me when I indulge in nostalgic memories of the past described in summary on another page. In fact, although I believe we must have a better life and more security through wiser laws such as Sir William Beveridge foreshadows, I am sure it is also necessary to recapture something of the pioneering spirit of our early days - if men's spirits as well as their physical needs, are to be satisfied.

And I am thankful to providence for the fun we had together when P&P was small and unproved and Miles aircraft were only just beginning to make their mark.

The Aeroplane for 9th April 1943 reported on the occasion thus: *A 'Miles Occasion' when more than 100 "founder employees of Phillips & Powis Ltd attended a recent reunion dinner. All had been with the company since 1930, and some since 1929 when P & P first entered the aeronautical field by acquiring an aerodrome and*

Roll of Pioneers:

1929
August: A G Boyd

1930
March: J Goddard

1931
May: Miss G E Hayes (later to become Mrs Kennedy)
August: S Dowling

1932
February: A H Johnson
March: G E L Avenhall
August: A V Bucknole
September: A Clarke (Bert Clarke's father), F G Miles,
Mrs M F Miles
October: Harry Hull

1933
March: C M Collard, A G Towndrow
April: G W Chapman, L Cooper, L M Williams
May: S B Grummett, L Waugh, A W Wilson
June: W H Clarke
July: F T Beasley, D S Broughton, W Curran,
R E Fullbrook, H Hall, M H A Longhurst,
A Marven, R Rudge
August: D J L Culver, C House
September: A J Pratt, H Willatts
October: B J Davies, C L Nash
November: C Hart

1934
January: W E Collins, R E Smith
February: A W Johnson, F W Stevens, C Sumner
March: R Marriner, A R Seer, G Snow, A E Tappenden
April: L Chapman, S L Goff, R E Miles
June: R H J Froomes, W H K Spooner
July: Miss L R English (later to become Mrs Condy),
M S Robinson
August: E W Brown, W Mathias, K P Godfrey

opening a flying club. Mr A H Johnson was in the chair, and speeches were made by Mr F G Miles (Chairman of the Company), Mrs Miles, Mr L A Hackett, Mr G McW Bennett, Mr S O Smith and F/L "Tommy" Rose.

On 1st April 1943, the South Marston factory was officially transferred to Vickers-Armstrong Supermarine for modification work on Spitfires, but this work had already been going on for some time under Phillips & Powis. The factory later completed assembly of Castle Bromwich built major Spitfire components and Supermarine retained control of the main factory at South Marston after the war for production of their Attacker, Swift and Scimitar aircraft.

In 1954 I had occasion to visit the factory in connection with my work for Supermarines and while having tea in the canteen later, I was surprised to see that the crockery and cutlery bore the inscription 'Phillips & Powis'. But, to my lasting regret, I never 'acquired' a piece as a souvenir!

On 5th October 1943, the name of the company was changed from Phillips & Powis Aircraft Ltd to Miles Aircraft Ltd as it was considered that the time had finally come to sever the link with the previous name, as by then neither Phillips nor Powis retained any interest in the company and the aircraft had always been known as 'Miles' anyway. Just prior to this change of name, the company had also been honoured with election to full membership of the Society of British Aircraft Constructors.

It was also during 1943, that the Minister of Aircraft Production, by then Sir Stafford Cripps, suggested to Miles that in order to increase aircraft production and alleviate the unemployment in Northern Ireland, it would be conducive to the war effort to set up a factory in the Province.

So, towards the end of 1943, a small team of 'pioneers' led by Walter Capley established a factory in a disused linen mill at Banbridge, Co. Down, in conditions which were far from ideal. The unit began by manufacturing Monoplane Air Tails (MAT), codenamed TORA, (these were stabilising equipment for air-launched torpedoes which had been designed by the firm) and components for aircraft in production at Woodley, and later it was also agreed that, of the 250 Messengers ordered for the RAF, the majority should be built in Northern Ireland.

However, Banbridge was 15 miles away from the nearest airfield, which was RAF Long Kesh, and the Messengers had to be transported there by road for assembly. The first Messenger to be built in Northern Ireland, RH420, made its first flight from Long Kesh in August 1945. Ten Messengers for the RAF and the first civilian Messenger were built at Banbridge, with probably the first five being test flown from Long Kesh, before production was transferred in early 1946 to a new purpose-built factory, rented fro the Northern Ireland government, at Newtownards, Co. Down.

In October 1945 it was planned to build M.28s, M.38 Messengers and M.65 Geminis there in order to leave Woodley free for the production of the heavier types envisaged and a new subsidiary company, Miles Aircraft (Northern Ireland) Ltd, was formed to run the operation with the talented Walter Capley as Manager.

Since the mid-thirties, Miles had expressed a great interest in large airliners of advanced form with an aerofoil section fuselage which blended into thick wings incorporating buried engines. He had designed a number of these airliners under the project title 'X' and by 1943 had been assured by the MAP that his latest 'X' design study would be looked on favourably by the Brabazon airliner committee.

The Brabazon Committee Report was actually delivered to the MAP and the Secretary of State for Air on 9th February 1943 but remained 'of a secret character' at the time. As Hansard reported for 17th February 1943: *Mr Perkins asked the Secretary of State for Air whether the Brabazon Committee have issued a report; and whether it will be available to Members?*

Sir A Sinclair replied that the Committee presented their report to my Right Hon Friend the Minister of Aircraft Production and myself on 9th February, the report is of a secret character, and I regret that it will not be possible to arrange for publication. Mr Simmonds asked: Does this Committee continue to sit, and will it make further reports, or has it completed its task? In response Sir A Sinclair said it has completed its task.

Nine years later, a letter from Don Brown appeared in *Flight* for 21st March 1952 on the question: *Did the Brabazon Committee Fail?*

On page 278 of the March 7th issue of Flight you quote Mr Peter Masefield's remarks on lessons to be learned from the work of the Brabazon Committee. He is also quoted as saying that the committee performed a national service of the first importance. No one will deny the unenviable nature of the task of trying to predict future requirements in the ever-changing world of air transport or the courage of any committee undertaking such a commitment: but surely the importance of such service to the nation should be judged by the measure of its success and, to judge by the particulars given by Mr Masefield, the recommendations of the Brabazon Committee were sadly wide of the mark.

The Brabazon I was envisaged as a 25-seater. It is hard to see how this was expected to be a paying proposition: while one might also question the wisdom of designing an aircraft with a cruising speed of only about 250 mph for a long-range, over-water route on which head-winds of 60 mph and more are encountered.

Be that as it may, the fact remains that after nine years and the expenditure of millions of pounds, the prototype has not yet completed its flight trials; and when it does, there appears little likelihood of its ever being used for the purpose for which it was proposed. The Brabazon II was specified by the Brabazon Committee to carry 24 passengers where, in fact, a machine of two to three times that capacity was required. Similarly, the Brabazon IIB was to carry 27 passengers, and has fortunately been capable of re-design to accommodate 40.

The Brabazon III never materialized.

The Brabazon IV was envisaged as a mailplane, whereas its success is due to the fact that it developed into something quite different - a very much larger aircraft to carry passengers.

The Brabazon Va specification was written around a private venture design put forward by Miles: and even that is not yet in service although pressure is being put upon an unwilling BEAC to use it.

The Brabazon Vb specification was, I believe, written to cover another PV design, the Dove, the success of which is due to the de Havilland Company.

So, out of the seven specifications with which the Brabazon Committee are credited, only one, the Brabazon III, appears to have been what was wanted: and that, ironically enough, was not ordered. With the exception of the PV Dove, not one of the other types is yet in use.

While making full allowance for the difficulties confronting the committee, how, in view of the results, can its work be regarded as other than a failure? Surely the first lesson to be learned from all this is not to put your trust in committees: or, as I heard it said the other day, "If Moses had been a committee, the Israelites would still be in Egypt!"

But I am getting ahead of myself!

From contemporary correspondence which has recently come to light, it is clear that the MAP never seriously intended to even consider the Miles project, despite their assurances, even though they accepted the fact that Miles was correct in his assumption that his 'X' design was far superior to the Bristol design actually chosen to meet the requirement. The reason for the Ministry's 'under-handedness', has still to be discovered but the surviving correspondence confirms that the relationship between Miles and the MAP throughout the war years was often quite 'stormy'! This correspondence also makes it abundantly clear that Miles was 'a doer' who had little or no time for bureaucracy, especially when he knew that the latter was not prepared to keep up with him!

A letter from Miles to Air Marshal R F Sorley, (CRD), MAP, dated 16th August 1943, brought forth a reply dated 8th October 1943 which was to firmly deny Miles the chance of being allowed to compete for the Brabazon project on the flimsiest of excuses, but it did however, make the very first mention of a 'sop' to Miles. This was that the Ministry wanted Miles to undertake a project of a very secret nature. No details of this project were given in the letter but it soon transpired that it was for a very advanced, jet-propelled, high-speed research aircraft, capable of speeds up to 1,000 mph.

This was, in essence, the answer to the oft asked question - why were Miles Aircraft Ltd, a relatively young, small company, renowned for their design and manufacture of monoplane touring and training aircraft in wood, and their 'weird and wonderful projects', approached by the MAP to design and build, what surely

must have been the most advanced aircraft at that time? The project was not put out to tender to the aircraft industry, as was normally the case - Miles was just given the job of designing the world's first supersonic research aircraft - and told to get on with it.

In 1943, the company was awarded the contract to design and build this most secret project, to Spec. E.24/43 and George Miles was to have overall design responsibility for the aircraft (although, in reality, he had little to do with its actual design at the time - it not being 'his kind of aircraft'). By February 1946 a very realistic mock-up of what was to become the M.52 had been completed, components for the first prototype had been made, the fuselage frames were being assembled on the jig, and the Power Jets W.2/700 engine had been flight tested in the rear fuselage of a Wellington bomber.

Ben Lockspeiser, Director General of Scientific Research at the MAP, was Chairman of the 'Problems of Supersonic Flight' Committee. This committee had been set up in 1943 and it is incredible to note that, while just about every department of the various Ministries concerned with the problems (and probably quite a few who were not!) were represented on this committee, neither Miles Aircraft nor Dennis Bancroft (the Chief Aerodynamicist of Miles Aircraft Ltd and who was deeply involved in the design of the M.52), even knew of the existence of such a committee. Dennis recalls that he had certainly never been invited to attend any of its meetings and in fact, were it not for Josh Spoor having given him copies of the Minutes of this Committee in 1996, 'he would have been none the wiser'.

Even by prevailing Ministry standards, this strikes me as being somewhat 'below the belt', as one would have thought that surely Miles Aircraft, who were after all designing and building the world's first supersonic aircraft, should have, if only out of courtesy, been invited to be attend this committee. If Miles had been represented on the Committee, and had been allowed to have their say then, perhaps, the ultimate outcome might have been different - who knows? See the appropriate chapter for details on the commencement of work on the M.52.

In 1944, F G Miles was made a Freeman of the City of London and a Member of the Worshipful Company of Coachmakers and Coach Harnessmakers, and on 9th August 1944, he wrote a very interesting letter to Lord Swinton of the War Cabinet, seeking post-war opportunities:

I was very disappointed to hear that you cannot find the time to come down and see us, but I see from the papers that you have had a bout of malaria and quite understand that this must be most enervating and annoying. However, I hope your holiday will give you a much-needed rest. We are trying very hard to establish ourselves in Africa, and have floated a company called Miles Aircraft of South Africa (Proprietary) Ltd with African rights. This company is under the chairmanship of Sir George Albu, the chairman of the General Mining and Finance Corporation. I have also become the chairman of Lunns Africa Ltd., which is a branch of Sir Henry Lunn Ltd, the Travel Agents, who are forming Feeder Line and Air Taxi Services.

As it is so difficult to get any information regarding post-war flying, I hope you don't mind me bothering you, but I would very much like to know whether we could negotiate with you to operate feeder services in the territories under your control, or taxi services, or if not yourself, who would be the right people for us to approach? We feel that when the big lines pass through places like Lagos, passengers will require delivering to outlying districts by air. We also feel that the American system of air mail pick-up and parcel pick-up and dropping could be very suitably introduced into the Colonies in order to save time and increase our efficiency.

We would like to be given the opportunity of running services such as these in conjunction with those that are being started in French Equatorial Africa by another Lunn concern registered in France.

We have the ideal aeroplane for the job to start with, which carries four people and lands and takes off within a hundred yards, a short distance which is eminently suitable for districts where there are poor landing grounds and no aerodromes. We also have a twin-engined aircraft that will carry up to one ton payload, with a remarkable performance.

If the Governments of the Colonies, through yourself, show official interest in these proposals, I would immediately send someone to visit you, and to enter into negotiations. (N.A. Ref: AIR 19/356).

The late John Justin, the famous film actor, was an RAF pilot during the war and was seconded to Miles Aircraft Ltd at Woodley as a production test pilot in 1944. Julian Temple tracked him down while he was researching for his book *Wings over Woodley* in the late 1980s, and in a letter to Julian, dated 12th June 1992, he wrote:

You are quite right, it was at Fred Miles' in 1944. I went there as a Test Pilot but he very soon showed me round the factory. We dropped in to what he called his photographic unit. Still pictures only but he happened to have, he said, quite a good 16 mm cine camera - it was a wow! Having caught my interest he suggested I take it over in my spare times making some movie records of his products - money no object. It was a joy to me, so I formed a unit. It had to be either the over-sixties or the under-seventeens. I chose youth so I'm sure some of them must still be alive. I know that my cameraman and my editor both went into the film industry after the war but cannot remember their names.

We completed two films, one of the Messenger for sales in South Africa and a film I made called "Fire in our Factory!" To my amazement it was bought for £1000 by some Ministry. I started an ambitious all-colour one to encourage ordinary folk to buy planes as they might a car, for business and pleasure. That was the M.28 I suppose but the work was cut short when I was posted to Pinewood to act in a film honouring Training Command (for the record, the colour film of the M.28 survives to this day and has been put on to video for The Miles Aircraft Collection - PA).

Another project I covered 'for the record' and very secret, was George Miles' super-sonic. It was just about ready to fly when I left (in October 1944 - PA).

Well then the answer to your questions; with Miles' connections colour film was no problem; the object of the Messenger and Mercury (M.28 - PA) films was, of course, post-war sales, especially to foreign parts. At least one copy of the Messenger film was sent to South Africa. I would dearly love to see some of the stuff shot between April and October 1944 - just for the laugh! I am so pleased Fred and George Miles are being remembered. Their contribution to the success of the air war was very great. Please let me know if the films are ever shown. Have you contacted George Miles?

The Aeroplane for 29th September 1944 gave details of films made during the latter stages of the war by firms to promote their products and an extract relative to those films produced by Miles Aircraft Ltd states: *A growing interest in the use of the cinema for publicity for the aircraft and accessory trades is a welcome sign that British industry is awakening to a realisation of the need for making its products known throughout the World. Some time ago we were shown a film by Miles Aircraft which gave a good impression of the extraordinary slow-flying qualities of an experimental development of the Miles M.28 single-motor monoplane. On a companion strip we were entertained by some air-to-air colour shots of Libellula, which proved conclusively that this unconventional type flew and manoeuvred like any conventional aeroplane.*

Miles was also very interested in the manufacture of non-aeronautical items, which would not involve much expenditure but could prove to be the salvation of the company in the uncertain days ahead. Numbered amongst these was Don Brown's suggestion for a pre-fabricated house which he felt was a fairly obvious choice as houses would be needed in large quantities after the war. Several other aircraft manufacturers were already producing these at the time, so a specification was drawn up. This was known as the 'Airoh' House and 'One prototype was photographed on the new MAP Track Assembly Line' in 1944.

The Miles 'Airoh' House.

On these two pages is the Air Ministry Record Site Plan of Woodley Aerodrome, dated September 1945.

SCHEDULE OF BUILDINGS

BLDG№	BUILDING	CONST	DRAWING№
1	CAR & CYCLE PARK, (M.A.)		
2	M/T PETROL INSTALL'N 2,000 GALS, (M.A.)	ST.	G.M.
3	GARAGE & DROP HAMMER SHOP, (M.A.)	C.I.	G.M.
4	STORES, (M.A.P)	S	G.M.
5	STORES, (M.A.)	C.I.	G.M.
6	MAGISTER SHOP & OFFICES, (M.A.)	B	G.M.
7	A.I. HANGAR, (M.A.P.)	C.I.	G.M.
8	FLIGHT SHED & BOILER HOUSE, (M.A.P.)	B	G.M.
9	TRAILER PUMP HOUSE, (M.A.)	B	G.M.
10	LUBRICATING OIL INSTALL'N, 1,000 GALS (M.A.)	ST.	G.M.
11	A.R.P. GARAGE, (M.A.)	B.	G.M.
12	FERRY PILOT'S OFFICE, (M.A.)	W.	G.M.
13	LABOURERS' & PAINTERS HUTS, (M.A.)	W.	G.M.
14	AVIATION PETROL, 5,000 GALS, (M.A.)	ST.	G.M.
15	WOOD & MACHINE SHOPS, (M.A.)	W.	G.M.
16	PLANT MANAGER'S OFFICE, (M.A.)	C.I.	G.M.
17	MILLWRIGHT'S SHOP, (M.A.)	W.	G.M.
18	ACETYLENE PLANT STORE, (M.A.)	B.	G.M.
19	CANTEEN, (M.A.P.)	B.	G.M.
20	V.R. MESS "HAWKHURST" (A.M.)	B.	G.M.
21	OFFICES "HAWKHURST" (A.M.)	B.	G.M.
22	TELEPHONE KIOSKS (2 №) AT SIDE OF A.R.S.	GP.TYPE	NIL
23	STORE, (M.A.)	W.	G.M.
24	MAIN OFFICES, (M.A.P)	B.	G.M.
25	MACHINE & FITTING SHOPS, (M.A.P)	B & ST.	G.M.
26	STORES & QUARANTINE, (M.A.P)	Do.	G.M.
27	DOPE SHOP, (M.A.P)	Do.	G.M.
28	A.R.P. REPORT CENTRE (M.A.P) & FIRE STATION	C.I.	G.M.
29	SCRAP BINS, (M.A.) (COMPOUND)	W.	G.M.
30	BOILER HOUSE, (M.A.P.)	B.	G.M.
31		B.	G.M.
32	AIR RAID SHELTERS, (M.A.P)	B.	G.M.
33	TIMBER STORE, (M.A.P)	C.I.	G.M.
34	SPARE RIB SHOP & WOODMILL, (M.A.P)	Do.	G.M.
35	CABIN STORE & PLYWOOD, (M.A.)	C.I. & ST.	G.M.
36	OLD PAINT SHOP, (M.A.)	Do.	G.M.
37	OLD ASSEMBLY EXTENSION (WIND TUNNEL) (M.A.)	Do.	G.M.
38	SUB ASSEMBLY & DOPE SHOP OVER, (M.A.)	Do.	G.M.
39	FABRIC SHOP, (M.A.)	Do.	G.M.
40	FOUNDRY & PRESS SHOP, (M.A.)		G.M.
41	LINE ASSEMBLY HANGAR, (M.A.P)	Do.	G.M.
42	FINAL ASSEMBLY HANGAR, (M.A.)	Do.	G.M.
43	NEW OFFICE, (M.A.)	Do.	G.M.
44	WING SHOP, (M.A.)	Do.	G.M.
45	OFFICE, (M.A.)	Do.	G.M.
46	DOPE ROOM, (M.A.)	Do.	G.M.
47	FUSILAGE SHOP, (M.A.)	Do.	G.M.
48	OLD EXPERIMENTAL SHOP, (M.A.)	Do.	G.M.
49	EXPERIMENTAL SHOP, (M.A.)	Do.	G.M.
50	OFFICES, LAVS. & STORES, (M.A.)	Do.	G.M.
51	EXPERIMENTAL OFFICE, (M.A.)	Do.	G.M.
52	DRAWING OFFICE & OFFICES, (M.A.)	Do.	G.M.
53	LAVS. & PHOTOGRAPHIC ROOM.	Do.	G.M.
54	FIRE STATION WITH TEST PILOTS OFFICE OVER (M.A.)	B.	G.M.
55	RADIO ROOM, (M.A.)	W.	G.M.
56	HOME GUARD STORE, (M.A.)	W.	G.M.
57/a	STORE HUT, (M.A.)	W.	G.M.
57/b	Do. Do. Do.	W.	G.M.
57/c	Do. Do. Do.	W.	G.M.
57/d	Do. Do. Do.	W.	G.M.
58	STATIONERY STORE, (M.A.)	W.	G.M.
59	STATIC WATER TANK, 20,000 GALS	C.	TP/4172/41
60	CLERK OF WORKS' OFFICE, (A.M.)	B.	CW/SHL/46
61	HARDSTANDINGS (7 №) (M.A.)	C.I.+COR	G.M.
62	AVIATION PETROL, 8,000 GALS, (A.M.)	ST.	3376/42
63	STORE HUT, (A.M.)	W.	G.M.
64	STORES, (A.M.) 50' X 18'	T.B.	NIL.
65			
66	PUMP HOUSE, (A.M.)	B	Do.
67	DECONTAMINATION CENTRE, (A.M.)	W.	Do.
68	LATRINES, (A.M.)	B	Do.
69	Y.M.C.A., (A.M.)	W	Do.
70	"WEST WINDS" SCHOOL, (A.M.)	W	Do.
71	SCHOOL & OFFICES, (A.M.)	B	WDY/7257/47
72	OFFICE EXTENSION, (A.M.)	B	WDY/7257/47
73	FLIGHT OFFICE, (A.M.)	B	S3/WDY/75
74	GUARD HOUSE, (A.M.)	B	NIL
75	BARRACK HUT WITH LAVS, (A.M.) 80'X 18'	W	WDY/3550/33
76	BARRACK HUT, (A.M.) 50' X 18'	W	Do.
77	HANGAR, (M.A.)	C.I.	G.M.
78	SERVICE HANGAR, (M.A.)	C.I.	G.M.
79	STATIC WATER TANK, (M.A.)	B	G.M.
80	LATRINES, (M.A.)	B	G.M.
81	OIL STORE, (M.A.)	B	G.M.
82	AMBULANCE SHED, (M.A.)	C.I.	G.M.
83	ASSEMBLY HANGAR STORE, (M.A.)	B.	G.M.
84/a	AVIATION PETROL, 3,000 GALS, (M.A.P)	ST	G.M.
84/b	Do. Do. 7,000 GALS (M.A.)	ST	G.M.
85	Do. Do. (M.A.)	ST	G.M.
86	STATIC WATER TANK, 50,000 GALS (U.G.)	C	G.M.
87	SIGNALS SQUARE	W	G.M.
88	ROBIN HANGAR, (A.M.) 50' X 60'	ST	6875/43
89	FLIGHT OFFICES, (A.M.) H.Q. F.T.C. 60'X18'	H	SHL/47
90	STORE, (A.M.) 38' X 18'-6'	H.C.	S3/WDY/78
91/a	BELLMAN HANGAR, (M.A.P)	ST & C.I.	8349/37
91/b	Do. Do. Do.	Do.	Do.
92	BOILER HOUSE, (M.A.P.)	B	G.M.
93	TRAILER PUMP HOUSE, (M.A.P)	B	G.M.
94	WELFARE CENTRE, (M.A.P)	B	G.M.
95	SALT BATH, (M.A.P)	B	G.M.
96	CANTEEN, (M.A.P. & M.A.)	B	G.M.
97	RESCUE VEHICLE SHED, (M.A.P)	B	G.M.
98	FIRST AID POST & CLEANSING STATION (M.A.)	B	G.M.
98	SUPER ROBIN HANGAR, (M.A.P) 60' X 150'	ST.	6909/43
100	SERVICE LIAISON, (M.A.P)	S	G.M.
101	PAINT & DOPE STORE, (A.M.)	B	S3/WDY/66
102	RIFLE RANGE		G.M.
103	S.A.A. STORE (A.M.)	B	CW/SHD/50
104	ASBESTOS HUT, (M.A.)		G.M.
105	ROBIN HANGARS (M.A.P) 50'X 60'	ST.	6875/43
106	FARM BUILDINGS & WIND TUNNEL (DAVIS FARM) (M.A.)	W	G.M.
107	APPRENTICES HUT, (M.A.)	W	G.M.
108	DRAWING SCHOOL, (M.A.P)	W	G.M.
109	AGRICULTURAL STORE, (M.A.)	C.I.	G.M.
110	GUARD HUT, (M.A.)	W	G.M.
111	BLISTER HANGAR, E.O.TYPE, (A.M.) 80'X45'	ST.	5392/42
112/a	DOUBLE BLISTER HANGAR E.O TYPE (A.M) 90'X 90	ST.	Do.
112/b	Do. Do.	ST.	Do.
112/c	Do. Do.	ST.	Do.
112/d	Do. Do.	ST.	Do.
113	REST ROOM GROUND STAFF (A.M.) 18' X18'	½H.C.	NIL
114	BARRACK HUT, (A.M.) 60'X18'	TH.	Do.
115/a	OFFICERS QUARTERS, (A.M.) 36'X18'	H.C.	3472/42
115/b	Do Do Do	H.C.	Do.
115/c	Do Do Do	H.C.	Do.
115/d	Do Do Do	H.C.	Do.

BLDG№	BUILDING		CONST	DRAW№
115/e	OFFICERS' QUARTERS (A.M.) 36'X 18'		H.C	3472
115/f	Do. Do. Do. Do.		H.C	Do.
115/g	Do. Do. Do. Do.		H.C	Do.
115/h	Do. Do. Do. Do.		H.C	Do.
115/i	Do. Do. Do. Do.		H.C	Do.
115/j	Do. Do. Do. Do.		H.C	Do.
115/k	Do. Do. Do. Do.		H.C	Do.
115/l	Do. Do. Do. Do.		H.C	Do.
115/m	Do. Do. Do. Do.		H.C	Do.
115/n	Do. Do. Do. Do.		H.C	Do.
115/o	Do. Do. Do. Do.		H.C	Do.
115/p	Do. Do. Do. Do.		H.C	Do.
115/q	Do. Do. Do. Do.		H.C	Do.
115/r	Do. Do. Do. Do.		H.C	Do.
115/s	Do. Do. Do. Do.		H.C	Do.
115/u	Do. Do. Do. Do.		H.C	Do.
115/v	Do. Do. Do. Do.		H.C	Do.
115/w	Do. Do. Do. Do.		H.C	Do.
115/x	Do. Do. Do. Do.		H.C	Do.
115/z	Do. Do. Do. Do.		H.C.	Do.
116/a	BATMEN'S QUARTERS, (A.M.) 36'X 18'		H.C.	Do.
116/c	Do. Do.		H.C	Do.
116/d	Do.		H.C	Do.
117/a	OFFICERS' LATRINE BLOCK (A.M.)		T.B	16330
117/b	Do. Do. Do.		T.B	Do.
118/a	STATIC WATER TANK, (A.M.)		C.	TP/4117.
118/b	Do. Do. Do. Do.		C.	Do.
119	OFFICERS' MESS (NOW SGTS.), (A.M.) (91 100)		T.B	SECO2
120	OFFICERS' BATH HOUSE, (A.M.)		T.B.	14438
121	DINING & RECREATION ROOM, (A.M.) (322 A/M & 18 SGTS)		T.B.	FTC/WT B13C
122	BARRACK HUT, (A.M.), 80'X 18'		T.B	NIL
123	OFFICERS' QUARTERS, (A.M.) (EXISTS COTTAGE)			B13C
124	RATION STORE, (A.M.)		T.B.	B13C
125	SGTS. & A/M BATH HOUSE & LATRINES, (A.M.)		T.B	B13C SHL/5
126	FUEL COMPOUND, (A.M.)		WIRE	1683/
127/a	BARRACK HUT, (A.M.), 36'X 18'		N.	B131/
127/b	Do. Do. Do. Do.		N.	Do.
127/c	Do. Do. Do. Do.		N.	Do.
127/e	Do. Do. Do. Do.		N.	Do.
127/f	Do. Do. Do. Do.		N.	Do.
127/g	Do. Do. Do. Do.		N.	Do.
127/h	Do. Do. Do. Do.		N.	Do.
127/i	Do. Do. Do. Do.		N.	Do.
127/k	Do. Do. Do. Do.		N.	Do.
127/l	Do. Do. Do. Do.		N.	Do.
127/m	Do. Do. Do. Do.		N.	Do.
127/p	Do. Do. Do. Do.		N.	Do.
127/q	Do. Do. Do. Do.		N.	Do.
127/r	Do. Do. Do. Do.		N.	Do.
128	OFFICERS' MESS & QTRS, (A.M) ("FALCON HOTEL")			FTC/WT
129				
130/a	STORE, (A.M.) 10' X 10'		B & W.	NIL.
130/b	Do. Do. Do.		Do	Do.
130/c	Do. Do. Do.		Do	Do.
130/e	Do. Do. Do.		Do	Do.
131	BATTLE H.Q. (A.M.) (A.R.S CONVERTED)			
132	SEWAGE WORKS, (A.M.) WITH DESTRUCTOR HOUSE & TOOL SHED			B86C/- S3/WDY
133	A/M LATRINES, (A.M.) (6 W.G'S & 3 URINALS)		T.B	NIL
134	KITCHEN, (A.M.) (DISUSED)		A.	Do.
134b	ABLUTIONS Do. Do.			Do.
135	BARRACK HUT & CREW ROOM, (A.M.)		TH	Do.
136	TIMEKEEPERS & FLT. COMM'RS HUT (A.M.)		N.	S3/TP/5
137	LATRINES, (A.M.)		T.B	NIL
138	SMALL HUTS, (M.A.P)		W.	G.M.
139	WIND SOCK, (M.A.P)			G.M.
140	FIRST AID POST, (M.A.)			G.M.
141	TEST & EQUIPMENT BUILDING, (M.A.)			G.M.
142	ENGINE TEST HOUSE, (M.A.)		C.I.	G.M.
143	STATIC WATER TANK, 60,000 GALS (M.A.)		C.	G.M.
144	SCAMMEL PUMP HOUSE, (M.A.)		B.	G.M.
145	25 YDS RANGE, (A.M.)		BRICK & EARTH	NIL
146	GAS CHAMBER, (A.M.)		B.	G.M.
147/a	DECONTAM. STATION, (M.A.)		B.	G.M.
147/b	Do. Do. Do.		B	G.M.
147/c	Do. Do. Do.		B	G.M.
148	PAINT SHED, (M.A.)		B.	G.M.
149	TRAILER PUMP HOUSE & DOPE STORE, (M.A.)		B.	G.M.
150	STORES, (M.A.) 50'X 18'		W	G.M.
151	SEWAGE WORKS, (M.A. & M.A.P)			G.M.
152	STORES, (M.A.), 10'X 18'		N	G.M.
153	ASBESTOS HUT, (M.A.) 30'X 20'			G.M.
154	STATIC WATER TANK, 20,000 GALS (U.G.)		C	G.M.
155	AVIATION PETROL, (M.A.P)		ST.	G.M.
156	HOME GUARD HUTS, (M.A.)		W.	G.M.
157	STORE HUT, (M.A.)		ST	G.M.
158	BUFFER STORE, (M.A.P)			G.M.
159	TRAILER PUMP HOUSE, (M.A.P)			G.M.
160	SEWAGE PUMP HOUSE, (M.A.P)			G.M.
161	SICK QUARTERS, (A.M.), (SANDFORD MILL)			NIL.
162	"SANDFORD MANOR" (M.A.P)			G.M.

RESTRICTED

WOODLEY
RECORD SITE PLAN
ALL SITES
BASED ON № II WORKS AREA DRG № WDY/1677/45

SCALE 1/2500

ABBREVIATIONS

T.B. INDICATES TEMPORARY BRICK   A. INDICATES ASBESTOS
C.I. " CORRUGATED IRON
ST. " STEEL
B. " BRICK   M.A. INDICATES MILES AIRCRAFT.
W. " TIMBER   A.M. " AIR MINISTRY.
C. " CONCRETE   M.A.P. " MINISTRY OF AIRCRAFT PRODUCTION
S. " SECO HUTTING
H. " HALL   G.M. INDICATES GUY MORGAN & PARTNERS (RESIDENT ARCHITECTS FOR MILES AIRCRAFT LTD)
H.C. " HANDCRAFT
TH. " THORBEX
N. " NISSEN.

P.S.W.   W.E. WINCH   SEP '45   40' X 30'

SECRET №   D.G. or W
REG № 4180 45   AIR MINISTRY

RESTRICTED

Key to 1945 Woodley Drawing Insets

The drawings of Woodley Aereodrome on the next five pages, courtesy of Tony Wingfield, show the factory and other buildings and their uses between 1939 and 1945. Insets 1 & 2 (on pages 38 and 39 respectively): Re-draws of Guy Morgan drawing (issue C, 22.8.45) with additional information from contemporary local residents. Insets 3, 4 & 5 (on pages 40, 41 and 42 respectively): Copies of Air Ministry drawing No 418/C (September 1945) with additional information from Guy Morgan drg (issue C, 22.8.45). the Museum of Berkshire, and contemporary local residents.

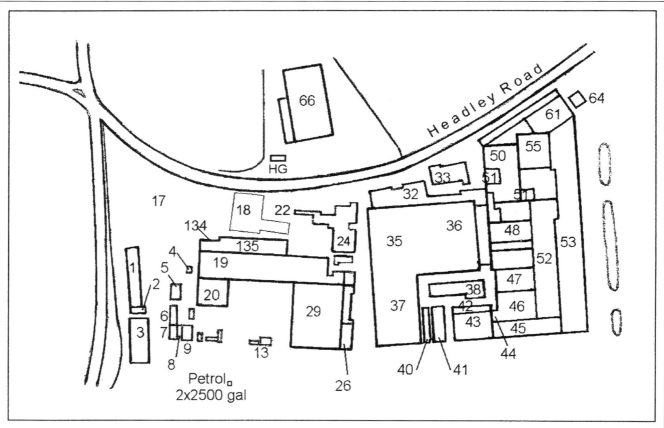

1	Garage	38	Spare Rib Shop & Woodmill
2	Drop Hammer Shop	40	Air Raid Shelter
3	Stores	41	Timber Store
4	Trailer Pump House	42	Cabin Store &Plywood
5	Millwrights' Shop	43	Old Paint Shop
6	Wood Shop	44	Fabric Shop
7	Wood Shop	45	Old Assembly (Wind Tunnel)
8	Wood Machine Shop	46	Sub Assembly
9	Plant Store	47	Foundry & Press Shop
13	Ferry Pilots' Office	48	Wing Shop
17	Car Park	50	Fuselage Shop
18	Bicycle Racks	51	Dope Room
19	Magister Shop	52	Final Assembly Hangar
20	A1 Hangar	53	Line Assembly Hangar
22	Hawkshurst	55	Old Experimental Shop
24	Canteen	61	Experimental Shop
26	Boiler House	64	Test Pilots' Office & Fire Station
29	Flight Shed	66	Buffer Store
32	Main Offices	134	Experimental Drawing Office
33	Boiler House	135	New Experimental Drawing Office
35	Machine & Fitting Shop	HG	Home Guard
36	Dope & Quarantine		
37	Dope Shop		

Woodley Main Factory 1945

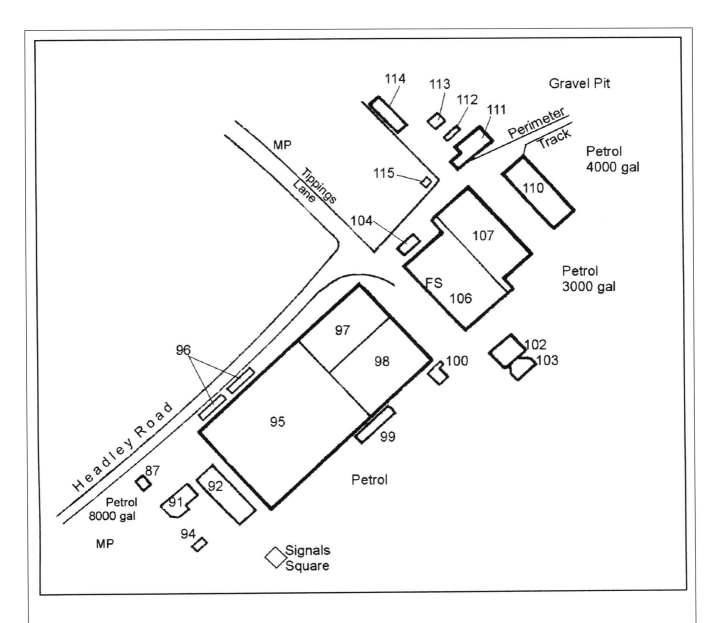

87. Guard Room
91. Flying School Building
92. Flying School Building
94. Flight Office
* 95. RAF No 10 FIS
96. Barrack Huts
97. Service Hangar
98. Service Hangar
99. Assembly Hangar Stores
100. Ambulance Shed
* 102. Robin Hangar - RAF Comm. Flt.

103. Flt. Commander's Office
104. Welfare Centre
** 106. Bellman Hangar No 1
** 107. Bellman Hangar No 2
110. Super Robin Stripping Hangar
111. Canteen
112. Air Raid Shelter
113. Cycle Shed and Car Park
114. First Aid Post
115. Rescue Vehicle Shed
FS   Fire Station
MP   Military Posn. - Pillbox Gun Posn.

*   See Appendix 40

**   These Bellman Hangars were constructed in the early 1940s to accommodate Spitfire repair and service - See Appendix 38.

Woodley Repair & Service 1945

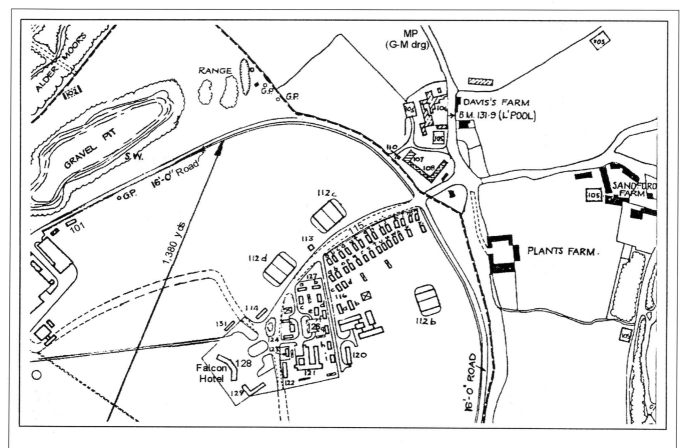

101	Paint & Dope Store	121	Dining & Recreation Rooms
102	Rifle Range	122	Barrack Hut 80ft x 18ft
105	Robin Hangars 50ft x 60ft	123	Officers' Quarters (Cottage)
106	Wind Tunnel	124	Ration Store
107	Apprentices' Hut	126	Fuel Compound
108	Drawing School	127	Barrack Huts (a-i) 36ft x 16ft
110	Guard Hut	128	Falcon – Officers' Mess & Quarters
112	Double Blister Hangar 90ft x 90ft	129	Falcon Annexe – Officers' Mess
113	Rest Room, Ground Staff	131	Battle HQ
114	Barrack Hut 60ft x 18ft	GP	Pillbox Gun Position
115	Officers' Quarters (a-z) 36ft x 18ft	MP	Twin A-A Gun Emplacement
116	Batmens' Quarters (a-d) 36ft X 18ft	BM 131.9(L'POOL)	Benchmark Height
119	Sargeants' Mess		

Woodley Falcon Hotel & Davis's Farm 1945

The house was apparently exhibited somewhere but Miles was not really very interested in this project and it is believed that no more were manufactured. The house was, needless to say, designed and built without the knowledge or approval of the Ministry!

Another unofficial project undertaken by the firm in 1944 was a method of wood pressings for parquet floors and this utilised waste wood from the factory - possibly the earliest recorded manufacture of the now famous 'chipboard' - a very early instance of re-cycling!

In the spring of 1944, Miles was introduced to Henry Martin, an American accountant who had arrived in England, bringing with him samples of a completely new type of pen which he had obtained from one Lazzlo Jozseff Biro, a Hungarian journalist refugee living in Argentina. This pen was revolutionary in that it used a small steel ball instead of a nib, which was supplied with a special ink via an open-ended capillary tube. Mr Martin held the patent rights for this new pen outside the USA and Miles was quick to see the potential of such an instrument and, in 1945, they formed the Miles-Martin Pen Co Ltd, with Miles and Martin each putting up £5,000 capital. Miles became Chairman of the new company, which was to bear all expenses and risks involved in launching the Biro pen, while the majority of the parts would be made by Miles Aircraft Ltd on terms which stated categorically that the latter would not be held responsible for any possible financial loss. For full details of the firm's involvement with the Biro pen see the next volume.

Dated 15th July 1944, a very interesting but of necessity rather brief history of the firm was written under the reference SEC/GB/GJW. This brief history gave facts and figures of bank overdrafts, aircraft production and development projects undertaken by the firm and is reproduced at Appendix 5.

Accidents to aircraft at Woodley were, fortunately, extremely rare but on 17th October 1944, Douglas C-47A, 42-24110, of 77TCS, 435TCG, US 9th Air Force, Welford, piloted by Foley D Collins Jnr landed there, probably due either to bad weather or poor navigation as Woodley was not far from his base at Welford, to the north-east, but on that particular day, this runway was downwind! As a result he touched down about mid-field and overshot through a row of Masters, which were parked adjacent to the fence alongside the road from the Repair & Service Department to the Miles Technical School/Wind Tunnel complex. The C-47A finished up on the other side of the road in a farmer's field, with the underside of the port wing severely gouged by one of the parked aircraft's propellers and sagging to about a foot off the ground and was rated LAC3 (landing accident Cat.3 damage) By the time Grahame Gates went to have a look at it the next day, it had already been stripped of instruments, radio and all the emergency food packages that aircraft used to

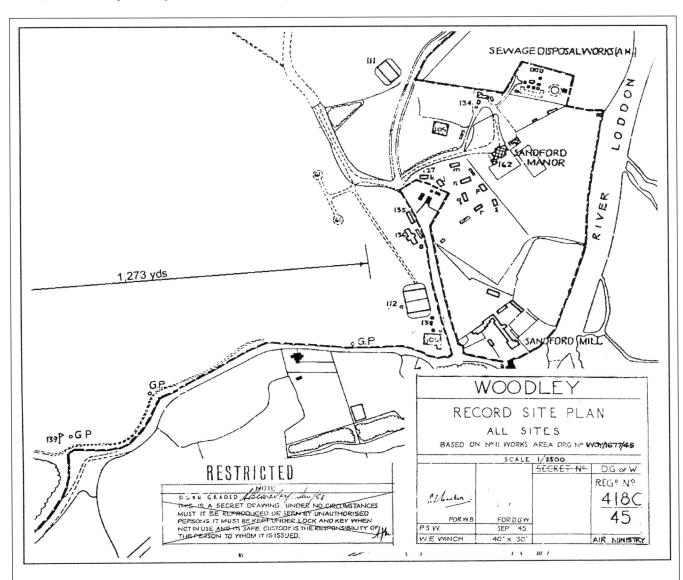

61	Hardstandings
105	Robin Hangar 50ft x 60ft
111	Blister Hangar EO Type 90ft x 45ft
112	Double Blister Hangar EO Type 90ft x 90ft
127	Barrack Huts (j – s) 36ft x 16ft
134	Kitchen
135	Barrack Hut & Crew Room
136	Timekeeper & Flt Commander
138	Small Huts
139	Wind Sock
162	Sandford Manor
GP	Pillbox Gun Position

Woodley Sandford Manor 1945

carry in wartime! It is interesting to note that three Master Mk.IIs, DK893, DK947 and DK972, were issued to Miles Aircraft on 17th October 1944 and SOC Cat.E on 24th October and it is possible that these may have been involved in the C-47 accident. DL204 was issued to Miles Aircraft on 17th October, having suffered a belly landing in Lincolnshire on 30th September 1944 but was re-Cat.E on 24th October, so it is possible that this was also involved.

The prototypes of four new aircraft, all designed by George Miles and Ray Bournon, were all built at Liverpool Road during the war, and these were given 'Liverpool Road' numbers as follows:

    L.R.1 - M.28
    L.R.2 - M.35 Libellula
    L.R.3 - M.39B Libellula
       (5/8th scale flying model of the M.39 Libellula)
    L.R.4 - M.57 Aerovan.

Although it was thought that both the M.35 Libellula and the M.57 Aerovan were built without the knowledge of the Ministry, it has since been discovered that only the latter was so constructed, for which the firm was duly admonished! The first prototype M.28 was later converted into the first prototype M.38/28, and this conversion was also undertaken at Liverpool Road.

George Miles also designed the M.25 Martinet and the M.33 Monitor high speed target tower at Liverpool Road but both these aircraft were to be built later at Woodley. The last new design to be undertaken at Liverpool Road, during the winter of 1944-45, was the L.R.5 M.64, which was designed and built by the staff in their spare time.

While it is not known for certain where the first true prototype M.38 Messenger and the ten Messenger Mk.Is for the RAF were built, it is strongly suspected that they were also built at Liverpool Road, as space was at a premium in the main factory at Woodley, but no L.R. number appears to have been given to these aircraft. After the war, George Miles designed the M.60 Marathon, the M.68 'Boxcar', the M.71 Merchantman and the L.R.6 M.65 Gemini at Liverpool Road, and the Gemini became the last new prototype to be built there.

George Miles, was unique in so far as he not only designed such a large number of new aircraft, but, being a qualified test pilot, he was not afraid to test fly his own creations as well. In fact it could be said that *never before in the field of aircraft design, had one person designed, produced and flown, so many widely diverse and successful new types, in such a short space of time.*

The story will continue in the next volume.

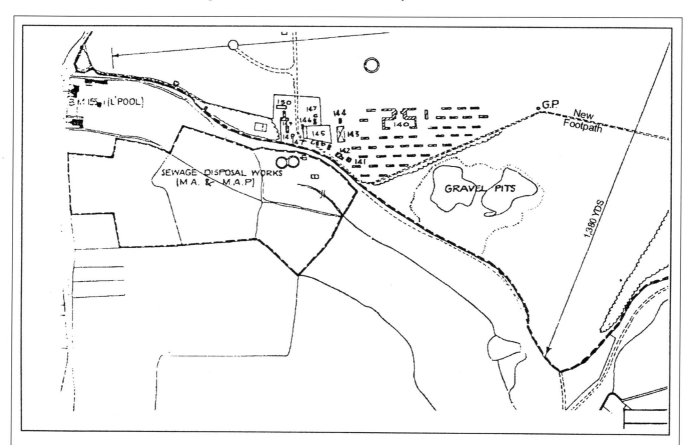

140	First Aid Post	147 a,b,c.	Decontamination Station
141	Test & Equip. Bldg.	148	Paint Shed
142	Engine Test House	149	Trailer Pump House & Dope Store
143	Static Water Tank 60,000 gal	150	Stores
144	Scammel Pump House	BM 155.1 (L'POOL)	Benchmark Height
145	25yd Range	GP	Pillbox Gun Position
146	Gas Chamber		

Woodley SW Corner 1945

Although very little is known about the activities of Phillips & Powis at Doncaster, in 1992 Eddie Pearce wrote to Julian Temple with a few details of his involvement there:

I told you I started work as an apprentice electrician with Westland Aircraft in December 1940 and have been trying to tax my brain about things that took place 50 years ago. I think that a lot of the wing components came from Cravens of Sheffield and they were badly disrupted by the air raids at that time, so for some time we were short of components to actually assemble (Craven Bros factory was rebuilt within three to four months and went on to produce wings for the Master (and later wings for the Airspeed Horsa glider - PA).

I left Westlands, because I was being paid for not doing any work! I know for a fact that I was not there at Christmas 1941, but returned later and worked for Phillips & Powis, and again we were held up for components, so using drawings available, mainly the camouflage colouring, I made a 1/36th scale Master II and the works manager used to comment about this when he passed my bench. When it was completed and painted, he came along and said "I know of a good home for this" and promptly took it, and put it on his own office desk. I was a little put out, but they were paying me and I used their facilities etc., so I suppose he was right. No ill feelings.

The main thing I remember, working on the Master II was having to nail tin plated copper strip along the main fuselage frame work. All joints had to be soldered and anything and everything made of metal had to be earth bonded throughout the whole aircraft. I cannot remember if we even completed or flew off one aircraft (at least one aircraft and possibly nine others were assembled and flown out of Doncaster - PA). I left to join the RAF on 27th April 1943 as a wireless fitter and stayed on until November 1947.

Geoffrey Oakes went on to say:

Meanwhile the factory had stopped producing Lysanders - the contract to build 500 had been cancelled and only 17 were built. A company called Phillips & Powis Aircraft in collaboration with Miles Aircraft (some understandable confusion here - PA) planned to use the site to build the Miles Master, a small training aircraft. However, because of production difficulties, only one aircraft was made. The factory was then taken over by Brooklands Aviation of Weybridge.

It is believed that the reason for the abandonment of Master assembly at Doncaster was that Brooklands Aviation, who had been repairing Wellingtons at RAF Lindholme, an active bomber station, had been told by the MAP to move to the larger hangars at Doncaster as they were more suited for the repair and overhaul of larger aircraft. This was recently confirmed by Doug Stringer, who wrote:

As far as I can recall, Brooklands Aviation took over the large hanger at Doncaster late in 1941, having had to give up facilities at RAF Lindholme (304/305 Polish Sqdns). We were handy for repairing their crashed Wellingtons. The RAF required their hangar for storage, hence our move to Doncaster. I am not sure whether Phillips & Powis had been building or repairing the aircraft, but remember two single-engined aircraft being moved to a nearby hangar, in order that we could move in with dismantled Wellingtons and have office and stores facilities.

It was about a month when the live aircraft were flown out and the RAF took over the nearby hangar for use by them with Mustangs.

This also seems to imply that more than one Master was actually assembled at Doncaster before Phillips & Powis relinquished the site.

DL200, the first Master Mk.II to be completed at Doncaster, was first flown, by F/L Hugh Kennedy, on 30th October 1941, making its landing an hour later at Woodley, to where it had been flown for acceptance checks. Hugh remembered seeing other Masters on the assembly line on this, his only visit to Doncaster, and it will be seen from the delivery dates for the next nine aircraft that they were probably also completed at Doncaster. All ten aircraft were delivered to the RAF between 4th January 1942 and 11th February 1942.

It is probable that a further 22 sets of components were completed in the Sheffield area but were then transported to South Marston for final assembly. However, the final 168 Master Mk.II from the 'Sheffield and Doncaster' contract were built at South Marston from scratch. The individual aircraft record cards tend to confirm that some aircraft owed their origins to the 'Sheffield and Doncaster' factories but seven months were to elapse between the delivery of the tenth Master Mk.II, DM209, from Doncaster and the eleventh, DM210, from South Marston. The remaining 190 Master Mk.II's from the 'Sheffield and Doncaster' contract, DM210-DM454, were completed at South Marston and delivered between 16th September 1942 and 26th March 1943. The final 100, which were originally to have been assembled at Doncaster, were cancelled.

The last aircraft to be delivered from the South Marston factory's original contract was the Master Mk.III, DL793, on 25th September 1942.

Strange tales abound in the world of aviation and one such concerns some Master Mk.IIs parked at 39 MU RAF Colerne at some time during the war. A number of these aircraft were apparently parked 'out to grass' on the airfield and when 'an old lag' was asked by an interested person the reason for this the inquirer was told that it was because 'they were all built at Doncaster and nobody likes flying them'! If this story is to have any substance then it is interesting to note that nine of the ten Master Mk.IIs which were assembled at Doncaster, DM201-DM209 were in fact delivered to 39 MU Colerne between 28th January and 11th February 1942 and some of them stayed there for well over a year before being delivered to a unit.

By late 1942, the North American Harvard was arriving in increasing numbers in the countries operating the Joint Air Training Scheme and production of the Master was scaled down accordingly. The last Master to be built at South Marston was delivered to the RAF on 26th February 1943, and the final contract for 360 Master Mk.IIs, which were to have been built at Woodley, was amended to 125, with the remaining 235 being amended to be built as M.25 Martinet TT Mk.I, also at Woodley.

Summary of production of the M.19 Master Mk.II and M.27 Master Mk.III at South Marston and M.19 Master Mk.II at Sheffield and Doncaster:

South Marston

First contract   **500** Master Mk.III and Mk.II

W8437-W9003	Master Mk.III	1st to 414th built; deld between 13.3.41 and 8.3.42
W9004-W9099	Master Mk.II	1st to 86th built; deld between 6.10.41 and 27.2.42

Second contract   **400** Master Mk.III and Mk.II

DL552-DL793	Master Mk.III	1st to 188th built; deld between 17.3.42 and 25.9.42
DL794-DM196	Master Mk.II	1st to 212th built; deld between 7.3.42 and 10.9.42; see also DM210-DM454

298 Master Mk.II were completed at South Marston on the original contract plus a further **190** from the Sheffield and Doncaster contract. The Master Mk.III was built only at South Marston and production ceased after **602** had been completed.

Sheffield and Doncaster

First contract   **300** Master Mk.II

DM200-DM209 Master Mk.II	1st to 10th built; deld between 4.1.42 and 11.2.42 (DM200 first flown 30.10.41)
DM210-DM454 Master Mk.II	11th to 200th completed at South Marston; deld between 16.9.42 and 26.3.43

DM200-DM231 are shown on the RAF record cards as being manufactured by Phillips & Powis Aircraft Ltd but from **DM232-DM454**, the makers are given as Phillips & Powis, South Marston. This therefore, gives rise to the speculation that the first **32** sets of components were manufactured at Sheffield and Doncaster (including the first ten aircraft which were probably assembled at Doncaster), with the final **168** sets of components being built at South Marston.

DM455-DM581 Master Mk.II	final 100 aircraft from the Sheffield and Doncaster contract cancelled.

The projected plans for Master production originally called for 140 aircraft per month from South Marston and 60 aircraft per month from Woodley, but these figures were never achieved. Average production rates for both Woodley and South Marston were as follows:-

Master Mk.I and Mk.II Woodley (where the assembly line had been in operation since early 1939) averaged 52 per month between July 1939 and December 1942, when Master production finally ceased there after 900 Master Mk.I and 1,250 Master Mk.II had been built.

Master Mk.III and Mk.II South Marston averaged 42 per month between February 1941 and March 1942, the first full year of operation. Over the first eighteen months to September 1942, production rose to an average of 50 per month and peaked between May and September 1942, when some 77 Masters of both marks were produced each month.

The final 190 Master Mk.II aircraft, which were originally to have been assembled at Doncaster, were produced at the rate of just 32 per month and this brought the average rate of production, for the two years in which the Master was built at South Marston, down to 46 per month.

It is believed that Ken Waller was the first and only resident test pilot at South Marston but unfortunately, his wartime log books are missing. However, it is known that after the first Master Mk.IIs arrived in South Africa, in 1941, he left to join the Phillips & Powis working party sent there to help with the introduction of the Master into service with the SAAF.

He was not replaced at South Marston as nobody could be spared but F/L Hugh Kennedy, the assistant test pilot at Woodley, took over the additional job of test flying the aircraft built at South Marston. Hugh flew there in the Sparrowhawk U-0223, usually at weekends, or when he could spare the time to test fly them, in batches.

For a summary of M.19 Master Mk.II and M.27 Master Mk.III production at all factories see Appendix 12. For individual aircraft histories of M.19 Master Mk.II built at South Marston, Sheffield & Doncaster and M.27 Master Mk.III built at South Marston, see Appendix 14, on CD.

Shortly before Master production ceased at South Marston, Phillips & Powis commenced modification work on Spitfire Mk.VBs and the earliest recorded delivery to South Marston was W3638, which was delivered on 6th June 1942. Correspondence between Mr J Reid Young of Vickers Armstrong and the MAP, dated 26th January

1943, confirmed a discussion with F G Miles, whereby the main site of the Phillips & Powis factory would be officially handed-over to Vickers-Armstrong (Supermarine) on 1st April 1943, a date presumably calculated to coincide with the completion of the last Master (which, in the event, was delivered on 26th March 1943). The MAP confirmed, on 9th February 1943, that Vickers-Armstrong could take-over the 'South Marston Aircraft Factory' almost immediately under its 'Castle Bromwich Aeroplane Factory'. It is believed that the name of the South Marston factory was changed to Vickers-Armstrong South Marston Ltd about this time.

Little is known about the early Spitfire work prior to the hand-over except that it was presumably carried out under contract to Vickers-Armstrong. The factory was then tooled up for the manufacture of the Spitfire Mk.21, although Spitfire modification work continued before full scale production from scratch could commence. Phillips & Powis's involvement at South Marston had come to a close but it is believed that the staff and workers stayed on.

No photographs of the factory or Master production at South Marston appear to have survived as it is understood that there were two catastrophic fires in the photographic department there during the war. A photograph of the first production M.27 Master Mk.III, W8437, in the archives of the Imperial War Museum, is recorded as having been taken at South Marston but this was actually taken at Woodley, probably immediately following its ferry flight from South Marston on 13th March 1941.

Of the 1,090 Masters built at South Marston only two outer wings, once attached to the Master Mk.IIs, DL906 (stbd) and DM384 (port), survive to this day. DL906 was purchased by Miles Aircraft Ltd, Woodley on 3rd December 1946 and DM384 was SOC at 58 MU Newark on 28th March 1946 and these somehow managed to survive to ultimately make their way to Booker, from where they were acquired in 1984 by Robin J Day of the then Berkshire Aviation Group.

Footnote: On 17th April 2003, Barry Abraham wrote:

In correspondence with EMI at Hayes in 1967 they confirmed that The Gramophone Co Ltd produced 340 sets of Master main frames, port and starboard wings, tail fins, rudders, ailerons and flaps. However, it is not known whether they were for Woodley, South Marston or both factories. They also produced about 500 sets of similar parts for the Magister and Martinet and carried out a lot of work on other aircraft, including Airspeed Horsa gliders.

With regard to the changeover from Phillips & Powis to Vickers-Armstrong at South Marston, the earliest records I have for Vickers-Armstrong Limited, South Marston Works (their new and correct title) are dated 30th June 1943. These show that Contract B.1951/C.23(c) was placed for 300 Spitfires Mk.XXI and this was received in April 1942 but none had been delivered by the time of the report, which would tend to imply that it was initially given to Phillips & Powis.

However, after the completion of the Master contracts, Spitfires were being modified into Seafires under Contract 2259/C.23(c) and also spares for Masters were being produced under Contract B.6659/C.23(c).

Following the changeover Vickers-Armstrong Ltd (Supermarine) provided technical advice, test flying and the like in a similar way to Castle Bromwich, w.e.f. 9th February 1943. The Phillips & Powis staff were taken over by Vickers-Armstrong. It is believed that the management control was handed over to Vickers-Armstrong after completing the Master contract.

South Marston was also apparently considered for production of the DH Mosquito, which would have been more in line with Phillips & Powis experience with wood but I haven't seen any contracts for this.

Walker's Linen Mill, Banbridge. *[Courtesy of P Flannagan]*

Chapter 3
Miles Aircraft Ltd – Banbridge, Northern Ireland

Sometime during 1943, the Minister of Aircraft Production, Sir Stafford Cripps, intimated to Miles that in an attempt to solve the unemployment problem in Northern Ireland and to increase the production of aircraft, a factory should be set up there.

In late 1943 Miles Aircraft were contracted to set up a factory in Northern Ireland and a small team of 'pioneers' led by Walter Capley crossed the Irish Sea to set up the unit in the recently closed Walker's Linen Mill, in Castlewellan Street, Banbridge, Co. Down. This factory had last been used by Walker's for making 'tent duck', from which tents were made. The factory was large but far from ideal as, apart from the roof being supported by many closely-spaced stanchions, it was still full of weaving machinery! However, these problems were soon overcome and within a short space of time the unit was manufacturing wooden Monoplane Air Tails (MAT) for air-launched torpedoes.

The secret MAT (code named 'Tora'), had been designed at Woodley in 1939 to a Ministry Development Contract to overcome control issues when dropping torpedoes from the air. They were later to be used with great success in naval operations, such as at Taranto, see **Footnote** for more details.

Variants of the MAT were continuously developed and produced at Woodley, with 358 Toras being built in 1940, 482 in 1941 and an unspecified number in 1942, before production was moved to Banbridge in 1943. Production of the MAT at Banbridge soon reached 50 units per week and as efficiency grew and the employees became more proficient this was increased to 150 per week by 1944. Components for aircraft in production at Woodley were also produced at Banbridge and at its peak, the labour force reached 300.

In October 1943, Contracts/acft/3261, dated 14th October 1943, was placed with Miles Aircraft Ltd for the manufacture of 250 M.38 Messengers to Spec A.17/43 for the RAF, but due to the shortage of space at Woodley, it was agreed that 208 would be built in Northern Ireland and 42 at Woodley. In the event, only 10 were assembled at Woodley, having probably been built at Liverpool Road, with the first, RH369, being delivered to the RAF on 27th October 1944 and the last on 25th June 1945.

Then, on 20th January 1944, the contract was cancelled, although various changes and negotiations brought about the eventual production of 20 aircraft, with 10 to be built at Woodley and 10 in Northern Ireland. Finally, on 22nd August 1944, a contract was placed on the authority of the Chief Executive (it is not known who this person was) for the production of 40 M.38 aircraft to be built in Northern Ireland (Contract Aircraft 4553/C23c).

Production of the Messenger commenced at Banbridge in October 1944 but as it was not possible to assemble the aircraft there due to the closely placed stanchions, the first five aircraft were taken by road to RAF Long Kesh, near Lisburn, about 15 miles away, where they were assembled, the engines installed and initial test flights carried out.

The Messengers were then ferried to Woodley for final inspection and painting. The first aircraft to be completed was RH420 and this was first flown from Long Kesh in August 1945, before being delivered to the RAF from Woodley on 30th November 1945. Billy Fyvie, who was probably the last surviving member of the workforce at Banbridge, recalled that, while working for Short Brothers & Harland Ltd, he had been 'talked into joining' Miles Aircraft at Banbridge as a Draughtsman/Carpenter by Bob Gillings. He also recalled that all ten Messenger Mk.Is for the RAF

Wings and fuselages take shape between stanchions of the roof of the factory at Banbridge.

were built at Banbridge, with the first five being assembled and test flown from Long Kesh, while the next five were assembled later at Newtownards where the new factory had been built.

A Story from County Down was written by Mary Williamson and published in the *Miles Magazine* for April 1946. This gives a good account of what it must have been like to work at Banbridge in the early days:

Recently I visited the Ulster unit at Banbridge, Co. Down, where in the latter part of 1943, a handful of fellows from Woodley, came "pioneering" on behalf of Miles Aircraft. Sitting in Mr Powis's office, looking at a most impressive perspective drawing of the new factory at Newtownards, it seemed a far cry from those early days when a soap box in the loft with no 'phone and no fire, comprised an office!

From this you will gather that it was not exactly a "palace of industry" to which they went. The factory at Banbridge was originally a linen mill, and when Miles Aircraft moved in, it was still full of weaving machines. These had to be removed and the

The Long Kesh Unit as at 2nd June 1942. Long Kesh was the Short & Harland Short Stirling assembly and wing production plant between 1942 and 1945, which was later used by Miles Aircraft (N.I.) for the assembly of Messenger Mk.Is in the latter half of 1945 and early part of 1946. The hangars were basically standard T2s but were 4ft 3ins higher than normal to accommodate the Short Stirlings assembly. All the structures were erected under the auspices of the MAP. This unit now forms part of a site which is a Scheduled Historic Monument and is now occupied by the Ulster Aviation Society. [Photographs courtesy of Short & Harland Archives via Ernie Cromie]

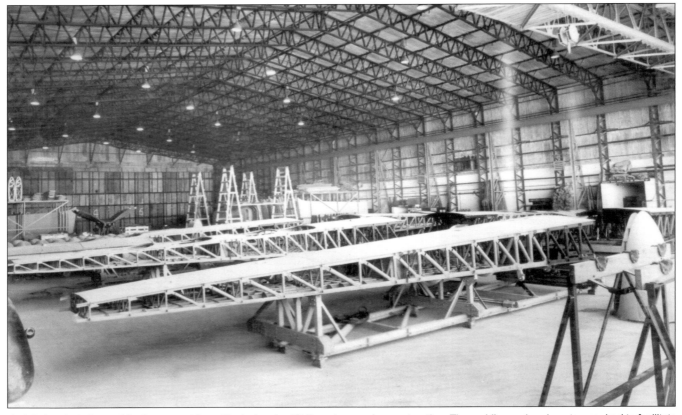

An interior shot of one of the hangars at Long Kesh showing Stirling wings under construction. The mobile overhead gantry required to facilitate their assembly is clearly visible.

decks more or less cleared for action. I say "more or less" because there still remained numerous stanchions supporting the roof, and therefore irremovable. From this point of view it was hardly suitable, but Fred Tuson, George Reynolds and the half-dozen others of the English team, who had followed from Woodley, got to work.

A large percentage of the workers were girls who had previously been working at the weaving looms, and they had to be taught woodwork. As George Reynolds said "some of them picked it up quickly, the others learned the hard way - but they learned!"

It was not originally intended to manufacture complete aircraft at Banbridge, and for the first year the factory was engaged on making aircraft equipment, but when the Messenger contract came in the opportunity of producing them was too good to miss, and they graduated to aircraft. Here arose another problem, for there was no airfield within 15 miles, and the aforementioned stanchions in the shop made the movement of even a wing a major operation. However, the use of the flying field and a large hangar (which had previously been used by Short & Harland for the manufacture of the Short Stirling - PA) at Long Kesh was obtained and made into a temporary base for the final assembly of aircraft. This was no mean feat as it entailed the transport of every component by road from Banbridge to Long Kesh, a distance of 15 miles or more.

However, they embarked on the Messengers in October 1944, and in August 1945 the first one was flown at Long Kesh. A great achievement - due to the dogged keenness of everyone concerned, in working under anything but ideal conditions.

At the peak period 300 people were employed - somewhat reduced now - but all Ulster labour, the total English staff being nine. They almost met their "Waterloo" just before "D" day when they were completely marooned in Ulster, the use of telephones was prohibited, no travel and no English papers - all this for a period of three weeks. The only means of communication being by telegram which took anything from ten days to a fortnight! At that time they had no alternative but to "hold the fort", and I believe it was the only time they really began to feel homesick.

A major disaster overtook them in February 1945 when Walter Capley was killed while test flying a Spitfire at Woodley. At that time negotiations were going ahead for a permanent factory in Ulster, and with the loss of Walter Capley many of the plans being

investigated had to be shelved. For the next few months the unit ploughed along with very little navigation until the arrival of Mr Charles Powis in July last year, who went over with the idea of establishing a permanent factory in Ulster. As a result of his efforts in this direction, the Government of Northern Ireland have agreed to build the new factory at Newtownards, which gives every sign of becoming a promising offspring of Miles Aircraft.

I'd like to mention here that I was more than impressed by the keenness of everyone at Banbridge and Long Kesh, and this was borne out when I learned that 60% of the people employed there have expressed their willingness to move to the new factory, even to the extent of uprooting their homes and families. I left them with the major problem of the move to Newtownards, which it is hoped will be accomplished without jeopardising the rather ambitious production programme for the current year.

Looking into the future, the potential is very high. Their new home certainly looks more like a proper aircraft factory; it has a first-class aerodrome with concrete runways, and when the small housing scheme is completed, will be provided with many amenities including squash courts, a gymnasium, and a theatre. The fact that it is also situated on Strangford Lough - a sea inlet of 20 miles - has, I gather, not been overlooked by the fishing and sailing enthusiasts.

So, the days of the Banbridge factory are now numbered, and I think it would be appropriate to give a final word for the few English personnel who went across some two and a half years ago, and to acknowledge the amount of work they have put in, and the domestic inconveniences with which they have had to contend. We wish them good fortune and prosperity in their new surroundings.

All thes aircraft built in Northern Ireland survived to be sold to civilian operators, becoming Messenger Mk.4As on the British civil register. Unfortunately, no photographs appear to have survived showing these Messengers in RAF colours but the following photographs at least show them all after they had been 'demobbed'.

It is not known when Banbridge finally closed but on 1st July 1946, a new company, Miles Aircraft (Northern Ireland) Ltd, was formed at Newtownards and the story of their fortunes will be told in the next volume.

G-AKVZ (RH427) at the Great Vintage Flying Weekend, White Waltham 17.5.98. It still has a current CofA in 2012.

G-AKZX (RH424), famously looped by Neville Browning in May 1962, survived until written-off at Rochester on 24th July 1965.

G-ALAC (RH420) at Shoreham for the start of the Daily Express Trophy Air Race on 22.9.51, during which it was DBR at Faversham.

G-ALAE (RH421) in early basic silver colour scheme, was declared a write-off following a forced landing at Epping on 2nd August 1958.

ZK-BED (RH425, G-ALAF). Sold to New Zealand in 1954 this Messenger remained active until 1967.

G-ALAG (RH422) was sold to France as F-BGQZ in 1953, returned in March 1956 with Rosenthal China Ltd as "China Clipper" seen here but was written off on a trip to Germany in December 1957..

G-ALAI (RH423) at Lasham 14.5.61 when operated by Sky Flying Group.

(M P Marsh).

Above: G-ALAJ (RH429) was to be wrecked in a gale at Christchurch in July 1956.

Left: G-ALAV (RH428) named "La Chauve-Souris" ("The Bat") was finally withdrawn from use at Coventry in February 1964..

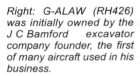

Right: G-ALAW (RH426) was initially owned by the J C Bamford excavator company founder, the first of many aircraft used in his business.

Footnote:

Further to the use of the Monoplane Air Tail (MAT) fitted to the torpedoes used in the air attack on the Italian Naval base at Taranto, Codenamed Operation Judgment, Cunningham and Lyster planned to attack Taranto on October 21st, Trafalgar Day, with aircraft from HMS *Illustrious* and HMS *Eagle*. This was later changed following fire damage to *Illustrious* and action damage to *Eagle*. While *Eagle* was being repaired, it was decided to press on with the attack using only *Illustrious*. Several of *Eagle*'s aircraft were transferred to augment *Illustrious*' air group and the carrier sailed on 6th November. In the days before the attack, several reconnaissance flights from Malta confirmed that the Italian fleet was at Taranto.

Aboard the aircraft carrier HMS *Illustrious*, 21 Fairey Swordfish biplane torpedo bombers began taking off. 11 of the aircraft were armed with torpedoes with MAT's, while the remainder carried flares and bombs. The British plan called for the planes to attack in two waves about an hour apart. The first wave was assigned targets in both the outer and inner harbours of Taranto.

Approaching the harbour from the southwest at 10:58 PM, the first wave of 12 Swordfish found 6 battleships, 7 heavy cruisers,

2 light cruisers, 8 destroyers in the anchorage. As they began their attack, the sky was illuminated by flares and intense, but ineffective, anti-aircraft fire. Around midnight, the second wave of 9 Swordfish arrived over the harbour from the northwest. Dropping their ordnance, they cleared the harbour and returned to their carrier.

In their wake, the 21 Swordfish left the battleship *Conte di Cavour* sunk and the battleships *Littorio* and *Caio Duilio* heavily damaged. They also badly damaged a heavy cruiser. British losses were only two Swordfish. In one night, the Royal Navy had succeeded in halving the Italian battleship fleet and had gained a tremendous advantage in the Mediterranean. As a result of the strike, the Italians withdrew the bulk of their fleet farther north to Naples. The Taranto Raid changed many naval experts' thoughts regarding air-launched torpedo attacks. Prior to Taranto, many believed that deep water (100 ft.) was needed to successfully drop torpedoes. To compensate for the shallow water of Taranto harbour (40 ft.), the British specially modified their torpedoes and dropped them from very low altitude. This solution, as well as other aspects of the raid, was heavily studied by the Japanese as they planned their attack on Pearl Harbor the following year.

A delightful shot of a Miles Master Mk.IA landing.

Chapter 4:
Miles M.9B Master Mk.I, Miles M.9C Master Mk.IA and the Miles 'Peregrine Fighter'

The story of the Miles Master in the service of the RAF continues from Volume 1 **Miles Aircraft - The Early Years**.

An Air Ministry order to Contract No.779602/38 was placed with Phillips & Powis Aircraft Ltd, Woodley, on 11th June 1938, for **500** M.9 Master Mk.I aircraft to Specification 16/38, issued 15th August 1938, for the 'Production of the Phillips & Powis Private Venture Trainer'. File No.788121/38/RDA3, which was issued to Phillips and Powis Aircraft Ltd on 5th September 1938, stated:

Requirements

To meet Operational Requirement OR.58, the aircraft shall be constructed in strict accordance with the drawings and schedules covering the construction of the "Miles Kestrel Trainer" aircraft N3300 in the form which that aircraft is accepted by DTD, as the prototype of the production aircraft, excepting for such amendments as may be introduced to meet the requirements of this specification and to make detail alterations to facilitate production.

Master fuselages under construction.

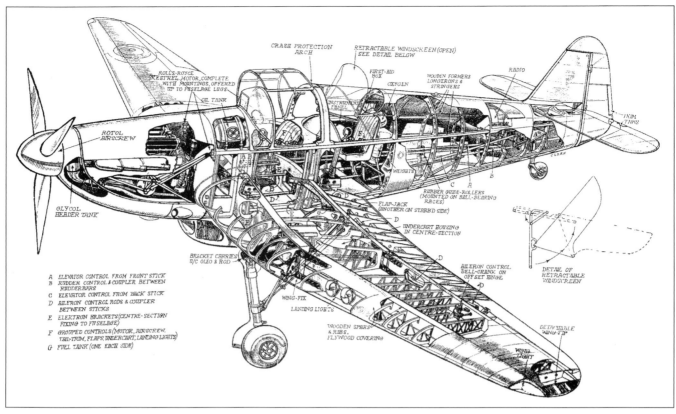

Cutaway drawing of the Miles M.9B Master Mk.I by JH Clark of The Aeroplane *26th July 1939.*

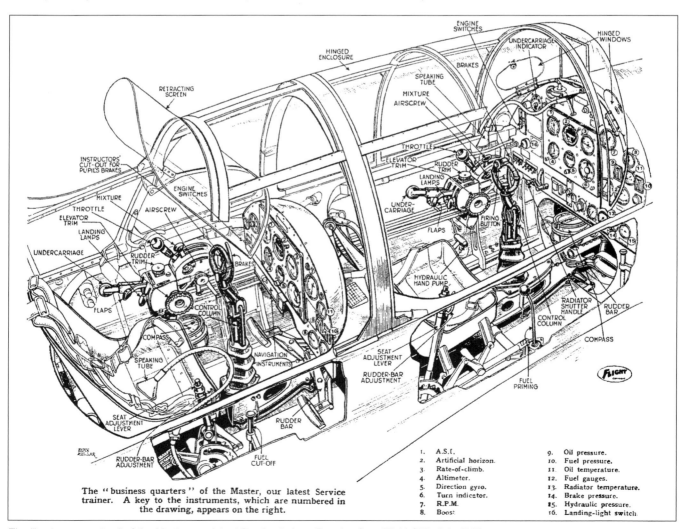

The " business quarters " of the Master, our latest Service
trainer. A key to the instruments, which are numbered in
the drawing, appears on the right.

1. A.S.I.	9.	Oil pressure.
2. Artificial horizon.	10.	Fuel pressure.
3. Rate-of-climb.	11.	Oil temperature.
4. Altimeter.	12.	Fuel gauges.
5. Direction gyro.	13.	Radiator temperature.
6. Turn indicator.	14.	Brake pressure.
7. R.P.M.	15.	Hydraulic pressure.
8. Boost.	16.	Landing-light switch.

The "business quarters" of the Master, our latest Service trainer. Drawing from Flight *27th July 1939.*

Engine: Kestrel engines supplied on embodiment loan are to be installed. The installation is to comply, as far as is practical, with the requirements of DTD.1028 paragraph 15 to 20 inclusive. The engines shall be suitably cooled for operation under tropical conditions. A constant speed airscrew of a type to be agreed by DTD shall be fitted and its strength shall be adequate for the conditions of the diving tests prescribed in ADM.292.

Consideration shall be given to improvements in respect of the Stability at the Stall, Rudder oscillation, and Control in a dive, with a view to reducing to a minimum the adverse features mentioned in the reports of A&AEE on the prototype aircraft.

Consideration shall be given to the following maintenance features: Engine mounting, Tail wheel (to be detachable), Fuel tank (improved shape), Elevators (to be detachable without removing tailplane), Wing tips (to be detachable).

Crew: 2 (Pilot and pupil).

Armament: One Browning gun with 300 rounds of ammunition.

Performance:

Maximum speed at 14,400 ft:	*226 mph*
at sea level:	*193 mph*
Range at economic cruising:	*484 miles*
Service ceiling:	*27,000 ft*

The 745 hp Rolls-Royce Kestrel XVI engine of the Miles M.9 Rolls-Royce PV Trainer/Kestrel was to be replaced in the Master by the 715 hp Rolls-Royce Kestrel XXX, which gave 585 hp at 2,750 rpm at 15,000ft (or 12,000ft given by other sources). This output compared unfavourably with the 745 hp at 3,000 rpm at 14,500ft of the Kestrel XVI engine fitted to the prototype. The maximum speed was also reduced from 295 mph at 16,500ft (although other sources gave the maximum speed as 296 mph at 14,500ft) to 250 mph at 15,000ft, however, the Master was still to be the World's fastest trainer. The reason for replacing the Kestrel XVI with de-rated Kestrel XXX given by the Air Ministry at the

time was that they suspected (wrongly, as it subsequently transpired), that pupils would be; *'incapable of handling such high power after the much lower powered Magisters and Tiger Moths of the EFTS's'.*

Jack Angell, the Rolls-Royce representative at Woodley at the time, recalled that the real reason the engine was changed was because the Rolls-Royce Kestrel XXX was *'more rugged'* and could therefore, *'take the extra strain imposed under training conditions with the great numbers of take-offs and landings'.*

However, be that as it may, the Rolls-Royce Kestrel XXX engines, with which the new build Masters were to be powered, were not new, as they were to be rebuilt and uprated by Rolls-Royce from existing Kestrel engines previously fitted to Hawker Hart variants.

Rolls-Royce were naturally disappointed not to have been able to provide the complete power-plant, with a brand new engine for the Miles Master, but at least they did obtain the contract to rebuild existing Kestrel engines, mostly Kestrel Mk.Vs, which had been taken from obsolete RAF Hawker Harts, Hinds and other Hart variants.

During 1938, with stocks of the liquid-cooled Kestrel XXX engine claimed to be running low, the Air Ministry asked Miles to consider substituting the 810 hp Bristol Mercury radial air-cooled engine in the Miles Master. This nine cylinder radial engine was still in full scale production at the time for use in the Bristol Blenheim bomber and was then claimed to be readily available. The necessary design modifications were immediately put in hand and the designation M.19 Master was allotted to the re-engined aircraft. However, the design was shelved when it was discovered that there were still stocks of Kestrel XXX's available after all and in the event, it was to be late 1939 before the prototype M.19 Master Mk.II was flown with the Bristol Mercury engine.

On 27th January 1939, three weeks ahead of schedule, Sir Kingsley-Wood, the Air Minister, had officially opened the new very large factory extension at Woodley, which had been built to

The photographs on this page and the next show M.9B Master Mk.Is on the assembly line at Woodley in early 1940. Note: the last photograph, shows four aircraft with part of their serials stencilled on the fuselage behind the rear cockpit, (N)7603-(N)7600. These were delivered to RAF Montrose, for 8 FTS, on 19.3.40, 27.3.40, 21.3.40 and 27.3.40 respectively.

The Performance

The most noticeable difference between the prototype and the production model is that the radiator has been moved back from the nose to a ventral position. The final position of the radiator was governed, not so much by cooling or aerodynamic considerations, as by considerations of weight distribution. (Note: this was in fact true, see Chapter 20 in Volume 1 - PA).

In fact, the performance and controllability of the Kestrel Trainer attracted a great deal of attention in the hands of Mr F G Miles himself and of Mr F W C Skinner, Chief Test Pilot of Phillips & Powis Aircraft Ltd, so that nobody was surprised and everybody was pleased when, on June 11, 1938, the Air Ministry officially announced that a very large order had been given to Phillips and Powis Aircraft Ltd for Miles Master advanced trainers developed from the prototype Miles Kestrel Trainer.

Eleven months after the placing of the contract the first production model of the Master, with a Rolls-Royce XXX motor, was flying. The most noticeable difference between the prototype and the production model is that the radiator has been moved back from the nose to the ventral position. The final position of the radiator was governed, not so much by cooling or aerodynamic considerations as by considerations of weight distributions (this was indeed the one and only reason, regardless of whatever else was reported at the time, and even later! - PA).

The aft part of the fuselage has been made deeper in the production model, the tailplane has been slightly raised, the areas of the fin and rudder have been increased a little. The cockpits have been made more roomy and the cockpit cover improved so that the person in the back seat can get a good view when landing.

The installation of the Rolls-Royce XXX, which gives a maximum of 585 hp at 2,750 rpm at 15,000 ft compared with the 745 hp at 3,000 rpm at 14,500 ft of the Kestrel XVI in the prototype has reduced the maximum speed from 295 mph to 250 mph but has still left the Master as the World's fastest trainer (Note: these were in fact 'second-hand' engines, having once been fitted to the Hawker Hart and its variants and which Rolls-Royce had been forced to de-rate in a cramped workshop in their main factory, as the Ministry had decided against the production of new engines, much to the chagrin of Rolls-Royce! - PA).

Production

In these days, when one has come to associate high-speed production with all-metal stressed-skin structures, the study of the construction of a comparatively large aeroplane in wood in large numbers and at a high rate is refreshing and instructive.

There is no doubt that for quickness of getting into production, the wooden aeroplane has advantages over its metal counterpart. In original design and construction the wooden prototype is also cheaper and quicker. For instance, the Kestrel Trainer was designed, built and flown in less than a year.

Mr F G Miles himself has said in an article in The Aeroplane of 9th November 1938, that "it is easy to design in wood, - provided one remembers one is designing in wood." He said in the same article, "I prophesy that if we are ever allowed really to adapt a modern high-speed design to wood that we will promise to cut down production time and put up the production rate to something really exciting."

Mr Miles also lays down four points in favour of wooden construction, to wit:

1. Aeroplanes can be built as fast, strong, stiff, and as durable in wood as in metal.

2. They can be built more quickly, either in small numbers or in mass quantities, than similar metal aircraft, if the designer,

works manager and the purchaser recognise certain fundamental simplifications inherent in the material, and take advantage of them.

3. There are unlimited supplies of suitable labour and suitable material. For metal there are neither.

4. If an emergency (polite term for war) makes us build really large quantities of fighters or light bombers, Mr Miles believes that sooner or later we shall place most of our faith in wood.

Mr Miles qualifies these remarks by saying that they apply to military aircraft or civil aircraft of fairly light types. He does not argue about really large civil transport aeroplanes. But he does believe in wood – for defence in war.

The Miles Master is a more powerful argument for wooden construction than the most eloquently expressed words. The achievement of quantity production in less than a year, including considerable redesign to Air Ministry requirements, is proof of the adaptability of stressed-skin wooden construction.

A complete equipment of jigs, naturally, is used for the production of the Miles Master. The wings and fuselages are assembled separately and then come together down two progressive and parallel production lines.

The fuselage jigs in particular are out of the ordinary and very neat. They have all been designed at Woodley. There are eight altogether, built on the cantilever principle, around a very stiff central metal tube. One end-support hinges down so that the whole fuselage can be slid off the end when complete. Removal from the jig takes only a few moments.

Another aid to fast production is the use of magnesium alloy castings wherever possible in place of forgings or complicated built-up fittings, as, for example, the undercarriage attachments to the spars. Thus there is a saving in cost and in man-hours on a large order.

The Layout

When the first Kestrel Trainer was planned the idea was to produce a really fast aeroplane to have all the characteristics of modern fighters. Thus the layout almost settled itself as a low-wing cantilever monoplane. The two-seat tandem arrangement was adopted to get the best performance and made the flying for the pupil more nearly like that of the fighters for which he would be preparing.
The Rolls-Royce Kestrel was chosen because of its combination of high performance with extreme reliability and the training it would give in the operation of water-cooled power plants.

Aerodynamic cleanness was studied very carefully, with the result that the drag coefficient of the whole aeroplane is probably very nearly as low as that of any machine yet built. As witness this, the Miles Master only needs 71 hp per 1,000 lb of loaded weight to cruise at 216 mph at 15,000 ft.

Throughout the design very careful attention was given to make possible the rapid removal and installation of all the various items of equipment.

Construction

Stiffness has been the criterion of the whole design, particularly with regard to the wing. This is very important where diving speeds of considerably more than 400 mph are likely. Mr F G Miles is convinced that weight for weight the wooden wing can be made stiffer, with a stiffer and smoother surface, than a metal wing, - at least up to an aeroplane of 60,000 lb of loaded weight.

The wing of the Miles Master is very thick. It has a thickness/chord ratio of somewhere about 24%; so thick at the root, in fact, that the front spar continues right through the fuselage and is hollowed out so that the legs of the front pilot can protrude through to the rudder bars. The Master has shown that high speeds are possible with thick wings without the expenditure of great power. At the same time they are very stiff indeed.

The wing section is the NACA 230, slightly tapered in chord and more so in thickness (see Specification and Performance Data - PA).

The wings are made in three parts, a centre-section and two outboard panels, all built up on two laminated box-spars with plywood stressed-skin covering. The thick centre-section is set at an anhedral angle on each side of the fuselage to make a clean juncture and to give greater ground clearance for the airscrew blades. The outer sections of the wings are set at a dihedral of 6 degrees.

The laminated silver spruce flanges of the two spars are made up in the wing shop. The laminations are glued together, put into a press, and left to consolidate. After setting, the flanges are spaced with spruce blocks. Five-ply webs, put on each side, complete the box spar. The plates for the wing fittings are built up of two, and in places three, laminations of high tensile steel bolted through the spars.

The split trailing edge flaps, curved to the shape of the centre-section, are made in special former jigs. They are hydraulically operated by Lockheed jacks and are normally depressed to 25 degrees for take-off and to 90 degrees for landing. An electrical indicator in the cockpits shows their position at all times.

The wings are assembled upside-down to simplify the assembly of the flaps and other details. The centre section can be turned in any position on a rotatable trestle for final completion. The whole of the wing is covered with Saro laminated plywood with madapolam fabric all over. The ailerons are also covered with 1-mm plywood, which makes them very stiff structurally.

The Fuselage

The fuselage is an oval semi-monocoque structure with spruce longerons and frames, entirely covered with stressed-plywood skin. It ends in a deep stern post, which also serves as the stern post of the fin.

The tail unit is fully cantilever, entirely covered with plywood except for the rudder, which has fabric covering. The elevators and rudder have damped trimming tabs operated by irreversible mechanisms close to the tabs. These tabs can be worked from both cockpits. Each has its own indicating system. The position of the tailplane has been carefully chosen to give good recovery from a spin.

The Undercarriage

The backwards fully retracting Lockheed undercarriage was designed and made by Automotive Products Ltd, Leamington Spa. It is the first of its particular type to be installed in an aeroplane in this country. As each wheel goes up backwards, it turns through 90 degrees at the same time, so that it lies flat inside the wing between the spars. In spite of this movement the mechanism is delightfully simple.

The Lockheed Airdraulic shock-absorber is attached through the angled universal joint to a big Elektron casting bolted on the front face of the front spar. There is a rotating and sliding collar on the leg. The side stay and the breaking arm at the back are attached to this collar. The side stay picks up another fitting at the other end of the big Elektron casting on the front spar.

The retracting ram and the knee-action breaking struts are behind the Airdraulic strut. A sleeve-lock secures the leg of the undercarriage in the extended position. A sleeve slides over the knee-joint so that it cannot move when the undercarriage is extended.

When the undercarriage is being retracted, the sleeve-lock first slides back, then the hydraulic ram attached to it, working at a pressure of up to 1,500 lb per sq in, breaks the knee-action strut and swings the leg up. As the leg swings up it turns on the universal joint. When the leg reaches the top of its travel it engages a spring-operated latch lock, which holds it firmly in position. To put the undercarriage down, the latch lock is tripped by the initial movement of the double-acting ram.

Emergency pipe-lines and hand pumps are installed should there be a failure in the main pump circuit. The position-indicator is inter-connected with the motor ignition switch and throttle control. A mechanical indicator is fitted as well, although the electrical indicator has duplicate bulbs.

Palmer wheels and tyres, 580 by 180 mm, or Dunlop wheels and tyres, 7.25 ins by 9 ins, are fitted. The Palmer brakes are air-operated. A hinged V-torsion bar keeps the wheel in the correct attitude.

The Lockheed undercarriage caused a great deal of interest when it was first shown at the SBAC show in 1937. Since then the rig has been slightly modified to take care of the increase in all-up weight from 4,200 to 5,500 lb and to allow for the higher requirements now adopted.

The Power Plant

The Rolls-Royce Kestrel XXX 12-cylinder liquid-cooled 60 degrees Vee motor, geared .477 to 1, develops 715 hp at 2,750 rpm at a boost of 5 lb per in for take-off at sea-level. It is rated at 535 hp at 2,400 rpm at plus ½ lb boost at 12,500 ft and has a maximum level output for five minutes of 585 hp at 2,750 rpm at 15,000 ft.

The Rolls-Royce Kestrel XXX was specified for production models in place of the Kestrel XVI because of the need to study production requirements now that the Merlins are being turned out from most of the Rolls-Royce Works.

In actual fact the Kestrel XXX's are not new motors but rebuilt and modified Kestrels taken from certain Service aeroplanes now obsolete. Auxiliary drives for the Rotol constant-speed airscrew and for the Lockheed hydraulic mechanism for retracting the undercarriage and working the flaps have been added to make the motor completely up to date.

A particularly interesting point is that the motor is supplied by Rolls-Royce complete with its steel tubular mounting which only has to be attached by four main fixing bolts and the various connections made at the bulkhead. The power plant can thus be detached when necessary, complete with vacuum pump and relief valve, the hydraulic pump and the constant-speed unit.

The motor drives a three-blade Rotol constant-speed airscrew which has Schwarz-covered wooden blades made by the Airscrew Company Ltd. The latest type of backwards facing ejector exhausts are fitted.

The low-drag ducted radiator has three elements, made up of two cylindrical water radiators with a single cylindrical oil cooler between them. The area of the exit is controlled from the front cockpit.

Two 35-gallon fuel tanks are slung in the centre section near the root of each wing. The tanks can be removed through doors under the wings.

The oil system is of a normal type with a tank mounted aft of the fire-proof bulkhead. A partial circulator is built in and there is provision for a different rate of circulation for warming up in varying weathers. The oil filter can be taken out of the top of the tank for cleaning.

A draining pipe is led to the side of the fuselage by way of a three-way cock in the tank sump. The oil-cock control is inter-connected with the starter ignition switch so that the motor cannot be started with the oil cock closed or open to drain.

A water header tank of 1 gallon 4 pints capacity plus 1¾ gallons of air space is mounted at the front of the motor on top of the reduction gear.

The motor drives a Lockheed hydraulic pump for the retraction of the undercarriage and for the operation of the flaps, a vacuum pump for driving the gyroscopic instruments, constant-speed unit for the airscrew and a 500-watt generator.

Accommodation

The Miles Master is normally flown from the front cockpit, although particular care has been taken to make possible landings from the back. The pupil begins his flying training in the back seat and then changes places with the instructor half-way through his training.

The transparent Perspex cockpit covers have fixed hinges on the starboard side and slide up in guide channels on the port side to fold over for ingress and egress. There are quick-release catches on both sides for emergency escape.

At the back a windscreen, normally folded back to form part of the roof, can be raised so that the pilot in the back seat can look out over the head of the occupant of the front seat when taking off and landing. For this purpose the back seat has 12 ins of vertical movement instead of the normal 4 ins.

Thus the pilot in the back seat has an excellent view forward over the leading edge of the centre section as well as straight forward through the windscreen over his companion in front. The necessary adjustment to the rudder-bar is made at the same time as the seat is moved.

A strong Elektron casting forms part of the frame of the cockpit cover between the two seats and serves to protect the heads of the crew should the aeroplane turn over on the ground.

An optical panel of Triplex in the front of the front windscreen gives an undistorted view forward for the reflector-sight of the gun. Two small panels in the vertical windscreen can be opened for flying in bad weather.

The view is excellent, largely because the moulded Perspex needs very little superstructure.

Built as a fighting aeroplane, the Miles Master would have been extremely formidable. As a trainer it is certainly at the top of its class. We know with what keen anticipation and enthusiasm the arrival of the production models is looked forward to at the training establishments. The Miles Master looks like going down to History as the "Rolls-Royce of Trainers, - Miles ahead of its rivals."

An article, couched in a similar vein, under the heading *Trainer De Luxe*, appeared in *Flight* for 27th July 1939. Other articles on the *Construction of the Miles M.9B Master Mk.I* appeared in 'Aeronautics' for November 1939 and an extremely detailed article on *The Miles M.9B Master Mk.I Production*, appeared in *Aircraft Production* for February and March 1940.

A very interesting letter, dated 2nd November 1939, recently discovered in the National Archives of Canada, detailed the proposed manufacture of the Miles Master by the Ottawa Car Manufacturing Company Limited, Ottawa, Canada. Sent by them to Air Vice Marshall G M Croil, AFC, Air Member for Air Staff, Department of National Defence, Ottawa, Ontario, it read:

We are enclosing for your attention specification covering the Miles Master I High Speed Advanced Trainer, designed and manu-factured by Phillips & Powis Aircraft Limited, Reading, England.

The latter company has been anxious for some time to commence the manufacture of the Miles Master in Canada and has now given this company the exclusive manufacturing and selling rights for this aircraft here and is prepared to proceed with production with the least possible delay.

The Miles Master was designed to meet Air Ministry requirements and has been purchased by them in large quantities for training in the Royal Air Force. The last order given by the Air Ministry was within the last month and according to our principals represented a large quantity.

In view of the advanced training programme to be carried out in Canada, we feel sure that the Miles Master I will be of particular interest to you having already proved its suitability for this class of instruction.

M Morris Lambe our Sales Manager has just returned from England after conferring with Mr. Miles, designer and joint Managing Director of Phillips & Powis and he was assured by the latter that they are prepared to give us every assistance in commencing the manufacture of the Master by sending over key men whose experience will be used to place this aircraft on a high production basis within the shortest possible time.

We would be very pleased to discuss this matter in further detail and trust that we may have the pleasure of hearing from you in this connection.

> *Yours truly,*
> *Redmond Quain,*
> *President*

Four notes, hand-written by indecipherable signatories were appended on the letter:

2. 3/11/39: AMAS (TC)
For remarks please.

This note was signed by GMC - CAS, to whom the letter had been sent.

3. 7/11/39: *AMDT*
Early reports from GB are good as regards this Advanced Trainer. It is therefore recommended that a full report be obtained from the CLO, unless one has already been obtained.

Some of the disadvantages of this aircraft from the Canadian point of view would appear to be:
  (a)   Wood-construction – effect of climate.
  (b)   Operation of Kestrel engine during winter weather.

This note was signed by G Howson and WG? - DAPT?

4. 30/11/39: *C.A.S.*
This appears to be a very good design but in comparison with the Harvard has the following disadvantages:-
  (a)   Wooden construction not as durable in dry climate.
  (b)   Being newer type will be subject to minor defects in design.
  (c)   Does not appear to have the simplicity that the Harvard has.

This note was signed by E Johnson - acan AMDT?

5. 4/12/39: *AMDT*
For reply please. We are not interested. Harvards in large numbers have been ordered and we are in no position to experiment with a new type now.

This note was signed GMC - CAS.

Air Vice Marshall G M Croil had had the final say - the Miles Master would not be produced in Canada - and that was the end of the matter!

However, it is ironic to note that Noorduyn Aviation Ltd of Montreal, Canada, eventually built 2,610 North American AT-16 Harvards (corresponding to the USAAF AT-6As) for the RAF and RCAF before being taken over by Canadian Car and Foundry in 1946 and this company then built a further 270 T-6G standard Harvard Mk.4s for the RCAF and 285 T-6Js for USAF Mutual Aid Programmes.

An extract from '*Some notes on Phillips & Powis Aircraft Ltd/Miles Aircraft Ltd's activities during the war*', for inclusion in the MAP Scientific War Records, dated October 1947 (N.A. Ref: AVIA 44/603), included the following on the Master:

The Master I was in quantity production at the outbreak of the War. It had an all-up weight of 5,000 lb, was powered by Rolls-Royce Kestrel XXX engine and had minimum strength factor of 9.0. The top speed was 228 mph at 14,500 ft, with a maximum climb of 2,400 feet per minute and a landing speed of 60 mph. The advanced training equipment included full dual fighter type controls, one .303 Browning gun, camera gun, two-way communication radio and night flying equipment complete with flares was standard. The instructor's location in the rear cockpit was fitted with a windscreen and seat raising mechanism such that he could elevate himself twelve inches above the normal position in order that his view during take-off and landing was equal to that from the front cockpit.

An early M.9B Master Mk.I showing the instructors windscreen and seat in the raised position for landing. Photograph 'Passed for publication' by the Press Section of the Air Ministry 24th July 1939.
[Flight photograph via Mike Hooks]

The design was evolved from the Miles Kestrel Trainer which had an all-up weight of 5,500 lb, was powered of the Rolls-Royce Kestrel XVI, and had a top speed of 295 mph at 15,000 feet, with basically the same equipment as subsequently specified for the Master I.

The intensified training programme during the war was such that any inexperienced handling, both in the air and on the ground, imposed unforeseen conditions on the aircraft, but nevertheless between 1940 and 1942 the number of structural defects and modifications was only 30% of a total of 1,750 reported defects and 400 modifications incorporated.

A 'g' limiting device was invented and developed by Miles Aircraft Limited to counter the effects of inexperienced aerobatic flying and a reduced wing span was also introduced for this reason. The contemporary system of specialised hydraulic equipment was replaced by a Miles design of unit assembly to facilitate maintenance, thus relieving inexperienced ground crews of complicated adjustments and replacement. Tail-wheel strut troubles caused by the rough surfaces of war-time emergency aerodromes were overcome by introducing lever-suspension and, as the aircraft rarely had the opportunity of being parked under cover, year in year out, plastic glues were introduced to avoid weathering effects on casein types of adhesive.

The fuselage construction was semi-monocoque, the frames being routered from multi-ply birch, the longerons made from spruce and the structure covered with three-ply birch varying from 1½ mm to 1/8" thick.

The wing and tailplane spars were box type beams having spruce booms and plywood webs. Many of the ribs were routered from multi-ply but a few main ribs were of spruce warren-girder construction. The covering was glued and screwed in position.

All flying controls were of the push-pull type, except those for trimming tabs which were cable operated.

Magnesium alloy castings were used wherever castings were applicable and all assemblies were designed in unit form for ease of production.

Immediately after Dunkirk, and number of Master I aircraft were converted - twenty-six in six weeks - to the role of a six-gun fighter. The guns were .303 Browning type with a reflector gun-sight, and a bullet-proof windscreen and plating were added for the protection of the pilot and engine.

With the Miles Master Mk.I in service with the RAF, and with the stocks of Kestrel engines drying up, the earlier design was resurrected and in June 1939, the M.9B Master Mk.I, **N7422** (c/n 1125), was taken from the assembly line to be fitted with the 840 hp Bristol Mercury VIII (as fitted to the Bristol Blenheim Mk.I), and with the increased span tailplane of the M.9C, it became the prototype for the new M.19 Master Mk.II. First flown, by chief test pilot 'Bill' Skinner, during October 1939. However, this prototype crashed during its service trials at the A&AEE at Boscombe Down on 10 the January 1940 so the M.9B Master Mk.I, **N7447** (c/n 1150), was hastily converted to the second prototype M.19 Master Mk.II in order for the trials to be completed, and this was first flown, by Flt Lt Hugh Kennedy, on 1st April 1940.

A second large contract for the Master, No B.44440/39, undated, was placed for the manufacture of **500** M.9C Master Mk.IA aircraft. The first **400** of these were delivered between 27th September 1940 and 15th April 1941, but the remaining **100** were completed as the M.19 Master Mk.II with the Bristol Mercury engine.

Production M.19 Master Mk.IIs were fitted with 870 hp Bristol Mercury XX or 30 engines and the introduction of this air-cooled radial engine reduced the length to 29ft 6in. However, the maximum speed of 275 mph at 14,000ft was a marked improvement over the Master Mk.I, even though the frontal area was increased. The cruising speed was 208 mph and the landing speed remained at 85 mph but the AUW was reduced to 5,341.5lb.

However, during 1940, the Ministry suddenly realised that the 'unlimited stocks' of Bristol Mercury engines, which they thought were available, had mysteriously disappeared, and so Miles was asked, yet again, to re-design the Master to take a third different engine. This time it was to be the American built 825 hp Pratt & Whitney Twin Wasp Junior R-1535-SB4-G, which had been chosen because, once again, '*supplies were considered to be plentiful*'. It is believed that these engines were originally intended for France but, following the collapse of that country in June 1940, they became available for other purposes. The M.9B Master Mk.I, **N7994** (c/n 1526), was fitted with the American engine to become the prototype M.27 Master Mk.III, but soon after this it was found that supplies of the Mercury engine were still available after all, so both the Mk.II and Mk.III were then produced simultaneously.

During the early stages of the war, Fighter Command had, in addition to their operational aircraft, an appreciable number of training aircraft on their strength, and in September 1940, when the Battle of Britain was at its height, practically every squadron had a Magister or Master attached to it. These aircraft were used for a multitude of different purposes, including ferrying pilots to collect replacement aircraft and picking up stranded pilots who had landed away from base for any reason. In one famous case, No 54 Squadron's Master Mk.I, N7681, was involved in picking up a downed pilot from Calais airfield in France and this was reported in the national newspapers and also in a full page advertisement for the Miles Master, which appeared in *Flight* for 11th July 1940:

Somewhere in England - MONOPLANE PILOTS NEED MONOPLANE TRAINING. Below a drawing of a Miles Master Mk.I in flight, was a newspaper cutting, which read:

The awards of the DSO to one RAF officer, the DFC to five others and the DFM to a sergeant who is posted as missing were announced last night. Acting Flt Lt James Anthony Leathart, who receives the DSO, flew a trainer aircraft to Calais Marck aerodrome to rescue a squadron commander who had been shot down but was uninjured. As he was taking off after the rescue an attack was made by 12 Messerschmitt 109s, but he shook off the enemy and landed without damage. Later he flew back to England unescorted. One day last month his squadron attacked 60 'planes. With his squadron he has shot down 15 Messerschmitts and possibly one Heinkel III and one Junkers 88.

Flt Lt Leathart, who was born at Upper Norwood, SE, in 1915, joined the Auxiliary Air Force in 1936, and was granted a commission in the RAF the following year.

David Masters, also wrote of this incident in 'So Few'; '*during the last days of the fighting in France in May/June 1940, Sqdn Ldr F L White DSO, of 74 Squadron, Hornchurch, flying Spitfire Mk.I, K9867 (ZP-J), attacked and shot down a Henschel 126 over France, but not before it had put a bullet through his radiator. The glycol cooling fluid began to pour out and he had to force land at Calais Marck Aerodrome. The other pilots of his squadron saw him land and reported the incident to their base. The Germans were already closing in around Calais but that didn't stop Sqdn Ldr White trying and obtain a new radiator! Hiding his Spitfire in the hedge as best he could, he sought help from the local Railway Transport Officer but this only got him into more trouble as he couldn't produce proof of identification and was promptly arrested! Eventually managing to sort that problem out he arranged for some swift enquiries to be made regarding the despatch of a spare radiator from England. He also learned that Flt Lt Leathart, of 54 Squadron, also from Hornchurch, was going to fly over in a Miles Master, with an escort, in order to pick him up.*

At about 12.30 p.m. on 23rd May 1940, Acting Flt Lt James Anthony Leathart took off from Hornchurch in 54 Squadron's Miles Master Mk.I, N7681, with the young New Zealander P/O Alan C Deere to act as escort. It was a lovely day, with a good deal of cloud at about 5,000 feet, and after about 15 minutes they arrived over Calais/Marck aerodrome. Noting the position of the bomb craters, Flt Lt Leathart made a successful landing between them while Deere circled the aerodrome at just under 1,000 feet. At first unable to find Sqdn Ldr White, Leathart took off but meanwhile White had arrived and was frantically waving to attract his attention! Returning to land again, Leathart saw a big dogfight taking place above the aerodrome so they both took shelter in a ditch until things quietened down. They then got into the Master and took off, White having left instructions with the remaining ground crews to destroy his Spitfire to stop it falling into the hands of the enemy. Fortunately, by this time the skies were clear of enemy aircraft and the Master returned safely to base. The rescue of Sqdn Ldr White proved just how highly the RAF prized the life of every single pilot'.

Further to my mention in the Introduction regarding the BBC TV programme on the 70th Anniversary of the Battle of Britain, the record, as portrayed by the BBC was not strictly accurate as it was not the Harvard advanced trainer on which the majority of the pilots who fought in the Battle received their advanced mono-plane training, but the Miles Master Mk.I and so an opportunity to finally publicly recognise the achievements of the Miles Master was lost.

In fact, only 200 Harvards were delivered between December 1938 and October 1939, with a further 200 being delivered between August 1939 and June 1940, whereas 500 Master Mk.Is were delivered between July 1939 and September 1940.

It must also never be forgotten that, not only did many of the future RAF and American fighter pilots (the latter who fought with the Eagle Squadrons in the Battle of Britain), receive their advanced training on the Master Mk.I, but they often also received further operational training on them when they arrived at the squadrons.

In January 1941, with the survival prospects for Great Britain still looking grim, bomb racks for the carriage of 8 x 25lb bombs were first fitted to the underside of the wings on Master Mk.IA **T8559** for trials, and provision was later made for the fitment of bomb racks to all subsequent marks of Master.

An interesting photograph showing a Master Mk.I, with possibly Ken Waller in the cockpit, with the first prototype Miles M.18, U2, in the back-ground. Note the sandbag pillbox at right end of the Repair & Service department.

Milestones ... 1939

MILES 'MASTER'

"Monoplane Pilots need Monoplane Training"

NO history of Miles Aircraft would be complete without reference to the now-famous Miles Master.

The Master was designed on the idea that the Trainers of the R.A.F. should be as advanced as the operational aeroplanes of the Hurricane and Spitfire class and have equal characteristics. It was a two-seat tandem low-wing cantilever monoplane, with a Rolls-Royce Kestrel engine, and was as fast as the single-seat biplane fighters of 1935, many of which were still then in service. Every fighter pilot in the R.A.F. now receives initiation into fighter tactics in a Master. He goes from initial to operational school with the confidence that comes of being familiar with the class of aeroplane he will fly in combat. Even the American Eagle Squadron—experienced flying men all—flew Masters before Hurricanes and their tribute to the trainers was high. In this small measure, credit which the designers would be loth to claim, the Master has thus contributed to the acknowledged superiority of Britain's fighting men in the air.

Over the remaining years between 1939 and now we must draw a discreet veil. And for the future, what can we say?—except that Miles Aircraft will be there with Wings for the World's air-minded in the form that best suits the needs of the great To-morrow that will dawn with Peace . . . .

Miles AIRCRAFT

CONSTRUCTED   BY   PHILLIPS   &   POWIS   AIRCRAFT   LIMITED,   SOMEWHERE   IN   ENGLAND

» M A S T E R S   O F   T H E   A I R «

(M6)

An advertisement for the Miles Master in Flight *for 26th November 1942.*

"World's Fastest Air Trainer. Over 500 miles per hour in dive from Oxford to Farnborough. The RAF's new training plane for fighter pilots now in full production and mass delivery has astonished the experts by its amazing high speed performance. The 'Master', fitted with a Rolls- Royce engine is constructed of wood and has stood the test of some terrific power dives and has been officially quoted as maintaining a speed of over 500 miles per hour in a dive from Oxford to Farnborough. Picture taken at dawn this morning shows a line of 'Masters' for fighter pilots newly delivered to an advanced training station (RAF Sealand - PA) that is hidden away near the mountains of the West Coast."

[Photopress 10th November 1939]

An evocative shot of Master Mk.I, N7622, taken before delivery to 8 FTS Montrose on 5th April 1940.

Master Mk.I, N7845, taken before delivery to 8 FTS Montrose on 2nd July 1940. Note radiator outlet flap open.

Master Mk.IA, N7547, delivered to Eastleigh for 759 Squadron, 10.2.40.

Master Mk.IA, T8559, with bomb racks and practice bombs. Note reduced span wings.

After the war the (Canadian) National Research Council in Ottawa published a booklet entitled The War History of the Division of Mechanical Engineering (RG77 archives). Apparently, "The British Ministry of Aircraft Production had expressed interest in the moulded plywood work of the Laboratories and had requested samples for examination by industry in Great Britain. A number of components, including various fairings, wing root fillet and pilot's seat, were then made for the Master and flown to Great Britain.

Reference RG77 Acc 85/86/237 File(s) Mechanical Engineering Director's Reports; Laboratories and Work of the Division, dated April 1941 gives details this work in *Components for Miles Master Aircraft by W T Reid*, as follows:

Wooden Aircraft (S2-1-26)

Miles Master Components for MAP

The British Plywood Manufacturers Ltd, 362-4 Old Street, London EC4 (based at Kings Langley, Herts), received a development contract from the MAP for the manufacture, in moulded wood, of wing and tail fairings and pilot's seat for the Miles Master. The company is proceeding to make these but desired samples made in America to show the MAP. Mr Sol Yager (of the Aircraft Plastics Division of British Plywood) inquired on 24th April if samples could be made in the laboratory. As this will afford the laboratory valuable experience, the President approved of the work being undertaken.

May 1941	Several moulds were designed and constructed.
June 1941	Mr Sol Yager visited the laboratory on 11th June. Work continued on the moulds for these components. A tail fairing was moulded and the pilot's seat was veneered.
July 1941	Mr Sol Yager visited the laboratory on 17th July prior to his return to England.

Labour and material costs on the four items, including moulds and part costs of bags was estimated as:

Pilot's Seat	225.00
Tail fairings	175.00
Wing Fillet - Front	150.00
Wing Fillet - rear	180.00

On 22nd July, Mr Yager was requested to confirm these prices were acceptable.

The pilot's seat and tail fairing were finished and displayed to the WT and SD Committee on 28th July and the wing fillet moulds were being made.

| August 1941 | The pilot's seat and tail fairings were shipped by air to England 1st August. The wing nose fillet was finished. |
| September 1941 | An invoice was issued 24th September for: |

1 moulded wood pilot's seat	348.00
1 moulded wood tail fairing	202.00
Express charges	2.87
	$552.87

The wing nose fillet was being packed for shipment at the end of the month.

Mr Sol Yager of British Plywood Manufacturers Ltd requests and is furnished information from time to time.

| October 1941 | The wing nose fillet and mould were shipped on 4th October. A sample of |

Plaskon 700 was forwarded at the end of the month.

November 1941	Nothing to report.
December 1941	The wing fairing mould is being finished.
January 1942	A wing fairing was moulded but was unsatisfactory due to defective gluing.
February 1942	The last of these components, the large wing fillet, was completed.
March 1942	The British Plywood Manufacturers Ltd were advised, on 4th March, that the last of the components had been made and inquiry was made as to its disposal.
10th April 1942	Sol Yager / W T Reid, NRC, Ottawa, reporting on his efforts with respect to building a Moulded Seat, which was to be tested at the RAE at Farnborough *"early next week"*, plus other technical matters. Included was the following comment: *I believe that the large Master Wing Fillet that you have made, will be of great interest over here and so when ship space is available, perhaps you will have this shipped.*

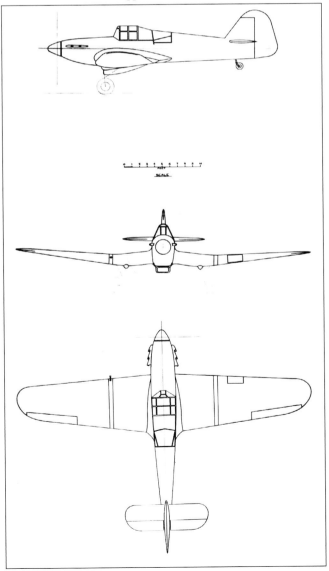

3-view G.A. drawing of the Miles M.9C Master Mk.IA.

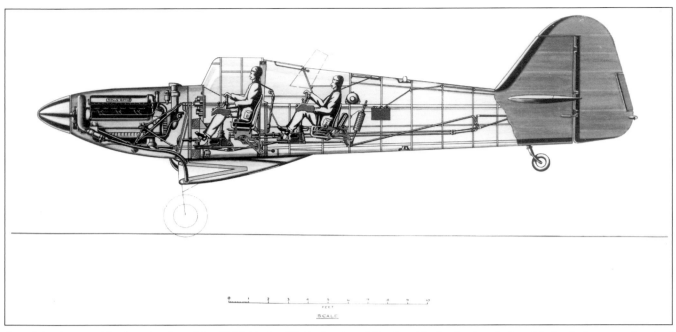

A partial cut-away side view drawing of the M.9C Master Mk.IA showing sliding hood to the front cockpit and instructor's screen in raised position, although seat in lower position.

Unfortunately, nothing further is known of these experimental moulded wooden component developments.

The other most noticeable difference in the production aircraft was that produced by the introduction of Modification No.150. This modification increased the span of the tailplane from 11ft 0in to 12 ft. 5½ ins, and increased its area by about 5 sq ft, in order to compensate for the extra weight caused by the installation of R/T equipment, which replaced the speaking tubes between the two occupants fitted in the early machines. These modifications increased the AUW of the M.9C Master Mk.IA to 5,450lb. The prototype M.9C Master Mk.IA was converted from the M.9B Master Mk.I **N7685** (c/n 1314) and was delivered to the A&AEE at Boscombe Down for service trials on 1st May 1940.

Immediately after Dunkirk, in June 1940, permission was given by the Air Ministry Development Branch, Harrogate, to convert 25 Master Mk.Is into Master Fighters, 'on the assembly line'. The Master Fighter was a basically a single-seat version of the Master advanced trainer, fitted with 6 x .303 Browning machine guns in the wings and was intended as a reserve fighter should the need arise. The prototype, with a single-seat and fixed cockpit canopy, a reflector gun-sight, bullet-proof windscreen and plating added for the protection of the pilot and engine, was converted from Master Mk.I **N7412** (c/n 1115).

25 were actually completed as M.24 Master Fighters on the assembly line and these were delivered to the flying training schools between 20th June and 28th June 1940, and yet, just two weeks after permission to convert the aircraft had been given, Phillips & Powis were instructed to stop work on the project.

The Master Fighter had been designed and built with such speed that it was not allotted a type designation number, and only after the Battle for Britain had been fought and won was it allotted the designation M.24, for record purposes, hence the Master Fighter's designation number being out of sequence.

An order for four Master Mk.I aircraft was received from Estonia in 1939 and Nos. 31 to 35 on the assembly line were allotted to this contract. These were to have been diverted from the RAF contract but unfortunately, war engulfed Estonia, which was over-run before they could be despatched and they were delivered to the RAF with their original serials, **N7438-N7442** c/ns 1141-1145.

The first 500 Master Mk.Is were delivered to the RAF between 4th August 1939 and 27th September 1940.

An A&AEE report, dated 12th April 1940, which dealt with maintenance trials following the discovery of certain defects and failures, concluded that:

The main wooden structure was a sturdy well-made job but the three-ply covering is considered too light to be satisfactory for Service operation. Although the machines are housed in hangars, the wing and fuselage coverings buckle very early in the life of the aircraft. Examination of a crashed aircraft showed that the gluing of the skin to the ribs was not always satisfactory; similarly during diving tests the three-ply covering became loose from the internal structure for the same reason. The combination of these two features (inferior gluing and buckling of the three-ply) is considered to be very unsatisfactory.

Other weak features included the sideways opening cockpit canopy and the rear cockpit windscreen handle but during routine maintenance, a number of other unsatisfactory features had come to light which needed to be corrected.

Modification No.133, incorporated into the Master on the assembly line in 1940, covered the introduction of a new windscreen and sliding hood for the front occupant, with hinged side panels to the rear cabin but with the rear top section still tilting forward to provide a windscreen for the instructor when in the raised position. This new arrangement replaced the hood originally fitted to the front cockpit of the earlier Mk.I aircraft, which was hinged on the starboard side, and found to be somewhat unmanageable in service. This modified version became the M.9C Master Mk.IA.

Structural problems, encountered shortly after the Master entered service, which weren't resolved until August 1940, meant that aerobatics were initially officially forbidden. Accident, Report No.Misc.4, which covered the first six accidents, was issued on 26th June 1940 by Group Capt Vernon Brown, Chief Inspector Accidents Investigation Branch at the Air Ministry. The 'General Review' of this report stated:

Since 10th January 1940 there had been six accidents to Master aircraft, five of which were definitely due to structural failure in the air, the remaining one being of a nature which makes it appear probable that a structural failure also took place.

The aircraft involved were:

N7422, *the prototype M.19 Master Mk.II which was being flown by a test pilot from the A&AEE when it lost its tailplane (it was fitted with the increased area type to Mod.150 - PA) during the recovery from a dive on 10th January 1940;*

N7551, *being flown by an experienced pilot* (from Warmwell - PA) *when it lost its tailplane following a roll off the top of a loop on 22nd April 1940;*

N7622, *being flown solo by a pupil from No 8 FTS Montrose on 28th May 1940 which suffered tailplane failure during spinning;*

N7556, *also being flown by a pupil pilot from No 8 FTS when on 31st May 1940 the aircraft was seen to be diving and turning with parts falling away from it, including the tailplane and most of both wings;*

N7630, *also of No 8 FTS being flown by a pupil pilot on 31st May 1940 when during the attempted recovery following a dive (or a spin) the aircraft began to break up, losing both wings and the tailplane;*

N7706, *the third Master to crash on 31st May 1940 and this one was being flown by a pupil pilot from No 15 FTS when, following an almost vertical climb into a bank of cloud it emerged in a spin and almost immediately after it broke cloud the port elevator came adrift.*

In four of the accidents there were also many failures at glued joints in those parts of the tail units, fuselages and planes which had broken away in the air. Four of the six accidents occurred on warm and damp mornings and during the first spell of warm weather of the year and the casein cement on parts of the scattered wreckage which had been exposed to moisture when lying on the ground was found to be soft. The average flying time of the six aeroplanes concerned in the accidents was under 50 hours.

It is of interest to quote three of the relevant paragraphs and the Conclusions from the report - viz:

Paragraph 4

As a result of the four last accidents, all of which happened within three days and three of which happened on the same day, acrobatics on Masters were immediately prohibited. The situation which arose as the result of this embargo was, of course, very serious and the normal methods for the investigation of an accident of this kind were, therefore, abandoned. The remains of the broken tailplanes were sent by road to the R.A.E. at Farnborough and immediately they had arrived a meeting was convened there to discuss the whole question. This meeting took place on 6th June and was attended by representatives of Aerodynamics and Mechanical Test Departments of the R.A.E., Phillips & Powis Aircraft Ltd, A.I.D. and R.T.O. from Phillips & Powis Aircraft Ltd, D.T.D. and Accidents Investigation Branch.

Paragraph 5

As the result of this discussion two tests were made at the R.A.E. on Master N7049 (error for N7409 - PA). *The fuselage was supported on its side by holding the main centre section wing attachment points and lateral load was applied to the fin and rudder by means of shot bags. The loading applied and its distribution corresponded to the design fin and rudder loads specified for the type and were roughly representative of the aerodynamic loads likely to arise in the course of using the rudder during aerobatics.*

(i)   As the load was applied the fin appeared to twist somewhat, causing early wrinkling of its skin, and some early buckling of the fuselage ply covering was noticed near the accumulator locker. The structure failed prematurely at loads corresponding to 0.44 of the design loading. The rear fin post broke away from the "upper" top longeron and the fuselage plywood there, the front fin post collapsed near its root by both bending and twisting, and the fuselage bulkhead at the rear spar came away from the "under" plywood and longeron. The fillets in the top of the rear fuselage aft of the same bulkhead were damaged.

(ii)   The fuselage which was damaged during the first test was then repaired and strengthened by a series of modifications. These comprised:-

(a)   Fitting of internal metal brackets and external metal straps to reinforce each of the four connections between the longerons and the rear fin post.

(b)   Substituting for the various corner fillets in the open top panels of the rear fuselage a complete covering of thick plywood, running from the stern post right forward to the accumulator locker.

(c)   Reinforcing the bottom of the front fin post by adding plywood with spruce strips to its front and rear surfaces to change it effectively into a wide box section strut from its root joint to the level of the lowest fin rib.

(d)   Reinforcing by light ribs and stringers the fuselage ply covering in the curved panel immediately ahead of the accumulator locker.

(e)   Reinforcing the diamond shaped hole in the underside of the fuselage below the accumulator locker by building up the front and rear corners of the hole with ply and spruce fillets.

For the purpose of this second test the original fin was replaced by a new fin off the production line with current improvements of ribs and cover incorporated.

Some buckling appeared in the fuselage ply below the accumulator locker at about 0.45 of the design load and more serious and extensive ones appeared at about 0.75 of the design load. At about 0.95 of the design load the ply fillets at the wing root fuselage junction were pulling away and buckling considerably; some evidence of creep appeared at 1.05 design load, and failure appeared imminent at 1.13 the design load when the test was discontinued to preserve the parts for further tests.

Paragraph 6

The results obtained in these tests indicate that distortion of some magnitude takes place throughout the length of the fuselage.

Conclusions

(i)   The accidents were the result of failures at the rear end of the fuselages due to weakness inherent in the design.

(ii)   The lack of adhesion in many of the casein cement joints is considered to be a contributory factor.

(iii)   The locking wire on the handles operating the emergency exit panels possibly delayed and may have prevented the pilots escaping by parachute after structural failure had occurred.

A footnote to the Report stated:

The series of modifications listed in paragraph 5 (ii) were approved by the local Modification Committee at Phillips & Powis Aircraft Ltd at a meeting held on 14th June 1940 and recorded in minute No.199. It was proposed that the modifications be incorporated in all Master Mk.I aircraft and that they should be returned to the contractor's works for this purpose.

It was further proposed that all present restrictions on flying the Master Mk.I aircraft should be rescinded when the modifications have been incorporated.

Master Mk.I, **N7893** was delivered to A&AEE, Boscombe Down on 18th July 1940 for further aerobatic and spin tests after strengthening modifications to the fuselage and fin structure had been incorporated. Following tests, particularly at extended aft c.g., it was found that the aeroplane behaved normally and it was then recommended, in an A&AEE report, dated 9th September 1940, that the restrictions on aerobatics in all Masters imposed earlier after a number of accidents in service with the RAF and one at the A&AEE should be removed.

Following the publication of Accident Report No.Misc.4, it was soon found necessary to issue Accident Report No.Misc.4B (of which no copy has been found) and this could have covered accidents to five Masters as follows;

N7625 from No.8 FTS whose tailplane broke off following recovery from a dive on 14.8.40;

N7987 from No.55 OTU which broke-up in the air 'cause not known' and crashed 20.9.40;

N8001 from No.8 FTS which was abandoned when part of a wing fell off 23.9.40;

N8002 from No.8 FTS which lost a wing, believed during aerobatics and crashed 2.3.41;

N7637 from No.8 FTS which broke-up and dived into sea 3.3.41.

Accident Report No.Misc.4C was issued shortly after these crashes stated:

Since the issue of Report Misc.4B, two further cases of structural failure in Master aircraft have occurred:.

*(a)   Master **N7704** of No.8 SFTS crashed at 1630 hrs on 7.6.41 2 miles NE of Laurencekirk. LAC Cook, HG (Pupil pilot) killed.*

The accident occurred in the course of a solo flight authorised for the practice of slow rolls and loops. About ½ hour after taking off the aircraft was seen spinning to the ground minus one wing; it was obviously out of control before being seen by any witness on the ground. The aeroplane crashed at high speed and was completely wrecked. The pilot did not abandon the aircraft and was killed instantly.

The aircraft was delivered new to the school on 10.5.40. Tailplane Mod. 199 - strengthening of front spar - had been embodied. Its total time-in-air amounted to 378 hours. The weather at the time was partly cloudy, 4/10 at 2,500 ft and 6/10 at 8,000 ft. The wind was easterly at 12 mph. Visibility 12 miles. The pilot's total flying experience amounted to 103 hours., 12 hours of which were solo in Master aircraft. His general flying ability was considered to be above average.

The main wreckage consisted of the entire fuselage, the tail unit less the rudder horn, the starboard outer plane and the centre plane with about 3 ft of the spars of the port outer plane attached. The wreckage of the port plane was distributed for a distance of about 2 miles down wind of the crash and the parts had fallen mainly on farmland interspersed with ditches. Standing crops covered most of the ground and a river ran through the centre of the line of wreckage. Recovery was, therefore, difficult and several parts, including the bottom boom of the front spar and the greater part of the rear spar, were not found. On examining the wreckage in detail it was found that the rudder had been struck in flight in two places on the port side and that as a result the trailing edge behind the horn balance portion had broken away, leading to the collapse of this component in a backward direction.

All damage to the centre plane could be attributed to impact. The severe damage sustained in the crash by the stubs of the port outer plane spars made an examination impossible but the fracture in the top boom of the front spar evidenced failure in upload. The timber from the top boom of the front spar as close to the fracture as possible was tested at the RAE with the following results:

Moisture content	*12.1%;*
Density	*24.7 lb/sq ft;*
Compression strength	*4840 lb/sq in*

The minimum compression strength for spruce having a moisture content of 12% is 5580 lb/sq. inch. This result indicates that the quality of the material was below Grade 'A' spruce requirements. There was no evidence of unsatisfactory gluing in any of the parts examined.

The 'Opinion' expressed in the Report stated:

The accident was due to structural failure of the port outer plane probably during an aerobatic manoeuvre involving up-loads on the wing structure. On the available evidence it is impossible to state whether the primary failure occurred in the front or rear spar.

*(b)   Master **T8819** of No.8 SFTS on 10.6.41 at Kinross station. The pilot, a Pole, was detailed for a cross country flight. He understood his instructions but later he was seen well off his course. He dived down on a Military camp and while pulling out of the dive a noise was heard and pieces fell away from the port plane. A Polish camp is in the neighbourhood. The aircraft crashed and the pilot was killed. The cause of the accident was attributed to the pilot 'shooting up' a Military camp, during which the wing structure failed as the aircraft was being pulled out of a high speed dive.*

However, accidents to Masters continued:

N7510, from No.56 OTU, lost a wing and dived into the sea on 25.7.41;

N7581, from No.9 SFTS, broke-up in the air during aerobatics and crashed 30.8.41, and the AID's Brief Description of this latter accident read:

Approximately one hour after a pupil pilot had taken off for the purpose of practising aerobatics the aircraft was seen to be diving with both wings broken. The pilot was killed instantly and had not attempted to bale out. Parts of the wing structure, fuselage and tail unit were scattered within a rectangle 80 yards by 400 yards. The accident was caused by a structural failure of the airframe during an aerobatic manoeuvre. It was not possible to determine whether the primary failure occurred in the front spar of the centre plane or in the fuselage. There were two splices of poor quality in the fuselage longerons.

N7574 from No.9.SFTS broke-up in the air during aerobatics and crashed 25.9.41 and the AID again issued a Brief Description of the accident which read:

The pilot took off with instructions to practise aerobatics. Forty minutes later the aircraft was seen diving steeply towards the ground with pieces flying from it. The pilot did not bale out and was killed instantly. The primary cause of the accident was a failure in the front spar of the centre plane which resulted in the complete collapse of the wing structure.

It is on record that a total of 19 Master Mk.I aircraft crashed as a result of structural failure, either due to the tailplane or wings departing in flight under certain manoeuvres. It is also possible that a number of other accidents, whose cause could not be determined due to the nature of the damage sustained in the crash, could also have been attributed to structural failure. The last three accidents to Master Mk.Is attributed to structural failure occurred in 1942;

N7598 from No.61 OTU broke-up in the air during a snowstorm and crashed 28.1.42;

T8852 lost a wing tip in a dive while on a test flight from the A&AEE and spun into the ground near Boscombe Down 6.5.42;

T8382 was abandoned after its port wing broke off 19.10.42.

Although these were very unfortunate accidents, casualties in training units were high, often due to the inexperience of the pupils and, inevitably in some cases, over-confidence, which invariably led to some pupils undertaking unauthorised low-flying, to the detriment of haystacks, trees and wires of various sorts in the locality of the schools. Apart from the aircraft, inexperienced flying instructors were sometimes to blame for not noticing pupils' errors in time and a number of accidents were also caused by engine failure.

A further report, dated 24th April 1941, concerning tests of Master **T8559**, which had Modifications No.133 and 150 incorporated and provision for four 40lb practice bombs under the wings, concluded

Above and below: Master Mk.IA, T8559, the first Master Mk.IA to be modified with reduced span wings.   *[Photographs via Phil Jarrett]*

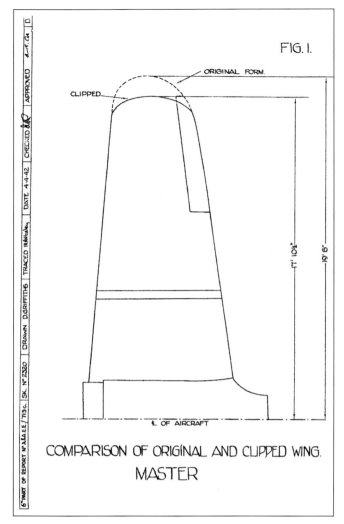

FIG. I.

ORIGINAL FORM.

CLIPPED.

COMPARISON OF ORIGINAL AND CLIPPED WING.
MASTER

A&AEE drawing showing 'Comparison of Original and Clipped Wing Master' but note that the reduced span wing shown is incorrect as it was clipped rather than rounded as on the original.

that: *There was a remarkable difference in the aircraft's behaviour at the stall between hood closed and hood fully open. This difference in behaviour was apparently mainly due to the last 1/3rd of the hood's travel.*

However, spinning, stalls and aerobatics with R/T installed were not recommended and it was suggested that these undesirable features in a training aircraft be removed if possible.

With a view to reducing the loads on the Master during aerobatics and recovery from dives, the M.19 Master Mk.II, **AZ543**, was allotted to CRD at Phillips & Powis, Woodley on 16th December 1941 to be modified with a reduced span wing. This was done by the simple expedient of removing 19½ inches from each tip to square them off, thereby reducing the span from 39 ft 0 ins to 35 ft 9 ins. AZ543 thus became the first Master to be so modified. Flt Lt Hugh Kennedy made the first 'Handling' flight with this modification, on 7th January 1942. Handling trials, comprising aerobatics, stalls, dives and spins, were then carried out by A&AEE Boscombe Down, between 6th February 1942 and 7th March 1942.

Further trials were then required to be carried out on a Master Mk.IA, with the same modified wing, and **T8559** (Kestrel 30), was delivered to the DGAP at Phillips & Powis, Woodley on 13th January 1941 in order to be modified.

The conclusions to the report on the flight trials of T8559, issued by the A&AEE Boscombe Down in March 1942 (with photographs of T8559 dated 24th March 1942 showing the 'Master I [Clipped Wings]'), stated:

In take-offs, landings and general flying there were no appreciable differences in handling and flying qualities except that the ailerons were heavier and the rate of roll slower. It also had the larger tailplane and stability was considerably improved. Stalling characteristics had deteriorated slightly and spins were very steep, the rudder becoming very heavy for correction. At full throttle and trimmed for level flight, the aircraft was dived at 330 mph and, although a strong push-force was necessary as speed increased, it was not excessive.

The report also noted that the Master Mk.II and Master Mk.III were cleared for a maximum of 300 mph IAS but no recommendation was made to increase that of the Master Mk.I above 290 mph.

All surviving Master Mk.I, Mk.IA, Mk.II and Mk.III aircraft were then retrospectively modified to have the reduced span wings, but the later production aircraft were all built with reduced span wings.

The A&AEE Boscombe Down produced a series of Reports on these Master trials under Report AAEE/719. The 6th Report on the trials, dated on about 22nd April 1942 is reproduced below:

Brief handling and spinning trials with a wing reduced in span.

Progress of issue of Report.

1st Part of A&AEE/719.a	Master I. - Ease of maintenance trials.
2nd Part	Master I. N7410 - Performance and handling trials.
3rd Part	Master I. N7893 - Aerobatic and spinning trials after modification.
4th Part	Master I. T8559 - Handling trials with larger tailplane and extended C.G. range including the effect of 4-40 in bombs under the wings.
5th Part	Master I. T8559 - Trials with inertia weight fitted in the elevator system.

Also see 7th Part of A&AEE/719.c - Master II. AZ543 - Brief handling and spinning trials with a wing reduced in span

1. Introduction.

   Further to the handling trials completed on a Mark II Master with a wing reduced in span, handling trials comprising aerobatics, stalls, dives and spins were required on a Mark I Master with the same modified wing. All tests were completed during March 1942.

2. Condition of aircraft relevant to tests.

   The aircraft was tested at two loadings:-

Loading.	All up weight.	Position of C.G.
Normal.	5,550 lb	37.6" aft of datum.
Extended aft limit.	5,590 lb	38" aft of datum.

The design C.G. limits are 32 inches to 38 inches (including aft extension). The above limits refer to the undercarriage down. At normal load, raising the undercarriage moves the centre of gravity from 37.6 inches to 38.4 inches aft of datum.

Except for the modified wing, the aeroplane was a standard Mark I Master with the large tailplane (see 4th Part of Report No,AAEE/719,a).

A sketch of the change in plan form of the wing is given in Fig.1.

3. Handling and flying qualities.

   At both loadings, in take-off, landing and general flying, there was no appreciable difference compared with the normal Master I, except that the ailerons were heavier.

At both loadings the aircraft was stable laterally and directionally under all conditions of flight. On the climb and in level flight the aircraft was stable longitudinally though the stability was not very positive on the climb. Comparing this with the prototype Master I aircraft it will be seen that the stability has considerably improved, especially on the climb; but it must be borne in mind that this aircraft, T8559, was fitted with the larger tailplane which is now standard on production Mark.I Masters. The larger tailplane makes the aircraft just stable on the climb (see 4th part of Report No.AAEE/719,a), which closely agrees with the results obtained in these tests.

4.   Stall characteristics.

(i)   Normal load.
Flaps and undercarriage up.

The stall occurs at 75 mph ASI. At 90 mph ASI, a slight oscillation of the control column commences, and at 78 mph ASI, the aircraft starts to pitch slightly, increasing until the nose and right wing drop sharply together at the stall.

Full aileron and some rudder is necessary to raise the right wing even when the nose is well down. The force on the control column, which is about 2-3 inches back at the stall, is light. Once the aircraft has stalled, the control column must be eased forward and the speed considerably increased before the aircraft recovers from the stall, as it remains in a semi-stalled condition at 20 to 30 mph ASI above the stalling speed.

After the aircraft has stalled, the control column can be brought right back, though the aircraft flicks violently from side to side. This can be checked by full use of aileron and rudder, and the aircraft can be kept from falling away for some time. During this period, the nose is remarkably low, but pitching commences at 80-100 mph ASI, until the aircraft can no longer be held up and it then flicks into a spin.

(i)   Normal load.
Flaps and undercarriage down.

The stall occurs at 55-57 mph ASI. There is no definite warning of the approach to the stall, although all the controls fall off in effectiveness. They remain much more effective than those of the clipped wing Master II.

At the stall, the nose and left wing drop fairly sharply and the wing cannot be picked up until the control column is eased forward. The recovery is then quick and normal. The force on the control column which is just aft of central, is light.

(ii)   Extended aft limit.
Flaps and undercarriage up.

The stall occurs at 74 mph ASI, and the behaviour of the aircraft is similar to that at the normal load.

(ii)   Extended aft limit.
Flaps and undercarriage down.

The stall occurs at 56-58 mph ASI and the behaviour of the aircraft is similar to that at the normal load.

5.   Spinning trials.

Spins were carried out to the left and right at both loading conditions. Characteristics during the spin and recovery are tabulated below:

(i)   Normal loading.

To right.
3 turns - height in: 12,000 feet.
        height out: 6,000 feet.

The first 1½ turns were rather jerky with some pitching, after which the spin became steady and slow.

There was infrequent but heavy buffeting on the rudder and elevator. The recovery was normal, taking ¾ of a turn, though the rudder was heavy for large movements and the aircraft took a long time to come completely out of the stalled condition. Another spin would result from an attempt to pull out too quickly.

To left.
3 turns - height in: 10,000 feet.
        height out: not recorded.

The aircraft was very reluctant to spin to the left, and the first two turns were very jerky with large pitch. The rudder was heavy to hold in and heavier still to reverse fully. Apart from this, recovery was quick and normal, taking about ¾ of a turn.

(ii) Extended aft loading.

To right.
8 turns - height in: 9,600 feet.
        height out: 4,000 feet.

The aircraft readily entered the spin with the nose well down and spun with an irregular rate of rotation with slight pitch. The attitude during the spin was slightly steeper than to the left. The recovery was satisfactory and took 1 turn.

To left.
8 turns - height in: 9,600 feet
height out: 5,500 feet.

The right wing was dropped sharply at the stall and full left rudder applied to force the aircraft into a spin.
The aircraft spun with the nose well down and was moderately steady with slight fore and aft pitching.
The recovery took ¾ of a turn, during which the rate of auto rotation increased and the attitude of the aircraft was almost vertical.

6.   Aerobatics.

The aircraft was looped and rolled satisfactorily at both loadings, there being little difference in the handling characteristics in both cases.

The loop is easy and straightforward even with an initial airspeed of 220 mph ASI. There is no tendency to roll off at the top of the loop even if a high rate of loop is maintained.

The slow roll, climbing roll and roll off the top are all normal with this aircraft, though the heavy ailerons give it rather a slow rate of roll.

7.   Dives.

The aeroplane was dived at the normal load with 2,400 rpm and full throttle. It was trimmed for all-out level flight.

The aeroplane was steady in the dive. As the speed increased, a push force was necessary to hold the nose down, but this force did not increase to a very large extent although the speed reached was 330 mph ASI. During early tests on a standard Mark I Master (see Part of Report AAEE/719,a dated 2/7/40), it was stated that the push force to hold the aeroplane in a dive was excessive at 310 mph ASI (the designed limiting speed) and the maximum permissible diving speed was, therefore, reduced to 290 mph ASI where it has remained since.

On the other hand, both the Mark II and Mark III Masters required a relatively small push force to hold them in the dive so that the maximum permissible diving speed on these aircraft has remained at 330 ph ASI. The characteristic of T8559 in the dive has already been mentioned in 5th Part of Report AAEE/719, dated 27.9.41 so that, although the reason for the change is not known, it seems clear that the diving characteristics of the aeroplane are not affected by the change in wing span.

The recovery was quick and straightforward on releasing the push force on the control column. There was no vibration nor control surface instability either in the dive or during recovery.

8. Conclusions

The aeroplane handles similarly to a Mark I Master with standard wings, except that the stalling characteristics have deteriorated slightly, and the ailerons are a little heavier in general flying. The aeroplane is considered satisfactory as an advanced trainer..

The Central Flying School, Upavon operated Master Mk.Is between April 1940 and September 1941 and the Air Transport Auxiliary sent potential ferry pilots on the CFS acceptance course there during 1940, where the pupils 'did the Master'. This short course consisted of a maximum of three dual flights before the pupils were sent off solo! However, such was the quality of the 'pupils' and the desperate nature of the course that, after six more solo landings the ferry pilots were classified as qualified to fly any single- engined RAF aircraft! By the severe winter of 1940/41, women pilots of the Air Transport Auxiliary were also ferrying training aircraft to the RAF Flying Training Schools.

Many 'outside' firms were sub-contracted to help with production of components for the Miles Master and Austin Motors was typical of these, producing 1,100 wings and centre sections.

In conclusion to the story of the Miles Master Mk.I and Mk.IA, it is of interest to note that an Instruction to Proceed (ITP) was issued, on 17th February 1943, to a company called Wood Development Ltd, Chingford, E4, for the manufacture of a 'Plastic plywood Master rear fuselage at an estimated cost of £1,750', but unfortunately there are no further details of this experimental fuselage recorded and no records of the firm appear to exist.

Master Mk.IA, N8049, with the AFTS ATA, White Waltham in June 1942. Note the M.27 Master Mk.III in the background.   *[Flight]*

All M.9B Master Mk.I and M.9C Master Mk.IA aircraft were built at Woodley; the M.19 Master Mk.II was built at Woodley, South Marston and 'Sheffield & Doncaster', but the Miles M.27 Master Mk.III was produced only at South Marston.

For a summary of the **900** Miles M.9B Master Mk.I and M.9C Master Mk.IA production and individual aircraft histories, see Appendix 8 on the CD.

(N.A. Refs: AVIA 5/19, AVIA 5/20 and AIR 2489. Air-Britain 'Aeromilitaria' 4/77).

Master centre sections under construction by Austin Motors at Longbridge.   *[The British Motor Industry Heritage Trust]*

The official caption to this photograph reads: 'WAAF at a Scottish Station of Flying Training Command'. Picture shows them working on the Rolls-Royce Kestrel of a Master Mk.I at 8 FTS Montrose. Air Ministry Photograph issued February 1944.   *[Via Phil Jarrett]*

A rare photograph of 9 Master Mk.Is flying low, possibly across their aerodrome but no further details are known.   *[Via Bert Clarke]*

Above and below: Magister P6546, port and starboard views of newly painted fuselage at 1 CRU Cowley.

(The British Motor Industry Heritage Trust)

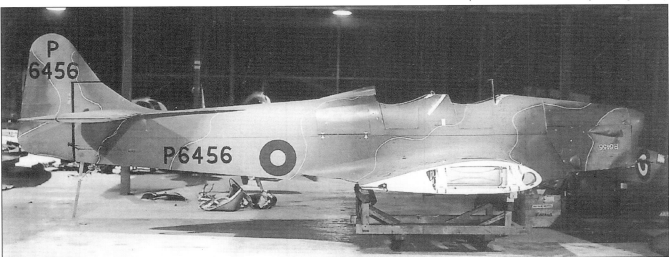

DIMENSIONS

Span	33 ft 10 in (10.31 m)
Length overall	28 ft 3 in (7.70 m)
Height	6 ft 8 in (2.03 m)
Wing area	176 sq ft (16.35 sq m)
Track	7 ft 4 in (2.24 m)

PERFORMANCE *(At aerobatic weight of 1,845 lb - 835 kg)*

Maximum speed	145 mph (233 km/hr)
Cruising speed at 2,000 to 2,100 rpm	125 mph to 130 mph (201 km/hr - 209 km/hr)
Landing speed	45 mph (72 km/hr)
Range	400 miles (643 km)
Take-off	170 yards (155 m)
Landing run with flaps and brakes	100 yards (91 m)
Maximum ceiling	22,000 ft (6,700 m)
Service ceiling	18,000 ft (5,480 m)
Rate of climb at sea level	850 ft/min (259 m/min)

WEIGHTS

Tare weight	1,240 lb (562 kg)
Pilot	200 lb (90 kg)
Petrol (21 gall - 95.5 ltr)	161 lb (73 kg)
Oil (2½ gall - 1.42 ltr)	22 lb (10 kg)
Payload (allowance for pupil or extra equipment)	222 lb (100 kg)
Total	1,845 lb (835 kg)

For non-aerobatic flying an increase in disposable load of 55 lb (25 kg) is allowable.

Contracts, which were raised at various times to cover work on Magister aircraft are listed below:

Loan of Magister to Contract B5907/39, dated 16th June 1939.

Repair of Magister aircraft at works to Contract 38589/39, dated 13th December 1939.

Magister spares in works, 59084/39, dated 22nd December 1939.

Drawings and technical assistance for Magister to Moms (Morris Motors), 76538/40, dated 16th April 1940.

Magister spares, Contract/Acft/672, ITP dated 22nd February 1941.

Fitment of towing hooks to a Magister, ITP dated 29th March 1941 (SB21851), transferred to C4(c) 28th August 1941.

Maintenance of overseers Magister aircraft, to Contract/Acft/2115, dated 7th May 1942, completed 17th December 1942.

Administrative services of the Magister, Master and Martinet, to Contract/Acft/2728, dated 10th June 1943.

Magister Exports

Details of the different types of RAF aircraft exported between 3/9/39 and 29/2/40 (N.A. Ref: AIR 8/367) included Magister aircraft: 'Egypt 1' (probably P6418 c/n 1773). Then, under the heading of 'Approved Releases', it stated 'France 3' with delivery rate and remarks – 'as soon as required'.

However, France was over-run by the Germans shortly after this and none were delivered. Details of the Magisters to be supplied to Turkey were also mentioned but these are dealt with in Appendix 11.

Although a note on the back of this photograph says '87 Sqdn Debden 1940', R1823 served only with the ATA, which would also account for the dark colour of the helpers uniforms.

[Via Bert Clarke]

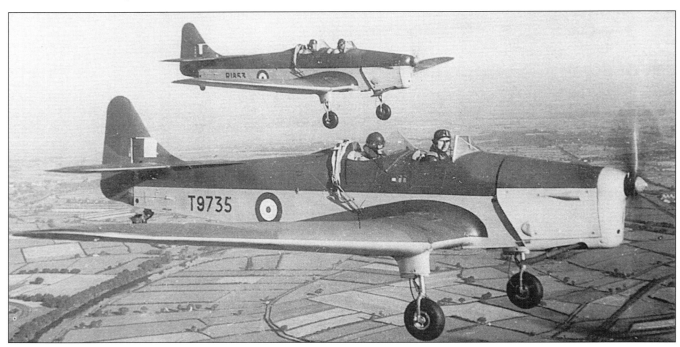

Magisters T9735 and R1853 of 15 EFTS Kingstown (Carlisle) in mid 1949.

In the column entitled 'Release under Consideration', it was stated: 'Iran 30' but in the remarks column it stated '50 second hand Moth Minors have been offered in lieu of Magisters. Iranians' decision not yet known'. Under Moth Minor in the same document, it was stated that supply was approved of second hand aircraft from RAF stocks if acceptable to Iranians in lieu of 30 Magisters applied for. In hand writing under Iran in the 'Approved Releases' column it was noted that; 'No reply from Iranians to date'. Only approximately 60 Moth Minors had by that stage been built in this country and thus the 50 offered would have had to come from civilian impressments.

Foreign Office file FO371/24574 states that on 9th January 1940 the (Iranian) Aero Club Commission want to purchase 30 Magisters, but on 27th January 1940, they said that they would purchase 50 Moth Minors instead. File FO371/24575 records on 10th January 1940 50 Moth Minor – no firm order; on 25th January 1940 - Re 30 Magisters and release of 20 more but on 27th January 1940 – "Could release 50 Moth Minor; not new but not heavily used".

On 6th May 1940, the file records that UK offer 20 Magisters and 30 second-hand Moth Minors. In the end it appears that they got fed up with waiting for Magisters and purchased a batch of Rearwin Cloudsters from America instead!

On 21st May 1940, Hugh Kennedy flew the Hawk Trainer Mk.III U6, on a bomb drop test, and on 25th May 1940 he recorded G-AEZS on a bomb drop test. However, it is believed that G-AEZS (c/n 538) became U6 for trials with the M.18 wing, so it must have reverted to M.14A Hawk Trainer Mk III standard later, while also retaining the 'B' mark U6 for the bomb drop tests, although still being recorded as G-AEZS! Either way, only Miles could have conducted bomb drop tests in wartime from a civil registered aeroplane!

In June 1940, with the risk of imminent invasion, desperate measures were called for and Miles was equally desperately trying to get the Ministry to at least consider and try out the ideas which the firm had regarding the use of training aircraft for fighting and bombing. The reason that this scheme came to nought is shown in ***'The History of the Chaotic Relations between Phillips & Powis Aircraft Ltd and the Air Ministry'***, which is reproduced in full in the Reading chapter. This document was written in July 1940 and extracts relevant to this episode are reproduced here:

After the interviews with Lord Beaverbrook it was taken that the Company might approach the Air Force and get their reactions and instructions, this was done. An aeroplane was fitted with bomb racks and the Director of Operational Requirements and the Assistant Chief of Air Staff both came to the aerodrome to discuss the idea and see it in operation. They were genuinely and definitely enthusiastic and within a day or so bomb racks were supplied to the Company and orders given to the appropriate Officers whereby arrangements were to be made to have all the aeroplanes in the country fitted ready for use.

Then suddenly through Mr Handley Page and Lord Beaverbrook came an order that the factory is subject to the Ministry of Aircraft Production and that all orders given by the Air Force were cancelled and all work on the Magisters was to cease (after about 15 Magisters had been equipped to carry eight 25lb bombs). No explanation was given and all appeals have failed to find one. Lord Beaverbrook, after promising to visit the factory and have a Conference with the Directors, at the eleventh hour cancelled this and for over a week nothing has been heard of him.

On the 11th June (1940) the telegram cancelling the order was received and on the 1st July the Aeronautical Inspection Directorate notified the Company that the work on the Magisters was to be suspended until it had been reconsidered on August the 1st next; this statement is made at a time when England herself is daily expecting attack.

When it is borne in mind that the purpose of the modification was to have available an effective and highly approved weapon against parachute troops or flotillas of landing forces the action of the Ministry in delaying a final decision, leaving aside the over-ruling of orders placed by active Air Force Personnel is as nearly a criminally actionable act as can be.

Nearly the whole 1000 aircraft could have been completed by now.

It was not recorded where the bomb racks were to be fitted, but photographs of Magisters of 15 EFTS Carlisle, show them to have been carried under the centre section. In the event, and luckily for all concerned, the threatened invasion never materialised and the 'Maggie bomber' was never called upon to play an operational role in the defence of the realm but, with this dangerous game of politics being played out in the background, one could hardly have credited that there was a war on.

Whilst on the subject of the dark days of 1940, it is a rather sobering thought to recall that during the disastrous campaign in France a total of 18 Magisters were lost, two in accidents and the rest abandoned in that country when we left in May 1940. These aircraft had been used on communications duties but none were ever recorded subsequently, so were presumably destroyed by the Germans.

It is of interest to note that an Instruction to Proceed was issued on 13th June 1940 to a company called Moulded Components (Jablo) Ltd, for '3 tailplanes for Magister at an estimated cost of £374' but no further details of these experimental tailplanes has been found. A full page advertisement was placed in Flight for 25th July 1940 by Phillips & Powis Aircraft Ltd entitled 'Somewhere in England' with the heading 'Monoplane Pilots need Monoplane Training'. It showed what has since become the famous photograph of Magister N3780 in pre-war colours, being flown solo (from the rear cockpit) serenely above clouds but, inset, was a cutting from a newspaper which read:

I met a new type of RAF man today. He is a squadron leader medical officer, a Welshman from Denbigh. He belongs to an RAF receiving station which got a message saying: "There is a wounded rear-gunner lying in hospital at a front town. The enemy is on the outskirts of that town." He took off in a tiny ancient Miles Magister, and, realising that he would be at the mercy of any Nazi plane spotting him, he hedge-hopped about a hundred miles. In the hospital he found the rear-gunner. He strapped him to a stretcher and put him on the plane. Although badly wounded, the rear-

Magister fitted with bomb racks and eight 25 lb bombs.

gunner had no complaints except "he seemed horrified at being flown by a doctor."

There were no comments - and any would definitely have been superfluous.

The most audacious attempt to escape from England was made by Luftwaffe officers, Lt Heinz Schnabel and Oblt Harry Wappler on 24th November 1941. They were prisoners in Camp No.15 near Penrith, Northumbria (formerly the Shap Wells hotel) and had forged papers that identified them as two Dutch officers serving in the RAF. They made their way to RAF Station Kingstown, near Carlisle and apparently without difficulty entered the station and with the help of a mechanic they started the engine of a Magister of 15 EFTS and took off heading for Holland. While over the North Sea they realised that with a distance of some 365 miles to go they would never make it as the maximum range of a Magister was 367 miles. They reluctantly turned back and landed in a field about five miles north of Great Yarmouth, where they were promptly arrested, returned to Camp No.15 and sentenced to 28 days solitary confinement each. After that episode, security at the station was considerably improved!

In 1941 the Ministry was rather concerned at the limited bomb load and range of the medium bombers then in use and they were considering means whereby these might be increased, at least until such time as larger bombers became available. One means suggested was the possibility of towing behind the bomber an auxiliary wing, loaded with either bombs or additional fuel. If such an arrangement proved feasible, it was estimated that the maximum bomb load would be more than doubled, or alternatively the maximum range correspondingly increased. Messrs Cornwall and Clare of Heston Aircraft Ltd also suggested to Supermarines in 1942, that an auxiliary wing, filled with fuel and towed along behind an aeroplane by means of twin booms attached to the wing trailing edge could be used to dramatically increase the range of the Spitfire.

Electrically operated explosive charges would break the towing attachments simultaneously for jettison purposes. The towed wing was the brainchild of Flt Lt Malinowski, a Polish fighter pilot who was also an engineer. He was introduced to Roxbee-Cox of RAE Farnborough in 1941 and showed him plans of his invention. The RAE studied the concept and were able to produce figures to prove to the inventor that his optimistic figures had not included drag; after all a combination of two monoplanes did add up to a form of biplane! The RAE did, however, have a rectangular aerofoil of 25ft span manufactured by a furniture company and, in order to test the feasibility of the scheme, Miles was asked to fit this wing to a suitably modified Magister to enable flight tests to be carried out, first by the A&AEE at Boscombe Down and then by the RAE at Farnborough.

A Miles Magister, now known to have been L8326, was given the RAF Experimental Aeroplane No.156 for identification purposes for 'Trailer-wing experiments'. Rather surprisingly, the identification drawing only showed the slots in the trailing edges of the wing where the tail booms were located and not the trailer wing attached.

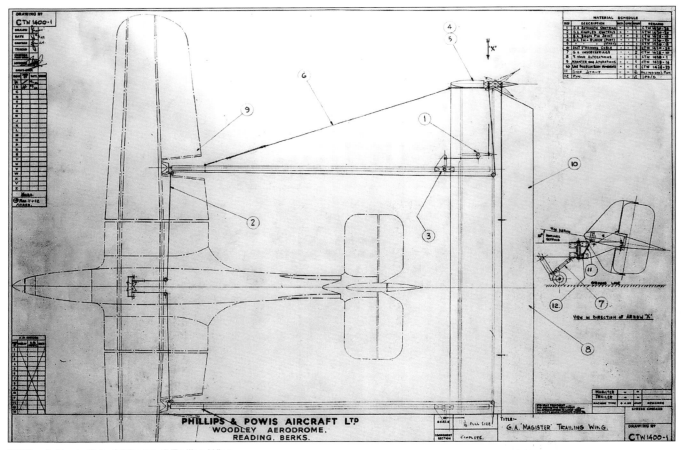

Phillips & Powis G.A.of "Magister" Trailing Wing.

An artist's impression of the Miles Magister with Trailer Wing, by S E Porter, of Phillips & Powis. Note larger rudder fitted to aircraft.

The initial tests were carried out at Boscombe Down, on account of the longer take-off space available, and the first attempted take-off was carried out on 12th May 1941, but this was not over-successful and a 30% extension was then added to the rudder to improve directional control - see drawing below.

Capt Eric Brown recalled in his book 'Testing for Combat' ...*after the rudder had been modified, directional control was critical but the longitudinal control was satisfactory and there was only a slight deterioration in aileron control. The maximum speed of the combination was only 80 mph in level flight and although the trailer wing behaved very well longitudinally, control was not too good about the other two axes. Laterally, the ailerons were heavy and rather ineffective and when bank was applied there was a difference of about 10 degrees between the main-planes and the trailer. Directionally, the control was very poor and just marginally acceptable for the tests. The next stage was to carry 2 x 110lb bombs on the trailer wing but this produced a form of directional snaking during take-off which was uncontrollable, probably due to oscillatory moments being set up in the trailer during the unstick process, so the take-off had to be aborted. This problem was cured when the rear wheels were locked to prevent the shimmying and the trailer payload was then increased to take 4 x 110lb bombs but again uncontrollable swing was experienced and the trailer took charge of the aircraft, swinging it through 50 degrees and causing it to charge into obstructions with resulting serious damage.*

This could have been the occasion recalled by Don Brown when one observer was almost killed by the device when it swung off the runway and headed straight for him! However, landing was normal, provided that the trailer touched down after the aircraft.

Four flights were carried out from Boscombe Down in May 1941, and the combination was flown to Woodley on 29th May for modifications. The booms had to be articulated directionally, and they were therefore hinged and geared to a pair of fins and rudders, which replaced the fixed fins on the trailer wing.

On 14th June, the Magister was returned for further tests by the RAE, and nine more flights were made. The combination flew to Woodley and return on 24th July and then to 'Wrington' (Wroughton?) and return on 29th. The combination was flown to Heathrow on 30th July and on 31st July and 1st August, to Woodley.

For the final stage of the tests Capt Eric Brown recalled: ...*the taxiing characteristics were still bad and on occasion, when a turn was attempted the trailer would take charge and turn the aircraft through 360 degrees, finally causing it to go backwards! In flight in smooth air the trailer maintained its correct position but if bumps were encountered it would pitch and yaw continuously. In calm air, turns with up to 60 degrees of bank could be made with the trailer behaving satisfactorily, although the lateral stick forces were high. In a dive to 120 mph the trailer kept good position until bumps were encountered at low altitude, when it began to pitch and yaw so severely that there was a grave risk of it taking charge of the aircraft.*

On 19th August, L8326 swung on take-off and headed off the runway to collide with an obstruction and, at this point it was decided to end the trials as, to quote Capt. Brown's own words: *From these tests it was apparent that flying with the trailer wing was a bit of a knife-edge operation, particularly on take-off and in bumpy weather, and for those reasons the experiments were not continued.*

Performance analysis showed that the most economic method to carry a fuel overload was in the accepted manner of hanging it in tanks under an aircraft's wings. The now famous 'drop tank' was then adopted for universal use and the trailer wing project was dropped. RAE Reports and Notes on the Trailer Wing Handling Trials are reproduced in Appendix 10.

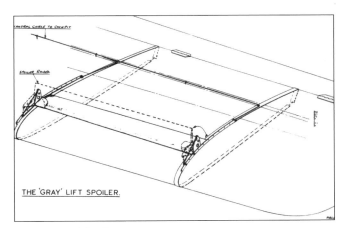

The 'Gray' Lift Spoiler.

In connection with the investigation of stall characteristics previously carried out on the Falcon, a number of experiments were made using a Magister as the test vehicle. One of these was the fitment of Gray lift spoilers. These consisted of small hinged slats mounted at about 0.10c and covering about a quarter of the semi-span near the wingtip.

In the closed position they were retracted flat on the upper surface of the wing and when required for use, were tilted forward about their leading edge so as to stand vertically. On test they certainly effected some improvement in the tendency to drop a wing at the stall, but the stalling speed was increased by about 5 mph.

Another device tried on the Magister was the 'diruptor', so named after an idea attributed to an Italian named Mattioli. Miles had already tried these diruptors on an M.2 Hawk, but it was decided to try them again on a Magister. The diruptors consisted of a small diameter rod passing through small fences with a number of holes in them in order to give various positions for the trials. The fences were mounted on the outer portion of the leading edge of the wing and the purpose of the rod was to cause small-scale turbulence across the wing and thus prevent the sharp stall which occurs when the laminar flow breaks away suddenly.

Rods of 1/8, 3/8 and 1/2 in were tried; the 1/8 in rod had little or no effect, but the 3/8 in rod effected a marked improvement in the stall but a loss in speed and rate of climb. The 1/2 in rod gave much the same results and, as in the case of the Gray lift spoilers, the disadvantages were felt to outweigh the advantages and the trials were abandoned.

The Mattioli 'Diruptor' fitted to a Magister.

A more elaborate idea, designed by the RAE was also tried on Magister L8168. This consisted of an alteration in aerofoil section for the complete outer portion of the wing. For this purpose, a thicker wing section was 'wrapped' around the existing wing, giving a tip section of NACA 4415 instead of the normal modified Clark YH section of 9% thickness. When this was fitted on 39% of the semi-span, little improvement resulted but, when the thicker section was increased in length to 56% of the semi-span, good stalling characteristics were obtained, although the ailerons became a little sluggish.

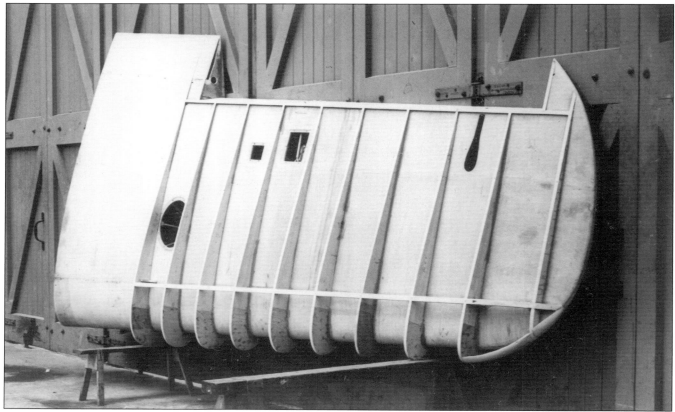

Above and below: The RAE thicker wing section fitted to Magister L8168.

Another suggestion, about which nothing further is known, consisted of the outer wing leading edge being built up, while the inner wing leading edge was fitted with a sharp triangular section. These modifications produced a gentle, predictable stall but at the expense of a 7 mph rise in stalling speed.

The last known suggestion was that of the Gray stabiliser fin. This consisted of a chord-wise flat plate fitted to the upper surface of the wing near the tip and intended to improve the stall by delaying the flow of turbulence out to the wingtip. With flaps up, the inboard portion of the wing stalled first, as intended, but when the stall passed the fin, control was lost and the aircraft spun. With flaps down, the wingtip stalled first, so that in neither case was the device successful.

With the advent of runways in place of grass airfields on which landings could always be made into wind, the ability to do cross-wind landings became of increasing importance. As the war progressed there was an ever-increasing output of rapidly-trained pilots, many of whom had not had sufficient flying experience to effect cross-wind landings in other than very light winds. In an effort to overcome the problem, in 1938, Owen Maclaren (later the inventor of the dreadful forward facing Baby Buggy) had designed a cross-wind landing undercarriage whereby the legs and wheels could be turned to any desired setting. This avoided the necessity

of either side-slipping into wind before touching down, or kicking off drift, both of which required a certain degree of skill and experience. With the Maclaren drift undercarriage, however, the final approach was made so that the flight path was in line with the runway, although the heading of the aircraft was at an angle to the flight path, dependent upon the magnitude of the cross-wind component. Having established the aircraft on finals, the undercarriage was set so that the wheels were in line with the runway heading. The approach was then continued until the aircraft actually touched down with the fuselage heading at an angle to the runway, but with the wheels aligned with the runway.

A visit was made by J M Gray of MAP, O F Maclaren and I J Rees of Maclaren Undercarriage Co to Air Service Training Ltd at Hamble on 3rd December 1941, in order to inspect the American aircraft there from the point of view of the possible installation of a drift undercarriage in one or other type. Machines inspected included the North American Mustang, Curtiss Tomahawk, Curtiss Kittyhawk, Curtiss Mohawk and Bell Airacobra, but they found that, whilst none of the types inspected appeared to involve great difficulties from the point of view of installation of the drift undercarriage, the first impressions were distinctly in favour of the Mustang. The visit concluded that: *'As Army Co-operation requirements might override our preference for the Mustang, it seems desirable that we should collect the Tomahawk drawings as soon as possible.'*

On 31st March 1942, a telegram was sent by the Air Ministry (Kingsway 0.7) to the Ministry of Aircraft Production (W/C Northway), HQ 41 Group, AM (ZE)E1 and HQ Army Co-operation Command, which read; *'Request you allot and arrange delivery of one Magister aircraft to CRD at Messrs Airwork Ltd, EFTS Denham for installation of Maclaren undercarriage prior to undergoing service trials in AC Command. A second Magister aircraft will be required for this purpose and further instructions will be signalled in due course.*

On the same day, Maclaren wrote a letter to J M Gray (MAP), on Airwork Ltd headed notepaper (which suggests that he was then working for Airwork) on the subject of the Maclaren Drift Undercarriage: *This is to confirm our telephone conversation of this day. We are very glad to note that approval has been given for* the fitting of a Drift Undercarriage to two Magisters. We also confirm that we can allot hangar space to these two machines at Denham. The delivery of one as soon as possible would be of great assistance for taking check measurements etc., but we do not think there is any urgency for the delivery of the second.

On 18th June 1942, Maclaren wrote to Mr Bowie, RD Inst, MAP: I should like to thank you for our recent discussion on the subject of installing torpedo sights in aircraft fitted with the above undercarriage in order to assist the pilot in lining up the machine when landing for the correct drift attitude. As I explained, we have an experimental Whitney Straight (Airwork owned Whitney Straight G-AFGK at the time and it was probably this aircraft - PA) fitted with this type of undercarriage which we use for development work and there is also an Airspeed Oxford fitted with the drift undercarriage, which is undergoing trials at Boscombe Down.

Above: Close up of undercarriage leg on P6456 showing the leg set at an angle and the Maclaren Drift mechanism.

We have also in the course of being fitted with this undercarriage 2 Magisters and a Mustang, Contracts 2136/C.23(c) and 2047/C.36(a) respectively, and it appears at the moment that the fitting of this type of sight will probably be very desirable on all machines fitted with the drift undercarriage. As arranged over the telephone I will 'phone you on Tuesday morning to ascertain whether you are likely to be free to give us your advice on the installation of these sights.

On 24th July 1942, P C Heming, RDL1(c) wrote to TL O/CRD regarding the Magister fitted with Maclaren undercarriage: Reference your enquiry of 20.7.42, in respect of the present position on the above installation. This is as follows, please -

The first Magister N3939. The installation of the undercarriage has been completed and it is now being examined by AID prior to taxying trials. It is anticipated that this aeroplane will be ready for delivery to A&AEE by 7th August.

The second Magister N6456 (in error for P6456 - PA) - Delivery instructions have been given to the firm through Contracts in the letter dated 20.7.42, ref: Aircraft 2136/C.36(b). The first aeroplane will go to A&AEE, and thence to Service Station, and deliveries anticipated with the second aeroplane will proceed direct to a Service Station as soon as A&AEE stated that the aeroplane is safe for Service pilots.

A 'Note on Position regarding application of Maclaren from TA to DTD, dated 14th August 1942, stated that: Large aircraft not being considered. (In a recent report from Bomber Command on landing characteristics of the "heavies" they expressed apprehension of any possible drift undercarriage on the grounds of added complexity for the pilot).

Application is only being considered for Army Co-operation types; these are as follows:-

(a) Oxford   Tests completed, A&AEE Report No.718f refers.

(b) Magister Two aircraft modified. First was damaged prior to delivery to A&EE; second aircraft is now complete and will go instead.

(c) Mustang   Design nearly completed, trial installation expected to be ready for tests early in September.

The Magister control system consisted of a hand winding gear which, by means of torsion cables and worm gears on each main wheel and tail wheel, controlled synchronously the relative heading of all three wheels. The tail wheel was steerable about the selected datum setting.

The A&AEE Report of the trials carried out at the Boscombe Down, dated 7th September 1942, was sent to The Secretary of the Ministry of Aircraft Production (RDL1c.): Tests of the Maclaren undercarriage have been made on Magister P6456 and brief check

Front view of P6456, the second Magister to be fitted with the Maclaren Drift Undercarriage, by Airwork Ltd, at Denham in mid 1942.

tests on N3939. Both aircraft handled identically. Cross-wind taxiing, take-offs, and landings were made in winds up to about 25 mph on grass and runways. The device works satisfactorily and its use presents no difficulty.

Taxiing across winds can be quite easily carried out making use of the angular wheel setting, no brake being necessary. With the wheels straight, some use of brake is necessary to taxi across wind. The only difficulty encountered was with the wheels set at an angle and the aircraft facing downwind, when it was found difficult to turn across the wind. The wheels had to be reset to normal to accomplish this.

Take-offs and landings were quite straightforward provided the correct methods were adopted. The device is not sensitive to wheel setting and satisfactory landings could be made with the wheels up to 10° off the correct setting. For comparison, take-offs and landings were made with the wheels set fore and aft, when it was found that the aircraft could still be satisfactorily taken off and landed across a 20-25 mph wind. This is, however, the maximum practical wind speed in which the landing could be done, and use of the Maclaren device facilitates the process considerably. The aircraft was also flown solo from the rear cockpit and found satisfactory for straight and level flight.

Copies of the report were sent to OC Royal Naval Air Station, Arbroath; Army Co-operation Command; RTO Phillips & Powis and 613 Squadron Twinwood Farm (613 Squadron had actually moved to Ouston on 28th August 1942). It is curious to note that a copy of the report was not sent to 4 Squadron.

Service Trials of Drift Undercarriage Installation were carried out on both aircraft by both 4 Squadron at Clifton and 613 Squadron at Ouston. 4 Squadron's conclusions were: i) it would be advantageous to have this drift undercarriage in landing and taking off from narrow strip aerodromes ii) the installation did not introduce serious increase or difficulties of maintenance and iii) tyre wear or damage more rapid than with a normal undercarriage, no comment. 613 Squadron's conclusions were similar to those of 4 Squadron but with regard to ii) above they added the comment 'even when hydraulic and mechanical lock is fitted up for the tail wheel' and iii) they felt that there was a slight increase in tyre wear. (N.A. Ref: AVIA 15/1544).

Capt Eric Brown, who was with the Fleet Air Arm Service Trials Unit (778 Sqn) at Arbroath in 1942, confirmed that the Maclaren undercarriage was capable of being rotated through 45° on either side of the centre line of the aircraft by means of a crank handle, angle indicator and lock. He flew P6456 on 16th and 17th September 1942, when a steady wind of 20 mph was blowing and, with a choice of three runways, he recalled that there were quite a number of computations possible to give the desired cross-wind components for the tests. On the first day he gradually worked up to 30° cross-wind landings and found these quite easy and comfortable to execute. On the second day he moved up the scale to the full 45° cross-wind landings and, although he found these were effective, they were neither easy nor comfortable to execute. He found that it was difficult to crab the aircraft accurately on the runway at the larger drift angles and that, after touchdown, braking had to be very judiciously applied to prevent side-loads on the undercarriage if the fuselage was not aligned dead into wind.

His conclusion was that the weight of the equipment did not justify the end, and that it was just as likely to cause accidents as prevent them at cross-wind angles above 30°. He felt that it could really only be applicable to light aircraft whose pilots were usually comparatively inexperienced.

Miles test pilot Hugh Kennedy flew P6456 with Don Brown on 30th March 1943 and Don recalled that it was hard to judge what it would have felt like to a novice, but as a normal pilot he found that it required a real effort of will to flare and touch down with what appeared to be a considerable angle of drift, even though one knew that the wheels were in fact aligned with the runway. In addition, it

seemed doubtful whether a pilot of limited experience, for whom the device was intended, would have sufficient skill for a crabwise straight approach, and to be able to judge the correct angle at which to set the undercarriage. He thought that it was probably for this reason that the idea was never developed.

Magister P6456 was purchased by O F Maclaren on 11th July 1946, probably because it still retained the Maclaren Drift undercarriage and was duly registered G-AIAI to him on 27th July 1946.

The Maclaren Drift Undercarriage was also fitted to an Airspeed Oxford and a North American Mustang for trials, but in the end the device was not considered for production aircraft.

Another modification was the 'Mock-up and test of canopy for Magister'. This canopy was to fit over both cockpits in order to provide more comfort for the crew when the aircraft were used on communications duties, and the ITP with this modification was issued to Phillips & Powis on 15th April 1942. Photographs of drawings of this modification survive to confirm that the work, at least on the first aircraft, was carried out by Phillips & Powis but it is not known for certain just how many Magisters were fitted with canopies.

The late Grahame Gates recalled that he was told that the windscreens used for these canopies were made from astrodomes from bomber aircraft and photographs show that the windscreen was roughly equivalent to half of an astrodome. The three

Magister fitted with cabin.

Photograph showing doors and canopies open.

Front view of Magister with cabin.

Magisters known to have been modified are N3890, P6407 and T9896; two of which had two separate upward opening hoods, while the other had a sliding canopy. One or two of these modified 'Maggies' were based at Woodley, where they were used for communications duties, but a photograph of P6407, taken in about May 1945, shows it at Cambridge (probably while with the Flying Training Command Comm Flt), in full camouflage and coded 'N'. All three modified Magisters were later sold and registered G-AKRW, G-AKJV and G-AKRV respectively. One ex RAF Magister G-AJRT (previously L8288), was fitted, after about 1955, with two separate sliding canopies which looked, from a distance, like a one-piece canopy.

The rear cockpit of Magister P6410 was fitted with a teardrop canopy with a sliding hood by an RAF unit at Barrow at some time, but when it was sold later (and registered G-AKGS) it had been returned to standard configuration with open cockpits.

During the course of research for this story, two photographs came to light which show a Magister tailplane manufactured from thermo-plastic by Aeroplastics Ltd. Interestingly the photographs had on the reverse '© The Fairey Aviation Co. Ltd. 19th March 1943 via Mr S C Hart-Still and John Maddocks'. Unfortunately, nothing further is known about this experimental tailplane or whether it was fitted to a Magister (see photographs on page 94).

Production of the Magister for the RAF ceased in January 1941, after a total of 1,230 aircraft had been delivered (see Production Summary below).

Sales of Magisters

Much 'misinformation' has been written about Magisters (and indeed also about other Miles aircraft types) being licence-built in foreign countries, especially in Turkey, and even Don Brown wrote that over 100 Magisters were built in Turkey, under licence, by Turk Hava Kurumu Ucak Fabrikasi. However, it is now known that 33 sets of 'raw materials' were supplied to Turkey by Phillips & Powis in 1941 and, after these had been completed, 'a considerable number' of Magisters were eventually built by the Turks, 'from scratch'. Following many years of research, Ole Nikolajsen has established that THK in Turkey actually built 80 Magisters from scratch (see Appendix 11 for further details of these).

Regardless of what may have appeared in the aviation press to the contrary, **no** other Magisters, nor indeed any other Miles aircraft of any type, were ever built under licence in any other foreign country.

A report detailing the supply of surplus RAF aircraft to foreign air forces after the war (N.A. Ref: AIR 2/10.191), implied that 15 Magisters and 28 Master Mk.IIs had been supplied to Austria. However, it subsequently transpired that: *The Austrian requirement depends on the signing of a Peace Treaty and may never come about.* This signing did not take place and no ex RAF aircraft were supplied to Austria.

A note entitled: 'Applications during the past twelve months for the export of aircraft or the sale of licences for manufacture abroad', dated 3rd December 1943, from PS15, stated, under 'Turkey' that: *The Turks have constructed a number of Magister aircraft under licence from Miles Aircraft Ltd and a representative of the firm was given permission to go to Turkey to help in the establishment of a Company for the repair of Magister and Master aircraft.*

While under 'Chile' the report states that: *An application by Miles Aircraft Ltd to sell manufacturing rights of the Magister, M.18 and M.38 is under consideration. One difficulty in the way of the proposal, is that of finding a suitable local timber in substitution of spruce. Arrangements have been made for the Chilean Ambassador and Air Attaché and certain Chilean industrialists to visit the firm.*

A letter from Mr Hawkes of PS4(b) at the MAP, dated 12th January 1945, to J V Perowne, CMG, at the Foreign Office, Whitehall, London stated: *Thank you very much for sending us copies of communications from Lima (of September-November 1944), regarding the prospects of business by Miles Aircraft Ltd in Peru. We saw Mr L A Hackett of Miles Aircraft here this morning, and he told us that from his firm's point of view these affairs were not sufficiently ripe as yet for him to put up any specific proposal for official consideration.*

In principle, however, his firm's policy of leading such a country as Peru towards establishing its own production of Miles types of aircraft in the future, by way of an interim stage in which it would be provided with a certain number of Miles training aircraft, together with facilities for setting up a repair and maintenance establishment for them out of which a production factory could later grow, is viewed quite sympathetically by MAP.

Of course, at the present time there is for various reasons no near prospect of making such aircraft (eg the Magister elementary trainer) available for that sort of purpose. But Miles are aware of that, and the position simply is that as soon as they believe that the time has come when they can reasonably put forward proposals to us, they may be expected to do so.

Comments from Mr Hawkes (Ministry of Aircraft Production) dated 12th January 1945 and attached to this letter stated: *As soon as Miles Aircraft Limited believe that the time has come when they can put forward proposals to the Ministry of Aircraft Production, they may be expected to do so.*

Minutes dated 20th January 1945 attached to the letter stated: *Miles Aircraft Ltd seem to be a very good firm for the purpose in view. They are certainly laying their plans with an eye to the future.* And on 22nd January 1945: *The new Air Attaché Lima, may be trusted to watch the opportunities in which the Miles Aircraft Co are interested, from the Peruvian end.* Unfortunately, nothing came of these plans.

Production Summary

M.14 and M.14A Magister Mk.I	1,225	(including 1 unidentified aircraft to replace the 'sample' aircraft supplied to Turkey) delivered against AM Contracts (a number of these were diverted to the air forces of Egypt and Eire)
M.14B Magister Mk.II	5	(with Blackburn Cirrus Major engines) delivered against an AM Contract
M.14 and M.14A Hawk Trainer Mk.III	25	for the civil home and overseas market pre-war
M.14B Hawk Trainer Mk.II	1	for the civil home market pre-war
M.14 and M.14A Magister Mk.I	23	supplied to foreign air forces
M.14A Magister Mk.I	1	'sample' aircraft sold to Turkey
Total complete aircraft	**1,280**	
M.14A Magister Mk.I	33	sets of raw materials for Turkey
Grand total	**1,313**	

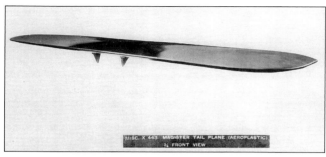

Front view of Magister Tailplane (Aeroplastic).

Rear view of Magister Tailplane (Aeroplastic).

A considerable number of surplus RAF Magisters were sold after the war and 148 were registered in the UK alone, under the designation M.14A Hawk Trainer Mk.III, although some were never overhauled and the aircraft were used for spares. Miles Service Bulletin No.3 August 1947 stated; *In order to clarify a point which frequently causes confusion, we advise all concerned that the civil version of the RAF Miles Magister aircraft is known as the Hawk Trainer Mk.III and that Certificates of Airworthiness are issued under the latter name.*

The first post war British aviation export order for South America, for 24 reconditioned ex RAF Magisters, was received from Chile in March 1945, although this was later reduced to 15 and it is possible that only 9 were eventually delivered. Due to pressures of work at Woodley, these aircraft were reconditioned at Cambridge by Marshall Flying School Ltd, under contract from Miles Aircraft Ltd.

A large number of ex RAF Magisters were also reconditioned by Miles Aircraft Ltd at Woodley for the air forces of Eire, Portugal and Thailand, and also for various home and overseas civilian customers. Included amongst the latter was one of the largest orders ever received for a British aircraft at the time - 151 - for the Argentine Government. The contract was arranged via H Hennequin y Cia in Buenos Aires and the Magisters were for use by flying clubs, being delivered between March and September 1946. Details of these and all other Magisters refurbished for overseas customers will be found in the next volume.

Many Hawk Trainer Mk.IIIs were much modified for racing purposes after the war, usually with the front cockpit faired over by their enthusiastic owners. A total of eight Hawk Trainer Mk.IIIs also took part in the 1950 King's Cup Air Race when Mr E Day gained first place in G-AKRV, at a speed of 138.5 mph.

For individual aircraft histories of Magister aircraft produced from 3rd September 1939 see Appendix 9. The individual aircraft histories of Magister aircraft produced prior to 3rd September 1939 are in Appendix 20 in **Miles Aircraft - The Early Years 1925 to 1939**.

(N.A. Refs: AIR 39/108; AIR 2066/2067; AVIA 15/1971 and B56721/39).

Probably the last Magister in RAF service was P6455 which was issued to the Reserve Command Com Sqdn, White Waltham on 11th July 1947. Photographed by the author at Shoreham in 1948, it went to 5 MU Kemble on 27th September 1949.

SPECIFICATION AND PERFORMANCE DATA

Engine:	M.14, M.14A 130 hp DH Gipsy Major I; M.14B 135 hp Blackburn Cirrus Major II
Dimensions:	span 33 ft 10 in; length 24 ft 7½ in; height overall, airscrew horizontal, tail down 6 ft 8 in; gross wing area 176 sq ft; net wing area 168 sq ft; aspect ratio 6.5; dihedral 6°; wing section modified Clark YM; thickness/chord ratio, root 19.2%, tip 9.0%
Weights:	empty 1,286 lb; fuel (20 gal) 150 lb; max fuel capacity 21 gal; oil (2½ gal) 22 lb; pilot 200 lb; passenger/pupil 200 lb; useful load 42 lb; AUW 1,900 lb, aerobatic 1,845 lb; wing loading 10.7 lb/sq ft
Performance:	max speed at sea level 140 mph, 130 mph at 5,000 ft, 125 mph at 10,000 ft; cruising speed 122 mph; stalling speed 52 mph IAS with flaps up, 43 mph IAS with flaps down; distance to unstick 630 ft with a 5 mph wind; distance to 50 ft 1,200 ft with 5 mph wind; landing run 420 ft with 5 mph wind; landing run from 50 ft 975 ft with 5 mph wind; initial rate of climb 750 ft/min; time to 5,000 ft 7.6 min; time to 10,000 ft 18.8 min; service ceiling 16,500 ft; absolute ceiling 19,000 ft; range 367 miles; duration 3 hrs

Chief Test Pilot 'Bill' Skinner 'Being strapped in' to the prototype M.19 Master Mk.II, N7422. This is one of only four photographs known to exist of this aircraft.
[Mrs A W Skinner]

Chapter 6
Miles M.19 Master Mk.II,
Miles M.19 Master GT Mk.II,
Miles M.27 Master Mk.III
and the Miles Mercury Fighter

In 1938, the Air Ministry asked Miles to consider the substitution of the Bristol Mercury radial air-cooled engine for the Rolls-Royce Kestrel liquid-cooled engine fitted to the Master Mk.I. The Kestrel engine was no longer in production and existing stocks were rapidly becoming depleted, whereas different versions of the Bristol Mercury air-cooled radial engine were in large-scale production for use in the Westland Lysander and Bristol Blenheim. The necessary design modifications to the airframe to take the radial engine were put in hand, and the M.9B Master Mk.I, N7422, was taken from the assembly line in June 1939, fitted with an 825 hp Bristol Mercury VIII 9-cylinder radial engine (as fitted to the Bristol Blenheim Mk.I), a sliding hood and the increased span tailplane of the M.9C, to become the prototype M.19 Master Mk.II.

Although the date of the first flight of the prototype M.19 Master Mk.II, N7422, is not officially recorded it can now be confirmed that it was in October 1939. The first four photographs shown on pages 95 and 96 were taken from the photograph album of Chief Test Pilot 'Bill' Skinner and the pencil notes written on the back of them are reproduced verbatim in the captions.

Therefore, it can be confirmed that it was chief test pilot 'Bill' Skinner who made the first flight of the Master Mk.II prototype and

not Tommy Rose, as stated by Don Brown and even published by the firm in '*A pictorial précis of some of the aircraft designed and built by Miles Aircraft Ltd!*'

'Bill' Skinner 'Examining the instruments etc before 'Starting up'.
[Mrs A W Skinner]

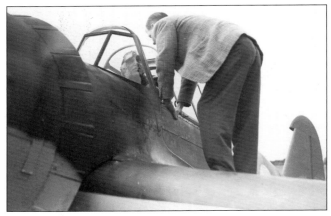

'A word with Mr F G Miles just before Taking off'.

[Photographs Mrs AW Skinner]

'After the test flight Bill gets out Mr F G Miles gets in'.

Tommy Rose therefore not only did ***not*** make the first flight of the new Mk.II prototype but he did not make the second flight either!

It is known that the prototype was flown by Flt Lt J F Moir, OC of 8 EFTS Woodley, on 13th October 1939, so it is highly probable that N7422 had made its first flight earlier in the day. Flt Lt Moir's previous experience as a test pilot with the A&AEE Martlesham Heath was obviously valued by Miles, as proven by his log book, which records test flights in many of the new Miles types very soon after they had made their first flight.

Following Bill's untimely death on 16th November 1939, the flight trials were completed by George Miles and Tommy Rose, who had been appointed the new Chief Test Pilot. The prototype Master Mk.II was delivered to the A&AEE Boscombe Down in November

1939 for its service tests, during the course of which it was proved to be 16 mph faster than the Master Mk.I. This was due to the Mercury engine giving 870 hp as compared with 585 hp of the de-rated Kestrel engine.

During the first full throttle diving test carried out during the performance trials at the A&AEE, Boscombe Down, on 10th January 1940, N7422 suffered structural failure of the tail unit or rear end of the fuselage, and crashed. The pilot fortunately escaped by parachute and landed unhurt. The M.9B Master Mk.I N7447 was hastily converted to replace it in order that the trials could be completed in the shortest possible time and this, the second prototype M.19 Master Mk.II, which was given the RAF Experimental Aeroplane No.105 for identification purposes, was first flown by Hugh Kennedy on 1st April 1940.

The installation of the Mercury engine reduced the fuselage length to 29ft 6in and gave the Mk.II a maximum speed of 275 mph at 14,000ft. This was a considerable improvement on the Mk.I even though its frontal area was increased. The cruising speed increased to 208 mph, but the landing speed remained at 85 mph, and the AUW was decreased to 5,341.50 lb.

All early production Master Mk.IIs had the 39ft 0in wingspan of the Mk.I, but the reduced span was introduced on the assembly line at an appropriate time, following the final M.9C Master Mk.IA, and all surviving aircraft were later retrospectively modified. The final 100 from the second contract for 500 M.9C Master Mk.IA were completed as M.19 Master Mk.II, with the 870 hp Bristol Mercury XX or 30 engine, being delivered from 16th April 1941. The Master Mk.II was fitted either with Rotol variable pitch, three blade constant speed wooden or metal propellers or de Havilland variable pitch, three blade constant speed metal propellers, both being left hand tractor.

The first batch of production aircraft were manufactured to 'Specification No. Master II/P.1. Production of Master II Aircraft', approved by W S Farren for Director of Technical Development, on 8th May 1940 and this stated that:

(i) *The aeroplanes are to be fitted with Mercury ME6M engine in lieu of Kestrel XXX engine. The modifications resulting from this change of engine, and the changes in other items of embodiment loan equipment consequent upon the change of engine, are to be embodied in all the aeroplanes.*

(ii) *Alteration to design of tail plane.*

(iii) *Alteration to design of cabin top.*

Modifications resulting from (ii) and (iii) above are also to be embodied.

etc, etc.

The second prototype Master Mk.II, N7447.

Another view of the second prototype Master Mk.II, N7447.

An Air Ministry photograph of Master Mk.II, N7447, dated May 1941.

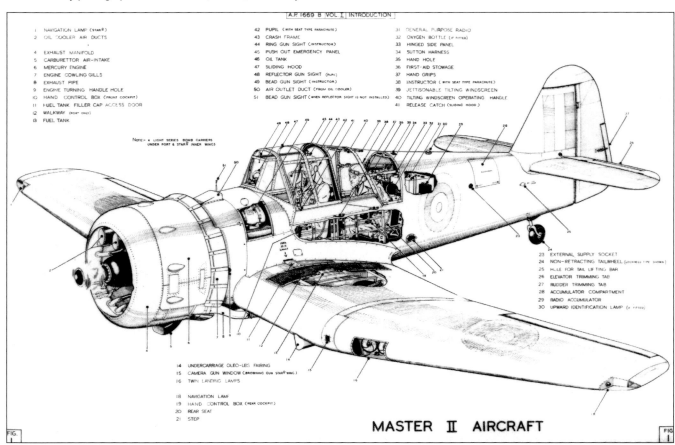

A.P. 1669 B VOL I INTRODUCTION

1 NAVIGATION LAMP (STAR'd)
2 OIL COOLER AIR DUCTS

4 EXHAUST MANIFOLD
5 CARBURETTOR AIR-INTAKE
6 MERCURY ENGINE
7 ENGINE COWLING GILLS
8 EXHAUST PIPE
9 ENGINE TURNING HANDLE HOLE
10 HAND CONTROL BOX (FRONT COCKPIT)
11 FUEL TANK FILLER CAP ACCESS DOOR
12 WALKWAY (PORT ONLY)
13 FUEL TANK

42 PUPIL (WITH SEAT TYPE PARACHUTE)
43 CRASH FRAME
44 RING GUN SIGHT (INSTRUCTOR)
45 PUSH OUT EMERGENCY PANEL
46 OIL TANK
47 SLIDING HOOD
48 REFLECTOR GUN SIGHT (PUPIL)
49 BEAD GUN SIGHT (INSTRUCTOR)
50 AIR OUTLET DUCT (FROM OIL COOLER)
51 BEAD GUN SIGHT (WHEN REFLECTOR SIGHT IS NOT INSTALLED)

31 GENERAL PURPOSE RADIO
32 OXYGEN BOTTLE (IF FITTED)
33 HINGED SIDE PANEL
34 SUTTON HARNESS
35 HAND HOLE
36 FIRST-AID STOWAGE
37 HAND GRIPS
38 INSTRUCTOR (WITH SEAT TYPE PARACHUTE)
39 JETTISONABLE TILTING WINDSCREEN
40 TILTING WINDSCREEN OPERATING HANDLE
41 RELEASE CATCH (SLIDING HOOD)

NOTE:- 4 LIGHT SERIES BOMB CARRIERS
UNDER PORT & STAR'd INNER WINGS

23 EXTERNAL SUPPLY SOCKET
24 NON-RETRACTING TAILWHEEL (LOCKHEED TYPE SHOWN)
25 HOLE FOR TAIL LIFTING BAR
26 ELEVATOR TRIMMING TAB
27 RUDDER TRIMMING TAB
28 ACCUMULATOR COMPARTMENT
29 RADIO ACCUMULATOR
30 UPWARD IDENTIFICATION LAMP (IF FITTED)

14 UNDERCARRIAGE OLEO-LEG FAIRING
15 CAMERA GUN WINDOW (BROWNING GUN STAR'd WING)
16 TWIN LANDING LAMPS

18 NAVIGATION LAMP
19 HAND CONTROL BOX (REAR COCKPIT)
20 REAR SEAT
21 STEP

MASTER II AIRCRAFT

Partial cut-away drawing of the Master Mk.II showing essential features.   *[Photograph from AP.1669 B Vol.1 Introduction]*

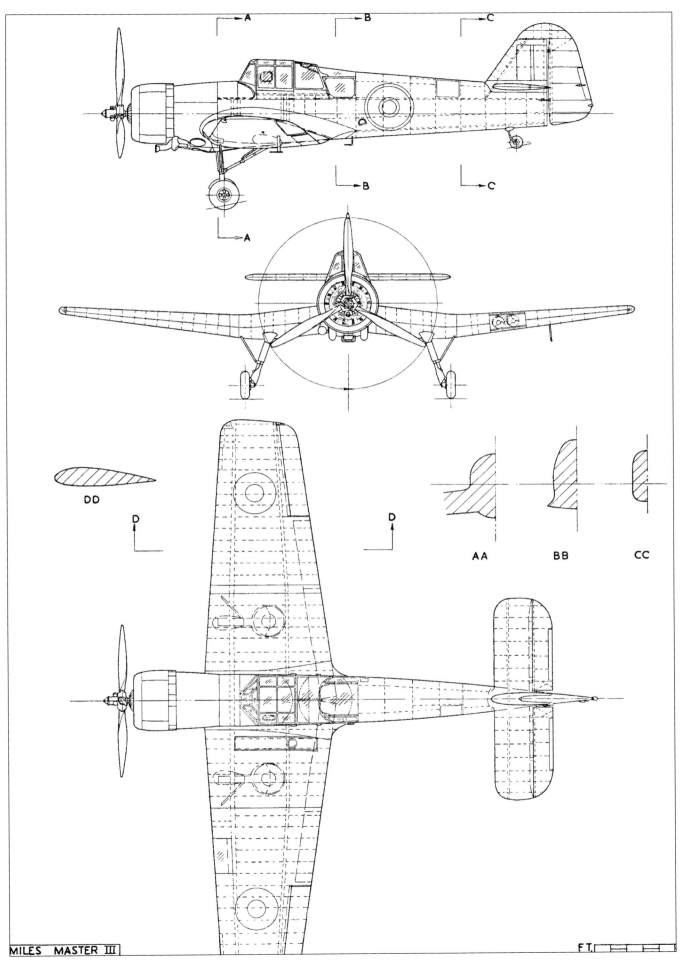

DD

AA   BB   CC

MILES MASTER III

F.T.

Three-view drawing of the Master Mk.III. Note reduced span wings.

Above: A Master Mk.II showing the reduced span wings and bomb carriers with 8 practice bombs.

The second prototype Master Mk.II N7447 at A&AEE Boscombe Down fitted with 8 practice bombs on under-wing racks.

The second batch of production aircraft were manufactured to 'Specification No. Master II/P.2. Production of Master II Aircraft' approved by N E Rowe for Director of Technical Development on 19th April 1941, and this differed from the earlier Specification with respect to the engine, as follows:

The aeroplanes are to be fitted with Mercury XX engines in lieu of Kestrel XXX engines. The modifications resulting from this change of engine, and the changes in other items of embodiment loan equipment consequent upon the change of engine, are to be embodied in all the aeroplanes.

etc, etc.

However, sometime in 1940, the Air Ministry suddenly realised that the 'unlimited stocks' of the Mercury engines had 'mysteriously' disappeared, and Miles was asked, yet again, to re-design the Master to take a third engine - this time the American built 825hp Pratt & Whitney Twin Wasp Junior R-1535-SB4-G 14-cylinder two-row air-cooled radial engine. This engine was chosen by the Air Ministry because 'supplies were considered to be plentiful'. It is believed that they were originally intended for France but following the collapse of that country in June 1940, they became available for other purposes.

The M.9B Master Mk.I, N7994, was modified to take the American engine with a Hamilton Standard variable pitch three-blade metal constant-speed, right hand tractor propeller and sliding hood, to become the prototype M.27 Master Mk.III. The M.27 prototype was first flown by Hugh Kennedy on 17th December 1940. The Master Mk.III originally also had the same span as the Master Mk.I in its original form, but this was later reduced in line with the later Mk.I, the Mk.IA and the Mk.II.

The maximum speed was reduced to 232 mph at 9,200 ft and the cruising speed was also reduced, to 170 mph, but the landing speed remained the same at 85 mph. The AUW was increased to 5,394.5lb but for the record, the maximum permitted AUW for all marks of the Master was 5,573lb, although this figure is often misquoted as being the AUW for various marks.

The Experimental Aeroplane No.122 was allotted to the M.27 Master Mk.III (with full span wings) for identification purposes, probably for the prototype, N7994.

'Specification No. Master III/P.1' was approved by N E Rowe for Director of Technical Development on 21th April 1941 and this stated that:

N7994, the M.27 Master Mk.III prototype at Woodley, note the Falcon Hotel in the background.

The aeroplanes are to be fitted with Twin Wasp Junior engines in lieu of Kestrel XXX engines. The modifications resulting from this change of engine, and the changes in other items of embodiment loan equipment consequent upon the change of engine, are to be embodied in all the aeroplanes.

etc, etc.

However, it was later found that supplies of the Bristol Mercury engine were still available after all and therefore both the Master Mk.II and Mk.III went into full scale production. The M.19 Master Mk.II was built at Woodley, South Marston and 'Sheffield and Doncaster', while all the M.27 Master Mk.III's were built at South Marston.

The projected plans for Master production originally called for 60 aircraft per month from Woodley and 140 aircraft per month from South Marston, but these figures were never achieved. The average production rates for both Woodley and South Marston were as follows:

Woodley

Production of the Master Mk.I, which had been in construction at Woodley since 1939, ceased in April 1941, and this was replaced on the assembly line by the Master Mk.II. The Master Mk.II was delivered from April 1941 and between July 1939 and December 1942 production of both marks averaged 52 per month. Master production finally ceased after 900 Master Mk.I and 1,250 Master Mk.II (including the 1 Mk.IV? and 125 GT Mk.II) had been built, with the final contract, for 360 Master Mk.II's, being amended to 125 (completed as Master GT Mk.II), with the remaining 235 being built as Miles M.25 Martinet TT Mk.I.

South Marston

During the first full year of operation, production of the Master Mk.III and Mk.II averaged 42 per month between March 1941 and March 1942 and during the first eighteen months to September 1942, it rose to an average of 50 per month. Production peaked between May and September 1942, when some 77 Masters of both marks were produced each month. The final 190 Master Mk.II

M.27 Master Mk.III prototype N7994 at the A&AEE Boscombe Down.
[MAP RTP Photographic Section]

Another view of N7994 at Boscombe Down in January 1941.
[MAP RTP Photographic Section]

aircraft, which were originally to have been built at Doncaster, were completed at South Marston at the rate of just 32 per month, and this reduced the average rate of production for the two years during which time the Master was built at South Marston, to 46 per month. A total of 488 Master Mk.II and 602 Master Mk.III were built at South Marston.

Doncaster

Components for Miles M.19 Master Mk.II aircraft were made by Cravens Ltd (*'an aeroplane manufacturer with propeller branch' in*

An interesting formation of RAF training aircraft of the Empire Central Flying School at Hullavington, prior to 28th March 1942. The Master Mk.III in the centre has its flaps partially lowered to help keep station with the slower Magister.

Master Mk.III, W8513, of ECFS Hullavington. Note, pilot shielding his eyes while looking at the photographic aircraft.

[The Aeroplane, via Mike Hooks]

Master Mk.III, DL630, being flown by chief test pilot Tommy Rose.

1919-20'), at their works in Sheffield. These parts, together with others made by smaller firms in Sheffield and the surrounding area, were assembled at Doncaster Airport in a large hangar which had been built for the Ministry of Aircraft Production and previously used by Westland Aircraft Ltd for the manufacture of Lysander aircraft. At least one Master Mk.II is known to have been completed at Doncaster and this was flown to Woodley by Hugh Kennedy on 30th October 1941. Hugh recalled seeing other Master Mk.IIs on the production line at Doncaster at the time of his visit and it is likely that a further nine were completed there, these being delivered by the ATA between January and February 1942. The

completion and assembly of the final 190 aircraft from this contract was then transferred to South Marston.

A total of 1,748 Master Mk.II and 602 Master Mk.III were produced (not including the prototypes modified from M.9B Master Mk.I aircraft), to make a grand total of 2,350 radial engined Masters, with the last one, a Master Mk.II, being delivered from South Marston on 26th March 1943.

During 1941, Miles suggested to the MAP that, if it was intended to keep the Master in production, a number of modifications and improvements based on Service experience could well be incorporated. These included a redesigned cabin top for the rear cockpit to provide the instructor with the necessary field of view on take-off and landing, without having to keep raising and lowering himself through the roof as on the standard Master. Other improvements suggested were a modified centre section and tailplane. The project was given the designation Miles M.31 Master Mk.IV, but at that time a considerable number of Masters were on order and these were considered to be adequate to meet the requirements of the Service for some years to come and, as the MAP was also considering asking Miles to design a target-towing version of the Master at about this time, the M.31 Master Mk.IV project was abandoned.

However, although the fuselage for the M.31 Master Mk.IV was actually built it is now known that it was not fitted to the first production M.19 Master Mk.II, T8886, as once thought. T8886 did incorporate many modifications, the nature of which have yet to be discovered but these did not, apparently, include the raised rear canopy. It is, presumably, because of these modifications, that T8886 was often referred to by test pilots as the Master Mk.IV. Indeed, on one occasion, Hugh Kennedy recorded a later flight in the 'Master IV', with 'B' mark U-0246 (T8886 later became U-0246) in his log book. The saga of T8886 is all very confusing!

The raised teardrop shaped rear cockpit of the M.31 was later incorporated in the Miles M.37 Martinet Advanced Trainer of 1946, and this configuration was to set the trend which was to continue to the present day. The fuselage of the M.31 was stored at Woodley until at least January 1945.

It was to be the Master Mk.II which was to give Don Brown his first experience of flying a high-powered aeroplane, and it apparently surprised him to note just how little different it was from either the Falcon or Nighthawk. However, owing to the large diameter of the engine, especially with the gills open, he found that the forward view when taxiing was rather poor, and it was necessary, as with all tailwheel aeroplanes, to steer a zigzag course to avoid the risk of hitting unseen obstacles ahead.

One of the unusual characteristics of the Master recounted by Don Brown, was its entry into a spin. On stalling the aircraft and applying full rudder, one wing would flick down sharply, as one might expect, followed by the nose in the normal way. The spin would then start, but at a surprisingly slow rate of rotation for a heavily-loaded aircraft, then, just as you were thinking what a slow and docile spin it was, more surprisingly still, recovery would apparently commence. The rate of rotation would slow down and the nose would start to come up. However, before you had time to recover from your surprise at this unusual phenomenon, the wing would flick sharply down again, followed by a rapid rate of rotation and the spin proper would then start; but if you had taken recovery action during the first two slow turns, you did not experience the proper spin because the latter was always preceded by the initial half-roll, the two slow turns and the partial recovery.

Capt Eric Brown carried out an interesting flight in an experimental Master Mk.II late in the war, and he described his findings, in his book **'Testing for Combat'**. These make interesting comparison with those experienced by Don Brown; *It was very representative in size of contemporary fighters, with a span of 35 ft 9 in, a length of 29 ft 6 in and a height of 9 ft 5 in (9 ft 3 in - PA). Its empty weight was 4,130 lb (4,293 lb - PA), and loaded weight 5,312 lb (max permissible 5,573 lb - PA). Top speed was 255 mph at 10,000 ft. From a handling point of view the Master II was fairly representative of what a naval fighter could have been in the 1940s, so it was chosen for an interesting experiment in relation to such fighters.*

The aircraft chosen, DL185, was in fact a hybrid, having a Master II fuselage with the old Mk.I wings of 39 ft span with squared tips. (This last statement is ambiguous however, as it implies that DL185 had the 39 ft wing span but with squared wingtips, whereas, in fact, all the surviving early Masters which had been built with the 39 ft span wing, with rounded tips, were later retrospectively modified by reducing the wing span to 35 ft 9 in, by the simple expedient of 'clipping' the wing tips to give a 'squared' effect. Unless, of course, DL185 had a completely new set of wings of 39 ft span but with square cut wingtips? However, it would appear to have had modified ailerons - PA.)

Spring tab wide-chord ailerons of short length were fitted, with the primary purpose of allowing larger-area flaps to be fitted to any wing thus equipped. Such an application would of course be of particular benefit to naval aircraft, and the behaviour of the ailerons was of especial interest at low speeds. In any case, a speed restriction of 200 mph was placed on this experimental aircraft for structural considerations. (Following trials on a Master Mk.I with 40% chord short span ailerons, these were later fitted to a Master Mk.II but with spring operated servo-tabs, on which the spring rate was adjustable on the ground, for the RAE Farnborough for experiments with short-span large-chord ailerons in order to allow aircraft to be designed with larger-span flaps - PA).

I made a flight on DL185 on 5th June 1945 and while making my control checks on the ground I found a very noticeable large amount of inertia in the ailerons, but this disappeared completely in flight, probably owing to the very weak spring used on the tab. The rate of roll at normal cruising speeds was an improvement over that of the standard Master, and there seemed to be very little increase of stick force from 100 mph to 200 mph, so the lateral control was definitely light. The aircraft was, however, laterally unstable (stick free), although the stick self-centred when released after displacement.

The all-up stall occurred at 79 mph and with no warning. The left wing dropped sharply, and though aileron control was positive right down to the stall, large stick movements could produce a premature stall up to about 84 mph. When the stall did occur the nose dipped with the stalled wing and so the speed rose at once, and only a 2 or 3 mph increase in indicated airspeed was sufficient to regain lateral control and raise the wing.

The all-down stall occurred at 58 mph without warning other than a slight lateral twitch. The right wing dropped gently and again the nose dipped sufficiently to give a slight rise in airspeed and allowed lateral control to be regained. The ailerons were still effective right down to the stall, although they were definitely sluggish and lacking in feel. At the stall there was about one inch of upfloat on the ailerons at the training edge, but this progressively decreased until there was none at 200 mph.

For the purpose of comparison I flew standard Master II DM352 on 7th June, which of course had rounded wing tips. (The observation; 'which of course' is very interesting, implying as it does that DL185 was in fact a 'one-off', 'with the old Mk.I wings of 39 ft span with squared tips'. However, all Masters should have had the mandatory reduced-span wings fitted long before 1945 - PA). *It proved heavier on the ailerons with a slower rate of roll, and there was a noticeable build-up in force with increase in speed from 100 mph to 200 mph. The lateral stability (stick-free) was neutral, although the stick self-centred when released after displacement.*

The all-up stall at 77 mph and all-down at 61 mph displayed the same characteristics as on DL185, although the ailerons seemed crisper, and certainly had more feel close to the stall. The interesting point, however, was that the all-down stalling speed was higher in spite of the increased wing area of this aircraft (implying that it did still have the 39 ft span wing - PA), *and the significance was that the stall occurred on the ailerons on both Masters.*

It was decided to investigate the stall characteristics further on both aircraft by making a series of powered stalls. The behaviour of the standard aircraft was more vicious, but in both cases the stall was entirely on the ailerons and the lateral control was less effective close to the stall with engine on than with engine off; consequently the wing could not be picked up until quite an appreciable increase in speed occurred. In that respect, however, the wide-chord ailerons showed up slightly better than the standard ailerons.

Approaches to the aerodrome were made in very bumpy weather at 85 mph with power on, and the hybrid Master was very difficult to control laterally, whereas the standard Master felt more secure although both required a high work rate.

My conclusion was that the wide-chord ailerons were not good enough in their current form for deck-landing on an aircraft carrier, but offered distinct possibilities as a rather better-than-usual application of spring tabs to ailerons. In fact I had at that time found only one case of really good spring tab ailerons for deck landing, namely those of the Grumman Hellcat III, which in its earlier marks without spring tabs had basically good aileron control anyway.

The instructor's seat in the rear cockpit of all marks of Master was adjustable vertically to enable him to raise himself, so that his head protruded above the canopy line, in order to obtain a better view over the leading edge of the wing for take-off and landing. The top of the rear canopy rotated about its front edge and was interconnected with the seat raising mechanism so that, when the instructor raised his seat, the canopy panel hinged upwards about its forward edge to act as a windscreen. However, care had to be taken on the initial climb after take-off so as not to allow the speed to build up above 160 mph, otherwise this windscreen was liable to fold back and catch the unsuspecting instructor an almighty crack on the head! Conversely, sometimes when entering a spin, the windscreen would flick open under the action of the forces acting on it, giving the pupil in the front cockpit the impression that the instructor was about to bale out!

With a view to reducing the loads during aerobatics and recovery from dives, a set of Master Mk.II wings was reduced in span by removing 19½ inches from each tip, i.e. the wing was reduced in span from 39 ft to 35 ft 9 ins. The ailerons were also cut away to suit the revised plan form and the ends of the wing were suitably faired off. These modified wings were fitted Master Mk.II AZ543, which was delivered to CRD at Phillips & Powis, Woodley on 16th December 1941. Hugh Kennedy then made flights as follows: 'Handling' 7th January 1942; 'ADM's' on 9th January 1942 and 'Levels' also on 9th January 1942. It was then delivered to the CRD at A&AEE Boscombe Down on 17th January 1942, for 'Brief handling and spinning trials with a wing of reduced span'.

The A&AEE Boscombe Down 7th Part of Report No.AAEE/719 on the trials, dated about 3rd April 1942 stated:

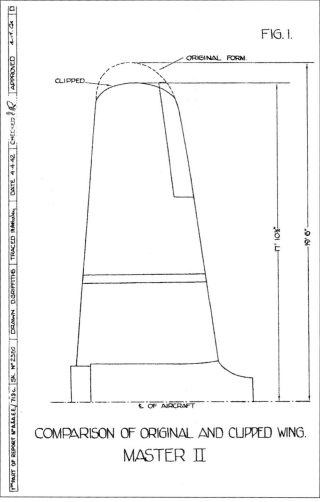

A&AEE drawing showing 'Comparison of Original and Clipped Wing Master' but note that the reduced span wing shown is incorrect as it was clipped rather than rounded as on the original.

Introduction:

With a view to reducing the loads during aerobatics and recovery from dives, a set of Master Mk.II wings has been reduced in span by removing 20 inches (19½ inches actually - PA) from each tip. The ailerons have also been cut away to suit the revised plan form

Master Mk.II, AZ205, with reduced span wings, at Woodley prior to delivery to DGRD at Phillips & Powis at Woodley on 12th July 1941. Delivered to RAE Farnborough on 14th July 1941.

and the ends of the wing have been suitably faired off. The photographs show the aeroplane fitted with the modified wings.

Condition of aeroplane relevant to tests:

The aeroplane was tested at two different loadings:-

Loading	All-up weight	Position of CG aft of datum
Normal load	5,575 lb	45.1 inches
Extended aft limit	5,575 lb	46.0 inches

The design CG limits are 40.2 inches to 45.3 inches aft of the datum (including aft extension). The above limits refer to the undercarriage down. At the normal load, raising the undercarriage moves the centre of gravity from 45.1 inches to 45.8 inches aft of the datum.

The aeroplane had no fairings on the undercarriage legs as is now the practice on Master aircraft. Two light series bomb racks with practice bombs were carried below the wings. The leading edge gun port and the ejector chute were sealed. The tests were made during the period 6.2.42 to 7.3.42. The aeroplane was fitted with a Rotol Jablo 10 ft diameter constant speed propeller.

Handling and flying qualities:

Take-off and initial climb: The take-off is not noticeably affected, although the initial climb away is not quite so good as that of the Mark.II Master with standard wings.

Stability: The aeroplane is a little less stable generally than the standard Mark.II Master. It exhibits similar characteristics, being unstable longitudinally on the climb and in level flight at low speeds. On the glide with flaps and undercarriage down, the aeroplane is stable, but with flaps and undercarriage up, it is unstable. Directionally and laterally the aeroplane is stable both on the climb and in level flight. The slight deterioration of stability compared with that of a standard Mark.II Master is particularly noticeable in tight turns which now tend to become tighter.

Stalling speeds: The following stalling speeds were obtained with both hoods closed.

	Normal load	Extended aft load
Flaps and undercarriage up	73 mph	71 mph
Flaps and undercarriage down	50 - 52 mph	50 - 52 mph

On a Mark.II Master with the standard wings the stalling speeds were 72 mph ASI, flaps and undercarriage up, and 56 mph ASI, flaps and undercarriage down (see 2nd Part of AAEE/719,c). It is possible that the indicated difference in speed at the stall, flaps and undercarriage down, may be due to change in the position error at low speeds. The pitot head is underneath the port wing tip on a strut 3 ft 7 ins to the rear of the leading edge and 5 ft 7½ ins from the tip of the clipped wing. As this makes the pitot head about 20 inches nearer the wing tip that that on a standard Master II, it is probable that the position error has changed at low air speeds. The position error, however, has not been checked.

Stall - flaps and undercarriage up: At both loads, as the speed is reduced the aeroplane becomes noticeably tail heavy, this tendency increasing as speed decreases. The forward position of the control column at the stall is nearly central, a slight forward movement being necessary to stop the nose from rising. At the stall the right wing drops sharply. Raising the wing by use of the aileron results in the left wing dropping, followed by the nose. Moving the control column further aft results in the aeroplane flicking from side to side.

Bringing the control column fully aft, and using all controls coarsely in an attempt to maintain an even keel results in the aeroplane flicking from side to side with some fore and aft pitching,

the speed rising to 100 mph ASI. Releasing the controls is sufficient to stop this and to effect recovery. The aeroplane showed no tendency to spin.

Stall - flaps and undercarriage down: At both loads the aeroplane becomes suddenly tail heavy at about 55 mph ASI and appears to sink, tail first, followed by a sharp drop of the nose. The elevators are almost completely ineffective and do not entirely arrest the tail sink, even when the control column is pushed forward. There is a slight tendency for the right wing to drop.

Bringing the control column fully aft results in a rock from side to side similar to the case with flaps and undercarriage up. The aeroplane then drops into a turn to the left, with the nose down. If the control column is held fully back the aeroplane will spin. The stalling characteristics were compared for various combinations of hood openings, but there was little or no noticeable difference in ASI or behaviour at the stall. The hood buffeting at the stall, which is so marked on the standard MarkII Masters, was not evident on this aeroplane but the elevator control appeared less effective at the stall.

Aerobatics: As has been previously stated, this aeroplane, with the "clipped" wings, is less stable that a Master II with normal wings. Besides the steep turns previously mentioned, the unstable characteristics are most apparent in loops. The minimum speed for a sustained steep turn of 60° bank is from 135 - 140 mph ASI.

Loop: The looping speed is higher than on a standard Master II. At 240 - 250 mph ASI a loop can be carried out. Care, however, is required to prevent stalling on top of the loop. The control column must be eased forward, and a tendency to yaw to the right must be checked; otherwise, this manoeuvre is straightforward.

Half roll off loop: It is difficult to get round in a half roll off the top of a loop unless the speed is about 260 mph ASI. If the loop is commenced at a lower speed it is possible to roll off the top by putting the propeller into fully fine pitch near the top of the loop.

Slow rolls: The roll is better than normal, it being possible to keep the nose up during the last half of the roll.

Gliding and landing: The approach and landing speeds are the same as those for a normal Master II (see 2nd Part of AAEE/719,c). At the gliding speed the poor elevator control becomes apparent, although it is still sufficient. The landing is normal, the tail coming down quickly.

Spinning tests: Spins up to 8 turns have been carried out at the normal and extended aft loadings. The characteristics of the spins are unaltered by the reduced wing span, and recovery is satisfactory.

Dives: Dives have been carried out up to the limiting speed of 330 mph ASI. The aeroplane was trimmed for full out level flight. The aeroplane is steady in the dive. There is a tendency to yaw to the left and drop the left wing, but this is easily corrected by use of the rudder. There is very little force required on the control column to hold the aeroplane in the dive and a slight pull is required to effect recovery. The recovery is normal and quick.

Conclusions:

The aeroplane is normal and straightforward, but the characteristics at the stall, flaps and undercarriage down are worse with the wings clipped and loops and steep turns are not so easily made. The aeroplane is, however, considered satisfactory as an advanced trainer.

In the early 1940s, a number of Spitfires were lost in combat because of structural failure. This was mostly caused by the light and powerful elevators which, while perfectly satisfactory for all normal purposes, were sufficiently powerful to break the aircraft when violently applied in the heat of combat. This problem did not

Above: Master Mk.II, AZ543, was the test aircraft fitted with the Anti-'G' device' in 1942.

occur on the Hurricane, whose elevators were appreciably heavier in operation than those of the Spitfire, so that at high speeds the stick forces per 'g' were insufficient to break the aircraft.

To overcome this problem, George Miles proposed that an inertia, or 'bob' weight was sprung to a neutral position until a pre-set 'g' was reached, after which its movement operated an anti-servo tab to significantly increase the stick force per 'g' as a warning to the pilot, while still leaving the Spitfire's pleasantly light stick forces in the normal operating range.

It has also been suggested that this inertia weight was fitted to the Master Mk.I in service, in order not to overstress the wings during pulling out from dives and that the pupils under instruction were warned about *'certain types of service aircraft which require a very large push force to keep them in a dive'* (e.g. early production Spitfires), which required considerable strength to prevent them coming out too rapidly when trimmed straight and level. However, it has not been possible to confirm this.

The 'Anti-g device', as it was known by the firm, or the 'Phillips & Powis 'g' Restrictor' by the Air Ministry, was designed by George Miles and installed in Master Mk.II T8852. Preliminary Tests were duly reported and further tests were carried out in Master Mk.II AZ543, being first flown, by Flt Lt Hugh Kennedy, on a 'Handling' flight on 7th January 1942.

However, the first reference by Hugh Kennedy to the 'Anti-g tab', was not made until a flight on 6th June 1942. The device was tested with complete success and it was found that, by adjusting the length of the lever arm to which the bob-weight was attached, it was possible to limit the maximum acceleration to any desired value.

George Miles found that carrying out a series of test dives followed by 6 'g' pull-outs was both uncomfortable and surprisingly tiring and this is hardly surprising! Following a number of test flights, Hugh Kennedy delivered AZ543 to the RAE at Farnborough on 9th August 1942, and collected it from Boscombe Down on 2nd December 1942. The last recorded flight with the 'Anti-g tab' was made on 28th April 1943, when Hugh delivered it to the RAE Farnborough; it was later delivered into service with 9 (P)AFU but it is not known if the anti-g device was retained in service.

453 M.19 Master Mk.IIs were shipped to South Africa for use by the South African Air Force in the Joint Air Training Scheme and

of these, 425 were built at Woodley and 28 at South Marston. Of these, 25 were lost at sea en route to South Africa. Further details on the M.19 Master Mk.II in service with the SAAF can be found in Chapter 9 and Appendices 16 and 17.

Miles was next asked whether he could quickly adapt the Master Mk.II for towing the General Aircraft Hotspur training glider and Don Brown described the circumstances behind this in *Milestones No.33* in the *Miles Aircraft Works Magazine* as follows:

Until 1942 the Hotspur glider was usually towed by obsolete types such as the Hawker Audax and the Hawker Hector. During the summer of 1942 the Ministry of Aircraft Production suddenly awoke to the fact that the stocks of these aeroplanes, which were no longer in production, were practically exhausted. They were thus faced with the prospect of having hundreds of Hotspur gliders and nothing with which to tow them. Presumably due to our reputation for being able to turn out things rather faster than most people, they turned to us and asked whether we could hurriedly convert the Master into a glider tug and, if so, how quickly we could let them have one to try out.

A hurried conference of the design staff was called and, to the amazement of the authorities, who expected that the job would take at least 3 months, promised to deliver the prototype within one week. The atmosphere of gloom prevailing a few moments previously was replaced by one of relief tinged with disbelief. Five days later a converted Master Mk.II was delivered to the service for trials.

The bottom of the rudder had been cut off and a hook had been installed in the rear of the fuselage with a release mechanism operated from the cockpit. All this involved quite a lot of modification and design work but when it was tested the Master was unanimously acclaimed to be by far the nicest glider tug the Service had yet had. Within a few weeks sufficient numbers had been delivered to relieve the shortage. Once again the situation had been saved by Miles Aircraft.

The prototype conversion, which also included the fitment of longer exhaust pipes, was made on Master Mk.II DL176 and this was first flown, by Hugh Kennedy, on a 'Handling' flight, on 11th April 1942. Hugh next flew DL176 (twice) at the AFEE Ringway on an 'Aircraft test (Ringway)' on the 12th April. An 'Instrument test' was carried out by Hugh on 13th April and then later the same day he carried out the first 'Towing flight Hotspur'. The next flight, also on the same day, was 'Towing full load Hotspur' and this appears to have been the extent of the recorded trials of the Master GT Mk.II made by the firm at the AFEE. While he was at Ringway, Hugh also made a 'Gliding' flight in a Hotspur (s/n B571?) on 13th April with Flt Lt Robert Kronfeld. DL176 had returned to Woodley by 28th April 1942. One anomaly is that although the trials were carried out on DL176, the official photographs taken at the A&AEE Boscombe Down show Master GT Mk.II DL302 and were dated July 1942.

Although the conversion had involved a considerable amount of design effort and modification, the resulting Master Glider Tower not only solved the supply problem but was also acclaimed by the RAF as the fastest and nicest tower that they had yet been given. As a matter of interest it should be mentioned that potential glider pilots were still first and foremost fighting soldiers and as such, had first to complete initial ground training, which was in the form of a modified battle course. Following this they then went on to train as glider pilots, in GAL Hotspurs, with day and night landings being practised. The men then were taught to make remote releases up to 20 miles from the landing zone, in order to provide practice in long glides during day and night conditions.

Following their initial training the pilots then went on to a Heavy Glider Conversion and Operational Training Unit, where they then mastered the heavier Horsa and Hamilcar gliders.

125 Miles M.19 Master Mk.II's were completed as GT Mk.IIs on the assembly line at Woodley, and a further 209 Mk.II have been accounted for as having been modified to GT Mk.II, either before delivery or later, see Appendix 15 for details of these.

The last Glider Training School to use Master GT Mk.IIs was 3 GTS at Wellesbourne Mountford, which disbanded on 3rd December 1947.

With the advent of rocket projectiles, with which it was proposed to equip certain types of operational aircraft, it was decided to fit these projectiles to an M.19 Master Mk.II in order to ascertain its suitability as a trainer in the use of these new weapons. DL852, an M.19 Master GT Mk.II, which was being repaired at Woodley following an accident while in use as a glider tower at Hanworth Park, was then transferred to CRD at Phillips & Powis on 6th November 1942 in order that the necessary modifications, including the fitting of a standard rudder, could be carried out.

Above and below: Master GT Mk.II DL302 at the A&AEE Boscombe Down. Note reduced bottom rudder to allow for the towing cable.

Master Mk.II DL852/G fitted with 6 rocket projectiles. Note the /G serial suffix applied.

An underside view of DL852/G showing the R/Ps and the reduced span wings to advantage.   *[A&AEE of 18th March 1943 via Phil Jarrett]*

Three rails were fitted under each wing on which to carry the six R/Ps and following completion of the installation, in December 1942, the Master Mk.II was marked as DL852/G (which signified that, being a new 'Secret' type, it had to be kept under guard at all times) and it was delivered to 'A' Squadron Performance, A&AEE Boscombe Down on 2nd February 1943.

DL852/G was damaged in a landing accident at Boscombe Down in April 1943 but the outer wings on which the rails were attached were undamaged and these were then fitted to Master Mk.II, DM159, in order that the trials could continue. This aircraft was delivered to the same unit at A&AEE Boscombe Down on 2nd August 1943. However, in the event, the requirement was apparently deemed unnecessary, no further Masters were so

modified and DL852/G was repaired and returned to standard, being delivered to 5 (P) AFU Ternhill on 15th May 1943.

On 14th October 1944, Master Mk.II, DL944 was delivered to the Admiralty, and it is on record that this aircraft was fitted with an experimental arrester hook for the Royal Navy, but no further details of this experiment are known.

In 1945, a chemical method of seeing boundary layer transition on wings was developed by the RAE at Farnborough. The wing to be studied was sensitized by a mist spray of potassium iodide, starch and hypo, which dried in a white layer. A trail of weak chlorine was laid alongside a trail of marker smoke by another aircraft, in this case a Master GT Mk.II which had been modified by the RAE to have a spray nozzle fitted between the undercarriage legs. The test subject, in one particular case a silver painted RAF Bell P-63A Kingcobra, FZ440, the inner wing of which had been covered with the paste, was then flown through the chlorine trail at a distance of about a mile from the spraying aircraft and transition from laminar to turbulent flow was shown by a darkening of the treated surface.

On 11th August 1945, Master II, DL429, which was on the charge at the RAE Farnborough, was allotted to General Aircraft Ltd at Hanworth Park for flight trials of the GAL TX.3/43 and Hotspur gliders for 6 months. On 12th October 1945 it was returned to Miles Aircraft by air to have hydraulic jacks fitted to the rudder and elevator, see later.

An HQ 41 Group Return (N.A. Ref: AIR 17/33) gave the numbers of Masters surviving as at 6th December 1945 as follows:

Master I	2 Stock as at 0900 29.11.45
	2 Stock as at 0900 6.12.45
	2 Awaiting/undergoing breakdown
Master II	167 Stock as a 0900 29.11.45
	167 Stock as at 0900 6.12.45
	3 Ready for issue
	16 Complete with equipment.
	4 Deficient of equipment
	2 Not checked in
	107 Long term storage
	34 Awaiting MAP disposal instructions. Non effective aircraft*
	1 Awaiting/undergoing breakdown. Non effective aircraft*
Master II Tug	17 Stock as at 090 6.12.45
	2 Ready for issue
	1 Complete with equipment
	14 Long-term storage

* These non effective aircraft require maintenance within 41 Group Units.

Fred Lynn visited Woodley on 14th June 1946 and noted a Master GT Mk.II, with no serial but 'fitted with hydraulic controls'. This aircraft was DL429, which was delivered to the Miles Aircraft CRD at Woodley on 12th October 1945, to have booster jacks fitted to the rudder and elevator. Although a 'Test' flight was made by Hugh Kendall on 16th March 1946, no details of the tests have survived, but this was almost certainly in connection with the Miles M.52 programme.

It is of interest to note that the Air Transport Auxiliary ferried a grand total of 9,532 Masters of all marks (although this total may have included some Martinets) as follows:-

843	15.2.40 to 14.2.41
1,675	15.2.41 to 14.2.42
1,913	15.2.42 to 14.2.43
2,681	15.2.43 to 14.2.44
1,808	15.2.44 to 14.2.45
612	15.2.45 to 30.11.45

As only 3,250 Masters of all marks were built in total, some of these aircraft must therefore have been ferried more than once!

During November 1945, 23 General Aircraft Hotspurs, towed by 23 Master GT Mk.IIs. all from 5 GTS Shobdon, were flown from Shobdon to Montford Bridge for breaking up by 34 MU Monkmoor - their task complete.

At the weekly Miles Aircraft Ltd Executive Management Board Meeting, held at Woodley on 23rd September 1946; 'It was agreed to purchase 20 Masters for re-sale'. In fact, Miles Aircraft Ltd purchased 30 Master Mk.IIs from 39 MU Colerne, between October 1946 and January 1947 as follows:

AZ251 11.10.46; AZ361 28.10.46; AZ701 1.11.46; AZ815 1.11.46; AZ842 11.10.46; DK834 11.10.46; DK858 22.11.46; DK864 29.10.46; DK881 13.10.46; DK964 27.11.46; DL196 22.10.46; DL253 11.10.46; DL349 3.12.46; DL403 12.11.46; DL414 12.11.46; DL465 6.1.47; DL468 3.12.46; EM380 19.10.46; DL828 8.10.46; DL829 22.11.46; DL860 5.11.46; DL906 3.12.46; DL962 22.10.46; DL963 27.11.46; DL967 22.10.46; DL970 22.11.46; DM121 22.10.46; DM183 14.10.46; DM228 22.10.46; DM352 5.11.46.

However, none were refurbished for re-sale and on 3rd February 1947, Mr Hackett the Sales Manager, stated that he could not sell the Masters lying at Repair & Service and it was decided they should be reduced for spares. On 20th July 1947, I saw the airframes of most of them, less engines, lying on their bellies at Woodley. I also recall sitting in one of them and relieving it of its fire extinguisher button!

A large number of M.19 Master Mk.IIs were exported to foreign air forces during and after the war and for details of those supplied to the air forces of South Africa, Portugal, Egypt, Eire, Turkey and the USAAF in Great Britain (under reverse Lease-Lend), during and after the war, see Appendices No.16, 18, 19, 20, 21 and 22 respectively. The story of those supplied to France under the Hartemann Agreement of 1946 will appear in Volume 3.

The 41 Group Return for 14th March 1947 (N.A. Ref: AVIA 57/17) stated 'Aircraft held in 41 Group available for sale (not included in 6th sale) showed that 118 Masters were available, but noted in the Remarks was; 'Foreign requirements for about 200. A few for Austria if approved under Peace Treaty'. An official report detailing the supply of surplus RAF aircraft to foreign air forces after the war, implied that 28 Master Mk.IIs and 15 Magisters had been supplied to Austria. However, it subsequently transpired that; 'The Austrian requirement depends on the signing of a Peace Treaty and may never come about' (N.A. Ref: AIR 2/10.191). In the event, approval was not forthcoming and no Masters (or Magisters, as related in the Magister chapter) were supplied to Austria.

M.19 Master Mk.II civilian sales:

T8886, the mystery Miles 'Master II/IV', which had been retained by the firm for TIs during the war, was reported as having been seen at Woodley on 14.4.46 as T8886, but this is at variance with the fact that Hugh Kennedy flew it as a 'Master IV' with 'B' mark **U-0246** on an 'Instruction' flight, of 1hr 45min duration on 21.8.44, having been acquired by Miles Aircraft in 1944. Don Brown flew it as a Master Mk.II, U-0246 (with a 840 hp Bristol Mercury engine) on 13.9.44, with George Miles as passenger. Given the 'new' c/n 6434 during refurbishment by the Repair & Service Department between 29.1.46 and 5.46, it was apparently allotted 'B' mark **U5**, although there is no record of it having used this mark.

Regd **G-AHOB** (CofR 10224 later 2574) 13.5.46, as a Master Mk.II, to Miles Aircraft Ltd, Woodley and painted in the cream and red 'house colours' of Miles Aircraft Ltd, Hugh Kendall made its first recorded flight as G-AHOB on 20.8.46, with further flights on 21/22.8.46 and he made a return flight to Andover on 4.10.46. G-AHOB took part in the flypast of Miles aircraft during the last Miles 'At Home' day held at Woodley on Sunday 20.7.47, flown by S/L Samuel E Esler, who recorded it as a Master II. The last recorded flight of G-AHOB was made by Hugh Kendall on 13.8.47, a 20 min 'air-air photo and PE Test'. Photographs confirm that G-AHOB was a Master Mk.II, with a Bristol Mercury engine and the 'clipped' wings of modified and later production Masters. Re-regd to Western Manufacturing Estate Ltd, Woodley, following change of name on 15.11.48. Cld 28.3.49 & regd 11.5.49 to Francis Charles Bettison, c/o British Air Transport Ltd, Redhill (but remained at Woodley). Cld 16.5.49 & regd 15.6.49 to Robert Alan Short, Thornton Heath, Surrey (but still remained at Woodley). No CofA issued. Scrapped at Woodley in 1950 and regn cancelled 12.10.51 as 'Aircraft broken up'.

Above: Master Mk.II G-AHOB at Woodley.
[G.S. Collection]

Right: Master GT Mk.II EM300 seen on the Southern Aircraft (Gatwick) Ltd dump in 1946.
[A J J Collection. Note E J Riding by rudder]

Left: Master GT Mk.II EM323 at AST Hamble in 1948.
[J D R Rawlings]

Below: Master GT Mk.II DM442 seen on the Southern Aircraft (Gatwick) Ltd dump in 1946.
[E J Riding]

DL224 Sold to British Air Transport Ltd, Redhill, from 39 MU Colerne 4.12.46. Not registered. Scrapped at Redhill in 1948.

DM442 Sold to Southern Aircraft (Gatwick) Ltd 27.11.46. Regd **G-AIZN** (CofR 11107) 30.12.46 to Southern Aircraft (Gatwick) Ltd. Application for CofA made 2.1.47 but cld 9.7.47. Regn cld 23.11.48 as 'to be used as spares'. Engine and spares sold to Sweden for use in their M.25 Martinets in 1949.

EM300 Sold to Southern Aircraft (Gatwick) Ltd 4.12.46. Regd **G-AIZM** (CofR 11106) 30.12.46 to Southern Aircraft (Gatwick) Ltd. Application for CofA made 2.1.47 but cld 9.7.47. Regn cld 23.11.48 as 'to be used as spares'. Engine and spares sold to Sweden for use in their M.25 Martinets in 1949.

EM323 Sold to S T Glanfield, Finchley, N.12 16.12.46. The reason for purchasing this Master GT Mk.II is not known but Glanfield also later tried to buy EM353. EM323 later appeared outside the ground engineering school hangar of Air Service Training Ltd, Hamble, where it was seen by the author in 7.48. It was ultimately broken up and sold as scrap to R J Coley 23.2.49.

EM353 Intended for sale as scrap to S T Glanfield, 407 High Street, Finchley, N.12 14.3.47 but purchase cancelled.

EM374 Sold to British Air Transport Ltd, Redhill, as scrap, 13.1.47. Not registered. Scrapped at Redhill in 1948.

M.27 Master Mk.III civilian sales:

DL670 went to 59 OTU Crosby-on-Eden on 2.7.42 but was seen flying over North Lancashire on 2nd July 1942 with full camouflage and the civil registration G-AGEK, underlined with the compulsory red/white/blue stripes. Regd **G-AGEK** (CofR 9368) 3.7.42 to The Secretary of State for Air, London, WC2, with the 'Usual Station' being given as Crosby-on-Eden. The reason for this registration was that, and I quote from 'Landfall Ireland': *By 1942, therefore, three Hurricanes were in the hands of the Irish Air Corps, having been purchased, together with spares – the pair of Mk.IIs at a bargain price of £7,200. Despite these 'windfalls', supply problems came to such a pitch that by mid-year the Army General Staff decided to disband the air arm and redeploy its personnel in a purely ground role. All ranks had already had infantry training and, indeed, an Air Corps AA battery was already in being. The RAF was somewhat taken aback by this development. The existence of a friendly and 'flying' Air Corps was proving of* *great value in terms of the highly un-neutral services it was rendering. Further consultations took place and, as a result, an RAF instructor, F/L Donald West (a flying instructor from 59 OTU - PA), arrived at Baldonnel in July 1942 in a Miles Master Mk.III trainer to conduct a conversion course in preparation for the release of more Hurricanes. Perhaps he was selected because his mother was from County Louth where her own mother still resided. 'Don' West's aircraft was finished in British civilian markings with Irish colours added to its undersurfaces. In this unique livery, the aircraft went into service at Baldonnel.* Returned to the RAF at 20 MU Aston Down on 22nd December 1942, the Master was again seen flying over North Lancashire as G-AGEK on that day, probably while en route. Regn cld 1.12.46 by the Secretary of State following the post-war census (although it has been recorded as 'Permanently Withdrawn From Use' 4.4.43). It reverted to DL670 and was issued to 81 Group Communications Flight, Aston Down 22.1.43.

In 1942, the registration **G-AGEO** was reportedly reserved for a M.27 Master Mk.III, but no previous RAF serial was quoted. The reason for this registration, which is not recorded in C.A. Form 113, is not known.

An advertisement was placed in *The Aeroplane* for 10th January 1947 by D J Hayles of Portsmouth who was offering three Miles Masters for sale; 'In good flying condition' at £375 each. Their mark was not given and they were not registered. Their previous identities were not quoted and these have never been discovered. Mr Hayles also purchased a number of surplus DH Dominies. Why he acquired them in the first place is also not known.

Southern Aircraft (Gatwick) Ltd placed an advertisement in *The Aeroplane* for 7th February 1947: 'Two Miles Master IIs without CofA for £400 each' and later, in *The Light Plane* for July 1947: 'Miles Masters Mk.II Trainers, 2 seaters with dual and blind flying equipment. Without C of A.'. These were registered G-AIZM and G-AIZN. However, it is believed that by then, the ARB had decreed that Master aircraft would not be granted CofAs. This was apparently due to their service record, which had included a number of structural failures in their early service life. The engines and other parts from both aircraft were later sold in Sweden as spares for the Swedish Miles M.25 Martinets.

Today, however, just six Master Mk.II outer wings survive and included in these are two from the aircraft which were scrapped at Woodley in 1947; two from the other aircraft disposed of; one

---

SPECIFICATION AND PERFORMANCE DATA

Miles M.19 Master Mk.II

Engine:	prototype 825 hp Bristol Mercury VIII, production 870 hp Bristol Mercury XX or 30
Dimensions:	span 39ft 0in (later reduced to 35ft 9in); length 29ft 6in; height 9ft 3in; wing area 235 sq ft (later reduced); aspect ratio 6.5; wing section, root NACA 23024, tip NACA 23006
Weights:	empty 4,293lb; fuel (68 gal) 496lb; oil (7 gal) 63lb; pilot 200lb; useful load 521lb; max permitted AUW 5,573lb; wing loading 23.7lb/sq ft (later increased due to reduced span)
Performance:	max speed at sea-level 221 mph, at 6,000ft 242 mph; max design diving speed 330 mph; initial rate of climb 2,120 ft/min; service ceiling 25,100ft; absolute ceiling 26,000ft; time to 15,000ft 9.8 min, to 20,000ft 17.0 min; distance to unstick 645ft; distance to 50ft 1,155ft; stalling speed, flaps up 78 mph IAS, flaps down 63 mph IAS; landing run 1,110ft; landing run from 50ft 1,776ft; range at economical cruise 393 miles; duration at economical cruise 1.8 hr

Miles M.27 Master Mk.III

Engine:	825 hp Pratt & Whitney Wasp Junior R-1535-SB4-G
Dimensions:	span 39ft 0in (later reduced to 35ft 9in); length 30ft 2in; height 9ft 3in; wing area 235 sq ft (later reduced); aspect ratio 6.5; wing section, root NACA 23024, tip NACA 23006
Weights:	empty 4,217lb; fuel (68 gal) 496lb; oil (7 gal) 63lb; pilot 200lb; useful load 597lb; max permitted AUW 5,573lb; wing loading 23.7lb/sq ft (later increased due to reduced span)
Performance:	max speed at sea-level 210 mph, at 9,000ft 231 mph; max design diving speed 330 mph; initial rate of climb 1,480 ft/min; service ceiling 27,300ft; absolute ceiling 28,500ft; time to 15,000ft 10.4 min, to 20,000ft 16.0 min; distance to unstick 630ft; distance to 50ft 1,260ft; stalling speed, flaps up 78 mph IAS, flaps down 63 mph IAS; landing run 870ft

recovered from a location near Langley and one which was SOC in March 1946. These wings comprise AZ361 port; DK964 stbd; DL349 stbd; DL906 stbd; DM384 port; and DL??? port (plywood cut away). Two of these are presently on display in The Museum of Berkshire Aviation, Woodley, while the other four were later sold to the Kent Battle of Britain Museum at Hawkinge. The best two of these will be used in the construction of a replica Miles Master Mk.IA for their display of trainer aircraft to represent the aircraft in which many of the pilots who took part in the Battle of Britain were taught to fly.

For a summary of Miles M.19 Master Mk.II and Miles M.27 Master Mk.III aircraft built at all factories see Appendix 12.

For individual aircraft histories of M.19 Master Mk.II aircraft built at Woodley see Appendix 13.

For individual aircraft histories of M.19 Master Mk.II built at South Marston, Sheffield & Doncaster and M.27 Master Mk.III aircraft built at South Marston see Appendix 14.

The Miles 'Mercury Fighter' Project

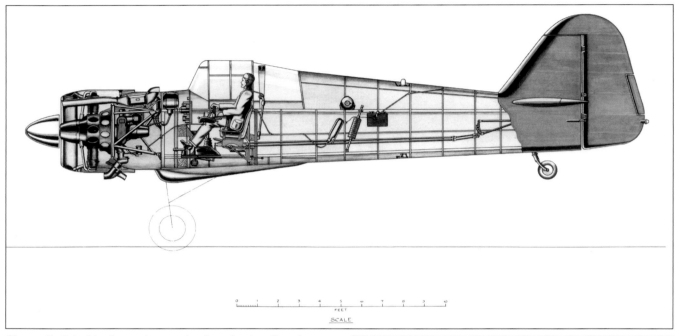

Above: Partial side-view cut-away drawing showing the six-gun 'Mercury Fighter'.

Recently discovered, but undated, Phillips & Powis photographs of a three-view drawing, are recorded as the Miles 'Mercury Fighter' in the negative index. The drawing depicts a single-seat, six gun, fighter version of the M.19 Master Mk.II trainer powered by a Bristol Mercury engine, probably the Mercury XX as fitted to the Master Mk.II, which could develop 870 bhp at 2,750 rpm.

The photographs, which were in numerical sequence, also depicted the Miles 'Peregrine Fighter', a similar, single-seat, six gun, fighter version of the Miles M.9C Master Mk.IA powered by a Rolls-Royce Peregrine I engine, and an artist's impression of this, dated November 1939, depicts the 'Miles Master Peregrine Six Gun Single Seater Fighter' in flight.

Below and right: Three-view drawing of the six-gun 'Mercury Fighter'.

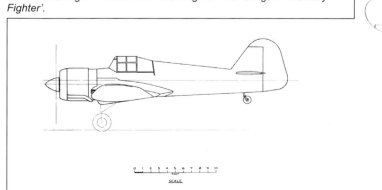

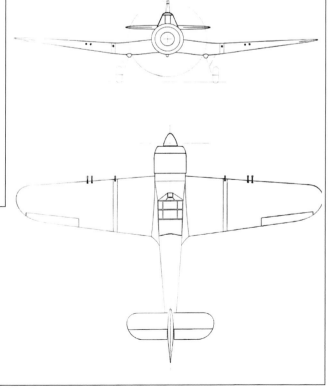

U9, the first prototype M.20/2.

Chapter 8
Miles M.20 Private Venture 'Munich' Fighter, M.20/2 PV Single-Seat Fighter to Spec. F.19/40, M.20/3 PV Fighter Bomber, M.20/4 PV Royal Navy Single-Seat Shipborne Fighter to Spec. N.1/41 and the M.20A Low Attack Fighter

In September 1938, at about the time of the Munich crisis, Miles decided that the RAF needed a fighter aircraft for defence, which would be cheap and easy to produce, to be of wooden construction, and to use the majority of Master metal components.

It was to have the gull wing of the M.9 Master, the radiator mounted under the centre section (interestingly, as the M.9 Kestrel still had the chin mounted radiator at the time), and it was to be powered by the new 880 hp Rolls-Royce Peregrine I engine driving a two-bladed airscrew. A 'top-secret mock-up' for the new design was built in the Experimental Department and this was shown by Miles and Bill Skinner to the Secretary of State for Air, Sir Kingsley Wood, on 27th January 1939.

It is not known if this mock-up, of what was known at the time as the 'Munich' Fighter, was allotted a c/n, although it was the practice in the factory at the time to allot c/n's to mock-ups. However, it was camouflaged and carried RAF roundels of the period. A photograph, probably taken in late 1938, shows it in the Experimental Department, mounted on a stand, but with no undercarriage visible (implying that it was retractable?) with the type number 'M20' painted in black aft of the red/white/blue/yellow fuselage roundel.

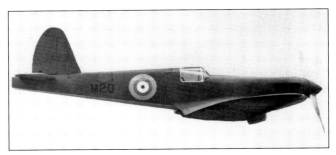

The 'Munich Fighter' mock-up, with type number 'M20' on the fuselage.
[Via Bert Clarke]

Undated Phillips & Powis photographs show side view drawings of a single-seat fighter type aircraft, obviously based on the M.9 Master/M.20 Fighter.

It is believed that the designation M.20/1 was retrospectively allocated to the 'Munich' Fighter in June 1940, when Miles decided to resurrect the original design idea, which ultimately became the M.20/2 and a paper on this subject, probably written by Miles, has survived to be reproduced here.

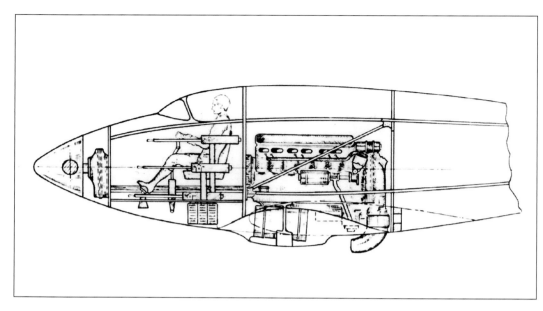

Left: M.20 Developments (Single Seater Fighter) October 1938. Note: engine mounted behind pilot and guns either side of the cockpit.

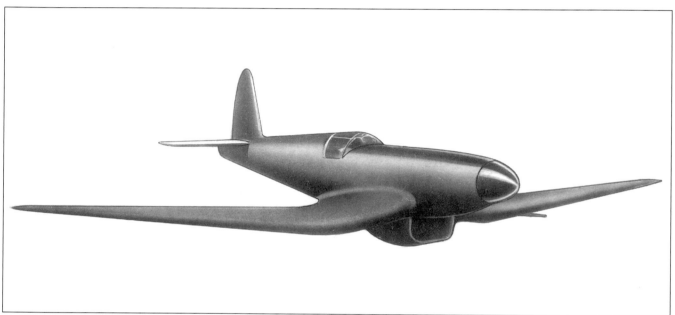

Above and below: Artist's impressions showing a fighter aircraft with apparently only one gun? Note Master type wing.

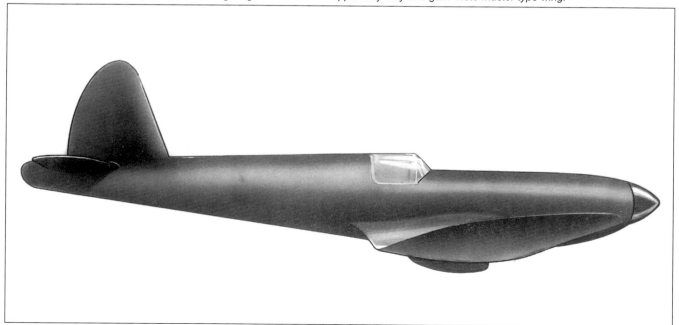

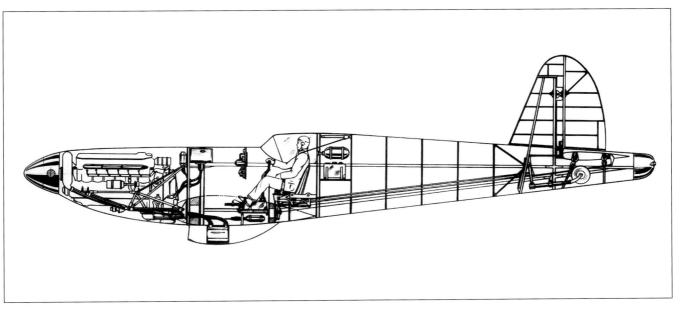

Cut-away drawing of an M.20 Development.

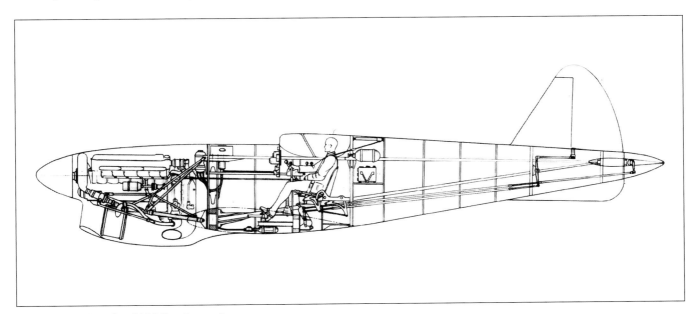

Cut-away drawing of an M.20 Development.

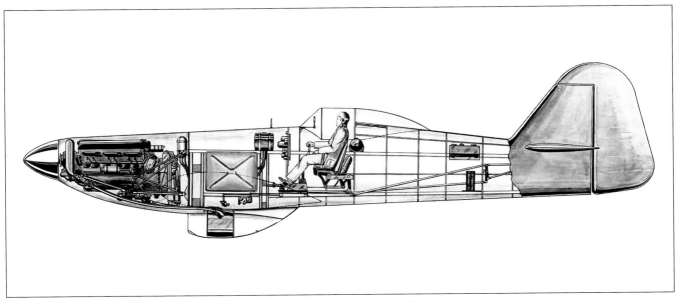

Cut-away drawing of an M.20 Development based on the M.9 Master but with a teardrop canopy.

Wooden Fighter

We have now put up a number of suggestions for a Wooden Fighter. Among these were:

1) A Conversion from the Existing Master.

2) The Munich Fighter which was to have had a performance in excess of the Spitfire, to have been of wooden construction and to have used the majority of the Master metal components.

3) A very high speed job with the Griffon engine to a special specification from Farren (possibly a 1,720 hp Rolls-Royce Griffon IIB - PA).

Of these I think the latter too advanced to be of practical use in view of the urgency today. Either of the others might still be of the greatest possible importance. I have had our existing Master conversion ideas re-examined from a practical point of view with the following results:

1) The wings can easily be fitted for 6 .303 Brownings. We are carrying out the necessary alterations on a pair of defective wings to demonstrate this.

2) Extra petrol tanks are being designed for the rear seat. These are standard tanks and only need mountings or connections. The duration will be increased as follows: (but no figures were given - PA).

3) The present aircraft carries 8 20 lb. bombs for instructional purposes. We are investigating the possibility of carrying a 250 lb. bomb with some form of mounting which can be jettisoned with the bomb; thus leaving the aircraft free from extra drag for the return journey without the necessity for internal stowage.

Another significant paper, again almost certainly written by Miles in 1940, is reproduced in full below:

Notes on the Design and Manufacture of Single Seat Fighter

These notes are based on the assumption that for the purposes of this war all control, except safety and performance should be sacrificed to the necessity of producing Single-Seater Fighters in very large quantities within a minimum period of time, say, one to two years from today. The use of the word 'sacrifice' does not mean that the manufacture shall be effected in a haphazard manner but I believe a very large proportion of the requirements which have been brought into force during the last few years could be jettisoned giving nothing but good results. If the influence on production by this minute control were measured I believe it accounts for an enormous number of man hours used in the production of the machine and these man hours are used particularly in respect of a number of non-essential requirements.

If these requirements were waived I estimate that the man hours as a whole could be cut down to about half of the present standard for metal aircraft and that the remaining one half could be made up of the skilled and unskilled labour of the type that is still available today in very large quantities, but cannot, because of the restrictions, be employed to the best advantage. Naturally a waiving of the restrictions could be effected through a mutual discussion with the authorities concerned, provided they appreciate the objects set out above.

These are the lines on which I would build a single-seater defence fighter realising that the paramount condition was quantity production in the shortest possible time. The aircraft performance and purpose would have to be approved and that standard would have to be set and attained.

The fighter would be of wooden construction, similar in all respects to the Miles Master. The experience gained with the Master has given us sufficient knowledge to be able to forecast performance and ability of the proposed fighter. All controls should be castings or press work thereby eliminating fitting work as far as possible.

The absolute minimum of equipment demanded by the fighting forces to be fitted to the machine and the requirements of the Ministry waived in regard to all fittings not so required or deemed absolutely essential. Internal treatment should be reduced to a minimum and proof can be given that today certain of the internal treatments cannot have the effect required from them and are therefore redundant. Strength requirements to be far more rational than as at present.

The design of the aircraft should not be controlled by the detachability of units. For example, the wings should be built in one piece thereby enabling the designer to give far better strength figures than is possible with removable wings. Ease of assembly should be left to the designer which would in itself give him the opportunity of creating the best machine without having to obey arbitrary rules which should be flexible. I suggest that interchangeability should be limited to the main covered components and the recent rule that all parts and spares lists must be checked by approved interchangeability gauges is another major reason for holding up design and production in the early stages.

Where inspection causes delay in production then the inspection department should be forced to increase its pace bearing in mind that the main object of inspection is safety in flight. This would probably mean that AID Inspectors would have to be available twenty-four hours a day. Where a regulation has been issued, the resident AID personnel should be given power to allow a commonsense discussion and where no agreement can be arrived at appeal should be allowed to the AID itself, but if no decision is given within 12 hours the designer should be entitled to make his own decision unless the refusal by the AID is on the grounds of absolute safety.

It is well known that in 99 cases out of a 100 the daily decisions required covering the methods of manufacture and detail design to improve production methods rest in the hands of the designer or manufacturer, but at present while the matter has to be submitted to the Air Ministry for a decision production is held up pending their reply. In the past this has, on numerous occasions, stretched into months rather than minutes and it is felt that where this delay is greater than is reasonable the designer, on whom after all lies the responsibility for the success or failure of the aircraft, shall be given the power to make a decision. These criticisms and suggestions are made by virtue of our experience with the design and manufacture of the Master aircraft.

The main reasons for putting forward this argument are:-

1) That the Company is in very close touch with the RAF and would not in any way sacrifice the possible life of anyone for the sake of cheapness in construction or any other reason.

2) Where the good name of the firm is at stake it should be obvious that every possible effort will be made to produce a satisfactory and reliable aircraft.

Miles M.20/2 Private Venture Single-Seat Fighter to Spec. F.19/40

In June 1940, at about the onset of what we now know as the Battle of Britain, Miles resurrected the idea of a utility fighter aircraft for the medium and high altitude, day and night roles and commenced construction of a private venture prototype. This was to be made of wood and powered by a Rolls-Royce Merlin XX, twelve-cylinder, liquid-cooled engine fitted with a two-speed, single-stage supercharger, driving a three-blade, constant-speed Rotol airscrew. The new fighter was given the designation M.20/2.

Miles then approached the dynamic Minister of Aircraft Production, Lord Beaverbrook and showed him his proposals. Beaverbrook realised that if the Supermarine or Hawker works got bombed, then there would be a real need for the Miles fighter. Jeremy Miles recalls that Beaverbrook was apparently quite impressed with the idea and told Miles that if he could build it in three months, he would pay for it, but if he couldn't, then Miles would have to pay for it! By then, construction of the prototype was under way and work proceeded at such a pace that the M.20/2 fighter was in fact designed, built and flown in the remarkably short space of just nine weeks and two days from its inception.

Walter Capley, designer of the Miles M.18, and second only to Miles in dynamic drive, was placed in charge of the new design and also oversaw its construction. The men building it 'worked until they dropped' and also 'slept on the job' in bunks, which they erected in the Experimental Department, into which they fell when could no longer stay awake!

Penny Jefferson, daughter of the late Eric Sibbick, recently sent Jean Fostekew of The Museum of Berkshire Aviation, Woodley, a copy of a hand-written document she had recently found while sorting through her father's papers. This document, of which she had been unaware but which could possibly have been part of a longer account of his memoirs (the rest of this document, which is equally absorbing, is reproduced in the chapter on Reading), gave

details of his time with Phillips & Powis/Miles Aircraft at Woodley and it is of more than sufficient interest to reproduce the section on his work on the M.20 here:

The M.20 was conceived in May 1940, a time of cloudless skies over Reading, with infinitely murky horizons across the seas in Europe. The supreme efforts of the Battle of Britain still lay in the future; however, things were hotting up for the Spitfire and Hurricane squadrons of the Royal Air Force, and meanwhile the opportunity to assist the late F G Miles in the design of an inexpensive, quick-to-build fighter of wooden construction came my way, as a contemporary to those illustrious aircraft.

My background, apart from an engineering apprenticeship, had included recent experience of stressed skin plywood and spruce structures for flying boats, in the comfortable yachting atmosphere at Cowes, Isle of Wight, but the coming of the war meant that my skills had to be put to a different use.

F G Miles expected the prototype to be flying in three months and, strangely enough, the target was accepted without demur - it was

The first prototype M.20/2 under construction in about August 1940. Note the unique 'teardrop' canopy under protective covering.

The wing under construction clearly showing the position of the gun bay for the four .303 Browning machine guns.

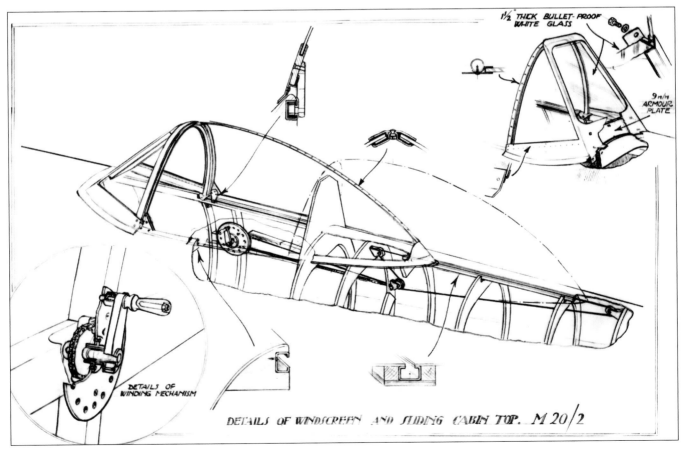

DETAILS OF WINDING MECHANISM

1½ THICK BULLET-PROOF WHITE GLASS

9 m/m ARMOUR PLATE

DETAILS OF WINDSCREEN AND SLIDING CABIN TOP. M 20/2

Details of windscreen and sliding canopy.

The completed M.20/2 showing its clean lines, ready for flight.

up to us to demonstrate the possibility! I well remember Miles' introductory discourse, which concluded that the words "If we win you can have everything, but if we lose, you get nothing". He was a superb speaker and equal to any occasion. I later learned that Miles had a wager with Lord Beaverbrook (newly appointed Minister of Aircraft Production) who considered such a program quite incredible.

Details of this aeroplane are given in Don Brown's book 'Miles Aircraft since 1925'. Don's boundless enthusiasm was always a great tonic in every situation.

I slogged out the fuselage frame drawings, directly on to plywood, with an allowance for the spruce 'capping' and laboured to sixteen hours each day on the monocoque structure of the Miles M.20. The nine-man team, led by Toby Heal, concentrating every waking hour for seven days each week, achieved the target with three weeks to spare! We borrowed a Bristol Beaufighter power-egg and compromised performance with fixed gear - tail dragger, of course - but nevertheless met the Air Publication 970 requirements of the day, without our eight-gun (Brownings) wooden weapon.

Flt Lt Tommy Rose, our Chief Test Pilot (and subsequent C-in-C Home Guard) taxied the M.20 from the experimental hangar across to the runway only to discover a severe oscillation in the rubber disc shock absorbers on the main gear, but, undaunted, the bird bounced off. Following a spectacular flight, the landing was 'very tricky' to say the least. Twenty-four hours later a pair of very effective dashpots, made by the nightshift workers of Sir George Godfrey's, cured the oscillation.

Flight trials progressed successfully and substantiated the fulfilment of all our design hopes, except in the reluctance of the aircraft to recover from a spin, in the hands of test pilot Hugh Kennedy, who came near to baling out. It fell to my lot to engineer a special six-inch extension to the fuselage, by which means the tailplane was moved aft, to cure the problem (another overtime drawing commitment, of course!). Later the Miles M.20, with its all-round view bubble canopy, was demonstrated at Northolt aerodrome in company with a typical Hurricane and Spitfire, in the presence of the most illustrious Brass Hats, including Sir Winston Churchill.

To the great disappointment of our design and experiment team the M.20 did not reach the production line. This I can only attribute to politics and official strategy. We subsequently developed a wooden

wing which was satisfactorily tested with four Hispano cannons at RAE Farnborough.

At its best, the M.20 established a worthy insurance policy, if only twelve months late in commitment. Further, as a backs-to-the-wall effort it was a truly fantastic achievement. I was left with a lifelong appreciation of the value of timber, properly used, for light aircraft structures.

With the M.20/2 almost ready for flight, the Air Ministry issued Spec F.19/40, dated 29th August 1940, to Phillips & Powis Aircraft Ltd, on 9th September 1940, to cover the construction of one prototype Single-Seat Fighter aircraft, which was built under Contract No. B.140247/40. This was based on the M.20 'Munich' Fighter and, with a view to ease of manufacture and time saving, Miles utilised as many standard Master components as possible, although he opted for a thick section, straight dihedral wing, both to simplify construction and to accommodate eight or twelve .303 Browning machine guns, with 5,000 rounds of ammunition.

The prototype fighter, fitted with eight .303 Browning machine-guns, was first flown, with 'B' mark **U9**, by Tommy Rose on 15th September 1940 (not the 14th September 1940 as stated in many reference works). Although it was confirmed that Tommy Rose's log-books were lost during the course of several of his moves, it has still been possible to confirm the date of the first flight of the M.20/2 from the log books of Hugh Kennedy, the firm's assistant test pilot. Hugh Kenney flew the Master Mk.II, N7447, on 15th September 1940, noting in his log-book: 'Guarding M.20 on its 1st flight'. Hugh Kennedy then flew the M.20 as follows: 'Handling trials' 21.9.40 and 23.9.40; 'Handling', and two 'Test Flights - ADM 293' 1.10.40.

Ken Waller, who had joined Phillips & Powis as a test pilot on 11th January 1940, made his first flight in the M.20/2, by then with serial **AX834**, on a 'Handling' flight, on 2nd October 1940. Hugh Kennedy also made further flights, without recording any marks, as follows: 'Handling Trials 9.10.40; 'Climb and Level' 10.10.40. However, on 27.10.40 Hugh noted M.20/2 AX834 against two 'Handling Trials' 27.10.40; 'Rated Altitude Test' 28.10.40; 'PE Measurements' and 'Diving and Rated Altitude Test' flights 29.10.40; 'Rated Altitude Test' 1.11.40; 'Aerobatics', 'Rated Altitude' and 'Climb' flights 5.11.40; 'Stalling Tests' 8.11.40; 'Climb' 17.10.40; 'Demonstration Flight' 24.12.40; 'Demonstration' 29.12.40.

On 1st January 1941, Phillips & Powis Aircraft Ltd produced the second issue of a booklet on the Miles Single Engined Fighter Aircraft - M.20/2 to Air Ministry Specification F.19/40.

BRIEF SPECIFICATION

PURPOSE

To produce a wooden aeroplane built with the minimum of light alloys and with more range and ammunition than existing types. It is essentially of simple construction - to be built in great quantities by available resources of semi-skilled labour and simple plant. In the first instance no elaborate hydraulic systems, retractable chassis, wing joints or other unnecessary complications are used. Now that the first aircraft has completed its first flight trials to our complete satisfaction, aerodynamic refinements including partial and full retraction of the chassis are being considered. Meant for war, all equipment necessary for fighting is fitted. A bomb load of 500 lb and long range tanks may be carried under the wings.

Production could be achieved on a scale hitherto unthought of, provided that the same spirit and conditions governing construction existed as during the design and building of the prototype, which took just over nine weeks. Its performance lacks nothing when compared with the most successful present day fighters in the world. With the one piece wing and simple design of the fuselage, empennage, etc, airframe production could easily be doubled and costs halved against existing forms of metal construction. If maximum production is required Canada provided the solution. Whilst first production requirements could be met in England, the work of organising output abroad could be going forward at the same time.

With energy and drive maximum production would be possible in less than 12 months as the materials, machinery and labour we require are there on the spot. In this country for every three tons of spruce shipped from overseas, we can only use one ton in aircraft construction. Moreover the aircraft is capable of being flown to England direct over the North Atlantic. Additional external tanks would be fitted for this purpose, which would give the aircraft duration of nearly nine hours. The weight in this condition, less fighting equipment which could be fitted in this country, would be 9,550 lb, wing loading 39 lb/sq ft, and power loading of 7.35 lb/hp for take-off. It must be agreed that these are very reasonable figures for such a condition of flight.

OUTSTANDING FEATURES

Throughout the basic design simplicity in all things has been aimed at. In addition to the deletion of hydraulic system, retractable chassis and wing joints, the following features have been incorporated:

STANDARD PARTS

These are used wherever possible, and include Miles Master control box and flying controls, Hurricane gun mounting fittings, standard Beaufighter engine installation complete with slightly modified cowling. Jigs and tools are therefore in existence for many components.

PILOT'S VIEW

Opinion has already been given by experienced Pilots that the view both forward and aft from the pilot's seat is far better than any present day single engined fighter. The cabin top may be opened to any position and can be jettisoned in the air.

PROTECTION

Protection is provided for the pilot by a sloping bullet-proof wind-screen and armour plating behind the seat which also protects the oil tank.

FUEL SYSTEM

Normally no fuel whatever is carried in the fuselage thus reducing the chance of injury to the pilot in case of fire and avoiding risk from fumes. The additional importance of these factors cannot be too highly stressed. The tanks are provided with electrically-driven immersed type fuel pumps, which deliver the fuel under pressure to the engine pump, thus preventing the fuel boiling at altitude in summer conditions. All tanks permanently fitted are rendered leak-proof against gun fire. When long range tanks are fitted fuel is carried under the fuselage in jettisonable tanks.

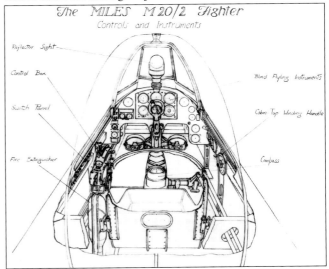

Sketch showing 'Controls and Instruments'.

The M.20/2 in camouflage with serial AX834.

OVERLOAD CONDITION

The design allows for the fitment of additional external fuel tanks and bombs. It is proposed to fit 100 or more extra gallons externally, together with 500 lb bomb load. The all-up weight would be 9,470 lb, giving a wing loading of 39.0 lb/sq ft and power loading of 7.3 lb/hp for take-off. The external tank may be jettisoned after reaching the objective, leaving the aircraft equipped purely as a fighter, with a cruising range of nearly 3½ hours.

AERODYNAMICS

We realised that in attempting to get an equivalent performance to current fighter aircraft with the handicap of a fixed undercarriage and the thicker wings necessitated by wooden construction, we had a difficult problem. This was overcome by cutting down the surface drag, leakage drag and interference drag to a minimum. The first condition is aided by the fact that the thick ply skin made an excellent surface which combined with a suitable paint finish, can hardly be bettered by any other form of construction. Leakage drag is always important. We have taken especial care that where any door or opening is required a form of fastening is provided which will enable a flush and air-tight fit to be obtained. Care has also been taken to see that this surface is sufficiently stiff not to deform under the high loads imposed in flight.

At 33 lb/sq ft the loads on the top surface of the wing under conditions of accelerated flight are very considerable, and the gun doors, which in themselves, form a large proportion of the total area of the wing, have had to be very carefully designed in order to attain the above conditions. The method of fastening which we have used is of our own design and we believe it to be an improvement on all previous methods. (The door is described in detail elsewhere). The wing section related to the angle of incidence throughout the span was chosen to give the best possible stalling characteristics. The very satisfactory results obtained in the flight trials to date have proved how correct our assumptions were.

GUN DOORS

Up to the present day gun doors in the top surface of a wing have been dependent on a large number of fasteners of the Dzus or Fairey Reed type. The Martin-Baker door is considerably improved by having only one control operating a series of bolts instead of a number of separate fasteners. This saves much time in servicing. We have considered it necessary to replace as much of the strength and stiffness lost by the cut-away skin as possible and to eliminate air leakage and excrescences which would otherwise cause considerable drag. The resulting door fulfils these conditions admirably, at the same time it gives rapid access to the whole of the gun installation including the ammunition boxes and feed necks. There are only three fixing screws per door and these are rapidly operated by a brace. The new design features include:-

1. Shear strength across the door panels is maintained by a series of dowels picking up the main structure.

2. The catches themselves are separate from the dowels and are positive. The load is transferred from the operating screws, through a torque tube, to a series of levers which engage beneath fastenings attached to the main structure.

The door is double skinned and hinges along the front edge. The operating screws act as jacks and through the medium of the series of levers they bed the door down tightly on to the sealing medium, thus ensuring the necessary air-tightness. When fastened, the door is capable of taking a lift load of 350 lb/sq ft and is completely flush with the wing surface.

GUN INSTALLATION

The four Browning guns with ammunition boxes in each wing are all conveniently grouped under the hinged door. The guns are all mounted on a single tubular chassis, which may be hinged upward to permit the gun barrels to be withdrawn without disturbing the guns on the mountings. Martin-Baker type quick release blast tubes

Photograph showing the hinged gun door in the open position.

are fitted. All these features we claim make the whole installation as accessible as any yet designed for rapid servicing.

Heating is provided from the radiator. A double duct is positioned at the back of the radiator near the inlet connection, and pipes are led on either side inside the leading edge of the wing to the gun bay. The hot air then passes through holes in the front spar, through the gun bay, and is forced to exhaust through a hole in the rear spar, due to the slight depression in the region of the aileron. It has, therefore, been possible, with the type of gun door used and previously described, to seal the gun bay from the rest of the wing, thus ensuring maximum efficiency for the gun heating arrangements.

UNDERCARRIAGE AND TAIL WHEEL

In making the difficult decision to use in the first instance a fixed type chassis, we were influenced by the urgent need for cutting down specialised work involving time, materials, and man power. This consideration has governed the complete design from start to

Close-up of the undercarriage with the front fairing removed showing the shock absorber unit.

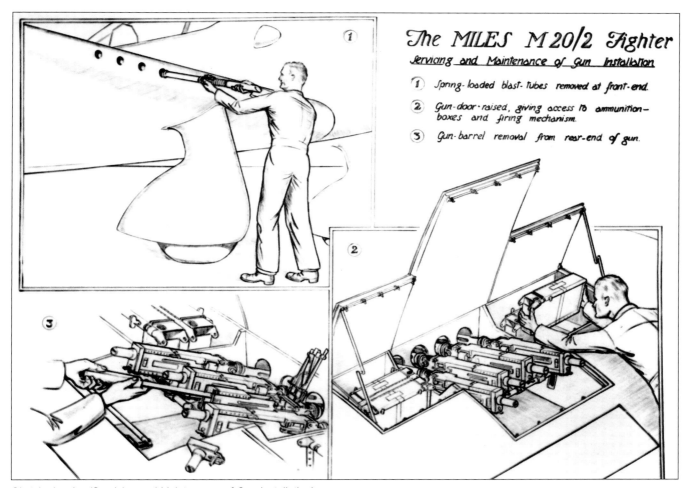

The MILES M20/2 Fighter
Servicing and Maintenance of Gun Installation

① Spring-loaded blast-tubes removed at front-end.

② Gun-door raised, giving access to ammunition-boxes and firing mechanism.

③ Gun-barrel removal from rear-end of gun.

Sketch showing 'Servicing and Maintenance of Gun Installation'.

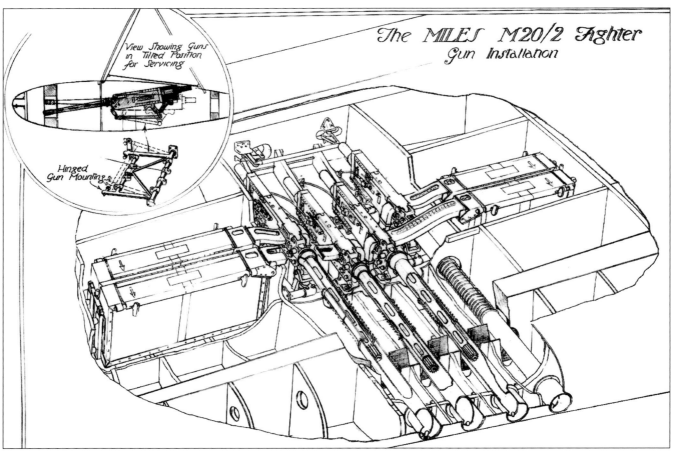

The MILES M20/2 Fighter
Gun Installation

View Showing Guns in Tilted Position for Servicing

Hinged Gun Mounting

Drawing showing the gun installation.

finish and in this particular instance permitted the deletion of all hydraulic circuits. Because of this and our desire to ensure production supplies, it was decided to place an order on Messrs Dowty Equipment Ltd for suitable chassis shock absorbing units, and at the same time to develop a chassis geometry which permitted efficient fairing and ease of maintenance. This was fitted to the aircraft for first trials and from our experiments to date we have confidence that this unit will give complete satisfaction in service.

This form of shock absorbing will eliminate the bulk of labour, material costs and complications of the more normal oleo-pneumatic types and conserve stocks of light alloy. It is the opinion of experts that this type of chassis can be produced and serviced better than any other form because of its simple construction and suspension. The shock absorber unit is completely accessible by removing the top fairing, which is secured by two captive bolts only. As mentioned previously, we have already developed a scheme for partial retraction of the tyre into the fairing to reduce drag. The possibility of complete retraction is now being investigated.

The tail wheel design is the same in principle as the main chassis, that is, lever suspension with "Dowty" shock absorbing unit in tension. The tail wheel is mounted in a streamline light alloy casting which is hinged on a bracket attached to the main strut. The shock absorbing mechanism is housed inside this strut and the complete assembly is free for complete rotation in large diameter brass bearings in the fuselage. The self-centring mechanism picks up two spigots in the top of the main strut and takes the form of a variable friction damper. The friction and a small righting moment are increased by loading up a spring as the wheel is moved away from the normal trailing position. The complete unit can be removed from the aircraft in a few minutes by unscrewing the large brass nut which forms the bottom bearing. Pressure check and inflation of the shock absorber are obtained through an aperture in the bracket at the bottom of the strut without removing the unit from the fuselage.

GLUEING

Past experience gained from a long series of wooden aircraft has led us to divide the use of glue into four categories. For these we make different assumptions as to the strength developed by the glued joint. For instance, where design or manufacturing considerations lead to any possibility that the full strength of the glue will not be fully developed, we assume in one category that the shear strength of the joint will only be one quarter of the figure we should expect to get on the actual test of a good glued joint. Thus a large safety factor is available to cover the risk of bad glueing and to allow for handling loads or adverse maintenance conditions.

SUMMARY

The following is a brief summary of the equipment which is fitted as on the standard fighter:-

8 Browning guns with 5,000 rounds of ammunition, and camera.

Recognition pistol and cartridge stowage.

One parachute flare and night flying equipment.

24-volt electrical system.

Graviner Fire extinguisher system (flame, crash and pilot operated).

Oxygen.

Wireless TR9D and R3003 with provision for TR1133A and contactor.

De-icing equipment for airscrew and windscreen.

Accommodation is also provided for blind approach transmitter R.1124A and receiver R.1125A.

The brakes, flaps and guns are all operated pneumatically and a compressor is fitted to the engine.

In the event, the M.20/2 turned out to be faster than the Hurricane, and only slightly slower than the Spitfire. The elimination of the retractable undercarriage also freed enough space in the wing for the installation of twelve .303 inch Browning machine guns, as compared with eight on the Hurricane and Spitfire. The M.20/2 could carry more fuel than existing fighters, which meant that it could remain in combat much longer without having to return to base to refuel and re-arm.

The M.20/2 was also fitted with a 'teardrop' hood over the cockpit, a most advanced innovation for the time, which gave the pilot a far better field of view than that possessed by any contemporary fighter. Although this was probably the first time that this type of canopy had been used on a fighter aircraft and other manufacturers of fighter aircraft must have seen the advantages of this, for some strange reason it was not adopted until much later in the war.

Michael S Wooding recently recalled: *Among many aircraft I worked on was the M.20, we were all proud to have worked on this aircraft. Built at record speed, working two shifts in the drawing office round the clock, five weeks elapsed from start of design work to completion of construction. A single engine, single seat 12 gun fighter, constructed of wood with as many standard parts as possible, it had a Rolls-Royce Merlin engine, and a performance superior to that of the Hurricane. The Germans had broken through at Sedan, and were speeding towards the French Channel Ports, it was thought that these rapidly constructed aircraft could help to plug the gap caused by our losses of Hurricanes and Spitfires.*

Almost no drawings of the prototype were produced, and I remember that two of us did the wing spar section calculations in the office, and then set out the spars on the wood in pencil in the workshops. From the lines we drew the woodworkers shaped the spars. In fact the Battle of Britain had been won by the time the aircraft had been tested, and so the project was stopped.

It is interesting to speculate that, if almost no drawings of the prototype were produced, just how many drawings for the earlier 'Munich' Fighter project (if any?) were made?

The M.20/2 AX834 was given the RAF Experimental Aeroplane No.118 for identification purposes and was recorded as being at Farnborough in early 1941 and flight tests continued into 1941, with Hugh Kennedy carrying out 'Spinning Trials' on 1.1.41. Although he made no comment in his log book, it was probably on this flight that he encountered the problem in recovering from a spin. This was found to have been caused by the tailplane blanketing the rudder, the cure for which simply entailed moving the tailplane further aft and squaring off the end of the fuselage in the side view. This was followed by 'Take-off Trials' 3.1.41; 'Diving Trials' 13.1.41 and 'Climb and Level' 5.2.41.

However, regarding the earlier spinning problem, Don Brown recalled: *On one of Hugh's early flights in the M.20 he had climbed the M.20/2 to a height of 25,000ft and then started a spin. After a few turns he initiated the standard recovery action but, to his dismay, nothing happened. He tried all the usual alternative recovery combinations of stick and rudder, both with and without the application of power, but still the aircraft continued to spin. As a last resort he used the tail parachute, which had been fitted for such an eventuality, but even this failed to stop the spin. Having tried all possible control movements normally calculated to stop a spin but still with no result, he then jettisoned the tail parachute and went through all the control movements once more but again with no effect. By this time he was down to 7,000ft and he felt that the time had come to abandon the aircraft. He released his harness, slid back the canopy, released the controls and was just about to bale out when the aircraft suddenly stopped spinning. Hugh refastened his harness and landed without further ado.*

On 6.2.41, Hugh carried out a 'Climb to Level and added the note in his log book (Fighter crashed)'.

With regard to the last entry, the official report read: *On 6th February 1941, Mr H Kennedy (Test Pilot) Phillips & Powis, Woodley, had completed a Climbing trial but whilst landing on the snow covered grass at Woodley, the wheels locked when the brakes were applied, the aircraft slid and crashed through a boundary fence and nosed over into a flooded gravel pit.* Unbeknown to Hugh, the wheel brakes had frozen in the 'free' position, probably as a result of the pneumatic brake system also having frozen during the long flight at altitude so, when he applied them after landing nothing happened. Hugh said later that he was *'unable to bring the aircraft to a halt within the confines of the aerodrome'*. The pit was in the south-west corner of the aerodrome and Hugh recalled later: *I was put unceremoniously into the gravel pit by the M.20!* The gravel pit was subsequently filled in to provide a much needed extension to the airfield!

The fuselage of AX834 survived on the dump at Woodley until at least 27th March 1948, with the serial erased on the starboard side but still visible on the port side.

The M.20/2 after Hugh Kennedy was "put unceremoniously into the gravel pit" by it and the aircraft was written off!

PERFORMANCE AND ENGINE PARTICULARS

Performance (estimated) – With Rolls Royce Merlin XX.

All-up weight:	7,865 lb.
Maximum speed at 21,000 ft:	350 mph.
Maximum speed at sea level:	282 mph.
Stalling speed:	79 mph.
Initial rate of climb:	3,000 ft/min.
Absolute ceiling:	35,0000 ft.

Performance of Rolls-Royce Merlin XX.

Maximum Power for take-off:	1,300 BHP.
International rating:	1,255 BHP at 10,000 ft in M.S. gear.
	1,190 BHP at 18,500 ft in F.S. gear.
Maximum power rating:	1,270 BHP at 12.250 ft in M.S. gear.
	1,185 BHP at 21,000 ft in F.S. gear.
Maximum cruising conditions:	1,120 BHP at 10,000 ft in M.S. gear
	1,045 BHP at 17,250 ft in F.S. gear.
Maximum economical cruising conditions:	1,000 BHP at 10,750 ft in M.S. gear.
	950 BHP at 17,800 ft in F.S. gear.

Normal fuel load carried is sufficient for two hours duration at economical cruising plus ¼-hour at full throttle at ground level, and at operational height.

POSSIBLE ALTERNATIVE LOADINGS

		All-up Weight
CASE I	Eight Gun Fighter to AM Spec. F.19/40.	7,865 lb. (33.4)
CASE II*	Four Gun with Two Cannon (800 rounds per gun, 180 rounds per cannon)	8,240 lb. (35.0)
CASE III*	Eight Gun Catapult Launching/Deck Landing.	7,985 lb. (34.0)
CASE IV*	Fighter/Bomber with 500 lb bomb load.	8,415 lb. (34.6)
CASE V*	Long Range Fighter (5 hrs economical cruising)	8,900 lb. (36.6)
CASE VI*	Long Range Fighter/Bomber (Cases IV & V)	9,470 lb. (39.0)
CASE VII	Long Range Ferrying (less fighting equipment)	9,550 lb. (39.3)

*Indicates that equipment not mentioned is similar to that carried in Case I to A.M. Spec. F.19/40, unless stated otherwise. Figures quoted in brackets are the maximum wing loading per square foot.

CASE III.   The following are the main differences from F.19/40:-
  (a)   Protection for pilot against fire from ahead only.
  (b)   Back type seat dinghy fitted.
  (c)   Provision for fitting Merlin XXX engine.
  (d)   Landing lamps and flare deleted.

LEADING DIMENSIONS

Span:	34 ft 7 ins	Gross Wing Area Minimum:	235 sq ft
Length:	30 ft 9 ins	Gross Wing Area Maximum:	243 sq ft
Height:	13 ft	Aspect Ratio:	5.1
Track:	12 ft	Root Chord:	100 ins
Airscrew Diameter:	11 ft 3 ins	Thickness Chord Ratio at root:	21 per cent
Normal Wing Loading:	33.4 lb/sq ft	Thickness Chord Ratio at tip	10 per cent
Power Loading:	6.0 lb/hp max	Dihedral:	3° 10 mins

John Webb, founder of The Reading Sky Observer's Club at Woodley, later gave the fuselage to an ATC Squadron at Brentford, Middlesex but in order to get it through the door of their premises, he and an ATC instructor (who told me the story recently but who wishes to remain anonymous as it is now something of which he is not too proud, being in later life deeply involved in the conservation of vintage aircraft!) had to saw it in half in the vertical plane! What happened to it after this episode however, is not known.

An additional wing was also built to take four cannon but it is believed that this was not fitted to either the M.20/2 or the later M.20/4.

M.20/3 Private Venture Fighter/Bomber

In late 1940 Miles submitted his proposals for a fighter/bomber version development of the M.20/2 to the MAP. This was designed to carry either two 50 gallon drop tanks or 500lb of bombs under the wings, in addition to the normal armament of eight machine guns. Nothing further is known of this variant and Don Brown made no mention of it in his writings.

M.20/4 Private Venture Royal Navy Single-Seat Shipborne Fighter to Spec. N.1/41

On 26th May 1940, the First Sea Lord (Alexander) sent a message to Lord Beaverbrook, the new Minister of Aircraft Production, it read:

I would like to have a word with you in the near future about production of Fleet Air Arm aircraft generally, but wish to bring to your notice the question of the Fulmar. It is already six months late and at the moment the Navy has no eight gun fighter in service. The most modern type is the Skua and this has poor performance (in fact a top speed of only 225 mph). I appreciate the urgent need for RAF fighters but learn, however, that FAA aircraft do not appear at all in the priority list sent out to the industry.

Beaverbrook eventually replied to Alexander's letter and from his reply it could be seen that he had other and more pressing things on his mind: *Give me six months and on 1st July ask what you like of me.* But Alexander was not to be put off and he told Beaverbrook: *After the raid on Scapa Flow on 16th March* (1940) *I need the Spitfire and recommend trials of it so as to replace the Skua. Although the Hurricane is 10 mph faster than the Ju 88 at 16,000ft, it is barely fast enough.*

The other pressing need was for a fighter aircraft of good performance and one which was cheap and expendable which could be catapulted from a ship and defend our convoys from attack from marauding Fw.200 Condors in the Atlantic. So, a development of the Miles M.20 was proposed to meet this naval requirement. It had a good performance and was also relatively cheap to produce, but it was stated that: *No production order would be placed until it was known that aircraft could be catapulted from light naval-type catapults and until the unsatisfactory spinning characteristics of the M.20 had been eliminated.*

The fact that the M.20's spinning problem had apparently not been remedied at this time helps to date this correspondence to about late September 1940. The Fleet Air Arm was in crisis but what it needed desperately was fighters, not advice. Beaverbrook attempted to help by writing again to the First Sea Lord. This letter was not dated but as it now claimed that the order for twelve Miles M.20s had apparently been placed, it must have been written after the spinning problem had been remedied, i.e. in early October 1940:

Thank you for your letter. It appears at first sight that the Miles M.20 fighter will be eminently suitable for catapulting from ships for convoy defence and we have already placed an order for twelve (no confirmation of this order can be found and there is no record

of serial numbers being allotted - PA). *Regarding the Mosquito, Sinclair (Secretary of State for Air) thought it would not be suitable as a carrier fighter. A number of M.20s will be lost at sea and it might, therefore, be desirable to use an engine less in demand than the Merlin XX.*

As the losses from this type of operation would inevitably have been high, it was thought that by fitting small wheels projecting below the fuselage instead of fitting a normal undercarriage, this would have also made for safer ditching and should the aircraft ever be required to land on a normal aerodrome, then nothing worse than a broken propeller and a shock-loaded engine should have ensued.

The M.20/4 to Spec. N.1/41, U-0228 in April 1941.
[MAP RTP Photographic Section]

The designation M.20/4 was given to the Royal Navy Single-Seat Shipborne Fighter development of the M.20/2, to Spec N.1/41, dated 3rd July 1941 and the specification (actually being written around Miles' proposals) was issued to Phillips & Powis Aircraft Ltd on 14th July 1941. One prototype aircraft was built, under Contract No B.140247/40, and this was fitted with a pointed spinner and a re-designed fixed, spatted undercarriage. According to the official specification; the undercarriage *'had to be capable of being detached easily, and the aeroplane must be capable of flight with or without the undercarriage'.* The wings were fixed to ease construction, catapult spools were fitted under the centre section and, although it has been reported that; *'an arrester hook was installed under the rear fuselage',* this was not shown in contemporary photographs. As the aircraft was meant to be expendable, it is not easy to see why an arrester hook would have been required anyway.

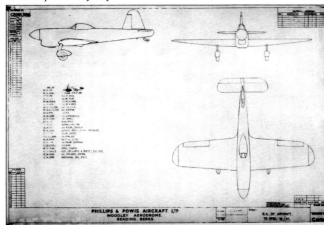

Three-view G.A Drawing of the M.20/4.

However, work had been proceeding on the M.20/4 since early 1941 and a surviving Miles Aircraft photograph shows a test rig with a notice above entitled: MT No.214 M20-4 Bottom Hinge Bracket Drg. No. 20.SK.2121 11th Feb1941. The M.20/4 was first flown, with 'B' mark **U-0228**, by Hugh Kennedy, on 'Handling Trials' on 8th April 1941. He then made the following flights: 'Handling Trials' 10.4.41; two 'Handling' flights on 11.4.41; 'Diving and handling' 12.4.41.

U-0228 was delivered to 'A' Performance Test Sqdn, A&AEE Boscombe Down on 15th April 1941 for a short assessment. Seventeen comments on construction and layout were made and

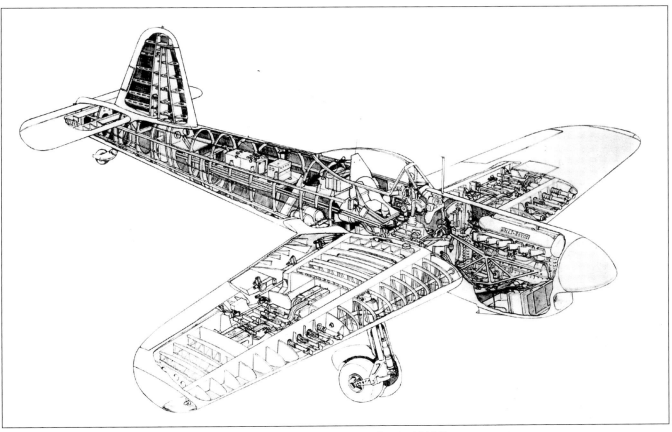

Cut-away drawing showing the 8-gun Miles M.20 Developments (Fighter Aircraft) - the M.20/4.

these included poor hood operation and lack of wing venting, but they considered that the view was excellent. At 7,560lb, and powered by a Rolls-Royce Merlin XX engine, U-0228 had somewhat heavy and slightly overbalanced controls and a conventional stall, but with the stick in the central position. Acceleration in a dive up to 450 mph was rapid in spite of the fixed undercarriage.

It was then given the serial **DR616** it was returned to the A&AEE in mid-1941 to be examined for use as a possible naval fighter. Performance was measured and it was found to be faster and at a greater height than the Wildcat, which came along later. Greater oil cooling was required and the cockpit needed more warmth but the eight .303 in guns were adequately heated. The internal fuel of 110 gallons gave a calculated range of 610 miles at 9,000ft.

Details of its performance at A&AEE were as follows: Take-off weight 7,566lb; take-off run 270 yds; to 50ft 450 yds (with 30° flap); max rate of climb 2,300 ft/min to 9,400ft; service ceiling 32,800ft; max speed and height at which achieved 333 mph 20,400ft.

Details of the Gunnery Trials undertaken on the M.20/4 by the A&AEE were given in 'Armament Ref: AAEE/A70/B15 21/8/41 Phillips and Powis N.1/41 Fighter - Gunnery Trials. Report No.1 8 x .303 Fixed guns' as follows:

In accordance with signal dated 23/4/41 full gunnery trials have been done at Boscombe Down. Trials started 26/4/41 in conjunction with performance trials and continued until 20/7/41, when performance trials were suspended as no satisfactory results obtained up to this time. The trials were started afresh and have now been completed.

Four .303 Brownings in each wing. Access to gun bay by means of a door hinged at front and anchored by claws mounted on torque tubes revolved by 3 screwed knobs operated by a hand brace. Guns fired pneumatically.

Ammo boxes adjacent to inboard and outboard guns, made from "Tufnol" and mild steel. Feeds anchored to guns by quick-release pins and spring-loaded clip holds them to ammo boxes. Capacity of boxes when aircraft received was 600 rounds per gun. Inboard boxes, however, had false bottoms and when these were removed their capacity increased to 900 rounds. Empty cases and links ejected through common opening in base of the wing.

Martin Baker type blast tubes used.

Trials were:

(a)   Re-arming and maintenance.
(b)   Ground functioning and jump cords.
(c)   Low altitude functioning.
(d)   Range of gun adjustment and harmonisation.
(e)   Characteristics of aircraft as fighter aircraft.

Results

(a)   Re-arming simple - took two armourers 20 min - could be reduced with practice. Guns could be removed for cleaning by two armourers in 20 min and replaced in 25 min. Removal not made any easier by raising the hinged mounting, therefore left in locked position. All breech-blocks could be removed in this position, but with mounting raised the recoiling portions could only be removed from the inner guns by unscrewing the barrel extensions. Special tools required to remove blast tube and to open gun bay panels, and stowages should be provided for these on aircraft.

(b)   27,200 rounds fired on ground. Aircraft had to be taken into the butts on a number of occasions to discover and remedy various defects: -

i)   ammo box guides not holding boxes rigidly - movement seemed to cause mis-feeds. Guides pinched until boxes were firmly held.

ii)   gun bay doors fouled feed shoots and forced them out of alignment with lips of ammo boxes, causing jammed belts. Top of chutes were filed down.

iii) in some cases feed chutes out of alignment with gun feed-way in vertical and horizontal planes. Adjusted by bending chutes and fixing lugs. Feed chutes unsatisfactory - need to be manufactured more accurately and to be more rigidly fixed.

iv)   pneumatic firing gear did not function correctly. "Bad lag" in response to operation of firing button and guns often stopped with breech-blocks forward - misfired side and rear sear releases. Messrs Dunlop and Phillips and Powis helped overhaul system to reduce lag in response, though never entirely eliminated. Breech-block - forward stops not resolved until Dunlop delay units were fitted in pneumatic lines - then complete load of 6000 rounds was fired with only one case of a breech-block stopping forward.

v)   heating ducts in gun bays led hot air direct into blast tubes. Will prevent proper cooling of barrels and inadequately heat breech-blocks. To be examined before heating trials are made in this aircraft.

vi)   Jump cords results satisfactory.

(c)   Approx 62000 rounds fired during low-altitude functioning trials.

(N.A. Ref: AVIA 18/816)

Sqdn Ldr Peter Whitworth, one of the pilots involved in the trials at Boscombe Down, recalled in a letter to *Aeroplane Monthly* in June 1976 that:

The M.20/4 was delivered to 'Per.T' (Performance Testing) for its main trials - its armament testing was quite secondary because the installation of its eight .303 machine guns was straightforward and sensible. When 'Per. T' pilots had done the main trials, the M.20 was passed to 'Arm.T' for one or two firing trials in Lyme Bay (our regular firing and bombing range). On 24th July 1941, I flew DR616 and fired the eight .303 guns in Sidmouth Bay, as, no doubt, Lyme Bay was not available that day. This aircraft was not very popular with the pilots who flew it, though it handled well - the trouble was it was fitted with a 'rogue' Merlin engine (a very rare occurrence), which had the nasty habit of 'sputtering and banging' for no apparent reason. The ground crew spent hours and hours searching for the cause of the apparent fuel starvation, but it was never cured as far as I know.

DR616 had a fixed undercarriage, and this was the real worry if there was engine failure - the prospect of landing at fairly high speed on any rough ground was somewhat daunting, as there would always be the likelihood of the aircraft somersaulting when the wheels hit even a small obstruction. Though I had been warned about it, I did not enjoy the sudden 'pops and bangs', which occurred only once on my flight, and I don't suppose lasted more than 2-3 seconds in all. We understood at the time that the M.20 would have no undercarriage in production, as it would be used only for catapult launch at sea.

In fact, the undercarriage was meant to be removed when the M.20/4 was mounted on the catapult, as the aircraft would invariably have had to have been 'ditched' at sea at the end of a sortie. A report that the Royal Navy version of the M.20, fitted with an arrester hook and a modified fixed undercarriage, was named the 'Miles Matador', appeared in *Aerogen* for June 1949 but no other reference to this name has ever been found and it is not known from where this report originated.

Following trials at Boscombe Down, the M.20/4 was flown to RAE Farnborough on 15th September, before returning to the makers on 31st December 1941. The M.20/4 was given the RAF Experimental Aeroplane No.138 for identification purposes. DR616 is on record as having been delivered to 24 Squadron, Hendon on 21st February 1942, but on 19th March it was returned to the makers. Stored in a Robin hangar on the Davis Farm site, where it was seen by Grahame Gates in early 1943. Although classified Cat.E1 and SOC on 22nd May 1943, the M.20/4 lingered on, finishing up in the Repair & Service Department, where it was subsequently broken up in November 1943.

Unfortunately, no photograph of the M.20/4 with the serial DR616 appears to have survived.

The requirement for an expendable convoy defence aircraft was eventually met by the use of suitably adapted Hawker Hurricanes fighters and the M.20/4 was consigned to history.

Miles M.20A Low Attack Fighter

In January 1943, Phillips & Powis Aircraft Ltd produced a booklet on **'Miles Specialised Aircraft for Specialised Purposes'**. This contained a summary of a selection of Miles aircraft which had either been built or proposed up to then and brief details of the M.20A Low Attack Fighter were also included. These are reproduced below:

This machine has been developed for anti-tank and anti-submarine attack and, for this purpose, extremely heavy armour and armament are carried. The armament consists of either 20 mm cannon or 40 mm cannon or UP (Universal Projectile). The pilot is very completely protected both from ground and air attack while the exceptionally high speed at low altitude makes it a very difficult target.

In view of the urgent need for a machine of this type, special attention has been given to the possibility of rapid production and, in this connection, it is interesting to note that the prototype was built and flown in nine weeks.

Span	34 ft 7 ins
Wing area	235 sq ft
Engine	Rolls-Royce Merlin 32
All up weight	8,500 lb
Max speed	330 mph at 5,000 ft
Armament	4 x 20 mm cannon or 2 x 40 mm cannon or 6 UP (Universal Projectile = rocket projectile)

An unorthodox aeroplane especially suitable for low attack duties, the M.20A is a development of the shipborne fighter.

Needless to say, nothing further was heard of this proposed variant.

SPECIFICATION AND PERFORMANCE DATA

M.20/2

Engine:	1 x 1,390 hp Rolls Royce Merlin XX
Dimensions:	span 34ft 7in; length 30ft 9in; height 13ft (the M.20/4 has been quoted as 10ft 5in?); min wing area 234 sq ft; max wing area 243 sq ft; aspect ratio 5.1; wing section, root NACA 23021, tip NACA 23009
Weights:	Tare 5,870lb; fuel (154 gal) 1,110lb; oil (8.5 gal) 77lb; pilot 200lb; AUW 7,865lb; normal wing loading 33.4lb/sq ft
Performance:	Max speed at AUW 7,865lb at 21,000ft 350 mph; max speed at sea level 282 mph; stalling speed 79 mph; run to unstick (30 deg flap) 810ft; distance to 50ft, 1,350ft; initial rate of climb 3,000ft /min; absolute ceiling 35,000ft; range at economic cruise 550 miles; 2 hrs duration at economical cruising plus ¼ hr at full throttle at ground level and at operational height.

Master Mk.I, N7809, completed as the six-gun M.24 Master Fighter, at Woodley before delivery to 5 FTS Sealand on 21st June 1940. Note partially blanked off rear cockpit and also apparent absence of gun ports.

Chapter 9
Miles M.24 Master Fighter/
Master Six-Gun Fighter Trainer

In early 1940, Miles suggested that the Master Mk.I should be converted to a single-seat fighter, equipped with six .303 Browning machine-guns, as a safeguard against serious losses of fighter aircraft by the RAF in the forthcoming battles which surely lay ahead. An undated document, found amongst George Miles' papers by Jim Pratt, gives a few details of the M.24 as follows:

The M.24 is a standard Master I converted to a single seater fighter, by the addition of extra armament in the form of Browning guns mounted in the wings. The dual control arrangement in the rear cockpit was dismantled, and the tipping windscreen was replaced by a fixed hood. Certain items of equipment such as flares etc, had to be removed to meet the requirements. All other details are as standard Master I. A number of these machines were produced fully equipped as a fighter.

CL Nash recorded that the prototype Master Fighter was converted from the M.9B Master Mk.I N7413, and that it was first flown, from Woodley, in June 1940. However, the official records state that the prototype 'Master six-gun Fighter Trainer' (as it was known in official parlance and not 'Master Fighter') was converted from Master Mk.I, N7412, and this was 'Test' flown by Flt Lt Hugh Kennedy on 30th May 1940. N7413 was allotted to AMRD (Air Member for Research and Development, i.e. RAE) on 25th July 1939 and then went to RAE Farnborough on 18th August 1939 before returning to Woodley later. Hugh Kennedy flew both N7412 and N7413 in May, June and early July 1940 and Ken Waller flew N7413 on 31st May 1940. N7413 was retained by Phillips & Powis as a Trials Installation (TI) aircraft, but there is no record of it being modified to take six machine guns.

The conversion of the Master to the 'Master Fighter' (as it is still more generally known) actually entailed removing the dual controls and instruments from the rear cockpit, fitting a fixed hood to the rear cockpit and blanking out its rear section, removing the cine camera gun and installing six Browning .303 machine guns in the wings.

The records kept by C L Nash of Miles aircraft production at Woodley, noted that 25 Master Mk.Is were completed as single-seat Master six-gun Fighters on the assembly line and Monty Cook, who worked for Phillips & Powis at the time, recalls that he worked on the Master Fighters and had gone on to night shift especially to progress them. He said that it was double British Summer Time (BST) at the time and he claims that the reason that they were abandoned was that the glue did not stand up to the gases induced by firing the guns. Although this is a very interesting hypothesis, it has not been possible to verify.

Likewise, Tony Wingfield recalls that Don Brown, in a lecture to 381 (Reading) ATC Squadron mentioned that when firing trials of the Master Fighter were carried out in the firing butts, the wings fell off after a while! Be that as it may, and admittedly the performance of such a 'utility fighter' would have been lower than that of the Hurricane and Spitfire or, for that matter, the Me109 which it would have been fighting against, this was before official policy (which had been on a stop-go since the idea was first suggested by the firm) delayed its introduction into service.

When it was realised, long after the excitement had passed, that the aircraft had not been given a Miles type number, it was given the

A close-up of the cockpit of N7809 showing the blanked off rear portion.

out of sequence designation M.24 Master Fighter. For the record, the 25 Master Mk.Is completed as M.24s were N7780-N7782 and N7801-N7822. All these aircraft, which had been completed in a very short time, were used for gunnery training by OTUs and FTSs and were delivered in June 1940.

A few strong words were written in 1940 about the 'Master Fighter' in the firm's internal memorandum: *The History of the Chaotic Relations between Phillips & Powis Aircraft Ltd and the Air Ministry:*

. . . we tried to persuade the Ministry that owing to the tragic shortage of fighter aircraft the Master could well be fitted with six guns and armour. Thus fitted it would at least be useful for home defence and each training school could probably look after itself to some extent. All schools have first-class pilots handy who could

help disorganise dive bombing attacks. We know that Mr Jones of Hawkers has recommended it. The Air Force was approached and the scheme met with their enthusiastic support and an order was placed with the Company to convert 25 of these machines. The work was actually started. The first machine was tested by the Air Force and was satisfactory; this was also knocked on the head by the Air Ministry.

I do sometimes wonder how we won the war!

SPECIFICATION AND PERFORMANCE DATA

Similar to Miles M.9B Master Mk.I but with single seat and six guns.

The M.24 Master Fighter, N7809, in service with 5 FTS Sealand.

[Via Peter Green Collection]

The Miles 'Hoopla' Radio Controlled Flying Bomb Mock-up being shown at Woodley. Note the cut away bottom fuselage to carry a 1,000 lb bomb. Note also the row of Spitfires in the background.

Chapter 10
Miles Hoopla Radio-Controlled Pilotless Aircraft

In 1940, with everything going in Germany's favour, it occurred to Miles and his team that, when the tide ultimately turned against the enemy and they finally had to accept the fact that the victory which had seemed so certain in the early days of the war had now, in fact, eluded them, they would be driven to desperate measures. In those days, bombing was mostly confined to military targets and neither side had yet resorted to obliteration bombing, which perhaps, more than anything else, finally brought the war to an end. Considering the desperate measures to which the enemy might ultimately resort, Miles felt that precision bombing of military objectives might well be replaced by the indiscriminate bombing of large cities, possibly by radio-controlled pilot-less bombs.

In discussion with the scientists at RAE, it appeared that from the technical angle such an idea was by no means impossible. In fact, fifteen years earlier, in September 1925 the RAE had started to develop a pilot-less flying bomb with a range of 300 miles and carrying a warhead of 250lb.

The automatic pilot for flying this aircraft was based on the same principles as the device already developed at RAE, known as the Pilot's Assister. This embodied monitoring by a magnetic compass, as proposed originally by the late R McKinnon Wood (under whom Don Brown had worked at the MAP in 1941), and F W Meredith, the real 'father' of the automatic pilot, as it was known during the war. No radio control of the automatic pilot was envisaged at that date and the navigation was to be done by dead reckoning with, it was hoped, a reasonable degree of accuracy.

The Larynx, a small pilotless aircraft was designed and built by the RAE and made its first flight on 20th July 1927, with extended tests being undertaken in 1929 in the desert country of Iraq. The same control and navigation concept installed in the RAE Larynx was later used in the German V1.

Foreseeing the possibility of such an attack against England however, it seemed to the Miles team in 1940 that the best kind of deterrent would be the ability to reply in kind and on a massive scale. Miles therefore built a full-sized flying mock-up of a small light aeroplane capable of carrying a 1,000lb bomb - the largest bomb in general use at the time - cheap to build and powered by a mass-produced engine. A radio-directed automatic control unit for the elevator and rudder was incorporated into the design and according to RAE calculations this weapon should have been capable of operating with a reasonable degree of accuracy up to a range of 400 miles.

The flying mock-up, named the 'Hoopla', was not given a Miles type number and it is not even known if it was ever test flown, or, if it was, from where.

The Hoopla project was duly submitted to the Ministry, with the suggestion that this weapon should be put into large-scale production, to be stored but not used except as a deterrent should the enemy first resort to such a means of warfare. Needless to say the idea was rejected by the authorities on the grounds that it might encourage the Germans to develop a similar weapon for use against us, and the fact that they considered such a weapon to be against the ideals of the Geneva Convention.

However, there was a fundamental difference between the Hoopla and the German V1 Vergeltungswaffe 1 – 'Revenge Weapon No.1'. The latter weapon was designed for short range indiscriminate bombing, whereas the Hoopla was designed for long range

Seen on this page are three different views of the Hoopla Flying Mock-up.

The Hoopla Flying Mock-up with 1,000 lb bomb.

precision bombing and would have been guided to its target by radio control.

Many years later, I discovered a Phillips & Powis file entitled 'Specification for HEC M VI. Carrier for 60 HE Mines'. This 'Carrier' was to be powered by a DH Gipsy VI series II or Menasco Buccaneer Type C.65 engine. The file contained four drawings of the machine, all dated April 1941. Although of poor quality, they are shown on this page and the next.

Below: The first drawing shows a 'Sectional View of Fuselage for 60 Mines'.

These mines were to be carried in 60 containers, each weighing 18.4lb including the release mechanism, giving a maximum payload of 1,100lb. This file also included weights and performance figures; a sectional view of the fuselage showing the positioning of the containers and equipment; a drawing showing the pilotless aircraft mounted on a 'Standard catapult or Accelerator Equipment' and performance curves. The letters 'HEC M' probably stood for 'High Explosive Carrier, Mines.'

The specification also showed that the HEC M VI was designed to be powered by either a 260 hp DH Gipsy Six or a 363 hp Menasco C6S engine *(the Menasco Super Buccaneer C6S-4 engine gave 260 hp and I can find no record of a Menasco engine giving 363 hp with this designation, or any other for that matter - PA)* and would have had a maximum speed of 200/220 mph at its operational height of 20,000ft. The only apparent difference between this aircraft and the Hoopla was that the HEC M. had circular fins and rudders whereas the Hoopla's were square. It is possible that Miles, having had his proposal for a pilotless aircraft capable of carrying a 1,000lb bomb rejected, resurrected the Hoopla in April 1941 and modified it to carry mines, thereby making it seem to be a less indiscriminate weapon, but one which would be a great asset for use against enemy shipping.

On D-Day, the 6th June 1944, the Allies invaded Normandy, whereupon the Germans decided that the time had come to unleash their weapons of mass destruction against the mainland of Great

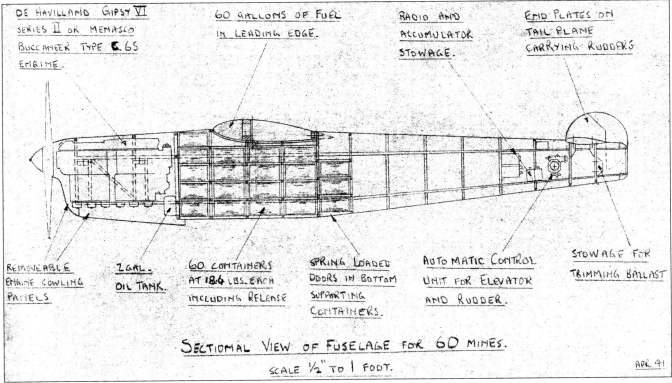

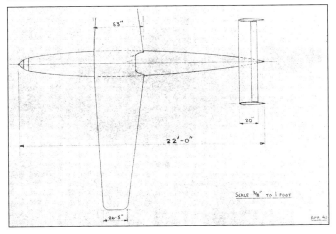

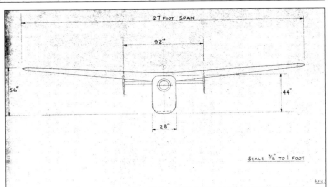

Above: Front view of the 'Carrier for 60 HE Mines'.

Left: Plan view of the 'Carrier for 60 HE Mines'.

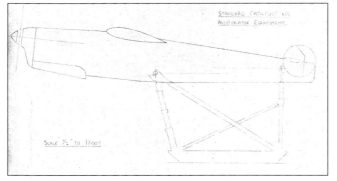

Drawing showing 'Standard Catapult or Acceleration Equipment'.

Britain. On 13th June 1944, they launched their first V1 'flying bombs' against London but due to their inaccuracy, in the course of the early attacks none of these pilotless weapons fell on the city of London although in the first five weeks of this indiscriminate attack over 3,000 of these 'reprisal' weapons were actually launched against the capital.

The rejection of Miles' proposal in 1940 was rendered all the more incredible when, in March 1947, it was revealed that, as early as October 1939, the Government of the day had been aware that the Germans were developing a pilotless weapon to carry an explosive charge. However, as the V1s, or 'Doodlebugs' as they soon became known (on account of the terrifying noise which they emitted, which I can still recall after all these years when I hear their name mentioned), began to fall in South East England in ever increasing numbers, the British public, very understandably, began to ask the awkward question of the government - how was it that the Germans

had this pilotless weapon but we in this country had apparently failed to think of it.

The Ministry had to act quickly, so they sent an urgent telegram to Miles, ordering him and his staff never to divulge, under any circumstances whatsoever, and least of all to the press, that his idea had in fact been put forward to the Ministry in 1940 and had been summarily turned down. Despite this, at least one newspaper 'let the cat out of the bag' but it was not until November 1945 that the official censor finally gave Miles Aircraft permission to inform the public that they had been working on a pilotless aircraft capable of carrying a 1,000lb bomb in 1940.

Thus, instead of being able to retaliate in kind, all we could do was to bomb the launching sites; a very dangerous operation as they were heavily defended, but one which the RAF completed with speed and precision. The V1 depended for its range on the quantity of fuel it carried which made it a very inaccurate weapon but considered to be adequate when aimed at a target the size of London. It really was only suitable for relatively short range indiscriminate bombing, whereas the Hoopla's use would have depended upon its known ground speed as ascertained by radar tracking. This would have enabled its impact to be directed by a radio signal to a reasonable degree of accuracy, probably within a few hundred yards at the designated range, thereby making it a relatively precision instrument.

Although his idea had been rejected, Miles decided to continue with the development of the autopilot, which he felt could be of use in both Service and civil aircraft. This design was a complete break from tradition, being the world's first electric lightweight auto-pilot and its development is described in the chapter on The Miles Co-Pilot.

The Hoopla, with 1,000 lb bomb, on the dump at Woodley on 11th April 1948. Note the fuselage of the M.20/2, AX834, and the M.64, U6, in the background.
[Via Phil Butler]

SPECIFICATION AND PERFORMANCE DATA - H.E.C.M. VI

Engine:	260 hp DH Gipsy Six Srs II or 363 hp Menasco Buccaneer C6.S (hp figures quoted are max at sea level); max hp at operational height 118/160
Dimensions:	span 27ft 0in; length 22ft 0in; height 4ft 8in; gross wing area 95 sq ft; wing loading 27.7/28.4lb/sq ft
Weights:	DH Gipsy Six engine, empty 875lb; fuel 480lb; oil 22lb; payload 1,100lb; AUW 2,477lb
	Menasco engine, empty 907lb; fuel 480lb; oil 22lb; payload 1,100lb; AUW 2,509lb
Performance:	DH Gipsy Six engine, speed at sea level 220 mph; speed at operational height (20,000ft) 200 mph; speed at absolute ceiling (24,000/25,500ft) 168 mph; stalling speed 83 mph; duration, including climb 3 hrs; time to operational height 30+ min Menasco engine, speed at sea level 240 mph; speed at operational height (20,000ft); 220 mph; speed at absolute ceiling (24,000/25,500ft) 174 mph; stalling speed 83.5 mph; duration, including climb 3 hrs; time to operational height 15 min.

An artist's impression of a later variant of the M.21 Aircrew Trainer.

Chapter 11
Miles M.21 Aircrew Trainer

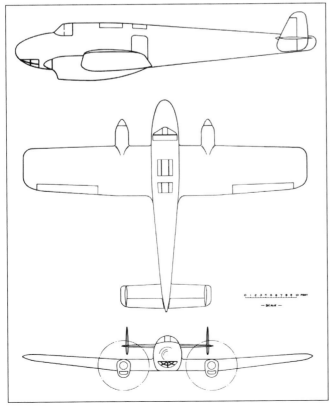

This unidentified and undated three-view drawing is believed to depict the initial design study for the in-line engined M.21 Aircraft Trainer.

Towards the end of 1940, it seemed evident that the RAF would initiate a large and increasing programme of bombing just as soon as enough of the new generation of four-engined heavy bombers became available. The introduction of these large aircraft, each with a crew of six or seven, meant that within the next few years some thousands of aircrew would need to be trained in their respective duties.

At that time the only crew trainers in service were the obsolescent twin-engined Avro Anson and Airspeed Oxford, and it seemed to Miles that there might be a need for a specialised aircrew trainer. He accordingly prepared a number of alternative project designs to provide for every phase of aircrew training in pilotage, navigation, radio, bombing and gunnery. All these projects were grouped together under the designation M.21 and they ranged from a comparatively small aircraft with a crew of four, powered by two 600 hp Pratt & Whitney Wasp engines, to a much larger machine designed to carry two full bomber aircrews, and powered by two 1,300 hp Rolls Royce Merlin XX engines.

Unfortunately, at that critical phase of the war the Ministry decided that, for the time being at least, the only new aircraft which could be considered for production must be operational ones and although a mock-up of 'M.21 Trainer' was built in 1941, none of the proposed M.21 projects progressed any further.

All the following photographs were unidentified and undated but are believed to show two basically similar versions of the projected M.21 Aircrew Trainer.

All these versions had twin fins and rudders, similar in shape to the later M.32 Glider project, but one had the windscreen in two halves with a central frame and had two large rectangular windows on

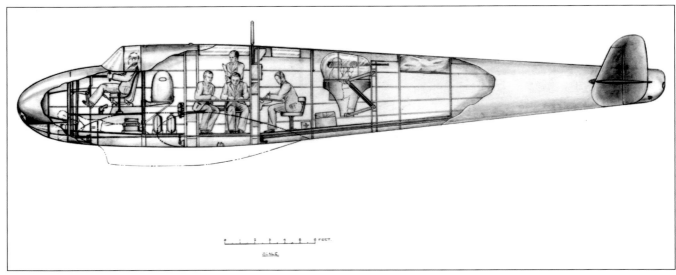

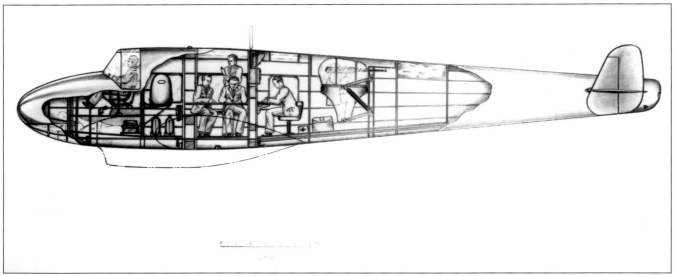

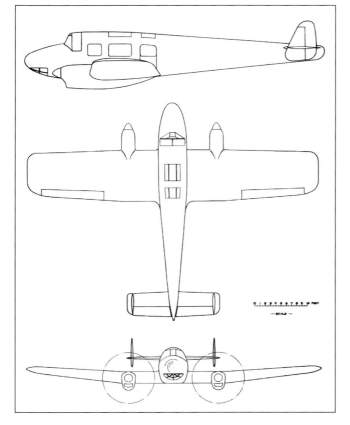

Above: These two cut-away drawings show interior details and crew positions with a crew of six. Note the bomb aimer's position in the nose and the retracted gun turret.

Below: Cut-away drawing showing the nose wheel retracting rearwards into the fuselage and the mainwheels retracting forwards into the engine nacelles.

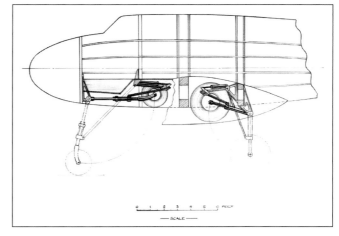

Left: Three-view drawing showing a slightly different version of the first project.

Right: An artist's impression of what it is believed to be a later version of the M.21 with radial engines. Note the different shaped wings, out-rigged fins and rudders and turret in raised position.

Below: A two view drawing of the variant seen on the right.

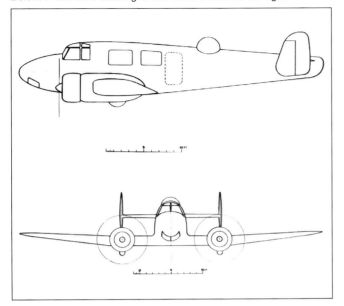

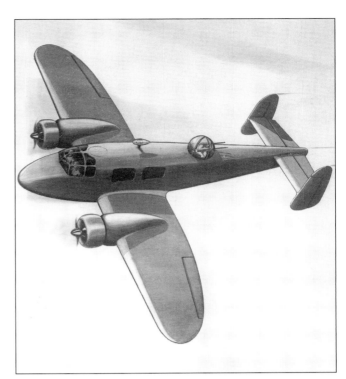

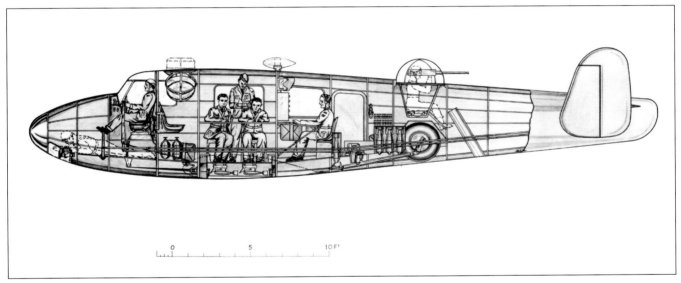

A cut-away drawing of this variant showing interior details and crew positions.

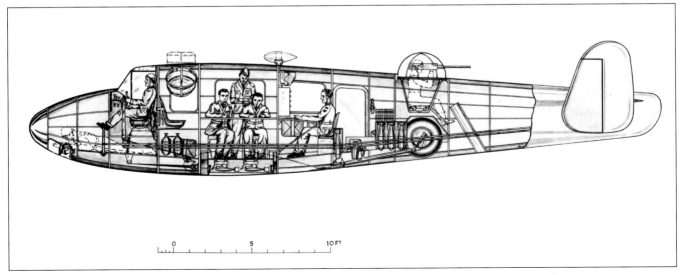

A cut-away drawing of the same variant showing interior details and crew positions but with a different windscreen layout.

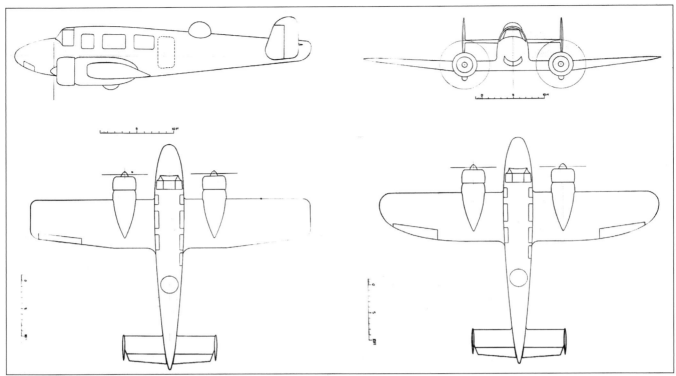

A four-view drawing shows a similar layout but with two different wing planforms.

each side of the fuselage, while the other had a wide flat windscreen and three large rectangular windows on each side of the fuselage. On both versions the entry door was on the starboard side.

Recently discovered photographs are shown below and include several interesting variations.

However, nothing further is known of either of these variants, or the significance of the 'M.8 Conversion'?

The Ministry weren't interested in the M.21 but, in 1942, Miles still felt that there was an urgent need for an aircrew trainer, so he offered the Miles M.36 Aircrew Trainer and in 1943, he offered the four-engined Miles M.55 Marlborough Aircrew Trainer. The Ministry however, did not share Miles' views and were content to soldier on with Ansons and Oxfords and so none of these projects progressed beyond the drawing board stage.

NO SPECIFICATION OR PERFORMANCE DATA HAS SURVIVED

A partial cut-away view of the Miles M.21 Developments (Twin engined Peregrine Trainer). Powered by two Rolls-Royce Peregrine engines, showing interior details. Note the single wheel retracted below the gun turret, i.e. reversed tricycle undercarriage on this variant and retractable cupola behind the cabin.

A cut-away view of the Miles M.21 Developments (M.8 Conversion Twin engined Trainer). Powered by two unspecified in-line engines. Note the retracted gun turret.

An artist's impression of the forerunner of the M.22, without the nose mounted machine gun nest.

Chapter 12
Miles M.22 Twin-Engined Fighter

Rolls-Royce ground ran their new 1,735 hp Griffon II engine in November 1939 but Miles obviously knew of its existence in 1938 as he had decided to utilise two of these engines in the design of a new twin-engined Fighter. It is not known if Miles originally designed the M.22 to meet AM Specification F.6/39 for a Fixed Gun Fighter (File No.S.50810), issued on 12th April 1939, or whether he designed it ahead of its issue and no further details of this specification are known. However, Supermarine produced a mock-up of their Type 334 to meet it. Westland also produced design studies for a Griffon powered twin tractor or pusher aircraft and Fairey undertook a design scheme, of which nothing is known.

The Specification was 'reconsidered in the 1940 programme' and was later issued as AM Specification F.18/40 for a Fixed Gun Two Seater Night Fighter (File No.SB.11632/RDT2(d)), dated 31st October 1940. On 10th November 1940, Specification F.18/40 was issued to Tender, to which Miles then offered the M.22A Twin Engined Fighter and for details of this see the next chapter.

What is believed to have been the original, undated, Miles design for the M.22, shows a twin engined fighter with the tailplane 'blended' into the fin. This however, was later modified to have a more conventional tailplane with the fins and rudders placed at the extremities with a bullet-shaped fairing covering the join.

To add confusion into the design for the M.22, a copy of the 'Minutes of Meeting on 23rd August 1940' gave details of the projected design for a 'Light Communication Aircraft M.22'. Present at the meeting were F G Miles, G H Miles, R N Bournon and W G Capley.

Right: Drawing showing details of the 10 x .303 Browning machine gun nest.

An artist's impression of the forerunner of the M.22 with nose mounted 10 x .303 Browning machine gun nest installed.

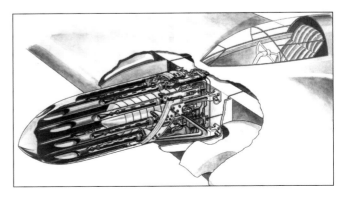

Although these minutes state that the 'Light Communication Aircraft M.22' was initially given the Miles type number M.22, it has been confirmed that the early Twin Engined Fighter project of 1939 was the actual M.22. However, by 1941, the 'Light Communication Aircraft M.22' had become the M.28, which resolved the problem.

Don Brown recounted that the M.22 Twin Engined Fighter appeared in 1941 but this was incorrect as an artist's impression shows it to have been painted silver with large pre-war type RAF roundels, thereby confirming its 1939 origins. Phillips & Powis produced an undated booklet on the M.22 Twin Engined Fighter, probably early in the war, and this is reproduced here in text form:

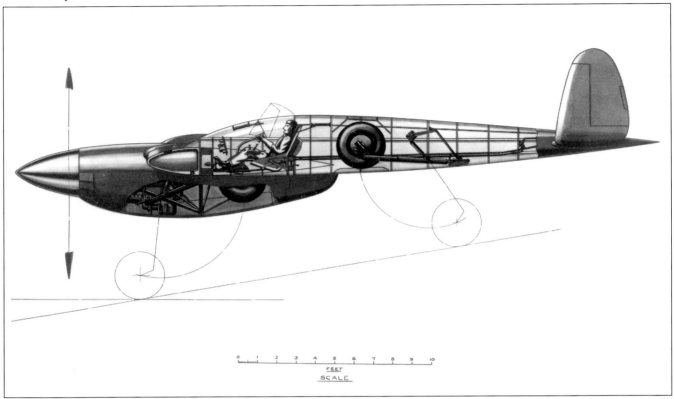

Above: Partial cut-away drawing showing details of the pilot's tilting windscreen and retractable undercarriage. Note reverse tricycle undercarriage with forward retracting rear wheel.

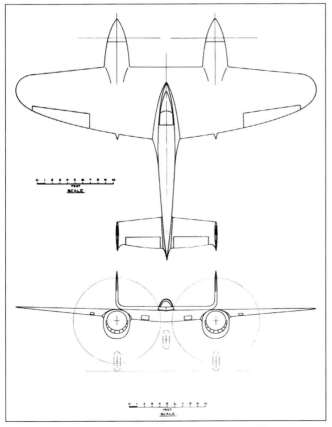

Above: Two-view drawing of the forerunner of the M.22.

LEADING DIMENSIONS.

Span	39 ft 0 ins.
Length	33 ft 0 ins.
Height	9 ft 0 ins.
Wing Area	325 sq ft.
Thickness/chord ratio at root	18 per cent
Thickness/chord ratio at tip	6 per cent
Dihedral	3°
Aspect Ratio	5
Root Chord	120 ins.
Wing Loading	40 lbs per sq ft.
Power Loading	4.05 lbs/HP Max.
Track	13 ft 0 ins.
Airscrew diameter	11 ft 6 ins.
Gross Weight	13,000 lbs.

BRIEF SPECIFICATION

PURPOSE

A twin-engined, low-wing monoplane to travel at the highest speed obtainable with a given horse-power, at the same time retaining all those flight characteristics most desirable in a fighter.

PERFORMANCE *With full loads (13,000 lb)*

Speed: Max level 504 mph at 15,000 ft. Landing speed 80 mph.

Climb: Initial rate of climb 5,180 ft/min. Time to 10,000 ft 2.4 min. Service ceiling 37,000 ft.

Range: 2 hours at 15,000 ft at economical cruising consumption after allowing for climb and ground run.

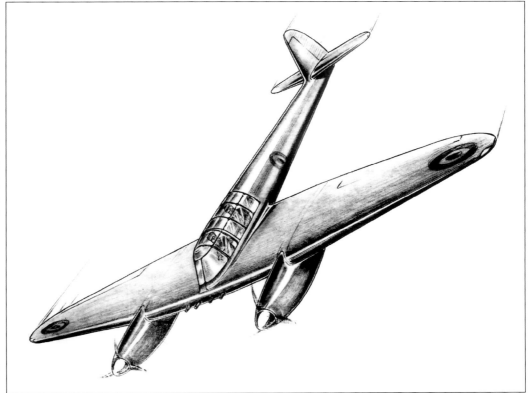

Right: An artist's impression of an entirely different version of the M.22 entitled 'F.6/39 Developments'. Note; two-seats, single fin and rudder and four guns mounted in leading edge of the wing in front of the cockpit.

Below: An artist's impression of the M.22 in pre-war silver colour scheme.

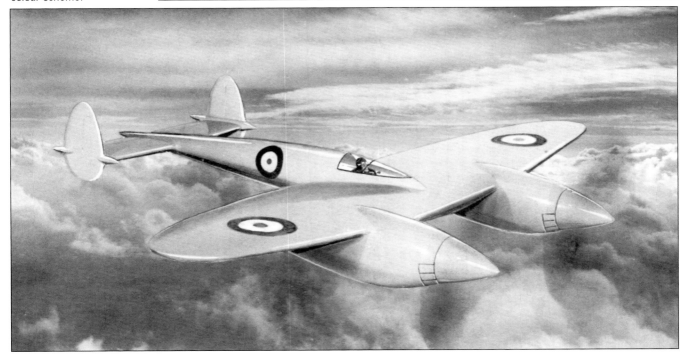

ENGINES

Standard Rolls-Royce Griffons - Water cooled vee-twelve, with constant speed airscrews. *(Actually R-R Griffon IIB engines - PA).*

Take-off: 1,600 BHP at 3,000 RPM (per engine).

Max level: 1,560 BHP at 2,750 RPM at 8,500 ft.

Cruising: 1,280 BHP at 2,400 RPM at 8,500 ft.

OUTSTANDING FEATURES

The outstanding features of this aircraft are:-
* Small frontal and wetted area.
* No protrusions (radiators, air intakes, exhaust pipes inside cowl).
* Leak-proof cowling.
* Miles special undercarriage and flaps.

The remarkably small frontal area of the fuselage has been obtained by accommodating the pilot partially in the wing where the underside is practically flat.

The pilot is given adequate view for landing and take-off by the use of a specially designed titling hood, and large seat-raising gear which enables him to raise himself 12" above his normal flying position. The cockpit hood forms the windscreen in this position. All the tricycle undercarriage units are retractable, completely faired and sealed to prevent air leaks.

The design and thickness of the wing section at the root have had the most careful consideration, it being our desire to guard against the slightest possibility of wing flutter. The spars are of metal construction. The entire surface of the aeroplane will have a very high finish to reduce skin friction.

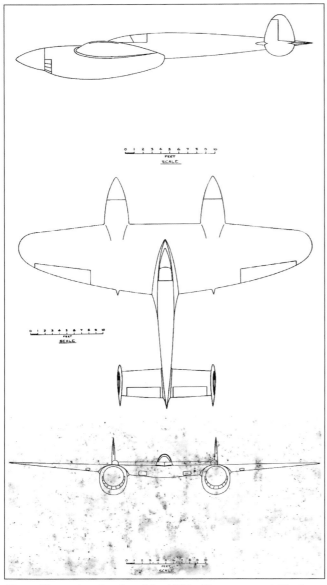

Above: Three-view drawing of the M.22 with no gun nest. The lower image was a poor quality original.

WETTED AREA

In order to produce an aircraft of such high performance, wetted area has to be reduced to the minimum. We believe the unorthodox layout shown here is the best possible when considered in conjunction with the view and comfort of the pilot.

FUSELAGE SHAPE

The fuselage shape as finally chosen is the result of careful consideration of all the essential points and gives, we think, the best practical solution of all the problems associated with high speed flight and operation.

PILOT'S POSITION

By positioning the pilot as far aft as is compatible with an excellent view for landing, the fuselage has been shortened and a large amount of wetted area saved over the more orthodox type with the pilot in the extreme nose. Care has been taken to ensure that the cockpit is as comfortable and soundproof as possible. Controlled cabin heating and ventilation have been provided, by by-passing the warm air in the radiator duct.

Above: Plan view of port wing showing engine installation. Below: Partial cut-away drawing showing details of the pilot's tilting windscreen and retractable undercarriage (Note: Both of these images were also taken from poor quality originals).

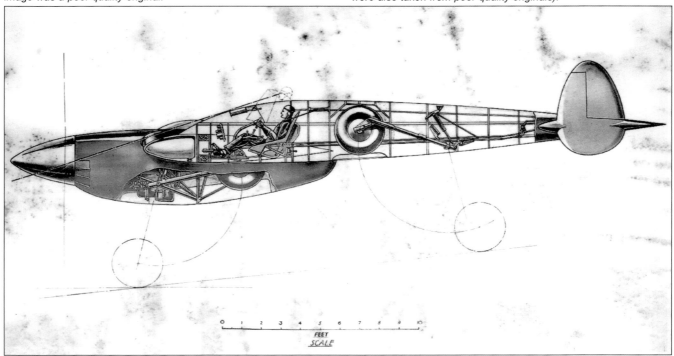

ENGINE NACELLES

The engine nacelles have been disposed so that the top line fairs into the wing near the leading edge and permits an uninterrupted air flow over the upper surface. Their length is a little greater than would appear necessary, but if the plan view is examined the usefulness of the length in providing a good form will be appreciated, besides providing a housing for the Miles flap mechanism.

WING DESIGN

The wing characteristics have been based on a wide range of flights on experimental aircraft which have been carried out for both the Air Ministry and ourselves.

The major points considered were manoeuvrability, freedom from adverse stalling characteristics, with a low drag profile and our new Miles flaps. Aspect ratio has been kept down to 5, whilst the thickness/chord ratio varies from 18 per cent at the root to 6 per cent at the tip. The wing section is of the most satisfactory low drag form.

To ensure that the necessary stiffness and torsional strength is obtained the complete wing is continuous between the wing tips, thus dispensing with the weight and complication of heavily loaded wing joints. With the tips removed the basic wing conforms with the ADM transport requirements.

GENERAL CONSTRUCTION

As a result of experience on the "Master" construction, we have no hesitation in adopting the same general principles of design. The fuselage, therefore, is of semi-monocoque construction with spruce longerons and stringers, with plywood frames and covering. The wings have metal built-up spars, spruce and ply ribs, and thick ply is used for bracing and to ensure a smooth skin covering.

UNDERCARRIAGE

The undercarriage is of the special Miles tricycle type and all three wheels are fully retractable; two into the engine nacelles and one into the fuselage. The rear wheel is provided with two operational positions so that the advantages of both the normal type of chassis and the tricycle can be fully used to assist take off and landing for night operation. Retraction is accomplished by hydraulic jacks, and shock absorbing by Dowty toggle-type mechanism. Brakes are fitted to all three wheels.

FLYING CONTROLS

The flying controls are orthodox and similar in construction to the well proved installation on the Miles "Master" Trainer. Many of the standard assemblies on the "Master", including as adaption of the engine control box, are incorporated.

VIEW

In the air, the view all round is particularly good especially forward and downward. For landing, this can be made unsurpassable by using the special hood and the extra 12" of vertical seat movement, which enables the pilot having landed, to see the ground directly in front of him at a distance of 40 feet.

ENGINE INSTALLATION

One of the most interesting features of the aircraft is the engine installation, which is being developed by Rolls-Royce and Farnborough. The Rolls-Royce Griffons are carried on simple steel tubular mountings attached to the wing spars and are cowled very tightly.

By the use of quickly operated tensioning devices, the cowling is made absolutely air tight, thus "leak-drag", an important factor, is dispensed with, whilst accessibility to the engine is improved.

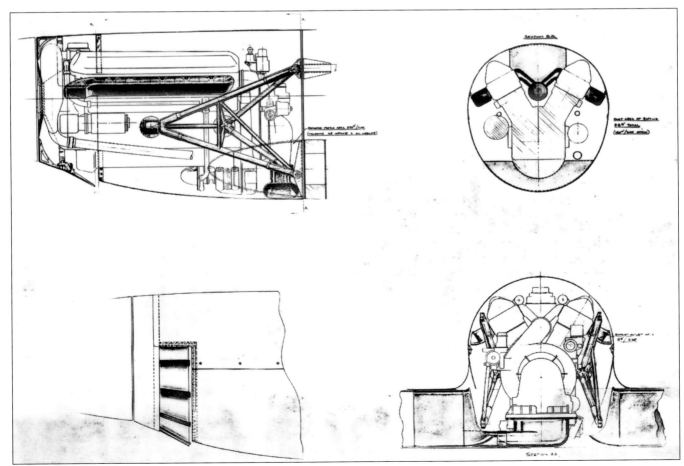

Drawings showing closely cowled engine installation.

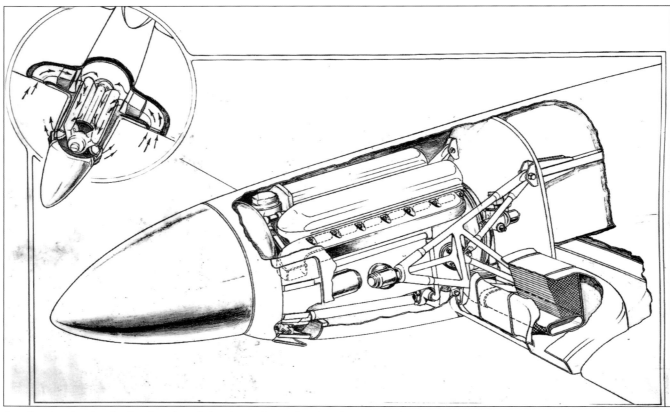

Drawing showing details of radiator installation. Inset shows direction of cooling air-flow.

Air enters through ducts in the wing leading edge, passes through the water and air coolers, which are mounted in front of the front spar, and then into the engine nacelle. After circulating round the engine, it is forced to pass over the exhaust manifold, generator and magnetos etc, finally being sucked out with the exhaust gasses through a semi-circular ring of controllable gills, which are placed immediately below the spinner. Thus a continuous stream of air, cooling all vital points is sucked out into the main airstream at a point which gives maximum flow velocity with minimum drag.

FUEL & OIL

Oil is carried in two tanks, one for each engine, in the nacelles behind the front spar and the fuel tanks are positioned between the spars at the root.

GENERAL

Summing up, the aircraft represents a distinct advance in high speed design, and incorporates all the latest developments which lend to greater efficiency whilst retaining simplicity of structural design.

FIGHTER CONVERSION

It can readily be converted to a truly formidable fighter, carrying either ten Browning guns with 500 rounds of ammunition per gun, or four 20 m/m cannon with 200 rounds per gun.

APPENDIX

As has been previously stated, the aircraft is intended for high performance work, but throughout the design, however, no step has been taken without fully exploring the advantage or otherwise of its application to a military aircraft. We are confident therefore, that as a fighter, fully equipped, the performance will not be unduly affected. Below is given a brief summary of the practical advance made on contemporary design of this type of aircraft.

1. Performance. Greatly increased speed range and rate of climb.

2. Increased operational range.

3. Ammunition. (Ten guns) 500 rounds per gun instead of 300 as at present fitted to fighters.

4. Undercarriage. New Miles two-position tricycle undercarriage: this with blind approach equipment renders the aircraft safer to operate at night.

5. Armouring for the occupant and all essential services against gun fire from all directions. The leading edge between the engines, sides and bottom of fuselage, windscreen and seat will be of bullet proof material.

6. Speed of production. A great number of the assemblies are identical with those used on the "Master", and since the basic principles of construction will be on the same lines, speed of production is assured.

7. Armament of 10 Browning guns or 4 Hispano-Suiza cannon.

(Note: Another black, but undated, brochure, entitled Miles Removable Gun Nest, states that 10 or 12 Browning guns with 500 rounds of ammunition per gun may be carried - PA).

MILES REMOVABLE GUN NEST

The object of this assembly is to provide more guns and ammunition than in contemporary design, and to cut down the time necessary to reload an aircraft. To do this, the guns, ammunition, cooling ducts, cowling piping, etc, have all been made one unit assembly which is removable by four quick release pins and one firing control plug. Thus the complete nest can be changed after use for a replacement already cleaned and loaded, in a few minutes. The used unit may then be attended to efficiently in the armoury instead of on the aircraft. Thermostatically controlled cooling can be fitted for automatic use when firing, combined with gun heating when guns are not in use. The cowling over the guns can be made readily removable in a manner similar to an airscrew spinner, and could be refitted to the aircraft with the new serviced gun nest.

Other advantages are:-
    (a)   Avoids cutting up wing structure and reduces drag.
    (b)   Firing services rendered less vulnerable by grouping.
    (c)   Wing structure simplified and easier to produce.

(d) May be arranged to give armoured protection to the pilot.

(e) Weight concentration practically on centre on gravity of aircraft.

(f) Recoil and inertia effects minimised.

FORM OF MOUNTING

Each gun is attached to forgings mounted to the stiff closed section ring, which in turn picks up the main attachment members. Individual gun adjustment is provided for initial setting, which

Artist's impression of the M.22 fitted with 'Miles Gun Nest'.

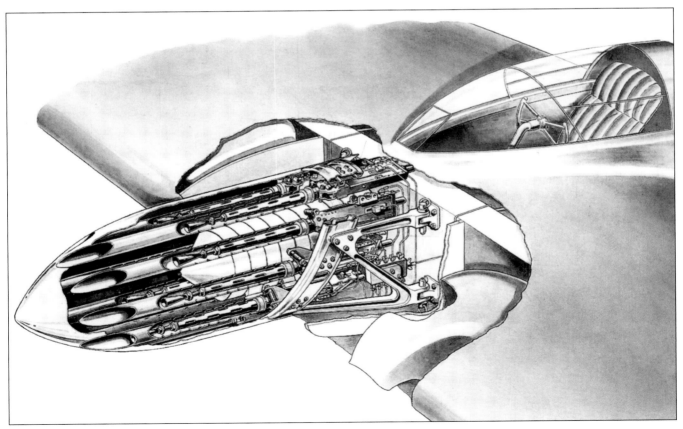

Close-up of the Miles Gun Nest installation.

coupled with adjustment on the main pick-up points of the aircraft structure, ensures interchangeability of the units without further adjustment on the aircraft after assembly.

DESCRIPTION OF COOLING

The cooling arrangements will be such that the inlet louvre is automatically opened by the operation of the gun firing button, but does not close except under thermostatic influence. This ensures that the guns are kept warm by the heating arrangements right up to the actual moment of firing, and are at the same time sufficiently cooled between and during bursts of firing.

COCKPIT CONTROLS

The gun firing button on the control column is normally used for firing, although this may be duplicated to permit firing in groups of, say, six guns at a time if desired.

SERVICING A USED GUN NEST

The whole operation can be carried out conveniently and efficiently in the armoury. It is suggested that the best means would be to transfer the unit from the aircraft by trolley and mount the whole assembly on a vertical type of jig. In this position the ammunition drums can be withdrawn or replaced, and each gun individually inspected and cleaned. The ammunition feed to the guns can also be done as the drums are assembled on to the central spigot.

The ammunition drums are so designed that when assembling, any drum will automatically register with any other, and ensure that the feed necks and chutes are correctly positioned relative to the guns. The design also caters for rapid reloading by handwheel, as will be seen in the photographs.

VIEW

A diagrammatic layout of the view obtained from the cockpit with the seat in the top position, produced by the Martlesham method, is shown below. This takes the form of a cube, of which the panels represent the six planes of vision with the pilot's eye centrally disposed about each plane. The panels are then opened up to give the projected vision in each plane. As will be seen the result is extremely satisfactory especially in the forward and downward direction.

The M.22 Twin-engined Fighter was seen to have been a very aerodynamically clean, twin-finned, low-wing monoplane, designed to travel at the highest possible speed with a given horsepower, while retaining the flight characteristics most desirable in a day or night fighter. This combination of engine and airframe would have given the M.22 a performance higher than anything envisaged at that time. With a maximum speed of 500 mph, the M.22 would have been 150 mph faster than the contemporary Spitfire and 100 mph faster than the new DH Mosquito.

The frontal area of the fuselage was restricted to a minimum in order to achieve maximum aerodynamic efficiency and this was partially effected by accommodating the pilot within the structure of the centre section of the wing. This arrangement enabled the engines to be mounted much closer together, thereby improving the single-engined performance, and minimising the effect of engine failure on take-off.

The M.22 was, unfortunately, destined to remain on the drawing board but had it been produced, it would probably have been the world's fastest piston-engined aircraft of the day. It was to be another four years before the DH Hornet (also of wooden construction) appeared on the scene and this aircraft, of a similar size to the M.22 but with a thinner wing, was to achieve only 476 mph on two more powerful engines than those proposed for the M.22.

SPECIFICATION AND PERFORMANCE DATA

Unfortunately, no details of these parameters, other than those shown above, have survived.

Below: Field of Vision Chart from a poor quality original.

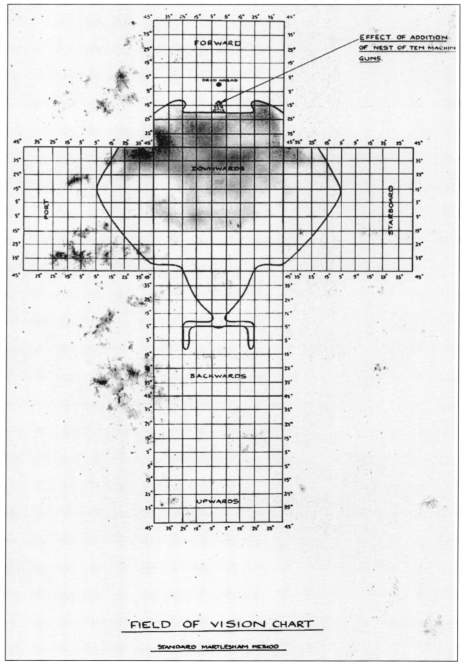

FIELD OF VISION CHART

STANDARD MARTLESHAM METHOD

An artist's impression of the M.22A.

Chapter 13
Miles M.22A Twin Engined Fighter

AM Specification F.6/39 for a Fixed Gun Fighter was issued on 12th April 1939 and although no further details of this specification are known, Miles offered the M.22 to meet the requirement. The Specification was 'reconsidered in the 1940 programme' and was later issued as AM Specification F.18/40 for a Fixed Gun Two Seater Night Fighter (File No.SB.11632/RDT2(d)), dated 31st October 1940. On 10th November 1940, Specification F.18/40 (reproduced below) was issued to Tender, to which Miles then offered the M.22A Twin Engined Fighter.

Requirements

To meet Operational Requirement OR.95, the primary role (of the aeroplane) will be the interception and destruction of enemy aircraft at night. In the interests of quick production, wood or composite construction will be accepted. This aeroplane must have a high performance and a powerful armament. Free and and obstructed vision for search for both pilot and for the AI operator is particularly important. The aeroplane will have fixed guns, good handling qualities is also an essential requirement and in particular the aeroplane must be easy to land at night. The aeroplane may be single-engined, twin-engined, a pusher or a tractor, and may best meet the requirements; a single- engined tractor is, however, preferred. Full night-flying equipment, including wing landing lamps, is required. Special attention is to be given to the cockpit lighting. A system of illumination by ultra violet light is preferred. Complete dimming of instrument lighting is required. Luminous instruments will not be fitted. A separate stand-by floodlight is to be provided.

Performance: The speed at 20,000 ft is to be as high as possible and is not to be less than 380 mph. It is essential that the engine or engines selected shall be equipped with two-speed blowers in order

that speeds at altitudes below 20,000 ft may be as high as possible. The normal fuel load is to be sufficient for a quarter of an hour flying at maximum power for take-off and climb plus 3 hours at the most economical cruising air speed at 15,000 ft plus a quarter of an hour at maximum engine speed for level flight at 20,000 ft. The service ceiling is not to be less than 35,000 ft. Not only should the aircraft form a steady gun platform capable of being sighted and held on target up to a maximum speed without difficulty, but also its handling qualities should be such as to give the pilot every possible aid during approach and landing and during take-off. It is also essential that the controls should be light, responsive and powerful, particularly in the rolling plane.

Engine: The aeroplane shall be fitted with British engines which shall have passed 100 hours Service type tests before delivery of the aeroplane.

Crew: A pilot and an AI operator/lookout with seat type parachutes.

Armament: 6 Hispano Suiza 20 mm cannons with 900 rounds of ammunition.

Signals: TR.1133, R3003, T.3065-R3066..

Corrigendum No.1. 9/12/40. Title - Two Seater Night Fighter. Armament changed to include Dorsal power-operated turret. ASR at Issue III. Endurance increased by 1 hour.

Gloster modified the F.9/37 second prototype (L8002), but the project was abandoned before the tests were completed. Hawker tendered its P.1008 night fighter design; Boulton Paul prepared its P.96 and PO.97 designs; Fairey also undertook a design study but,

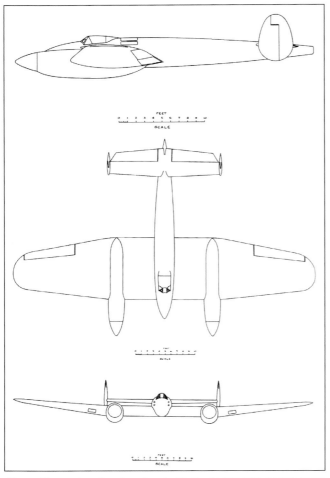

Above: Three-view drawing of probably the first M.22A design study.

as the requirements with regards to armament and performance were so very different from those envisaged for the M.22, Miles prepared its M.22A design, based on the use of the Rolls-Royce RM.6SM engine. None of the aircraft tendered were built as the MAP did not proceed with the design.

Early in the war, Phillips & Powis Aircraft Ltd produced an undated booklet on the M.22A Twin Engined Fighter, 'For day and night fighting based on Air Ministry Specification F.18/40' reproduced below:

PURPOSE

Design: To develop a basic design of a simple straightforward nature, the main objectives being ease of production, the maximum assistance to the crew in the execution of their duties in the air and facility for maintenance on the ground. It is understood that the F.18/40 specification is under revision with regard to performance. The design described in this book attempts to anticipate these alterations and the main points of difference are as follows:

1. Performance. A top speed of 425 mph at 29.750 ft and an absolute ceiling of 43,000 ft when using Rolls-Royce engines RM.6SM. With standard Merlin XX engines a top speed of 405 mph at 22,500 ft with an absolute ceiling of 40,000 ft can be obtained.

2. Range. Provision is made in the wings for a total Tankage giving a duration, allowing for take-off and climb, of 4 hours normal and 6 hours maximum for patrol.

3. Armament. The four cannon are placed on either side of the cockpit and are capable of angular setting. Thereby any angle of fire may be obtained between the horizontal and 7° upward inclination.

4. Pressure Cabin. In view of the extremely high ceiling we suggest it may be necessary to make the two cockpits in the form of a pressure cabin. Schemes for accomplishing this in a simple manner are at present under discussion.

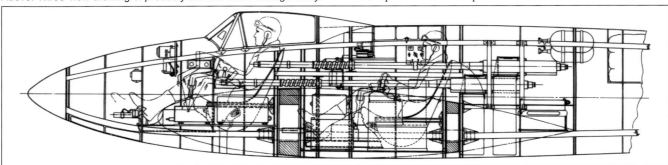

Above and below: Cut-away drawings of the forward fuselage showing the crew positions.

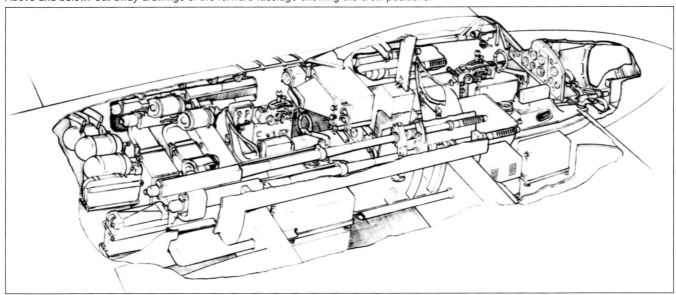

We are confident that, with the simple type of structure and materials we propose to use, the prototype could be flying within six or seven months of receiving the ITP, if it were constructed under the same conditions as the fighter to Specification F.19/40. This aircraft was designed, built and flown in nine weeks.

GENERAL DESCRIPTION OF AIRCRAFT

The aircraft is a low-wing monoplane, chiefly constructed of wood. The engine nacelles as arranged for Rolls-Royce Merlin XX or RM.6SM engines are of the new drag-less type. Water radiator, oil cooler and air intake ducts all have their entry in the leading edge of the wing. The chassis of double wheel type completely retracts into the engine nacelles and full access is provided for maintenance. The cantilever tail plane carries the twin fins and rudders at the extreme ends. The pilot is positioned forward of the front spar and has an exceptionally good view in all essential directions. The plan form and sections of the wing chosen has been based on tests giving the best stalling and spin recovery characteristics.

STRUCTURE

Wings.   The wing is designed in one piece; is entirely of wooden construction and has been calculated to give satisfactory stiffness criteria at a diving speed of 500 mph. We have now had much experience in building wooden wings for high speed aircraft and further research work is in hand on this subject. On the F.19/40 fighter, also of wooden construction, the wings housed the fuel and 8 Browning guns, with 5,000 rounds of ammunition, yet there was no difficulty in having them cleared by the RAE for a diving speed of 500 mph, this despite a wing density figure of 2.3 lb/cu ft.

The wing consists of normal box spars and thick ply covering with the grain at forty-five degrees. The fuel, oil tanks and cooling systems can be assembled and completed before the attachment of the wing to the fuselage, thereby greatly assisting assembly and production. This permits both top and bottom skins to be continuous right through to the fuselage. The wing design allows for detachable wing tips. Frise balanced ailerons and split double flaps.

Fuselage.   The fuselage, which is of semi-monocoque construction, can be entirely of wood. The structure width is sufficient to flair into the Boulton Paul type A, Mk.IID gun turret (*as a result of Corrigendum No.1 to the Specification, dated 9/12/40 - PA*). The attachments for the cannon are arranged outboard of the fuselage side panels. They can be covered by thick gauge easily detachable panels which also form additional side armouring for the crew. In this way a clean interior of the cockpits, the best means of protection, and freedom from fumes and noise for the crew are assured.

Experiments are now in hand with cannon mounted on wooden structures which will include actual firing tests. At the rear end, the fuselage is kept as wide as possible to provide a good base for the tail plane and to accommodate the retractable tail wheel.

OPERATIONAL FEATURES.

The basic requirements of the specification have been met with regard to the crew arrangements:

Forward Cockpit will include full flying controls and blind approach equipment with those instruments necessary for the flying duties as indicated under. This cockpit also has control of the cannon firing and is provided with the best possible view. Full armouring for the occupant and the essential part of his equipment is provided.

Duties.   The member of the crew in the front cockpit is assumed to engage the enemy, taking over control of the aircraft when requested to do so by the AI operator. No illuminated instruments whatever need be used for this part of his duties. Care has been

taken that there is no reflection from any of the lights used in other parts of the aircraft. He will not be responsible for the control of the aircraft until engagement with the enemy. As he will probably be the senior member of the crew and has the advantage of view and position, it is assumed that he will land the aircraft at the conclusion of the flight.

Second Cockpit in one case is provided with full set of flying controls and instruments, with AI equipment, wireless etc. The design assumes that this member of the crew will take the aircraft off, carry out the patrol, and keep in wireless touch with ground staff. He will also operate the AI and bring the aircraft within range of the enemy so that the front occupant can take over. In the other case the Boulton Paul type A, Mk.IID, four gun turret is fitted here.

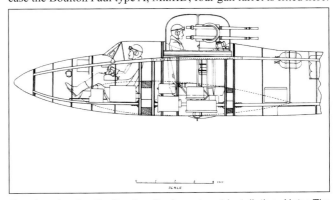

Drawing showing the Boulton Paul gun turret installation. Note: The drawing is entitled 'Miles Twin Engined Fighter (Fighter Developments)', as were others in this sequence.

Escape Doors.   Escape for the crew is arranged through the floor except for the gunner. There seems no alternative to the gunner using the hinged dome as on the "Defiant". The cabin top over the pilot will be capable of being completely jettisoned.

DESIGN FEATURES

Cannon Installation.   The provision for the four cannon will be on the outside of the continuous fuselage section and will be extremely accessible when the detachable panels have been removed. The Mk.I feeds are attached to the cannon, the ammunition boxes being carried within the fuselage. Access for reloading will be from the rear cockpit. If it is preferred to replace the box complete with ammunition, guides will be provided.

Heating tubes from the radiators are led along the leading edge of the wing with the outlet as close to the cannon breeches as possible. A 2-way outlet is provided to control the hot air exhaust either to atmosphere or to provide cockpit heating. The tests carried out with this form of gun heating on the Miles M.20 aircraft indicate that it should be very satisfactory. It avoids such complications as additional heating radiators, etc.

Engine Installation is of the new dragless type which Messrs Rolls-Royce are developing with us. The radiators and oil coolers are carried in the leading edge portion of the wing, together with the inlet ducts. The warm air may then be carried in the nacelle to the rear end, through the thermostatically controlled aperture, to atmosphere. Fully feathering airscrews will be used if available.

Fuel & Oil Systems.   We attach great importance to the fact that there are no parts of the fuel or oil systems in the fuselage, which reduces the risk of immediate injury to the pilot in the case of fire and avoids cockpit fumes. All tanks will be proofed against leakage from 20 mm shells, the fuel tanks being of the completely flexible type, and piping will be rendered leak-proof against bullet penetration.

The Graviner fire extinguisher will have the usual connections in the engine nacelles and may be extended to the fuel tank bays in the wings if required.

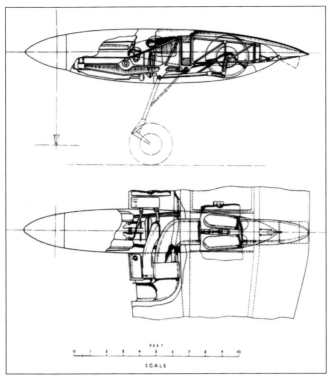

Drawing showing engine and radiator and retractable undercarriage installation.

member of the crew. The sectional view of the fuselage indicates by heavy lines the location of the armour plating, which is fitted in addition to that at the sides of the fuselage. It will be seen that this is adequate for the crew and ammunition against attack from ahead or behind, whilst as much of the essential equipment including the oxygen, has been positioned as advantageously as possible.

AERODYNAMICS

The aerodynamic cleanliness of the whole aircraft has been most carefully studied in conjunction with the required armament and equipment. With the arrangement whereby the cannon are situated on either side of the cockpit a fuselage of reasonable width has been maintained. At the same time the occupants of the cockpit are provided with ample room. The design allows for twin fins and rudders to aid easy handling and spin recovery. The engine nacelles shape relative to the wing has been chosen from tests carried out at the RAE Farnborough.

The aspect ratio of the wing has been kept as low as is consistent with high performance. This produces the maximum stiffness and strength of wing for a given area. The plan form of the wing has been designed to give the best possible anti-spinning characteristics. In this respect attention has been paid to experimental work which has been carried out by the NACA in the USA.

Electrically operated immersed type fuel pumps are used in the tanks to prevent fuel boiling in the pipes at extreme altitude. As previously stated, provision has been made in the wings for the accommodation of long range tanks.

Undercarriage. The undercarriage illustrated is of the lever suspension type arranged to retract into the aft portion of the engine nacelle. In order to cut down the wheel diameter to aid retraction and to decrease vulnerability, a double tyre unit is proposed. The tail wheel, also of the lever suspension type, retracts into the fuselage. Either hydraulic or electric power can be used and special care has been taken in design to ensure that accessibility of the undercarriage units will be good and removal from the aircraft easy.

Protection for Crew, Ammunition, etc. A bulletproof windscreen of adequate height and width provides protection for the front

LEADING PARTICULARS *(equipped as Night Fighter)*	
Span	51 ft 0 ins.
Length	35 ft 0 ins.
Height	11ft 6 ins.
Track	16 ft 0 ins.
Airscrew diameter	12 ft 0 ins.
Normal Wing Loading	36 lbs per sq ft.
Power Loading	6.3 lbs per BHP
Nett Wing Area	390 sq ft
Gross Wing Area	460 sq ft
Aspect Ratio	5.6
Root Chord	11 ft 0 ins
Dihedral	4°

Although other aircraft manufacturers also prepared designs to meet this Specification, none were ordered, as the MAP later decided not to proceed with the requirement.

Note: the following unidentified and undated photographs show what are believed to be further proposals to meet this specification.

A model of an early variant of the M.22A. Note reverse tricycle undercarriage.

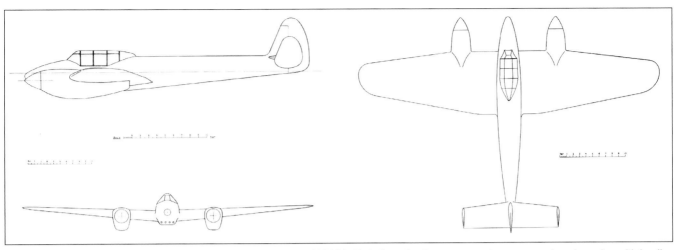

Three-view G.A. drawing showing an early variant of the projected M.22A. Note the raised canopy over two crew seats, a low wing with leading edge radiators between the fuselage and the engine nacelles, three fins, with the rudder on the central fin only and four cannon/ machine guns mounted in the underside of the nose.

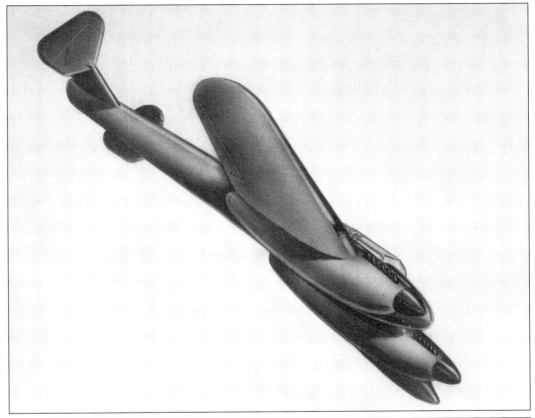

Right and below: Two artist's impressions of another variant of the M.22A in flight which show it to have a slightly raised canopy over two crew seats, leading edge radiators and twin fins and rudders.

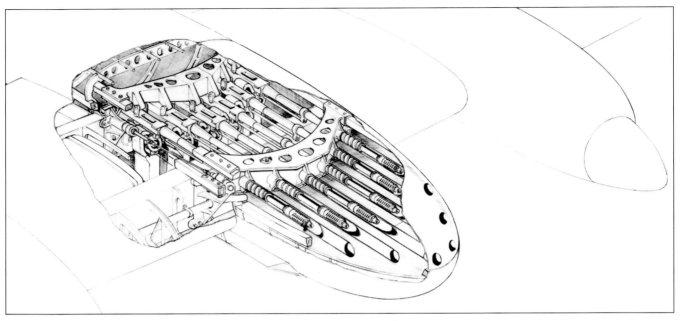

Cut-away drawing of the six cannon mounted in the forward fuselage below the wing.

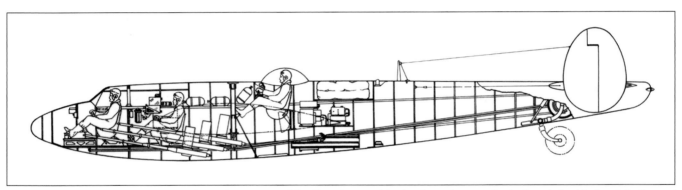

Cut-away side-view drawings showing: (above) the canopy faired into the top of the fuselage, three-seats, dual control, mid-wing, twin-fins and rudders, with the radar operator seated in a mid-positioned cupola, six cannon mounted three either side of the cockpit at a slight angle and with a retractable tailwheel; (below) two seat dual control, mid wing, twin fins and rudders, six cannon mounted three either side of the cockpit at a slight angle and with a retractable tailwheel; (bottom) three seat, dual control, mid wing version with twin fins and rudders and a dorsal power-operated Boulton Paul turret with four machine guns situated behind the cockpit, six cannon mounted three either side of the cockpit at a slight angle and behind, and with a retractable tailwheel.

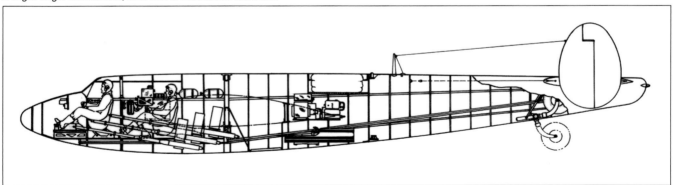

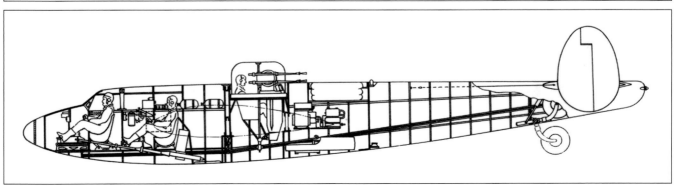

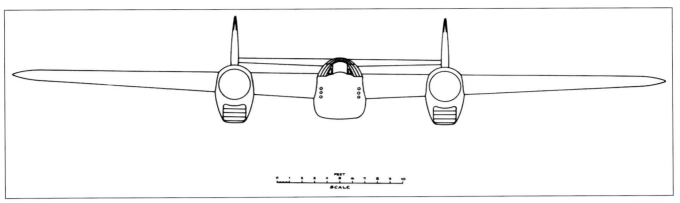

Above: Front view showing mid-wing, twin fins and rudders, six cannon mounted three on either side of the fuselage and radiators under the engines; (right) cut-away drawing showing the two crew positions and mountings for the cannon.

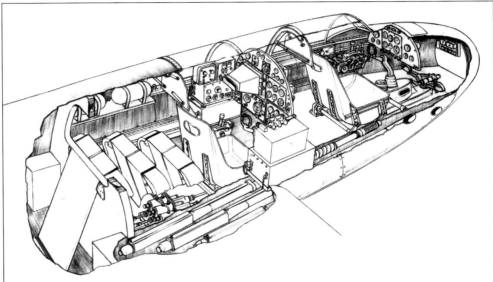

Below: An artist's impression of the M.22A on the ground, with mid-wing, engines with radiators under, and six cannon; and (bottom) an artist's impression of it in flight.

An artist's impression of a similar variant to the previous version but with the canopy faired into the top of the fuselage. Note: Although not shown by the artist, the radiators were in the leading edges of the inboard wings.

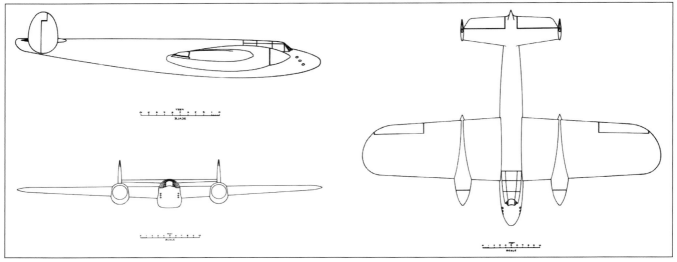

Above: A three-view G.A. drawing of this version.

Below: A side view cut-away drawing showing what appears to depict a later variant of the M.22A, with a slightly raised cockpit just for the pilot, with the radar operator situated just in front of the front spar but possibly with a window. This variant had a low wing and 4 cannon mounted in the fuselage sides above the wing.

None of these photographs gave any details, apart from the negative number, on the reverse. It is these numbers which have given me a clue as to the possible order in which these proposals were projected. It would appear possible that the Merlin engined version had a mid-wing while that with the Rolls-Royce RM.6SM had a low-wing.

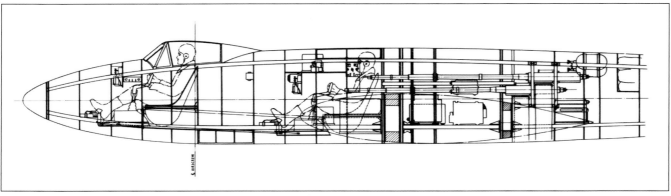

SPECIFICATION AND PERFORMANCE DATA

Engine:	2 x 1,280 hp Rolls-Royce 60 rated RM.6SM or 1,390 hp Rolls-Royce Merlin XX
Dimensions:	span 51ft 0in; length 35ft 0in; height 11ft 6in; wing area 460sq ft; aspect ratio 5.65
Weights:	AUW 16,500lb; wing loading 36lb/sq ft
Performance:	max speed (2 x Merlin 60) 425 mph at 29,750ft, (2 x Merlin XX) 405 mph at 22,500ft; absolute ceiling (Merlin 60) 43,000ft, (Merlin XX) 40,000ft; normal duration 4 hrs; max duration 6 hrs.

An artist's impression of the M.23 High Speed Aircraft.

Chapter 14
Miles M.23 Single Engined High Speed Aircraft

Early in the war, Phillips & Powis Aircraft Ltd produced an undated booklet, stamped Secret and Confidential, reproduced below, on the Miles Single Engined High Speed Aircraft, which did not give a Miles designation, but Don Brown recounted that it was in fact the Miles M.23 and that it had appeared in 1941. It was to have been powered by either a Rolls-Royce Merlin or Rolls-Royce Griffon.

The 1,735 hp Griffon II engine was first ground run in November 1939, so it is possible that this project was not designed until 1941, or it could have been designed somewhat earlier and not given the designation M.23 until later. Although the Master is mentioned in the text as being in production, there is no mention of the M.20, which first flew in September 1940.

LEADING DIMENSIONS.	
Span	31 ft 0 ins.
Length	28 ft 8 ins.
Height	8 ft 0 ins.
Wing Area	185 sq ft.
Thickness/chord ratio at root	20 per cent
Thickness/chord ratio at tip	6 per cent
Dihedral	4°
Aspect Ratio	5.4
Root Chord	89 ins.
Wing Loading	40 lbs per sq ft.
Power Loading	4.62 lbs/H.P. Max.
Track	12 ft 10 ins.
Airscrew diameter	11 ft 0 ins.
Gross Weight	7,400 lbs.

BRIEF SPECIFICATION - GRIFFON ENGINE

PURPOSE

A single engined, low wing monoplane to travel at the highest speed obtainable with a given horse-power, at the same time retaining all those flight characteristics most desirable in a fighter.

PERFORMANCE *With full loads (7,400 lb)*

Speed: Max level 470 mph at 15,000 ft. Landing speed 80 mph.
Climb: Initial rate of climb - 4,680 ft/min. Time to 10,000 ft - 3 min. Service ceiling 38,000 ft.
Range: 2¼ hours at 15,000 ft at economical cruising consumption after allowing for climb and ground run.

ENGINE

Standard Rolls-Royce "Griffon" - Water cooled vee-twelve, with constant speed airscrew.
Take-off: 1,600 BHP at 3,000 RPM.
Max level: 1,560 BHP at 2,750 RPM at 8,500 ft.

BRIEF SPECIFICATION - MERLIN ENGINE

PURPOSE

A single engined, low wing monoplane to travel at the highest speed obtainable with a given horse-power, at the same time retaining all those flight characteristics most desirable in a fighter.

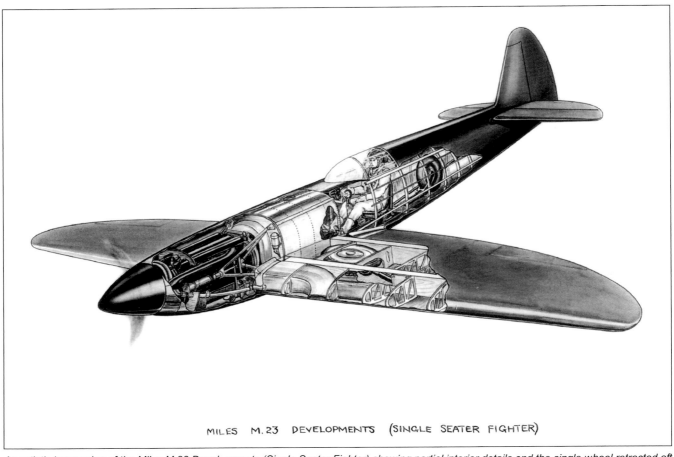

MILES M.23 DEVELOPMENTS (SINGLE SEATER FIGHTER)

An artist's impression of the Miles M.23 Developments (Single Seater Fighter) showing partial interior details and the single wheel retracted aft of the cockpit.

PERFORMANCE *With full loads (6,200 lb)*

Speed: Max level 411 mph at 17,750 ft. Landing speed 76 mph.
Climb: Initial rate of climb - 2,770 ft/min. Time to 10,000 ft - 5.3 min. Service ceiling 26,000 ft.
Range: 3¼ hours at 18,300 ft at economical cruising consumption after allowing for climb and ground run.

ENGINE

Standard Rolls-Royce "Merlin" - Water cooled vee-twelve, with constant speed airscrew.

Take-off: 1,075 BHP at 2,850 RPM.
Max level: 1,010 BHP at 3,000 RPM at 17,750 ft.
Cruising: 666 BHP at 2,600 RPM at 18,300 ft.

OUTSTANDING FEATURES

The outstanding features of this aircraft are:-
   Small frontal area.
   No protrusions (radiators, air intakes, exhaust pipes inside cowl).
   Leak-proof cowling.
   Miles special undercarriage and flaps.

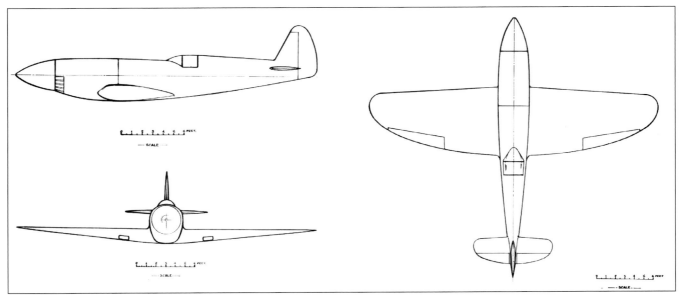

Three–view drawing of what is believed to have been its initial conception.

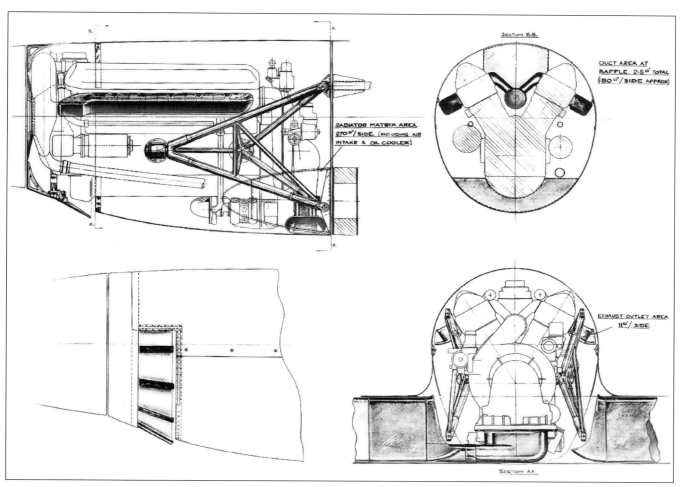

Above: Drawings showing details of engine installation.

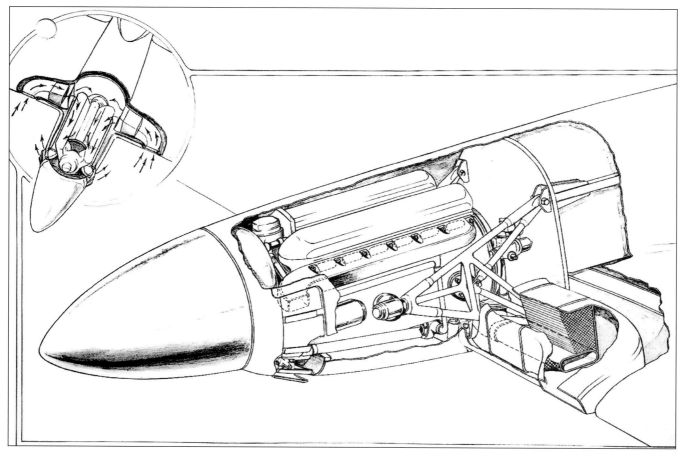

Drawing showing details of radiator installation. Inset shows direction of cooling air-flow.

The small frontal area of the windscreen is made possible by the depth of the fuselage at this point. The pilot is given adequate view for landing and take-off by the use of a specially designed titling hood, and large movement seat-raising gear which enables him to raise himself 12" above his normal flying position. The cockpit hood forms the windscreen in this position. All the tricycle undercarriage units are retractable, completely faired and sealed to prevent air leaks.

The design and thickness of the wing section at the root have had the most careful consideration, it being our desire to guard against the slightest possibility of wing flutter. The spars are of metal construction. The entire surface of the aircraft will have a very high finish, reducing skin friction to a minimum.

GENERAL OUTLINE

The highly efficient shape of this aircraft incorporates design data taken from recent aerodynamic research, ensuring the maximum speed, manoeuvrability and ease of handling.

PILOT'S COCKPIT

Considerable care has been taken to ensure that the cockpit is as comfortable and soundproof as possible. Padding and upholstery will be used where possible and thick glazing employed in the cabin top. Controlled cabin heating and ventilation have been provided, arrangements having been provided for by-passing the warm air from the radiator cooling ducts.

WING DESIGN

The wing characteristics have been based on a wide range of flights on experimental aircraft which have been carried out for both the Air Ministry and ourselves. The major points considered were manoeuvrability, freedom from adverse stalling characteristics, with a low drag profile and our new Miles flaps. Aspect ratio has been kept down to 5.4, whilst the thickness/chord ratio varies from 20 per cent at the root to 6 per cent at the tip. The wing section is of the most satisfactory low drag form.

To ensure that the necessary stiffness and torsional strength is obtained the complete wing is continuous between the small detachable wing tips, thus dispensing with the weight and complication of heavily loaded wing joints. With these tips removed the basic wing conforms with the ADM transport requirements.

GENERAL CONSTRUCTION

As a result of experience on the "Master" construction, we have no hesitation in adopting the same general principles of design. The fuselage, therefore, is of semi-monocoque construction with spruce longerons and stringers, with plywood frames and covering. The wings have metal built-up spars, spruce and ply ribs, and thick ply is used for bracing and to ensure a smooth skin covering.

UNDERCARRIAGE

The undercarriage is of the special Miles tricycle type with the single wheel aft; all three wheels are fully retractable and completely faired. The rear wheel is provided with two positions so that the advantages of both the normal type of chassis and the tricycle can be fully used to assist take-off and landing for night operation. Retraction is accomplished by hydraulic jacks, and shock absorbing by the normal oleo leg. Brakes are fitted to all three wheels.

FLYING CONTROLS

The flying controls are simple and extremely rigid, guided push and pull tubes being used as installed in the Miles "Master" Trainer. Many of the standard assemblies fitted on the "Master" are incorporated, including an adaption of the engine control box unit.

FUEL & OIL SYSTEM

The fuel tank is carried in the fuselage and the oil tank in the leading edge of the wing. The fuel system is fitted with emergency hand pump and all parts are cooled against risk of vaporization.

ENGINE INSTALLATION

One of the most interesting features of the aircraft is the engine installation, which is being developed by Rolls-Royce and Farnborough. The Rolls-Royce "Griffon" engine is carried on a simple steel tubular mounting, which in turn is attached to the fuselage at the top longerons and front spar by four bolts. This cuts down the time required for engine removal to a minimum. An entirely new departure in cowling design is proposed which will be leak-proof.

Air enters the radiators and oil coolers, which are placed forward of the front spar, via ducts in the leading edge, and from there passes into the leak-proof engine cowl where it is directed over the exhaust manifold, generator, fuel pump, magnetos etc, finally being sucked out with the exhaust gases through a semi-circular ring of controllable gills, which are placed immediately below the spinner.

Thus a continuous stream of air, cooling all vital points is sucked out into the main airstream at a point which gives maximum flow velocity with minimum drag. The sealed cowling consisting of essentially two panels, permits no other air whatsoever to enter the cowling: therefore "leak-drag", an important factor, will be practically removed. This design, incorporating the latest available data, represents a definite advance in high-speed research, yet owing to the simplicity of construction it is readily convertible into a formidable fighter.

APPENDIX

As has been previously stated, the aircraft is intended for high performance work, but throughout the design, however, no step has been taken without fully exploring the advantage or otherwise of its application to a military aircraft.

We are confident therefore, that as a fighter, fully equipped, the performance will not be unduly affected. Below is given a brief summary of the practical advance made on contemporary design of this type of aircraft.

Performance	Greatly increased speed range and rate of climb. Increased operational range.
Ammunition	(Eight guns) 500 rounds per gun instead of 300 rounds.
Undercarriage	New Miles two-position tricycle undercarriage: this with blind approach equipment renders the aircraft safer to operate at night.

Armouring for the occupant and all essential services against gun fire. The leading edge over the coolers, sides and bottom of fuselage, windscreen and seat will be of bullet proof material.

Speed of Production	A great number of the assemblies are identical with those used on the "Master", and since the basic principles of construction will be on the same lines, speed of production is assured.

Alternative Armament of 8 Browning guns or 2 Hispano-Suiza cannon.

Heating will be provided.

For the record, it should be noted that the wing area was substantially less than on existing fighters, being only 185 sq ft, compared with 242 sq ft on the Spitfire and 258 sq ft on the Hurricane, which gave a higher wing loading. Although nothing came of this project, it certainly had a great number of very novel and advanced features.

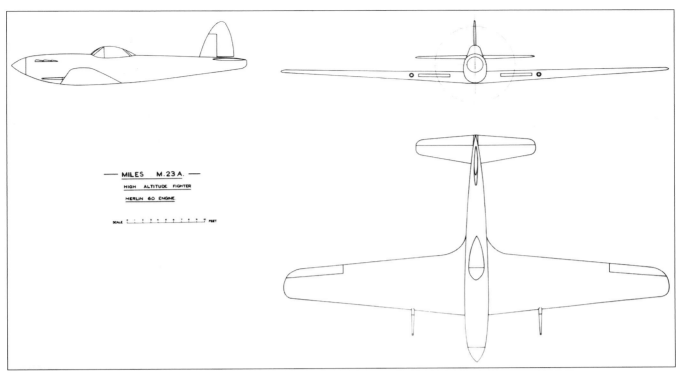

Three-view drawing of the M.23A High Altitude Fighter.

Chapter 15
Miles M.23A High Altitude Fighter

In 1942, existing RAF fighters were finding difficulty in reaching the high altitude at which the Luftwaffe was operating over the British Isles with their Junkers Ju.86 bombers and as a temporary expedient, two modifications to the Spitfire were put in hand. The first was an extension to the wingtips of the Mk.V, to increase the aspect ratio and decrease the induced drag, especially at low indicated air speeds and also to increase the service ceiling. This version became the Spitfire HF Mk.VII. The other variant was basically a Mk.IX but fitted with a more powerful version of the Rolls-Royce Merlin.

It was felt that a pressurised high-altitude fighter should be designed as quickly as possible to combat this threat and Don Brown prepared a project design, which became known as the Miles M.23A. This design bore no resemblance to the previous M.23 and it is, therefore, rather surprising that the same basic Miles designation was given to it.

In September 1942, Phillips & Powis Aircraft Ltd produced a booklet on the M.23A High Altitude Fighter - Merlin 60 Engine, which is reproduced below:

Miles M.23A has been designed as a pressurised high altitude fighter to supersede the Spitfire IX, which can only be regarded as a temporary expedient.

The armament provided consists of two 20 mm cannon with 60 rounds of shells per cannon. After allowing 120 lb for armour and oxygen and carrying the same fuel as the Spitfire, the span loading is 2.97 lb/sq ft.

This compares favourably with the figure of 4.63 lb/sq ft on the Spitfire and 3.30 lb/sq ft on the Welkin and, coupled with the power of the Merlin 60 engine, should give an exceptional performance at high altitudes. With the greater powers which will no doubt shortly

be available from developments of this engine, the performance at altitude will be still further enhanced. Additional fuel in jettisonable tanks would be carried at take-off and, with the ample wing area provided, sufficient fuel for a long patrol could easily be provided while still retaining a reasonable take-off. It will be seen from the drawing that ample control volumes have been allowed to ensure good manoeuvrability at high altitudes.

In January 1943, Phillips & Powis Aircraft Ltd produced a brochure entitled 'Miles Specialised Aircraft for Specialised Purposes'. Contained therein was a summary of a selection of Miles aircraft which had either been built or proposed up to then. Brief details of the M.23A High Altitude Fighter were included and these are reproduced below:

With the constantly increasing altitude at which combat is now joined, the need arises for a specialised fighter designed for this purpose.

The single engined types used hitherto are merely adaptations of the most successful medium altitude fighters and, although they have put up a remarkably fine performance in their new role, the need for a specially designed fighter is becoming increasingly apparent. To this end the M.23A has been designed to have a performance hitherto unattained.

Span	48 ft 0 in (note: the span was quoted as 50ft in the original September 1942 booklet)
Wing area	262 sq ft
All up weight	6,800 lb *(Note difference in AUW to that quoted above - PA)*
Engine	Rolls-Royce Merlin 61
Max speed	440 mph at 30,000 ft
Service ceiling	48,000 ft
Armament	2 x 20 mm cannon.

MAIN PARTICULARS		Protection for tanks	115
		Armour	45
Span	50 ft.	Oxygen	75
Gross wing area	262 sq ft.	Accumulator	45
Aspect ratio	9.55	Miscellaneous equipment	30
Normal AUW	7,440 lb.		310
Wing loading at take-off	28.4 lb/sq ft.		
CPF factor	12	2 Cannon	230
		Ammunition magazines	60
ANALYSIS OF WEIGHT (lbs)		Shells (120 rounds)	70
Wing	1,220	Radio	70
Fuselage	850	Camera, flares, etc	50
Pressure cabin equipment	200	Pilot	200
Undercarriage	350		680
Empennage	150		
Engine mounting and cowling	160	Fuel	600
Controls	100	Oil	50
Tanks (bare)	90		650
	3,120		
		AUW	7,440
Power plant	2,640		
Fuel and Oil systems	40	PERFORMANCE	
	2,680	Speed at 30,000 ft	440 mph
		Service ceiling	45,000 ft

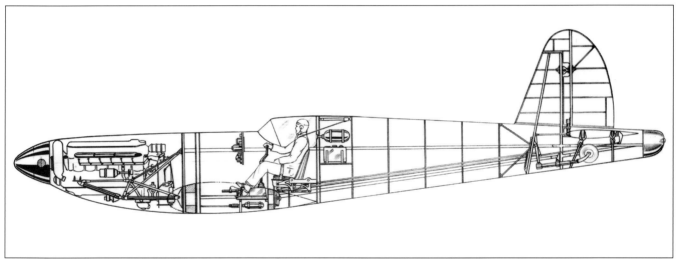

Cut-away drawing showing the M.23A with wing mounted radiators.

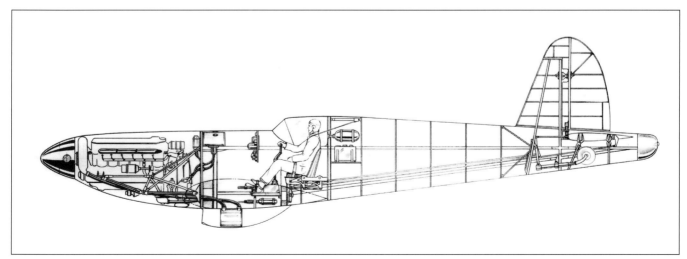

Cut-away drawing showing the M.23A with radiator positioned centrally under the fuselage.

The Miles M.23A was the first Miles design to employ a thin, high aspect ratio wing, with cooling being provided by two ducted radiators mounted in the leading edge of the wings, or as the second drawing shows, a radiator positioned centrally under the fuselage. Although nothing came of this project, it was certainly very advanced for its time and could undoubtedly have been produced and in Squadron service long before the Westland Welkin, which had been designed specifically to deal with high altitude German bombers and which was still under development long after their threat had gone.

LR241, the first prototype M.25 Martinet Mk.I.

Chapter 16
Miles M.25 Martinet Mk.I Target Tower to Spec. 12/41 and M.25 Martinet Mk.II

Until 1941, target-towing duties had been performed by various obsolescent types of aircraft which had originally been designed for other tasks. As supplies of these began to run short, Miles was asked by the Ministry whether he could design and put into rapid production a specialised target-tug based on the Master, using as many standard parts as possible but deleting the dual flying controls and substituting a winch and stowage for the targets.

Miles M.9B Master Mk.IA N7716, was retained by the firm 'for towed target duties' and Contract No. B.109329/40, with an Instruction to Proceed dated 5th June 1940, was raised for two Master Target Tower conversions 'to investigate possibility of using Master for Target Towing purposes - Mock-up stage only', at an estimated cost of £2,500 each. It has not been possible to identify the second machine but Phillips & Powis photographs show one of them with a mocked-up wind driven winch installed on the coaming of the rear cockpit and an arrangement of wires and pulleys in the fuselage for the towed target.

Specification 12/41/PP for a 'Target Tower "Martinet" Direct Production developed from "Master"' was issued to Phillips & Powis Aircraft Ltd, on 1st June 1942 and the Miles M.25, as it was designated, was originally to have been known as the Miles Master TT.

Specification No. Martinet I/P.1: *'Production of Martinet I Target Towing Aircraft; Specification of particular requirements to accompany and be regarded as forming part of the Contract Agreement and subject to the same general conditions'*, was approved by N E Rowe (DTD) on 21st May 1942. The detailed

Specification was set out in Appendix "B" dated 27th June 1942 (signed by EMT at Air Ministry) (Target Towing Aircraft. Martinet I/P.1) and Amendment No.1 dated 19th August 1942; as follows:

The Naval and Air Staffs require the Martinet I target towing aircraft for the following purposes *(to meet OR.110 - PA)*:-

Air to air firing practice

Ground to air firing practice

Ship to air firing practice.

Each aircraft is to be equipped with the fixed fittings necessary for any of the purposes listed in para 1. The aircraft is to be capable of service in any part of the world.

PERFORMANCE

The speeds required for the various duties of the aircraft are:-
Air to air firing, when towing a 4 ft. target on 1,500 ft. of cable:-
(a) A continuous cruising speed of 175 mph at 2,000 ft.
(b) A most economical speed of 140 mph at 2,000 ft.

Ground to air, when towing a 5 ft 5 in flag target on 7,000 ft. of cable:-
(a) A continuous cruising speed of 165 mph at 10,000 ft.
(b) A most economical speed of 130 mph at 10,000 ft.

The endurance required is two hours at the continuous cruising in para 4 (ii) (a), plus two hours at the economical cruising speed in para 4 (ii) (b), plus ten minutes at take-off power.

When taking-off from a grass surface with normal load the aircraft is expected to be capable of crossing a 50 ft obstacle within a distance of 400 yards from rest in still air conditions. When landing with normal load the aircraft is expected to be capable of coming to rest within 450yards after crossing a 50 ft obstacle in still air.

TOWING GEAR

The aircraft is required to carry either type 'B' or type 'E' winch as alternatives. Either winch shall be easily removable for servicing.

A guard is to be provided to prevent the towing cable from fouling the empennage and tailwheel.

CREW STATIONS

A crew of two (pilot and target operator) is required for target towing. The target operator's station shall be fitted with a comfortable seat and back rest with safety harness to accommodate the operator at take-off and landing and while unoccupied during flight (note: this refers to the operator, not the seat! - PA). A point of attachment in the floor for the operator's safety harness is required when changing targets.

The target operator's station is to be laid out so that the operator can stream targets conveniently. The type 'E' winch is to be controllable from the target streaming position. Provision is required for operating the type 'E' winch from the ground starter battery socket. Electrical inter-communication shall be provided between pilot and target operator at the seated and target streaming positions. Fittings for a speaking tube will be required on aircraft allocated to the Royal Navy. RN Units will fit the tubes.

On these two pages are six photographs showing the first mock-up of a wind-driven winch strapped to the sill of the rear cockpit of a Master Mk.IA. Note fairing behind rear cockpit.

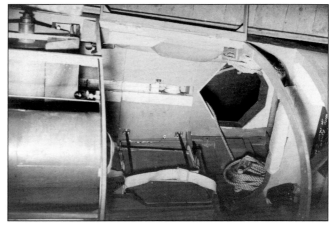

EQUIPMENT

Full night-flying equipment is required. Two-way RT to be operated by the pilot. For this purpose the alternative installations of TR.9D (or TR.1196) or TR.1133 is required. Also IFF. Pyrotechnics - a fixed Verey pistol and eight cartridges are required stowed in the pilot's station.

Targets and release:

Four flag targets 5 ft 5 ins vertical or horizontal, and two 4 ft sleeve targets.

Five 4 ft low-drag sleeves or four 4 ft flags with releases. An additional target with release will be carried in position ready for immediate streaming.

Three target release triggers one on each cable of 'E' winch.

One final release weight.

Spring loading of targets in containers is required to ensure unhampered release. Halyard pegs and flag release knobs are to be coloured for identification purposes to indicate sequence of operation. If external target containers are required for one role they should be detachable in the interest of higher performance in any other role.

Navigation Equipment. - One magnetic compass in the pilot's cockpit and one navigational computer Mark III D is required with a stowage in the pilot's station. Dinghies - Two 'K' type dinghies, stowage for one of these is to be provided in the rear cockpit.

Tropical. - Air cleaners, sand excluders and desert equipment stowages.

Miscellaneous. - Wire cutters to be stowed in the drogue operator's cockpit. Necessary tools for airborne servicing of the winch. One first aid kit.

Armament. - No bombing gear or guns are required.

Specification No. Martinet I/P/1 also stated that the aeroplane shall be fitted with either one Mercury XX or one Mercury 30 engine and the installation shall be suitable for use under tropical, temperate and sub-arctic conditions (see ADM.491 - Aircraft Design Memorandum), when towing 4 ft low drag sleeve target from a type 'B' winch at maximum weak mixture cruising power at the critical boost altitude for this power condition.

In May 2012, a Miles Aircraft document entitled 'Private Development' was discovered and confirmed that, in 1941 a 'Mock-up of Martinet (later officially ordered)' was in fact ordered. However, just what this entailed though was not specified.

Two prototype M.25 Martinets were then ordered to Spec.12/41, with serials LR241 and LR244. The first prototype, LR241, built to Contract No. Acft/1639, was completed in a very short space of time and was first flown, by chief test pilot Tommy Rose, on 24th April 1942. The second prototype Martinet Mk.I, LR244, was fitted with a Bristol Mercury 30 engine and the 'E' type winch. First flown, by Hugh Kennedy, on 4th July 1942, LR244 was delivered to 'D' Performance Test Squadron, A&AEE Boscombe Down on 19th July 1942.

An extract from 'Some notes on Phillips & Powis Aircraft Ltd/Miles Aircraft Ltd's activities during the war, for inclusion in the MAP Scientific War Records', dated October 1947 (N.A. Ref: AVIA 44/603), included the following on the Martinet:

An investigation of the Master design at the latter end of 1942 indicated that a major re-design was necessary to meet

Above and below: LR244, the second prototype Martinet Mk.I.

requirements specified at that time for target towing and thus another version, eventually named the Martinet, was evolved. Experience with the Master and the then prevailing difficult material supply position made Miles design staff revert to a type of airframe construction very similar to that used in 1936 on the original Miles Kestrel while retaining the proved aerodynamic features of the Master series. This construction consisted of box form beams consisting of spruce booms and three-ply birch webs for fuselage frames, and wing and tailplane ribs. The Master power- plant, undercarriage and controls were the only major components retained and the all-up weight was 6,600 lb with a minimum strength factor of 8.0. The top speed was 242 mph at 5,800 feet, the climb 1,700 feet per minute and stall 58 mph I.A.S.

Pre-formed leading-edge skins were used to get a high degree of wing smoothness. Reinforced phenol resin mouldings were used as substitute for light alloy castings in a large number of instances, an example of which was the hand control box unit containing the throttle, mixture, flap, undercarriage, trim tab and landing lamp controls.

The Martinet's principle role was that of target towing for which it was equipped with either an electric winch for targets suitable for air to air fighter practice, or a wind-driven winch capable of towing large flag targets for ground to air practice. The large type of target was carried in a special container faired into the underside of the fuselage and large enough to hold 4 flag targets which were launched by remote control from the observer's cockpit. Normally six low-drag (flag or sleeve) targets were stowed inside the aircraft, together with the necessary towing cable but nine could be accommodated if necessary.

The Martinet was also equipped and used as a glider tug and towards the end of the war as a single seater fighter trainer (Note: In fact only one Martinet was modified for glider towing, and the two prototypes of the M.37 Advanced Trainer were modified from standard Martinets - PA).

In 1945 a certain number of Martinets were modified to take ground operated radio controls which consisted of electro-hydraulic power units monitored from a radio receiver. The aircraft remained unchanged aerodynamically, the modification being confined to structural items to take the additional equipment. These radio controlled aircraft were named Queen Martinets and had an all-up weight of 6,780 lb.

The Miles M.25 Martinet, although externally apparently based on that of the Master Mk.II, had little in common with it, being, in reality, a completely new design. Therefore, apart from an outward family likeness, the Martinet and Master detail design and construction had little in common, with major technical problems having to be overcome before the requirement could be met.

The heavy winch and towing gear required necessitated moving the engine further forward to compensate for the change in the centre of gravity, while special attention had also to be given to the engine cooling arrangements, owing to the severe conditions imposed by target towing.

Modifications to the engine cooling were therefore made to allow for the lower speed and higher power output when towing, and longer exhaust pipes were fitted to the production aircraft.

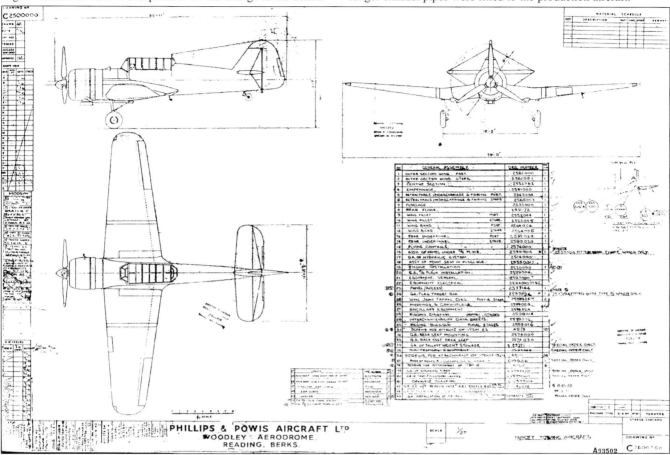

Phillips & Powis Aircraft Ltd three-view G.A. drawing of the M.25 Martinet Mk.I.

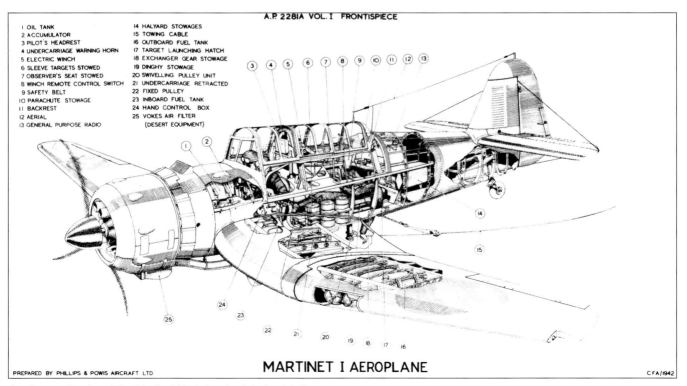

A cut-away drawing of the Martinet Mk.I showing interior details.

The electric 'E' type winch was generally used for targets suitable for air-to-air fighter practice, and the wind-driven 'B' type winch, which was capable of towing large flag targets, for ground to air practice. Ultimately, at least four different types of winches were to be installed in the Martinet to give the following different types: Martinet I, Martinet I 'B' Winch (wind), Martinet I 'E' (electric) and Martinet I 'F' (electric) winch.

Stowage for two drogue targets were to be provided for use with the Type 'B' Winch and provision for one target in position ready for use and stowage for a further five targets were to be provided for use with the type 'E' triple drum winch.

Provision was initially to have been made for the carriage of 8 - 11½ lbs HE Practice Bombs on two Light Series Bomb Carriers but this requirement was deleted by Amendment No.1 to Specification No. Martinet I/P.1 on 19.8.42. The AUW was 6,600lb with a minimum strength factor of 8.0. The top speed was 242 mph at 5,800ft, the climb 1,700 ft/min and the stall 58 mph IAS.

We now have to move forward in time to the 2nd July 1945 as a document, prepared by JH Lowden, the chief draughtsman, with that date, obviously in preparation for the Investigation at Miles Aircraft Ltd by the Industrial Advisory Panel on 4th and 5th July 1945, throws new light on the problems the firm had experienced in early 1942 with the MAP over the piecemeal ordering of the aircraft and embodiment loan equipment. This document is reproduced below:

MARTINET

Start of design	1.11.41
MAP Examination of Master II re target towing	8.11.41
MAP Mock-up Conference	9.12.41
First flight	1.5.42
(Note: this date is in error as LR241, the first prototype Martinet, was first test flown, by Tommy Rose, on 24.4.42- PA).	
MAP Final Conference	29.5.42

Memo from Mr Bennett, dated 12th February 1942 Re small quantity ordering:

"......the method the AM adopt in arriving at orders to be placed for aircraft, i.e., they give orders for no more than a year's supply at any one time. This order is given six months before deliveries commence as this period is considered sufficient to allow for all purchases to be made.

The order we have in hand, therefore, for 600 Martinets takes us to June 1943. By June 1942 we shall have another order for a further 480 which will be for deliveries from June 1943 to December 1943.

Although the Ministry recognises that 2,000 of these machines will be required they refuse to order for this quantity in one lot".

Delay in MAP authorisation for supply of embodiment loaned items

The Martinet original Appendix 'A' was compiled by us and taken personally to MAP on 19th December 1941 in the hope that we would get sanction to indent for equipment prior to the compilation of the Ministry document. The suggestion was rejected and the head of the department told me to stick to my own job.

An MAP representative visited us on 5th February 1942 to enquire into the matter and pointed out that we could not indent for the equipment until an agreed Appendix 'A' had been compiled and circulated.

We received four draft copies on the 11th February 1942, but these were so hopelessly inaccurate that we had prepared dozens of amendments before we could use it. These amendments had to have seven copies each and sent to MAP to get their agreement that their document was in error.

Hydraulics

We used the Miles Theed hydraulic unit in the Martinet design because it had given so good service in the Master III as compared with the Lockheed installation which comprised so many small parts and a mass of intricate piping.

Although the design was completed and the aircraft had flown on 1st May 1942, we did not get MAP agreement to use the unit, which was of course already in production for the Master III, until 20th June 1942.

MAP Modifications

MAP New requirements	48%
Improved Design	38%
Production Easements	14%

22% of the above were common to the Master.

Sgd J H Lowden

Martinet HN884 '6D-K', of 20 Sqdn, Llanbedr, being flown by Gp Capt KWT Pugh, seen towing a drogue over Cardigan Bay in 1949.
[Via Andy Thomas and the P H T Green Collection]

The 5th Part of the A&AEE undated Report, No. A&AEE/792, was entitled: Brief performance and handling trials and relevant extracts from this are reproduced below:

Period of tests: July - August 1942.

Brief performance and handling trials were required on Martinet LR244 fitted with the 'E' type winch. This part of the report contains the results of the performance on climb and in level flight, the position error correction and handling trials. The handling trials were curtailed since the aeroplane was allotted away before these could be completed. The results of the performance tests were reported to MAP in letters of reference AAEE/4487/ 53-AT156, dated 7th and 25th August.

This aeroplane is the second prototype Martinet I and is equipped with an 'E' type electrical winch. It is a derivation of the Master II *(although the Martinet may have borne a family resemblance to the Master II, that's where the similarity ended. This is a common misnomer as the Martinet was certainly not 'a derivation of the Master II' but was a completely new design - PA).* The principal differences are a change in wing section, redesign of the rear cockpit and installation of target towing gear. The rear cockpit is provided with a folding observer type seat placed aft and to starboard, together with a lap strap. The type 'E' winch is installed at the forward end of the cockpit.

The cockpit hood is a sliding type instead of the hinged type as on the Master II *(this statement was incorrect as the Master II had a sliding hood, it was only the early Master Is that had a hinged hood - PA).* The installation of the target towing equipment includes a target hatch, a pulley-guide for the cable and guards on the tail unit. No wireless masts or aerials were fitted. Close fitting inter-cylinder baffles and long tail pipe exhausts were fitted to the engine. The aeroplane was delivered with an air intake incorporating an ice-guard and a Vokes air cleaner. This intake arrangement was replaced by a normal intake, which also incorporated an ice-guard, during the course of the trials.

A Mk.VIIIc pressure head is fitted beneath the port wing, about 7 ft inboard of the wing tip. Full details of its position and setting are given in Fig.5. A 4-view photograph of the aeroplane is attached at the end of this report.

Then followed technical details of the trials, with tables of figures and graphs.

Scope of tests:

These tests consisted of climb and speed measurements with the normal intake and ice-guard, and an intake incorporating a Vokes air cleaner and ice-guard, fitted in turn. The position error was measured over a speed range of 100 mph to 225 mph with flaps and undercarriage up, in level flight. The tests were done at the provisional TSL.

These trials consisted of general handling, and tests to ADM.293 at the provisional TSL, and dives at a forward CG position. The aeroplane was allotted away before the handling and diving characteristics could be checked over the complete CG range as determined from subsequent information obtained on the first production aeroplane HN862.

Results of tests:

Climbs and level speeds - The results of these tests have been reduced by the method of A&AEE Memorandum dated 27th August 1942. With the normal air intake and ice-guard fitted, the maximum speed is 240.50 mph TAS at 5,800 ft. Fitting the intake incorporating the Vokes air cleaner and ice-guard reduces the maximum speed to 231 mph TAS at 4,600 ft. The corresponding figures for the maximum rate of climb are 1,420 ft/min up to 3,400 ft and 1,340 ft/min up to 2,500 ft respectively.

Layout and comfort of cockpits - Front cockpit. Except for the re-design and re-positioning of the fuel cocks, the cockpit layout of the Martinet is the same as in the Master II. The fuel cocks have been re-positioned about 6 in higher on the Martinet and consist of two levers mounted on a gated box. One lever operates the port tanks, the other the starboard. The system is considered to be very satisfactory as the cocks are easy to operate and in a convenient position.

Rear cockpit - The suitability of the layout for target towing operations is not dealt with in this report since this aspect of the work remains within the province of RAE.

Handling trials - Detailed handling trials were not made on this aeroplane as it was found that the behaviour was similar to the Master II (see 2nd Part of Report No. A&AEE/719c). The main points of the differences are given in the following:

Take-off and initial climb - The take-off run was not measured but is thought to be longer than the Master II, and the climb away not as good. The swing is no more marked than the Master II and can be held quite easily on the rudder. Climb - There is still insufficient rudder trim on the climb and the footload on the left rudder is tiring. The rudder is heavier than on the Master II owing to the removal of the balance tab.

General - Longitudinally the stability is slightly better than on the Master II, but the aeroplane is still unstable on climb and in level flight at low speeds with engine on. The controls are similar except for heavier rudder and slightly less effective aileron. The tendency to "weathercock" in rough air conditions is much less marked.

Tests to ADM.293 - These trials were made at a weight of 6,572 lb, CG 54.4" aft of the datum. These were made with flaps and undercarriage UP and with flaps and undercarriage DOWN and these comprised: Behaviour at the stall (Tests 1 and 3 of the ADM), Slow glide (Test 2 of the ADM) and Slow speed turns (Tests 4 and 5 of the ADM).

Diving trials - Diving trials were made at the forward CG position of 49.6" aft of the datum, at a weight of 5,376 lb. The limiting diving speed is 330 mph ASI. The aeroplane had to be held in the dive with moderate pressure on the control column, and was stable about the three axes. On applying 10° yaw in either direction the aeroplane banked in that direction until the rudder was returned to neutral when the normal diving path was regained. There is more than sufficient rudder trim at the maximum diving speed and it is considered that this would allow the fitting of a fixed tab or cord on the rudder trailing edge to improve the climb condition.

Approach and landing - The best approach speed is 90 mph ASI without engine, ie about 5 mph faster than for the Master II. On lowering the flaps there is a marked change of trim making the aeroplane very tail heavy, and if this tail heaviness is not checked by elevator the aeroplane will stall. Once the flaps are fully down, the aeroplane settles into the glide and little or no adjustment of the trimmer is necessary. This characteristic is more marked on the Martinet than on the Master II. The landing characteristics are similar to those of the Master II.

Further developments - Further handling and diving trials and measurement of the take-off run will be made on Martinet I HN862, the second production aeroplane, which is fitted with the type 'B' winch.

LR244 was delivered to 'D' Performance Test Squadron, A&AEE Boscombe Down again on 13th May 1943, for performance and handling tests, still with a Mercury 30 engine installed, and the results were as follows:

Take-off weight	6,555lb
Take-off run	275 yards
Take-off run to clear 50ft	500 yards.
Max rate of climb	1,420 ft/min to 3,400ft
Max speed and height at which this achieved	240 mph at 5,800ft.

On this page are four A&AEE photographs of LR244, the second prototype Martinet Mk.I.

At some stage in the trials, LR244 was fitted with a 4 ft, low drag sleeve target and a Bristol Mercury 25 engine, which reduced its top speed by 25 mph but was accompanied by slight engine overheating.

It has recently been discovered that, by January 1944, LR244 had been modified to be the prototype for the M.50 Queen Martinet pilotless aircraft, and I must thank Tony Adderley for recently kindly confirming this, as it was his father, Sqdn Ldr M C Adderley, who was with the Pilotless Aircraft Unit, Manorbier, who recorded his first flight, 'Handling of aircraft', in LR244 on 26th January 1944, with Mr Spuir. Sqdn Ldr Adderley flew many other 'Auto Test' and 'Auto Check' flights in LR244, recording his last flight in it on 8th September 1945.

While the use of different winches being fitted to Martinets is mentioned in the narrative, it is fitting that details of their various uses and methods of operation should be explained. Therefore, courtesy of Barry Ketley, editor of *The Long Drag - A Short History of British Target Towing* and Don Evans its author, the following extracts from this book can now be reproduced here:

Winch Type 'B'

The Type 'B' winch was probably the most widely used winch of all time, coming in to service before World War II. The Type 'B' winch consisted principally of a cable drum driven by a four bladed windmill, which was exposed to the airstream. The drum was supported in a rectangular frame mounted in the operator's cockpit with the arm supporting the windmill extending through the side of the fuselage. A windmill speed control and a drum brake were provided by a worm and segment mechanism mounted on the windmill arm, both controls being operated from the rear cockpit. The windmill propeller was mounted on the windmill head, which was attached to the windmill arm. Rotation of the windmill arm changed the angle of the blades relative to the slipstream, thereby varying the speed of the drive to the cable drum.

When paying the cable out, the windmill was de-clutched from the cable drum allowing the cable to be hauled out by the drag of the target, the speed being controlled by the brake, which was adjusted by the brake control handwheel. To haul in, the windmill was turned to face the slipstream. This action automatically released the brake and engaged the clutch, thus transmitting the drive to the cable drum. The speed was variable over a wide range by use of the windmill control, which changed the angle of attack of the windmill and therefore its speed. When winching in, the brake was

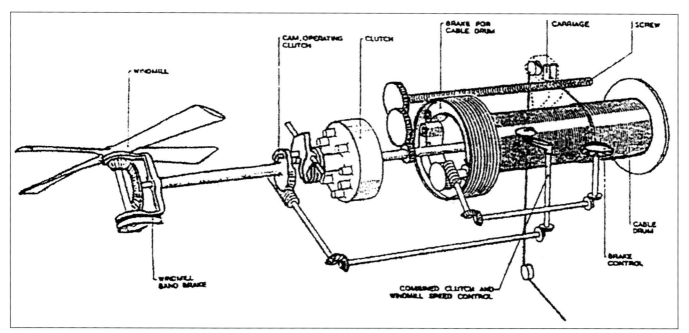

Above: Wind driven 'B' Type Winch.

only used to slow and finally stop the winch when hauling in the last few feet of cable.

The drum contained 7,000 ft of 10 cwt cable, which was wound on the drum evenly by the laying on gear, and the winch was capable of hauling in a 2 x 10 sleeve target at a rate of 1,000 ft per minute. Total weight of the winch complete with cable was 340 lbs.

In most aircraft, the operator sat facing forward with the winch in front of him, operating it by the use of the brake and windmill controls. The brake was applied by turning the handwheel in a clockwise direction, while the combined clutch and windmill speed control was operated by a cranked handle. During the first part of the movement the windmill was automatically freed from its small band brake and further movement engaged the clutch, which was connected to the cable drum. A speed indicator, a footage indicator and a revolution counter were also provided.

In a typical installation, such as the Martinet, the cable was fed out of the aircraft over a pulley in the floor and the cable end was pulled up into the cockpit to attach the rigging lines of the sleeve.

The folded target was then pushed through a hole in the floor and into the slipstream. Once the target was streaming the winch was set to pay out. When hauling in, the cable end had to be hauled right up into the cockpit to release the sleeve. To assist the operator, the last 100 ft of cable was painted; red from 100 ft to 20 ft and yellow for the last 20 ft. If the end of the cable had been shot away, the operator had no idea of how much cable was left trailing, the footage indicator not being particularly reliable. In such cases it was not unknown for the end of the cable to come thrashing into the cockpit causing injury to the operator. I heard of at least one fatality caused in this way.

The 'B' winch was far from being perfect, but it had a long and distinguished career, dragging more targets than any other. It dragged sleeves, banners, winged targets and anything else that came along.

Winch Types 'D' and 'E'

The Type 'D' winch was a simple frame carrying three drums of cable, which were used one after the other. It was similar to the American 'Jupiter' winch but once a cable was paid out there was no way of hauling it back in again.

The Type 'E' winch was basically the same as the Type 'D', but was fitted with a 0.4 hp electric motor, which was not powerful

enough to winch in a target, but could manage to winch in a bare cable. The reason for this development was to make use of a new type of release gear which had been introduced. Targets were fitted to the cable in the normal way, but the connection was made using the new release.

The target was released from the aircraft and the winch set to pay out. When the target was damaged and needed replacing, a metal block or messenger was sent down the cable striking the release gear and slipping the target off the end. The empty cable was then winched in and a new target fitted. If the cable was damaged, preventing the messenger sliding down, it could be slipped from the drum and the second drum used, followed by the third if necessary.

The winch was fitted with an internal expanding brake to control the speed when paying out and a tumbler switch to energise the motor for winding in. When the winding in switch was in the 'off' or 'stop' position, a push button switch could be used to inch in the cable for the last 100 ft. No automatic laying-on gear was provided but a hand lever was fitted to guide the cable tidily on to the drum.

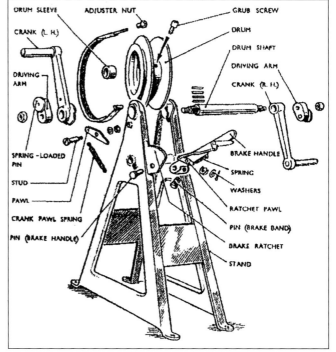

Above: Manually operated 'D' Type Winch.

Winch Type 'F'

The Type 'F' winch was a further development of the old type 'D' winch. It was fitted with a 0.5 hp electric motor and was provided with an automatic laying-on gear for the cable. On the type 'E' it had been found that the third drum was seldom, if ever, used so the type 'F' used two drums only.

Another improvement was the control system, which employed a single lever to control all operations of the winch. The 'One-Hand Control', as it was known, activated the motor or applied the brake respectively by the forward or backward movement of the lever.

The Types 'E' and 'F' winches were installed in the same position as the type 'B' winch and although they had none of the power of the type 'B' winch, they were simple to operate and did away with the drag of the windmill, which allowed slightly higher towing speeds to be used.

The first production Martinet HN861 was first flown, by Hugh Kennedy, on 23rd July 1942 and the Martinet then replaced the Master Mk.II on the assembly line at Woodley. The second production Martinet HN862, fitted with the type 'B' winch, was also fitted with external flag stowage. HN862 was delivered to 'D' Performance Test Squadron, A&AEE Boscombe Down on 25th August 1942, and the A&AEE later turned the exhausts 70° away from the fuselage to cure cockpit contamination. Maximum continuous towing speed was 200 mph (true) at 4,100ft and the modified rudder trim contained the yawing moment caused by the side mounted winch. Handling, including spinning, was

HN861, the first production Martinet Mk.I.

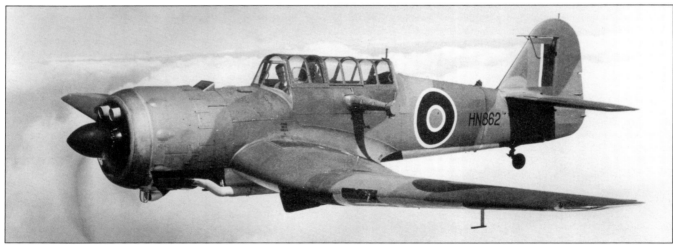

Above and left: HN862, the second production Martinet Mk.I.

satisfactory between 330 mph and the stall at 58 mph (flaps and undercarriage down). Endurance at 200 mph (true) was 3.44 hrs.

The famous Charles Brown photograph of Martinet HN862 being flown by Tommy Rose was, at some later stage, 'doctored', by an 'artist' at Miles Aircraft Ltd, to show it in a landing attitude with an arrester hook protruding from the rudder sternpost, a shortened rudder similar to that of the Master GT Mk.II and the undercarriage down. Although the rudder looks as if it has been genuinely modified, the actual hook and the undercarriage can clearly be seen to have been added later by the artist and this tends to confirm that serious thought was probably being given for modification of the M.25 Martinet to meet a Fleet Air Arm requirement.

Although Martinets were not adapted for deck landing it is known that 5 Martinets from 269 Squadron, were transported to the Azores on the escort carrier, HMS *Premier* (below deck), and flown off without any problem by their RAF crews, just before they reached their destination. Also, during the post war period at least, Home-based Fleet Air Arm Martinets were transported by aircraft carrier, along with squadrons of first line aircraft, on overseas detachments to Gibraltar, being flown off to the shore station. However, it is not known how they arrived on the deck in the first instance, although more than likely they were hoisted aboard from the dockside or barges.

An official MAP photograph, dated May 1945, claims that RH121, the last production Martinet, was 'Martinet Mk.II', with a Mercury

Photograph of HN862 'doctored' to show a proposed 'navalised' version with arrester hook and undercarriage down.

engine. This aircraft was delivered to RNAS Evanton Storage Section on 1st June 1945 and appears to be indistinguishable from a standard Martinet Mk.I. Fitted with the pylon for a wind-driven

Five Martinets of 'B' Flt, 269 Squadron, seen in the background, struck down in the hangar of HMS Premier *en route to the Azores in April 1944.*
[Photograph courtesy FAA Museum]

Two of 269 Sqdn's Martinets about to take off from HMS Premier.   *[Via Phil Jarrett]*

Three FAA Martinets running up at Gibraltar, note the tail unit of a Barracuda at left of photograph.   [IWM via Phil Jarrett]

RH121, the last production M.25 Martinet, shown on these MAP photographs to be a Mk.II.

Our trainer the Master, who does his stuff
Where the ground is hard and the going tough.
He's now to be seen on the end of a wire,
Exposed to the trainees' withering fire —
With cabin new and a little more span,
With stripes of black daubed over his tan,
He blossoms forth as a new silhouette —
His name? Oh, yes — it's the Miles Martinet.

This Oddentification, by Wren, of the Martinet just had to be included!

winch on the port side of the fuselage as on the Mk.I, but with no propeller. Unusually, it had a white band painted around the rear fuselage. RH121 is also referred to as a Martinet Mk.II in the official records but unfortunately, the Ministry of Supply record card for this aircraft is missing.

Although nothing is known about this variant, it is possible that the Mk.II referred to a modification especially for the Fleet Air Arm and in this connection it is of interest to note that Contract/Acft/5849, dated 17.12.45, was raised for 'Modifications to Naval standard of 10 Martinet aircraft'.

Martinets were used by the RAF at home, in Iceland and the Azores, with some remaining in service until at least May 1953. Some 400 Martinets were transferred to the Fleet Air Arm, where they were used at home until at least 1950 and in units overseas, from the Caribbean to Australia, at least until the end of the war.

A note giving details of: 'Applications during the past twelve months for the export of aircraft or the sale of licences for manufacture abroad', dated 3rd December 1943, stated under the Argentine that: 'Miles Aircraft Ltd have been authorised to supply details of the Martinet, and arrangements have been made for the Argentine Naval Attaché to visit the firm.' Nothing further is known of this proposal.

Martinet Mk.I, MS796 was fitted with a glider towing hook in early 1946, in order to establish the performance of the aircraft, and cooling of the engine, when towing a fully loaded Hotspur glider. AFEE Beaulieu Report No.AFEE/T.47 was written by C J Evans BSc to report on tests from March to May 1946 as follows:

A Martinet showing the wind driven winch with the propeller in the stowed position.

The Martinet MS796 at Woodley after modifications for Hotspur glider towing. Note cut-away bottom rudder as per the Master GT Mk.II.
[Via Phil Jarrett]

Summary

Tests on the Martinet I loaded to 6,500 lb towing a Hotspur at 3,600 lb show the performance to be adequate when corrected to temperate summer conditions and the engine and oil temperatures to be just within the limitations. The tests included determination of the effect of fitting tighter cylinder baffles and an additional Potts oil cooler and both these modifications have a slight beneficial effect on cooling and are recommended for use in service.

Introduction

Tests were required to establish the performance and cooling of the Martinet I when towing a fully loaded Hotspur under temperate summer conditions; in addition it was required to determine the effect of fitting close fitting type cylinder baffles and an additional Potts oil cooler.

Condition of Aircraft and Engine Installation

The tests were made on Martinet I MS796, a standard target towing aircraft with the winch removed. *(Note: the lower part of the rudder was also cut-away similar to the Master GT Mk.II – PA).* The engine was a Mercury 30 (manufacturer's number 103881, AM number 284035) fitted with a DH/4/8 propeller. Normal open type cylinder baffles and the normal Serck oil cooler were incorporated but tests were also made with close fitting type baffles and an additional Potts oil cooler. The engine limitations for towing at the time of the tests are shown in the table at the bottom of the page.

Results obtained

Take-off tests were made using 2400 rpm, 4.25 lb/sq in boost with gills fully open, 23° flap at a speed of 78 knots ASI. The net ground run reduced to standard atmospheric conditions and zero wind was 1,125 yards and the gross distance to reach a height of 50 feet was 1,810 yards. Under temperate summer conditions these results would be increased to 1,260 yards and 2,030 yards respectively.

Climb tests were made at the optimum climbing speed of 96 knots, using 2,400 rpm, 4.25 lb/sq in boost with the gills fully open and 23° flap and the initial rate of climb was 350 ft/min. Under temperate summer conditions this would be reduced to 280 ft/min.

Level flight - Cruising tests were made in rich and weak mixture at 3,000 feet with gills fully open and 23° flap and the minimum practicable speed was found to be 90 - 95 knots.

With the normal open type baffles and the Serck oil cooler, cooling on climb and in level flight was just satisfactory under temperate summer conditions using the 100% correction for both cylinder and oil temperatures. With close fitting baffles fitted there was a very slight reduction in cylinder temperatures while with the additional Potts oil cooler fitted the oil temperatures were reduced by amounts up to 5°C.

Range calculations have been made for the combination for cruising under weak mixture conditions at 3,000 feet. The still air range under ICAN conditions is 375 nautical miles whilst the corresponding practical range is 281 nautical miles. Under temperate summer conditions these results would be reduced to 361 nautical miles and 271 nautical miles respectively.

Conclusions

The performance of the Martinet I at a weight of 6,500 lb when towing a Hotspur is adequate under temperate summer conditions and engine and oil cooling are just within limitations. Slight improvement in oil cooling characteristics may be obtained by the fitting of close fitting cylinder baffles and an additional Potts oil cooler and it is considered that both these items could with advantage be used in service.

HN959 was used by the FAA and was once recorded as a 'GT Mk.I', but it is thought that this designation was a local, and probably unofficial, designation recorded because this Martinet was used to tow target gliders. Its history card simply records it as a 'Martinet TT. However, on 28th December 1944, it stated 'Winch mods with Wilmot Mansour' (for development of TT gear with non-radar towing cord) and it arrived at Wilmot Mansour (possibly at Marwell as their works were in Totton, near Southampton) on 2nd January 1945, ex 48 MU Hawarden. To AFEE Beaulieu, where 'Winch mods flight tests at AFEE' were carried out on 3rd September 1945. It was with the Naval Section of 'A' Flight at AFEE Beaulieu in January 1947. To RAE on 22nd June 1948 for 'experimental target towing work' and to 27 MU Shawbury '(surplus)'.on 1st April 1949.

For the record, Charles M Wilmot and Joseph N Mansour had previously been directors of International Model Aircraft Ltd (part of Lines Bros, Merton, who were manufacturing target gliders amongst other things) and who had resigned in 1944 to set up their own company at Totton, Southampton, in a Robin hangar acquired from Marwell. They then manufactured rocket-propelled target gliders for the Royal Navy and later developed the 'Jetex' jet engine for model aeroplane use.

On 17th December 1945, Martinet HP413 was allotted to Miles Aircraft for trials of proposed trainer cockpit hooding in mock-up form to ascertain effect on aircraft handling and Contract 6/Acft/16/CB.9(a), dated 11th July 1946, called for this aircraft to be converted to a prototype (or semi-prototype) standard as the Martinet T Mk.I. In actual fact this meant that a wooden mock-up of the proposed raised 'teardrop' type rear cockpit canopy was to

---

Engine Limitations for Towing

	RPM	Boost lb/sq in	Oil temps °C	Cylinder temps °C
Maximum for take-of	2650	4.25		
Maximum for climb	2400	4.25	90	210
Maximum for cruising rich	2400	2.75	90	210
Maximum for cruising weak	2400	0.5	90	210

The aircraft was loaded to an all up weight of 6,521 lb as follows:

Tare weight	4,748
Service load	721.5
Fuel (130 galls) 87 octane	975
Oil (8.5 galls)	<u>76.5</u>
Total weight	<u>6,521</u>

The CG was at 52.1 ins aft of datum and the CG limits were from 47.5 ins to 54.4 ins aft of datum. The Hotspur was at the standard load of 3,600 lb.

Martinet HP413 with mock-up raised rear cockpit for aerodynamic trials for the proposed M.37 Martinet Trainer.

be fitted over the rear compartment of the Martinet HP413 for aerodynamic trials with this new hood shape (which was similar to that which had been envisaged for the earlier proposed M.29 advanced trainer).

On 21st March 1946, following makers' trials, HP413 was delivered to A&AEE Boscombe Down ('D1' Squadron) for completion of handling and spinning trials. On 24th September 1947, it was conveyed to 71 MU scrap dump, 'surplus to requirements'.

On 4th February 1946, Martinet JN275 was allotted 'To Miles Aircraft for trial installation of Martinet conversion to trainer', the M.37 Martinet Advanced Trainer; on 3rd January 1947, it was 'Handed over to C.R.D. charge at the firm'; on 14th July 1947, 'Surplus to CS/A at Miles Aircraft and despatched to EFS on 20th June 1947'. The Miles M.37 incorporated a raised 'teardrop' canopy fitted over the rear seat, which was mounted higher than the seat in front in much the same manner as that envisaged for the earlier M.29 advanced trainer project, and for details of the M.37 see the appropriate chapter

On 12th July 1948, Martinet JN296 was allotted to Miles Aircraft from 27 MU Shawbury for 'mods and flight trials' and this was seen at Woodley on 10th September 1948. On 23rd December 1948, it was 'declared surplus to CS (A) requirements' and on 1st February 1949, it left Reading for 48 MU Hawarden. A Memo from Mr Fielder of Handley Page (Reading) Ltd dated 20th December 1948 stated that Martinet JN296 has been re-allocated to 48 MU 'Please arrange 530 etc'. The last unit shown on the individual aircraft record card for this aircraft was 'to the makers' but a Handley Page (Reading) Ltd, 'Work-in-Progress Civil Contracts - 31st December, 1948', stated: 'Prepare Martinet JN296 for Maintenance Unit. Total Costs £38. 6.11'. JN296 was test flown by Hugh Kendall on 6th January 1949 and this was also the last recorded flight of a Martinet from Woodley.

On 4th March 1946, Martinet JN668 (fitted with a Bristol Mercury XXX engine), was allotted to Miles Aircraft for trial installation of advanced trainer requirements. It was then modified to become the

second prototype Miles M.37. On 25th (February?) 1946, JN668 was handed over to CRD charge at Miles Aircraft Ltd, Woodley and on 10th September 1946, it was 'loaned to SBAC Radlett for exhibition'. Displayed in the static aircraft park at the last Miles Aircraft 'At Home' day held at Woodley on 20th July 1947, on 1st December 1947 JN668 was declared surplus to requirements and was sold to Gloucester Flying Club, under sales/contract No.12/Sale/34785/ DA12a. The engine from the second prototype still survives to this day, in The Museum of Berkshire Aviation, Woodley, with a panel attached which has 'JN668' stenciled upon it.

On 10th July 1946, Martinet NR598 was allotted to 'TDF (now Lines Bros) for towing winged targets under development' (presumably at Reading but more likely at Oakley) and on 25th April 1949, it was declared 'surplus to requirements and sent to 48 MU Hawarden from Reading'.

Martinet PX133 was delivered to International Model Aircraft at Oakley on 20th July 1944 (the name International Model Aircraft was changed to Lines Bros on 19th June 1946) for towing trials with their winged target gliders. In September 1944, it was used for flight trials by RAE. Flown from Chalgrove to RAE Farnborough on 4th February 1949, on the following day for flight trials with '32 ft winged target' but it is not known if these 'winged targets' were of IMA/Lines Bros or RFD design. On 1st April 1949, it left Farnborough for 27 MU Shawbury, following completion of the trials.

It should be mentioned here that, although Martinet HP216 is also recorded as having 'only' been used by International Model Aircraft in connection with these trials, it was sold as scrap on 4th September 1947, so this is considered to be unlikely.

On 12th June 1946, Martinet, RG907, went to Wolverhampton (Boulton Paul Ltd) - albeit only for use of its engine for first flight trials of the (prototype) Boulton Paul T.7/45 (Balliol advanced trainer); apparently the engine was later replaced and on 16th September 1948, and it was despatched to 48 MU Hawarden as '(surplus)' - however, it was issued to 2 APS Acklington later.

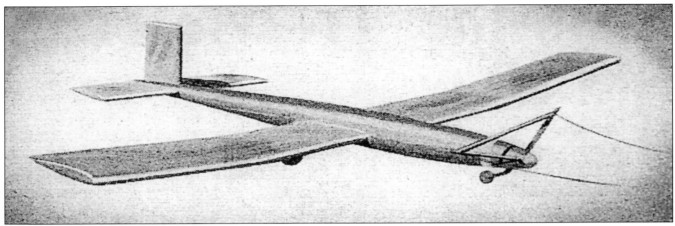

Above: A Winged Target, with Martinet in attendance, at RAF Templeton 'for glider target experiments'. [Via Ivor Thomas]

Left: A rare photograph showing a Martinet towing a 16 ft Winged Target over Orkney. ['Sky over Scapa' - Haslam]

On 16th December 1943, Martinet EM500 was 'Allotted to Miles Aircraft (6 months) for Fitment as 2nd prototype pilotless aircraft', i.e. the prototype M.50 Queen Martinet Radio Controlled Target Aircraft. There has been some confusion over the years as to which aircraft was actually the first prototype M.50 but it can now be confirmed that it was the second prototype M.25 Martinet, LR244. Therefore, this statement is correct. For the record, EM500, was issued to Miles Aircraft Ltd some 7 months earlier than Martinet PW979, which became the third prototype M.50.

On 27th January 1944, EM500 was 'Retained by firm 'for trial installation and test of drone equipment' and on 29th November 1944, it went to RAE for flight trials. On 5th October 1945, a replacement engine was fitted and on 28th April 1946, it was damaged due to heavy landing and 'flown (?) into Miles Aircraft provisionally for Cat.B repair'. On 21st March 1947, the engine was removed and sent by road to 2 MPRD at Stockton on Tees. On 7th May 1947, it was recorded as 'Aircraft burnt on site - 49 MU' and was 'Allotted to 49 MU Lasham as scrap, Cat.E2 on 28th May 1947.

On 7th July 1944, Martinet PW979 was allotted to Miles Aircraft for trial installation of Drone equipment on 6 month loan (later extended to 20th July 1945); this then became the second prototype M.50 Queen Martinet. On 9th August 1945, it went 'To PAU Manorbier for investigation by the Pilotless Aircraft Unit'. PW979 next went to RAE for 'Flight trials re: pilotless aircraft development programme on 14th December 1945 and on 21st March 1947, the card read 'Engine sent to 2 MPRD'. On 7th May 1947, it was recorded that the 'Aircraft was burnt on site' and on 25th May 1947, it was Cat.E2 Scrap to 49 MU Lasham.

A further 22 M.25 Martinets, including two prototypes, were later modified to M.50 Queen Martinets, including the 2 prototype M.50s, by Miles Aircraft Ltd at Woodley and for details of these and their individual histories see Appendix No.30.

The joys of towing winged targets was aptly explained in an article entitled *Glider Towing* by W H Stevens, published in the Air Training Corps Gazette - Vol.VI No.4 April 1946:

For the Navy pilot eagerly awaiting his first operational appointment a spell of service with a second-line squadron often seemed like purgatory; yet his work was frequently an invaluable contribution to the war effort, and even if it was away from all the fighting is still involved some difficult tests of good flying.

"Toe-Joe" was just such a task. Pilots avoided it like the plague, although many lived to bless training it had given them. For the "Joe" who towed the gliders had an unenviable job, but a job that demanded some degree of skill. It was no easy task to land a

An HQ 41 Group Return (N.A. Ref: AIR 17/33), gave the numbers of Martinets surviving at 6th December 1945 as follows:

Martinet I	4 (for repair – Non-Effective aircraft)
Martinet IB Winch	155 comprising 2 (complete with equipment); 151 (in long-term storage) and 2 (for repair – Non-Effective aircraft)
Martinet I E & F Winch	593 comprising 5 (ready for issue); 6 (complete with equipment); 1 (not checked in); 572 (in long-term storage) and 9 (for repair – Non-Effective aircraft)
Martinet Overseas	13 comprising 3 (ready for issue); 1 (complete with equipment) and 9 (deficient of equipment)

pilotless 16-foot glider on to an uneven runway without mishap from the front seat of a Martinet; and the technique was so much akin to that of landing on to a carrier's deck that few later regretted the monotonous hours they had spent circling ships' or shore-based gun crews while their glider received a fair sprinkling of busting shells and shrapnel.

Thirty-two-foot gliders came to be used for these target practices, but for a long time the Navy relied upon the smaller "winged target" that became known to all and sundry as a "Harry Winger".

Taking off with one of these was always an occasion for the 'goofers', who would drop tools in the expectation of little light entertainment. They were seldom disappointed.

With her Bristol Mercury XXX engine ticking over the Martinet would be taxied into position on the runway by a ground-crew man, while another took the cable running from the winch to the floor of the gunner's cockpit, and out over pulleys, then to the tow-bar of the glider. The aircraft would then be taxied forward until the slack been taken up, when a signal from a rating would give the pilot the "all clear".

Flaps dropped, the engine would be opened up to 2,650 revs, giving maximum power of 850 hp, and the machine held on a steady course until, about 60 knots, the pilot would feel her coming unstuck. Thus he would have attained sufficient altitude to clear the boundary fence with his target, and incidentally he would have performed a carrier take-off.

If all went well speed was allowed to build up 80 knots, and at 200 feet the boost reduced to +2½ in. At 500 feet flaps were raised and the engine throttled back to +½ in, giving a comfortable 120 knots. It took time to gain height, and often it was some minutes before the speed showed signs of building up, but at least tug and glider were airborne.

All too often take-off was not nearly as smooth. A slight cross-wind was enough to send the winged target drifting on to the grass, where it would trip and snap the cable. Occasionally the glider rose too rapidly and fouled the elevators with the cable, so steepening the angle of climb that the aircraft was in danger of stalling.

A gunner who forgot to lock his winch provided the funniest spectacle. The aircraft took off with the cable drum turning and laying out more and more cable. Naturally, the glider remained where it was, and to those of us watching from the squadron office it appeared to have broken away.

Several thousand feet of cable had run out, and the Martinet was now but a distant murmur, when the winch ceased revolving and the cable drew taut. With a wild leap the glider jerked forward 120 knots, as if jet-propelled. Unable to see the cable, an old man who had been trimming the grass at the far end of the runway watched the object hurtling towards him with mouth open wide. Then, at the very last minute, he decided to accept the evidence of his senses, and dived into a convenient ditch. The glider splintered and dissolved against the boundary fence above him, with a great deal of noise, while the wire went singing past uncomfortably close.

"Streaming", the process of letting out a greater length of wire once the tug and target were airborne, was usually performed over the sea, and away from other aircraft. Length of tow depended upon the type of exercise, or "shoot" required. At low levels it was not possible to stream too great a length of wire, because the gliders' drop in height relative to the tug increased the farther behind it got.

An attitude of 1,000 feet generally entailed a tow of 1,000 feet, although three times that length could no doubt have been used with safety.

"The greater the speed the less the drop" was a useful maxim when a ship demanded an attack with the glider skimming the waves. Unfortunately, many a pilot forgot that there was a slight drop in speed when making a dumb-bell turn on to a fresh run sufficient to close the gap between target and sea. The resultant jerk as a wing sliced into the water was always followed by the gunner's gleeful shout: "Target away, sir"!

High-level runs were less troublesome. But the accuracy the guns was proportionately worse, so that a watery grave was best avoided by lengthening the tow to 3,000 feet.

Winged targets flew smoothly, following the aircraft in most of its manoeuvres, but it must be remembered that they had no lift, and the wings merely gave a steadying effect as the feathers on a dart. For this reason the term "glider" is actually inaccurate.

Although the glider was successfully looped, any manoeuvre more violent than a Rate 3 turn was inadvisable. Up to that angle of bank

A drawing of Royal Navy winged targets and their towing requirements.   [ATC Gazette April 1946]

the target followed the aircraft quite smoothly, although there was always a slight lag while movement was transmitted along the cable. Pulling out from a dive the target's momentum sent it lower than the tug at the end of the dive, and for this reason care had to be taken when losing altitude at any great rate.

Constructed of all-welded steel, the fuselage of a 16-foot glider had a triangular cross-section. Wings and tail unit were made of either wood or steel and were interchangeable, as was the nose fairing, which, being also of wood or metal, allowed the c.g. to remain the same for either type of wing.

A main skid, 10 feet long, of ash, had a facing of mild steel, and there were twelve small coil springs to absorb the shock of landing. Spring-steel strips provided wing-tip skids.

Difference in weight between wood and metal versions of the target, which seldom lived longer than six flights, was not very great. The wooden target weighed 144 lb; a metal one was 13 lb heavier.

In order to obtain an accurate estimate of their sighting abilities gun crews generally requested the use of a marking aircraft. This was, if anything, slightly worse than towing.

The marking Martinet, its pilot suffering from an acute pain in the neck from staring through his canopy up at the comrade above, remained in position directly beneath the tug and on a level with the target for the whole of the shoot. From the rear the observer would mark upon a chart the approximate positions of bursting shells, reporting by radio to the gunners at the close of each run.

Marking was an exasperating task. With the Mercury grinding away in front, the ship politely informing you at regular intervals that you were fouling the range - which happened every time you lagged a little behind the tug - and the "looker" complaining bitterly because the aircraft's tail obscured his vision, two hours was the limit of anyone's endurance.

But when the marking aircraft became mistaken for the target even the strict discipline of R/T procedure could not hide the anguish of the unfortunate soul buried in a cloud of black-puffing shells.

Bringing a "Harry Winger" home was always a fascinating business, but if the tug pilot or his gunner had a date the target became mysteriously lost on some convenient hillside.

The target was wound in to within a few yards (never done at speeds in excess of 110 knots) and a request was made to land the glider. To do this a dummy approach was made, and the glider cut loose by the gunner as it skimmed over the runway, with the tug remaining airborne and about 100 feet. A "welcome home" committee stood by in a control van when word was received that a glider was coming in, ready to clear the airfield of the (usual) wreckage.

A normal circuit was made, but on the downwind leg speed was reduced to 100 knots, and flaps lowered by degrees, to ensure no sudden deceleration that would leave the target to overtake the tug under its own impetus. The approach was made longer than normally, with a low rate of descent that should never have exceeded 400 feet a minute.

Imagining that he was landing on a spot at the farthest end of the runway, the pilot aimed to cross the downwind boundary at some 250 feet, losing height very steadily, and with a speed of 80 knots. Gunner watching the runway below would order "Port, port, port", "Steady", or "Starboard", according to the drift, cutting away the target when he judged the time was ripe, but not if more than three-quarters of the runway had been wasted.

Skilful pilots could drop their targets at the runway's near edge, and continue with the landing without a second circuit. The rest of us considered the flight successful if we landed the target all in one piece.

An article entitled "*In Search of a Target*" by Flight Lieutenant A F Hailey, appeared in the Air Reserve Gazette for April 1947 and an extract from that regarding the target gliders is reproduced below:

One type of aerial target was developed from a system in use by the Royal Navy. Since the early part of the war they had been training light ack-ack gunners by using large model gliders. These gliders had a wing span of just over six feet. They were launched from a winch and, by the automatic application of rudder, could be made to circle a particular area at about 40 mph. Later on, this system was improved by the introduction of a rocket glider - span four feet - which stepped up the speed to some 100 mph.

It was more or less logical that from this point designers should toy with the idea of producing a glider - or rather a winged target - which could be towed by an aircraft at much higher speeds. As a matter of fact, this idea was by no means new. Before the war, both here and in other countries, experiments were carried out with this object in view. But they were not at all successful; the United States, for instance, decided the project was a dead loss and abandoned it altogether. But the RAF did not give up entirely and, as a result of our long experience coupled with much trial and error, a workable towed winged target was at last developed. In September 1942 this target, made of balsa wood and with a wingspan of four feet, was successfully towed by a Hawker Hart.

It seemed, until recently, that two winged targets were in the running for official adoption by the RAF. One had a wingspan of sixteen feet, and the other of thirty-two feet. At first, the former was the more successful of the two, but now some snags in the larger model have been ironed out, and you can safely put your shirt on the thirty-two-footer.

This winged target - see artist's impression below - has a fuselage of steel, with the mainplane and tail assembly of steel and fabric. The weight is comparatively light, being about 780 lb. This factor, and the target's streamlining, mean that the towing aircraft is not slowed up to any great extent. The tug, by the way, is at present a Martinet, though the Tempest V is likely to take its place fairly soon.

Landing and take-off with the winged target is an interesting business, though apparently not as tricky as one might expect. With take-off, a pilot has to be careful to fly very steadily, and to climb at certain pre-described speeds. For landing, the tug pilot takes his instructions over the radio from another pilot who is seated in the runway control wagon. Experiments have shown that this system works out very well, and targets which have been badly shot up have been landed quite successfully.

Although the winged target has not been universally adopted for the RAF (it is still capable of improvement and trials are continuing), it seems fairly certain that it will be making a general appearance within a short time.

As to the future, it is obvious that when aircraft speeds get above the subsonic range even winged targets will have had their chips. Then the only effective means of practising air combat will be to have pilotless target aircraft controlled by radio. And - between ourselves - that's exactly what is going to happen.

Overseas Sales

In an MAP letter dated 17th May 1944, it was stated that we were to transfer to 'such Governments as had been agreed', a specified number of aircraft. In answer to this, the Americans replied in a letter dated 24th June, to the effect that they had concurred to our course of action, and one of the Governments to whom supplies of aircraft had been agreed, was Portugal. Included amongst the first batch of specified aircraft for foreign governments were 4 Martinets for Portugal, and these were probably those which were ultimately supplied to the Portuguese Navy. For details of M.25 Martinets supplied to Portugal see Appendix 25 on the CD.

A 32ft span winged target.

[ATC Gazette]

A very long, 'Top Secret' Telegram, dated 18th November 1944, was sent from Washington to the Air Ministry, Whitehall, the contents of which went to great lengths to outline our export policy and its implications on the Lease-Lend arrangements between ourselves and the United States of America. This telegram also expressed concerns over just to which foreign governments the Americans thought that we could or could not export aircraft. The Americans certainly wielded the big stick over what we could and couldn't do with aircraft supplied under the controversial Lease-Lend agreement.

The Royal Egyptian Air Force also apparently placed an order (having presumably expressed an interest in acquiring a suitable aircraft for target towing), for 4 Martinets, but in Air Attaché Report 18, dated 1st May to 21st October 1945, it was stated that, although the first one had been delivered to Suez in September 1945, acceptance of it was refused by the Director of the REAF because production of the Martinet had ceased. This machine remained in its packing case at Suez Road Stores depot but it is not known what happened to it or the other 3, which were en route from the UK at the time. They were replaced with Defiants from Ceylon (Report 20), which the Egyptians presumably hadn't noticed had been out of production for even longer than the Martinet! It then got worse because the Half Year Report on the REAF, dated 31.10.46, stated that 4 Defiants (instead of Martinets) had been received from Columbo, Ceylon, as a gift from the RAF, but were found to be in such a poor state that it was doubtful if repair would have been economical! (N.A. Ref: AIR 23/8346).

On 26th August 1946, it was recorded at a weekly meeting at Woodley:

Martinet. Sweden: An order had been received for 5 reconditioned aircraft. Turkey and Switzerland also looking at it. However, nothing came of the last two countries 'looking at it'.

Hugh Kendall flew Martinet TT Mk.I RG906 to Radlett on 11th September 1946, for the seventh SBAC Show, held at Radlett (on 12th and 13th), where it was demonstrated (probably by Ken Waller), before being flown back to Woodley by Hugh on 13th.

During 1946, Miles Aircraft Ltd reconditioned 2 Martinets for the Irish Air Corps (and these still stubbornly refuse to reveal their previous RAF identities, despite much research on both sides of the Irish Sea) and for details of these see the next volume. In 1947 they reconditioned 3 for the Portuguese Air Force, see Appendix 25, and

5 for AB Flygleveranser, Stockholm, Sweden, the latter for banner and target towing duties for the Royal Swedish Air Force, details of these and another, which was reconditioned for Sweden later in 1947 as a replacement for one lost in a crash, will be found in the next volume.

An undated, document (N.A. Ref: Air 2/10.191), entitled: 'Sales of surplus military aircraft', referred to aircraft despatched to foreign countries as at 1st April 1948. Included in this were 41 ex RAF Martinets supplied to France under the Hartemann Agreement of 1946 (some of these being fitted with the type 'F' winch); 9 to the Belgian Air Force (although 2 were later exchanged for 'new' aircraft); 3 to Portugal (although 3 had already been supplied to the Portuguese Air Force and 4 to the Portuguese Navy during the war) and 6 to Sweden. The sales to France, Belgium, Sweden and Eire will also be covered in Volume 3.

Also mentioned in the above document was the fact that the Danes have also purchased 6 Proctors, 3 Martinets, 3 Spitfire PR.XIs outside the agreement – 'these have all been supplied with the exception of 2 Spitfire PR.XIs which are now awaiting delivery. 95 per cent of the equipment due under the agreement has now been supplied'. Unfortunately the previous identities for the 3 Martinets were not given and indeed none were ever delivered to Denmark.

Two Martinets, MS902 and MS 903, were despatched to Iceland on the SS *Isobell* on 18th December 1943, arriving in Reykjavik on 8th January 1944. Of these, MS902 was last used by RAF Reykjavik from 1st November 1945 and rather than bring it back to the UK it was sold locally on 18th July 1949 to the Akureyri Flying Cub, Iceland and registered **TF-SHC**. MS903 was SOC on 15th November 1945.

UK Civilian Sales

Although the RAF individual aircraft record cards note that 3 Martinets were sold to the West London Flying Club/Group at White Waltham on 14th March 1947, they were in fact purchased by Mr D E Masters, who was probably only a member of the club. They were for sale in Sweden and there is no record of them having been refurbished before delivery nor were CofAs issued:

EM646   Sold to West London Flying Group 14.3.47. Regd **G-AJJL** (CofR 11351) 27.2.47 to Donald Ernest Masters, Blandford, Dorset. Regn cld 23.5.47 as sold abroad. Regd **SE-BCO**.

HN913   Sold to West London Flying Club, White Waltham 14.3.47. Regd **G-AJJO** (CofR 11354) 27.2.47 to Donald Ernest Masters, Blandford, Dorset. Regn cld 23.5.47 as sold abroad. Regd **SE-BCN**.

HP145   Sold to West London Flying Club, White Waltham 14.3.47. Regd **G-AJJK** (CofR 11350) 27.2.47 to Donald Ernest Masters, Blandford, Dorset. Regn cld 23.5.47 as sold abroad. Regd **SE-BCP**.

W S Shackleton Ltd placed an advertisement in *The Aeroplane* for 4th April 1947 as follows: 'Three Martinets - "to clear" at £175 each.' These were MS794, MS836 and MS 871, sold by the RAF on 10th March 1947 and although only two were registered to W S Shackleton Ltd, these were delivered to Bovingdon (believed by air), where they languished in the open, becoming derelict by May 1948. The third aircraft was not reported as being delivered to Bovingdon:

MS794   Sold to Lancashire Aircraft Corporation Ltd, Salmesbury 1.3.47 but not registered.

MS836   Sold to Lancashire Aircraft Corporation Ltd, Salmesbury 1.3.47. Regd **G-AJZB** (CofR 11716) 18.6.47 to W S Shackleton Ltd, London, W1. Regn cld 26.2.48. Broken up at Bovingdon in 1948. PWFU 5.3.48.

MS871   Sold to Lancashire Aircraft Corporation Ltd, Salmesbury 1.3.47. Regd **G-AJZC** (CofR 11716) 18.6.47 to W S Shackleton Ltd, London, W1. Cld 26.2.48 Broken up at Bovingdon in 1948. PWFU 5.3.48.

MS849   Sold to Robert Alan Short, Thornton Heath, Surrey 2.1.50 but not registered. Seen, painted silver, parked outside Willis Hole Aviation, Plough Lane, Croydon Airport but with no markings other than the serial.

In the Reading Sky Observers Club 'Skywriter' (No. Ten, dated 20th August 1947) it was stated that: *Group Captain Bandidt of Miles Aircraft is very kindly making available to us a Martinet complete with wings and engine* but it is believed that ever nothing came of this most generous gesture and there is no confirmation of this actually happening.

A total of 1,724 Miles M.25 Martinets were built. For a summary of Miles M.25 Martinet TT Mk.I production see Appendix 23 and for individual aircraft histories see Appendix 24 on the CD.

(N.A. Refs: AIR 941, AIR 1798 and AIR 2489).

Left: Martinet RG988 'R8K', 776 Squadron, Woodvale, in 1945.   [Via Bert Clarke]

*Below: Martinet HP218 '4M-A', 695 Squadron, Horsham St. Faith, on 20th June 1948.
[M P Marsh via Bert Clarke]*

SPECIFICATION AND PERFORMANCE DATA

Engine:	870 hp Bristol Mercury 25 or 30
Dimensions:	span 39ft 0in; length 30ft 11in; height 11ft 7in; wing area 242sq ft; aspect ratio 6.3; wing section root NACA 23024, tip NACA 23009
Weights:	empty 4,640lb; fuel (130 gal) 975lb; oil (8.5 gal) 76lb; crew 400lb; useful load 659lb; AUW 6,750lb; wing loading 27.9lb/sq ft
Performance:	max speed 221 mph at sea level, 240 mph at 5,800ft, 238 mph at 10,000ft; max cruising speed 199 mph at 5,000ft; max design diving speed 330 mph IAS; stalling speed 83 mph with flaps up, 62 mph with flaps down; run to unstick 780ft; distance to 50ft, 1,380ft; landing run 1,275ft; landing from 50ft, 1,614ft; time to 5,000ft, 3.5 min and to 10,000ft, 8.0 min; range 694 miles; duration 5.0 hrs.

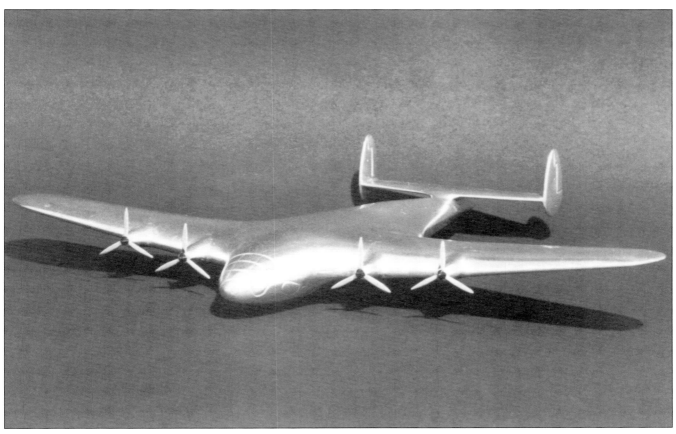

A model of the proposed Miles X.2 Transport Aeroplane.

Chapter 17:
Miles X.3 Transport

In 1940, Miles produced a design study for a 100 passenger transport version of the Miles X.2 Transport Aeroplane Project, to be powered by six 900 hp engines developed from the Rolls-Royce Kestrel.

Below: An artist's impression of the proposed Miles X.3 Transport.

This he called the Miles X.3 and an artist's impression of this shows that the engines were apparently partially buried in the wings, with rather 'stubby' nacelles protruding from the leading edges. Like the Miles X.2 project, the X.3 had twin fins and rudders and a tricycle undercarriage but nothing else is known of this variant.

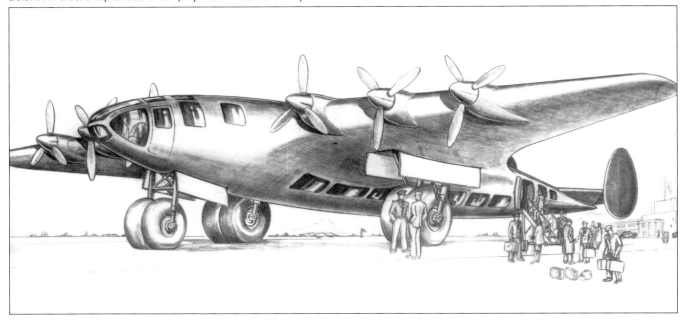

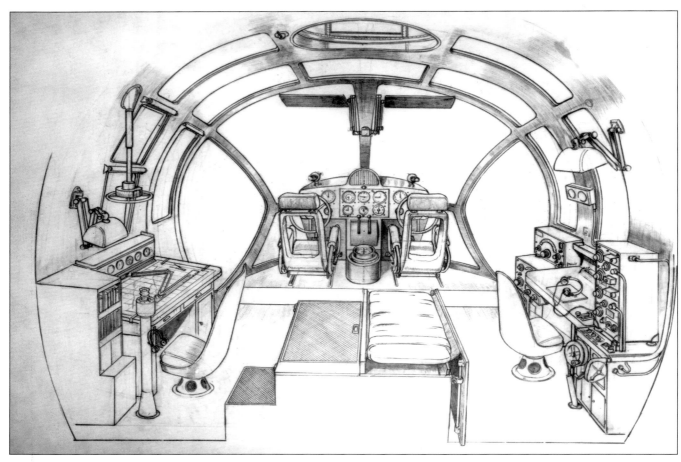

Above: A drawing of the 'office' looking forward.

Right: A drawing showing the galley on the left, note the 1930's cooker and sink(!) and the flight engineer's work station on the right, complete with engineers vice and tools!

SPECIFICATION AND PERFORMANCE DATA

Engines:	6 x 900 hp developed Rolls-Royce Kestrel
Dimensions:	span 99ft 0in; length 78.8ft; wing area 1,762 sq ft; aspect ratio 6
Weights:	not known
Performance:	not known

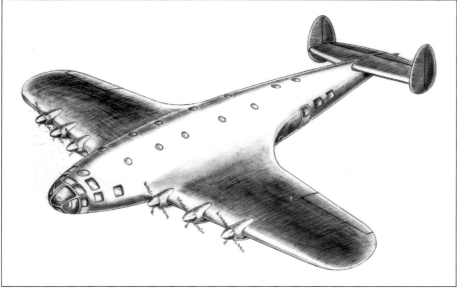

Left: An artist's impression of the X.3 in flight.

An artist's impression of the Miles X.7 in flight.

Chapter 18:
Miles X.4, X.5, X.6, X.7, M.26H X.7 Mod
and M.26I X.8 Transports

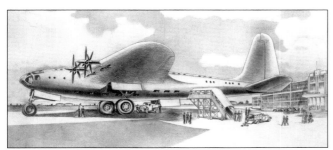

Above: An artist's impression of the Miles X.7 loading at a typical pre-war airport.

Right: A cut-away drawing of the Miles X.7 showing the interior and engine installation with gearboxes.

Miles X.4, X.5 and X.6

Miles continued to work on the 'X' projects as and when he could spare the time but of the next three design studies, the Miles X.4, X.5 and X.6, nothing is known. However, in 1941 Miles produced the X.7 design study.

Miles X.7

The Miles X.7 was a 50 to 100 seat passenger Trans-Atlantic Transport, powered by eight 2,300 hp Rolls-Royce Merlin engines

buried in the wings driving four contra-rotating airscrews through gearboxes and extension shafts, and was the largest of the 'X' series of transport aeroplanes proposed at the time.

The X.7 was readily distinguishable from all the other 'X' variants as, apart from the X.8 (which had no windows and a different cabin) it was the only variant to have a single fin and rudder. The X.7 probably had a single-wheeled tricycle undercarriage, although an artist's impression produced at about the same time shows only the forward portion of an 'X' project (which could possibly have been the X.7), with twin-wheeled tricycle undercarriage and boarding stairs. Three different versions of the X.7 were proposed:-

50 passengers, long-range	3,450 miles
100 passengers, medium range	2,000 to 2,500 miles
100 passengers, short range	1,100 miles

Above: The Main Lounge fitted with 34 seats.

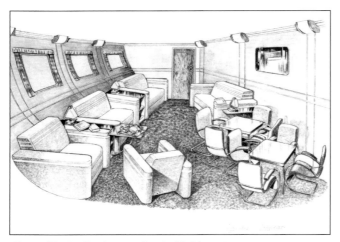

Above: The Ladies Lounge fitted with 20 seats.

SPECIFICATION AND PERFORMANCE DATA

Miles X.7 and M.26H X.7 Mod

Engines:	8 x 2,300 Rolls-Royce Merlin
Dimensions:	span 150ft 0in; length 110ft 0in
Weights:	AUW 165,000lb
Performance:	max speed 350 mph

Miles M.26I X.8

Engines:	4 unspecified, but would probably have been 1,740 hp Rolls-Royce Griffon II

All other details were probably very similar to the X.7.

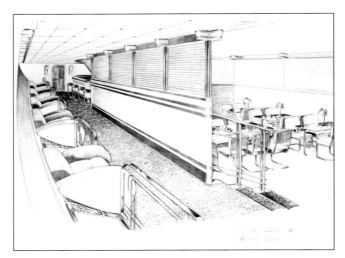

Above: Promenade Deck and Dining Room.

The designation M.26 was given to the X.7 during 1942 and all subsequent 'X' variants used this designation. It was also during 1942 that the X.7 was resurrected as the M.26H X.7 Mod., and a project drawing dated 7th April 1942 shows this version as a two-deck 550 seat Troop Carrier. The lower Deck 'A' seated 290 troops and the upper Deck 'B' 260 troops. The single fin and rudder was retained but twin-wheels were fitted to the tricycle undercarriage.

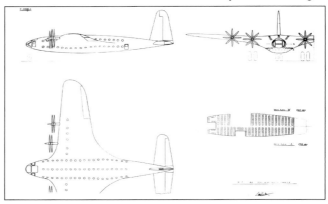

Above: Three-view drawing of the Miles X.7 as a 550 Seat Troop Carrier.

Miles X.8

Although little is known about the Miles X.8, a photograph of a three-view general arrangement drawing, unfortunately with an illegible date, shows the M.26 Scheme 'X' freighter version of the X.7, and it is believed that this was probably the X.8. The Scheme 'X' had four engines of unspecified type (but probably Rolls-Royce Griffon II) mounted normally in nacelles on the wings. There were no windows in the fuselage and it had the single fin and rudder of the X.7 and a large single-wheeled tricycle undercarriage. An unusual feature, however, was the 'bug-eye' teardrop cockpit for the pilots, which was mounted centrally on the top of the front fuselage.

In 1941, Miles decided to build a reduced-scale, twin-engined flying model at his own expense, in order to confirm that the hoped for benefits of the 'X' principle were in fact attainable. The new machine was known as the Miles M.30 'X' Minor and this should not be confused with the original reduced scale flying model of the Miles 'X', which had been projected before the war, as that was a markedly different design. The Miles M.30 'X' Minor flying scale model is detailed in the appropriate chapter.

During my researches into the Miles 'X' Transport Aeroplane Projects, it was found that each project was also given a letter, e.g. A for the X.1, B for the X.2, C for the X.3 etc and this practice went on until at least K for the X.10.

The first prototype M.28 undergoing initial engine runs prior to its first flight, which was made by George Miles, with 'B' mark U-0232, on 11th July 1941. Note a young Jeremy Miles standing with F G and George Miles by the port wingtip. *[Via Richard Almond]*

Chapter 19
Miles M.28 Training and Communications Aircraft

During 1939, George Miles started work on the design of a replacement aircraft for two very successful Miles aeroplanes; the Whitney Straight of 1936 and his first design, the Monarch of 1938. However, on the outbreak of war in September 1939, the project had to be dropped.

Amongst some documents recovered in June 2002 from the estate of the late Mr. Readings, was a minute of a meeting held on 23rd August 1940 with F G Miles, G H Miles, R N Bournon and W G Capley present. This minute was entitled 'Light Communication Aircraft - M.22' and it suggested that George Miles was intending to resurrect this design study of 1939. This ultimately developed into the Miles M.28 and the minutes are reproduced below:

Light Communication Aircraft - M.22

Preliminaries

1. DO at Liverpool Road. Schedule of office equipment put forward by Mr Bournon approved by Mr F G Miles.
2. Mr Bournon to be taken off Tora *(the code name for the Monoplane Air Tail - PA)* by 31st August and transferred to Mr G H Miles.
3. Mr Reading *(actually Ken H Readings - PA)* will be allocated to Mr Bournon. No further DO help to be engaged for the time being.
4. Office and Shop space at Liverpool Road will be allocated to Mr G H Miles.
5. Necessary labour etc will be made available for this job and will work to the instructions of Mr G H Miles. From a disciplinary and wages point of view, all labour will come under Mr Tusen.

Design Points

A. Two seater with occasional third seat. All seats to be very comfortable. Cockpit width to be 43" inside.
B. Maximum all-up weight for overload case to be limited to 2,000 lbs. This will necessitate a wooden airscrew.

C. Wing area to be approximately 160 sq ft. Aspect Ratio of wing to be about 6.
D. Cruising speed to be 150 mph. Engine Gipsy Major III 150 hp.
E. Wheel control.

Although these minutes were entitled 'Light Communication Aircraft - M.22', this is not thought to be a typing error but was probably due to the Miles type designation system having reached that number at the time of the meeting.

However, it must have been realised later that there were other design studies on the drawing boards at Woodley, including the twin-engined Day or Night Fighter project of 1939, and that these would also require Miles type numbers so, in 1941, this project was therefore, re-numbered M.28 and in 1941, the Day or Night Fighter project of 1939 was given the type number M.22.

However, these minutes appear to have heralded the start of the final design for a modern training and communications aeroplane

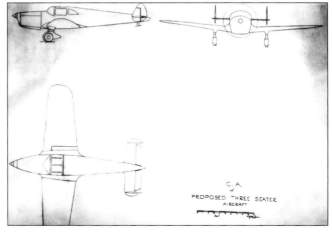

Three-view G.A drawing of the pre-war Proposed Three Seater Aircraft, later to form the basis for the M.28.

Right: Photograph showing the push-pull wheel controls fitted to the first prototype M.28.

that was to be more efficient than anything in that class produced to that time. Don Brown later wrote:

During 1941 official consideration was being given to a completely re-designed version of the Proctor.

We were convinced that a machine having the same accommodation and performance as the Proctor could be produced with a 140 hp Gipsy Major engine instead of the 200 hp Gipsy Six used in the Proctor.

We accordingly embarked upon the design of the M.28 and the prototype flew in September 1941. It entirely vindicated our ideas in that it fully equalled and in some respects exceeded the accommodation, pay-load and purpose of the Proctor, using only two-thirds of the power of the latter.

No official interest was displayed at the time and the first prototype M.28 was subsequently converted into the M.38 which will be described later.

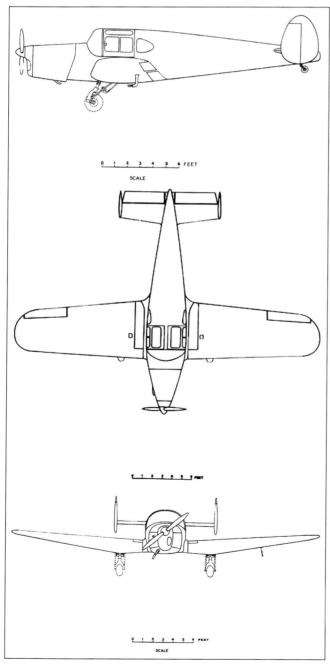

Three-view G.A. drawing of the first prototype M.28.

Phillips & Powis Aircraft Ltd later produced an undated booklet on the Miles M.28 Training and Communications Aircraft, reproduced here in text.

LEADING PARTICULARS

GENERAL

| Type | 2 or 3 seater low wing monoplane. |
| Duties | Ab-initio or intermediate training, communications. |

PRINCIPAL DIMENSIONS

Span	30 ft 6 in
Length overall	22 ft 1½ in
Height overall, including airscrew (tail down)	8 ft 6 in
Width of cabin	4 ft 0 in
Wing area (gross)	160 sq ft
Type of undercarriage	Retractable.
Track	9 ft
Shock absorber strut	Oleo type with lever suspension.
Brakes	Bendix mechanically operated.

PRELIMINARY SPECIFICATION

The Miles M.28 has been designed to fulfil two major functions:-

   (a)   Two-seater ab-initio and/or intermediate training aircraft.

   (b)   Three-seater communications aircraft.

The major features of the design and the reasons for their incorporation are dealt with briefly hereunder.

Since the beginning of the war there has been a growing tendency towards the opinion that ab-initio training should be carried out on an aeroplane which embodies as many features as possible of the operational types. Alternatively, the gap between the simple elementary trainer and the high powered advanced trainer should be filled by an aircraft closely approaching the latter type, but capable of economical operation and maintenance by relatively unskilled personnel. At the same time the machine should retain the features of safety and ease of handling which have hitherto been associated with small training aircraft.

For reasons of economy, maintenance and the conservation of petrol supplies, it is also important that the engine should be as low power as possible consistent with the duties of the aeroplane. The M.28 is designed to take any engine in the region of 150 hp. It has a retractable undercarriage, constant speed airscrew, high lift auxiliary aerofoil flaps and many other features which have not previously been incorporated in a low powered trainer.

The pronounced difference between the elementary trainer and the advanced type is particularly marked for those pilots who graduate to multi-engined aircraft. The M.28 has side by side seating, an enclosed cabin and wheel control. The cabin and instrument layout are deliberately very similar to that of the average twin engined type. The main objection which has been raised in the past to side by side training aeroplanes has been the restrictions of view on the opposite side to the pupil or instructor. This point has received careful study and the forward view of the M.28 is superior to any type of open cockpit ab-initio training aircraft in current use. Large transparent panels are also provided for rearward vision.

A feature of the design not hitherto considered necessary on light training types is the very complete instrument equipment. A standard service blind flying panel is fitted in addition to a complete set of engine instruments, including those normally associated with supercharged engines.

The need for a large number of small aircraft for inter-station communication and specialised purposes has been met until now partly by utilising unsuitable service types and partly by impressing privately owned aircraft. The result is that a very large number of different types of aircraft are now in use for this purpose, and provisioning and maintenance problems must present great difficulty. The performance of many of these aircraft is inadequate for the purpose for which they are used and in many cases their comfort leaves much to be desired.

The cruising speed and range of the M.28 will be considerably in advance on any existing aircraft with the same power plant (Gipsy Major or Cirrus Major engine) and compare well with aircraft of much higher power. The side by side cabin is unusually large, being 4 inches wider than the Proctor at the pilot's seats and 5 inches higher from the bottom of the seat pan to the roof structure. The machine can be adapted for a number of specialised applications among which are: field ambulance work, army co-operation purposes, radio and navigational training, air crew training and freight carrying.

As a light freight carrier the aircraft has interesting possibilities owing to the very large disposable load/horse power ratio. This works out at 7.3 as against 3.4 for the Bombay heavy transport aircraft. With the fixed pitch wooden airscrew at the designed all-up weight of 2,500 lb the disposable load is 1,100 lb. Allowing

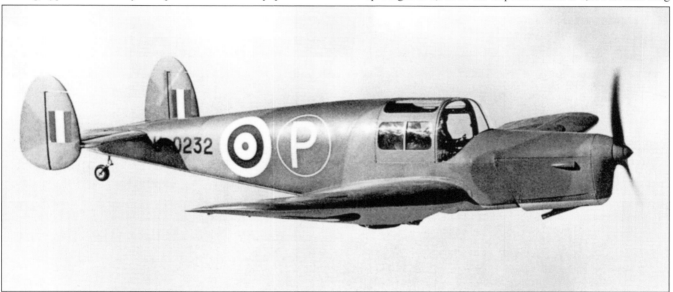

Above and below: U-0232 the first prototype M.28.

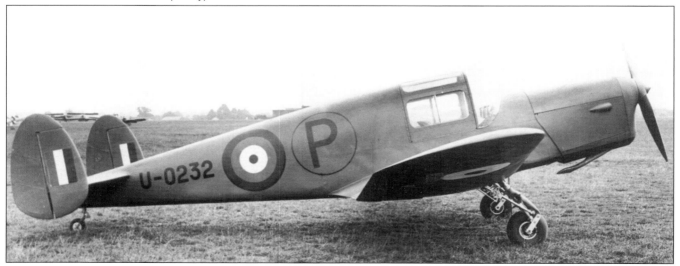

200 lb for pilot and 170 lb for fuel and oil the pay load is 730 lb, representing two spare Gipsy Major engines and airscrews, 40 Bren guns, nearly 100 gallons of petrol or 70 gallons of water. The version with constant speed airscrew will carry an even greater load without sacrificing take-off run but the strength factors will be reduced.

As a light ambulance the machine will carry one stretcher case and nurse as well as the pilot. When adapted for this purpose the cabin will be heavily sound-proofed and the stretcher supports will be mounted on rubber shock absorber and vibration dampers. A full length 6 ft detachable panel and special track arrangement; combined with the low height of the aircraft will make loading and unloading relatively simple.

SPECIAL FEATURES

Some noteworthy detail features of the design not usually to be found on aircraft of this size are:

Exceptionally large windscreen giving unequalled forward view.

Miles low drag auxiliary aerofoil flaps combined with fuselage air brake and drooping ailerons.

Retractable undercarriage with knee action oleo-pneumatic shock absorbers.

Undercarriage designed to confine damage to airscrew when landing with chassis retracted.

Lever suspension oleo-pneumatic tail wheel unit with quick release attachment feature. (The complete assembly can be removed for servicing or replacement in one minute).

Dual range fuel tanks.

One piece removable cabin for quick loading on freighter version.

Exceptionally large cabin accommodating standard seat type parachutes for instructor and pupil.

Full instrument equipment including standard Service instrument flying panel.

Quick access to instruments.

PERFORMANCE *(Based on an all-up weight of 2,050 lb - Trainer Version)*

Case 1:
Gipsy Major Series III Engine with constant-speed airscrew -

Maximum level speed at sea level	160 mph
Cruising speed at rated altitude 3,500 ft	150 mph
Initial rate of climb	1,250 ft/min
Stalling speed (with flaps)	40 mph
Cruising range (full tanks)	715 miles
Duration	4.75 hours

Case 2:
Gipsy Major Series III S Engine with constant-speed airscrew -

Maximum level speed at rated altitude (7,000ft)	176 mph
Cruising speed at rated altitude (7,000 ft)	166 mph
Initial rate of climb	1,400 ft/min
Stalling speed (with flaps)	40 mph
Cruising range (full tanks)	700 miles
Duration	4.25 hours

Case 3:
Cirrus Major 150 or Gipsy Major Series IIA Engine with fixed pitch airscrew -

Maximum level speed at sea level	155 mph
Cruising speed at 1,000 ft	140 mph
Initial rate of climb	950 ft/min
Stalling speed (with flaps)	40 mph
Cruising range (full tanks)	700 miles
Duration	5.00 hours

WEIGHTS

Case 1:
Gipsy Major Series III Engine -

	Two-seater Trainer	Three-seater Communications
Tare	1,460 lb	1,460 lb
Fuel	(20 galls) 150 lb	(35 galls) 262 lb
Oil (2 galls) 18 lb	(3 galls) 27 lb	
Instructor/pilot and parachute	200 lb	200 lb
Pupil and parachute	200 lb	
Two passengers and parachutes	-	400 lb
Total	2,028 lb	2,349 lb

Case 2:
Gipsy Major Series III S Engine -
Two-seater

	Three-seater Trainer	Communications
Tare	1,400 lb	1,480 lb
Fuel	(20 galls) 150 lb	(35 galls) 262 lb
Oil (2 galls) 18 lb	(3 galls) 27 lb	
Instructor/pilot and parachute	200 lb	200 lb
Pupil and parachute	200 lb	
Two passengers and parachutes	-	400 lb
Total	1,968 lb	2,369 lb

Case 3:
Cirrus Major 150 or Gipsy Major Series IIA Engine -
Two-seater

	Three-seater Trainer	Communications
Tare	1,480 lb	1,400 lb
Fuel	(20 galls) 150 lb	(35 galls) 262 lb
Oil (2 galls) 18 lb (3 galls) 27 lb		
Instructor/pilot and parachute	200 lb	200 lb
Pupil and parachute	200 lb	
Two passengers and parachutes	-	400 lb
Total	2,048 lb	2.289 lb

ODDENTIFICATION—CLII

If by Bradshaw you must fly
As you travel through the sky,
Choose a craft which will assure
A view of all that lies before—
A craft with comfort and stability,
With bags of room (despite utility),
A craft which will approximate
To Miles's new M-28.

With acknowledgments
to The Aeroplane.

The booklet ended with this delightful Oddentification, by Wren, of the M.28.

In January 1943, Phillips & Powis Aircraft Ltd produced a brochure entitled 'Miles Specialised Aircraft for Specialised Purposes'. Contained therein was a summary of a selection of Miles aircraft which had either been built or proposed up to then.

A note on the M.28 was included:

M.28 ab initio Trainer or Communications Aircraft

The M.28 combines perfection of view and ease of handling with a performance never before attained in a light training type. It is fitted with high lift flaps and a retractable undercarriage and its side-by-side seating makes it especially suitable for the training of pilots who are destined to fly multi engined types. As a communications type it provides a roomier cabin, a higher top speed and a lower landing speed than any similar type of aeroplane yet produced. It is available with either stick or wheel control and with a variety of engines both British and American.

Span	*30 ft 6 in*
Wing area	*160 sq ft*
Engine	*Gipsy Major, Cirrus Major, Walter Scarab, Lycoming, Menasco*
All up weight	*2,100-2,500 lb*
Max speed	*175 mph*
Landing speed	*40 mph*

M.28 Mk.I

The design work on the M.28 was carried out by Ray Bournon, a young project engineer, under George Miles' direction in the Experimental Department at Liverpool Road, Reading. The project was the first complete aircraft to be designed at Liverpool Road and was also given the designation LR.1.

The first prototype M.28 was built at Liverpool Road and it had a low aspect ratio wing fitted with retractable and external aerofoil flaps to give a high-lift coefficient. It also had a very deep moulded Perspex windscreen giving a far better view than any aircraft then in service and the cabin doors hinged to fold on the horizontal centre line before opening upwards, being guided in rails at each end. The first prototype was built as a dual control ab initio trainer with horizontal push-pull wheel control. It is also of interest to note, that the weights, wing area, aspect ratio and cruising speed originally specified in the minutes, were almost exactly achieved in the aeroplane.

The M.28 was the first aeroplane designed to convince the RAF of the desirability of side-by-side cabin training, a feature about which the Miles brothers had been preaching for many years, instead of the usual tandem open cockpits.

Although it was the original intention to fit a constant-speed propeller to the M.28, George Miles recalled that the prototype and most subsequent variants had fixed pitch propellers, mainly because the available Gipsy Major engines lacked the necessary accessory drives and the smallest of the DH constant pitch propellers was a new development.

The prototype M.28 was first flown, with 'B' mark **U-0232**, by George Miles, on 11th July 1941 and was given the RAF Experimental Aeroplane No.162 for identification purposes. From the pilot's point of view, it was found to have light and very effective controls with exceptional directional stability, provided by the twin fin and rudder unit, but marginal inherent stability. These features were characteristic of nearly all the aeroplanes designed by George Miles, whereas the earlier aircraft designed by F G Miles had very marked stability and moderately heavy controls. The low aspect ratio of the M.28 had a noticeable effect on its handling characteristics, especially on the approach. While the controls remained crisp and effective right down to the stall, the high induced drag at low speeds, consequent upon the low aspect ratio, produced a marked rate of sink which had to be counteracted

either by the application of power or by increasing the approach speed. This technique was easily mastered, and was in fact no disadvantage as the actual touchdown speed was very low and the landing run short, even without the use of brakes.

A letter sent by Ray Bournon to Ken H Readings (who had probably been 'called-up' for the armed forces by then), dated 12th October 1941, makes for most interesting reading:

I must apologise for the long delay in answering your letter but I have been waiting for the M.28 bonus to be paid out. A PO value £6 enclosed represents your portion of the £100 which was allowed although the machine was nearly 2 months overdue. The a/c flew quite successfully (GM pilot) with ailerons drooped 17° (not 25°) and the only criticism was TP too small, elevators too small and not enough up movement. Both these points have been rectified with alum. The a/c will leave the ground flaps down at less than ½ throttle - lands at about 33 mph (not a misprint) lightly loaded; also top speed will be nearly 165 mph when wheel wells are faired - good eh!

The third day F G landed it u/c up (forgot all about it) (said he was too busy watching ASI) also with flaps down. (see below - PA) Broke off drag flap and bent inboard rail of left flap and broke prop. Pitot head and exhaust. We lifted a/c wound u/c down wheeled it in and had a/c in the air 21 hours later. Everybody very satisfied. About a week later F G was flying could not get u/c to lock down one side (small plug end in dural con-rod cracked) - landed OK but when he put on brakes u/c both sides folded back - damage as above. Quite an eventful career to date.

She looks fine in the air and on the ground - the only thing I don't like is that she is 100 lb. heavier than I expected but 30 lb. of this is in the engine. We have started the 2nd m/c and are taking things steadier now. We have - or will have soon - two females in the office now but no one else new. Everybody in the offices wishes to be remembered to you also my wife. I hope you are getting on OK and that the life suits you, it must be a bit different from Liverpool Rd etc but you must be used to it by now.

Well that is all for now, come and see us when you can and all the best of luck - I think "Happy landings is the toast." Yours Bournon

PS. Let me have a note about the money some time as I had to sign for it.

Norman Angell (brother of Jack Angell) who was on the 'flight line' at Woodley at the time, told me recently that he had accompanied F G Miles on both these flights and that after the first occasion he had 'got the blame for the accident for not reminding Miles that the undercarriage red lights were still showing before he landed!'

Miles alighting from the cabin shortly after landing the prototype M.28, U-0232, with the undercarriage retracted!

[Via Richard Almond]

The M.28 being recovered.

Miles was apparently very angry with himself for bending the new aeroplane but immediately instructed the works to have it ready for flight 'first thing in the morning!' The Experimental Department worked all night, straightening the underside, checking the engine and fitting a new propeller and it was duly wheeled out the next morning ready for flight! On the second occasion Norman recalled that the very same thing happened again but as this story was not quite consistent with the facts outlined by Ray Bournon in his letter above, it definitely couldn't have been his fault that time!

Ken Readings must have later been invalided out of the service, as Ray Bournon sent him another letter dated Saturday 15th August 1942:

Thanks for your letter of 22/7. I am very sorry to hear about your health, although it is a blessing that your complaint is not one that will affect you in normal life - if any life is normal these days. Well,

to cut a long story short we should be very pleased to have you back in "civvy street" in general and P&P in particular. I have pulled strings and got machinery in motion to secure first option on your services and from preliminary reports I expect some measure of success but as you know it may take time and then of course things may have happened at your end that we know nothing of. We have enough work on for twice the staff and more in store. By the way we now have a staff of eight PBD's ('poor bloody draughtsmen'! - PA) one woman, a stressman - and myself.

Well Ken we all here wish you the best of luck and hope that things will go well for you in the near future. If I get any definite news I will let you have it and please do the same. I am having your favourite corner prepared for you in anticipation. Yours Ray

I think that these two letters give a good indication of the enthusiastic attitude of the staff at Liverpool Road. For the record, Ken must have returned to Phillips & Powis, as a letter to Mr K H Readings, dated 21st June 1948 and signed by S R Hogg, FCA, Receiver and Manager, Miles Aircraft Ltd, read:

Dear Sir, This will serve to confirm that one week's notice of termination of employment has today been exchanged between yourself and the Company, effective on 25th June 1948.

The first prototype M.28 was later modified to become the prototype M.28/38, the forerunner of the M.38 Messenger, first flying in this guise, with 'B' mark **U-0223**, on 12th September 1942.

M.28 Mk.II

Of the M.28 Mk.II, Don Brown later wrote: *The second prototype was built for the firm's own communications purposes, but it created such interest and such a favourable impression by various RAF officers who saw and flew in it, that it was embraced for No.41 Group.*

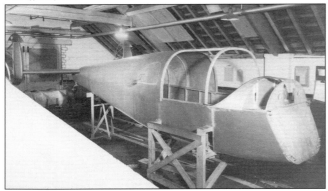

Above: The fuselage of the M.28 Mk.II under construction 'in the roof' at Liverpool Road, Reading.

Above: This photograph shows that the elevator and rudders were made of light alloy, a hitherto unrecorded fact.

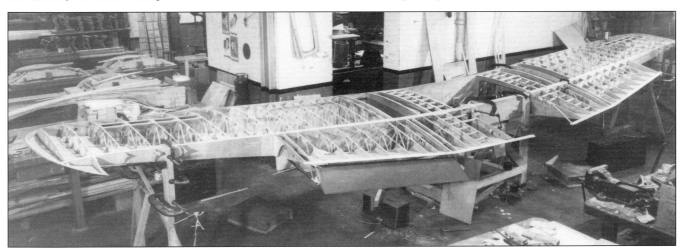

The wing under construction.

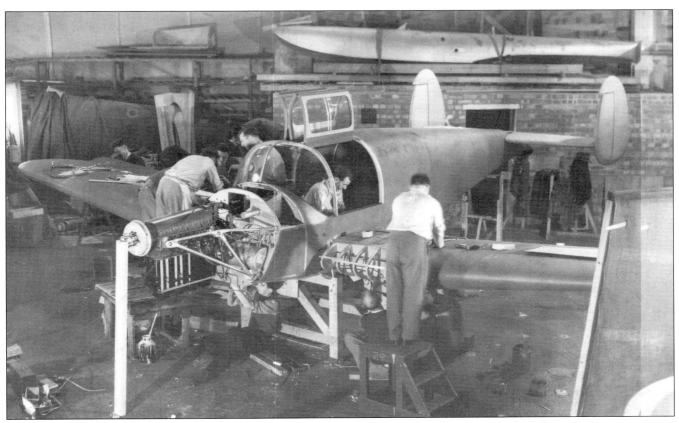

Final assembly. Note the single float hanging from the rafters behind the aircraft. The reason for this being at Liverpool Road remains a mystery.

The M.28 Mk.III was first flown, by George Miles, on 22nd May 1943. This photograph shows it flying with serial PW937.

The M.28 Mk.II was a three-seat dual-control trainer and was fitted with either a DH Gipsy Major or Blackburn Cirrus Major engine. It had a hydraulically operated undercarriage and vacuum-operated flaps and was evaluated by the RAF, with serial **HM583**, before being used for communications.

M.28 Mk.III

Of the M.28 Mk.III, Don Brown later wrote: *The third prototype was started when a contract was received to convert this machine into a triple-control trainer for tests at ECFS (with serial PW937 - PA). These tests proved so successful that for the first time in the history of the RAF a decision was made to adopt side-by-side training in future trainers. The result of this decision is now seen in the specification for the Boulton Paul T.7/45 advanced trainer, a contract for which has recently been placed.*

This statement confirms that the M.28 Mk.III was originally built as a two-seat trainer, with dual controls, and was later modified, under Contract/Acft/3176 dated 21st July 1943, at an estimated

cost of £7,000, to become a three-seat trainer with triple-control, for evaluation as a triple-control elementary trainer. The idea behind this thinking being that two pupils would occupy the front seats while the instructor sat on a raised seat placed centrally behind them. This was made possible by the exceptionally deep windscreen and the excellent all-round field of view. This version of the M.28 was fitted with a 150 hp Blackburn Cirrus Major III engine and was the first to be fitted with a new uniform taper (thin) wing with identical root and tip thicknesses as the M.38 although the aspect ratio was 5.8 on the M.28 (with a span of 30.7ft) as against 6.81 on the M.38 (with a span of 36.2ft), and this thin wing allowed the wheels to protrude when retracted which would also have lessened the damage in the event of a wheels-up landing. The M.28 Mk.III was allotted 'B' mark **U-0242.**

The M.28 Mk.III was also fitted with a vacuum operated retractable undercarriage (with re-designed 'straight' legs), vacuum operated retractable lift flaps and drag flap, and a raised central rear seat for the instructor, to enable him 'to observe the mistakes of the pupil in front!'

An extract from a somewhat biased Ministry Report (N.A. Ref: BT/28/1195) dated 30th May 1945 on the development work carried out by Miles Aircraft Ltd, which will be reproduced in full in the next volume, stated that:

Publicity was given to the M.28 in Flight *(4.2.43 and 29.4.43).*

An M.28 was later fitted with triple controls as an experiment at the request of DTF. This, however, was not liked by ECFS Hullavington and was later abandoned.

The Report also stated: *Unofficial development work, initiated by the firm without any known official recognition (included) M.28 -*

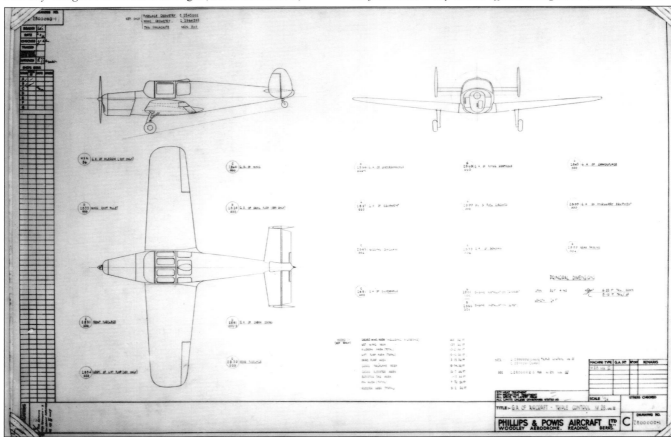

Three-view G.A. of Aircraft - Triple Control M.28 Mk.III.

Photograph showing the seating arrangement in the M.28 Mk.III.

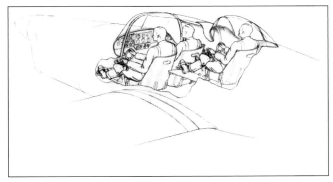

A sketch showing a View of Seating Arrangement for the M.28 Mk.III Triple Control aircraft.

Up to 27th May 1943 this type was a private venture. DOR then stated a requirement for one aircraft to be fitted with triple controls.

Although it is believed that DOR stated their requirement on 27th May 1943, the M.28 Mk.III had, in fact, made its first flight on 22nd May 1943 and by the time the ITP was issued, on 21st July 1943, the flight trials must have been well under way - things moved quickly at Woodley in those days!

The M.28 Mk.IV, Mk.V and Mk.VI were civil versions based on the airframe of the M.28 Mk.III and for individual histories of these variants see Appendix 27.

M.28 Mk.IV

Of the M.28 Mk.III, Don Brown later wrote: *The fourth M.28 was then built for the firm's own use, and has resulted in this type being ordered for the use of Mr Peter Masefield, who has just gone to the USA as this Country's representative on the field of Civil Aviation.*

It was announced in *The Aeroplane* for 23rd February 1945 that the name "Mercury" had been given to the civil version of the M.28 Mk.IV and it was generally known by this name in the factory. However, it is said that the Bristol Aeroplane Company objected to its use because of the confusion they felt it would cause due to their engine of the same name, even though this was out of production. However, Hugh Kendall regularly recorded 'Mercury' in his log book whenever he flew a civilian M.28.

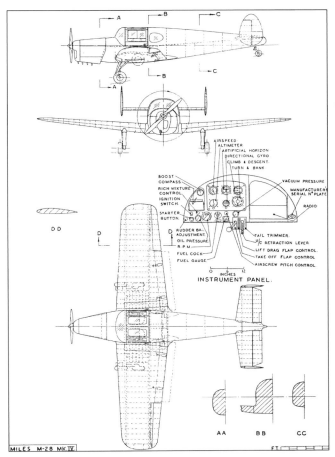

Three-view drawing of the M.28 Mk.IV.

The M.28 Mk.IV was a four-seat light transport, with single 'broken-stick' control, intended as prototype taxi aircraft for the ATA and was built by the Experimental Department, Liverpool Road, Reading in 1944. Fitted with a 145 hp DH Gipsy Major IIIS engine, with separate exhaust stubs and a constant-speed propeller, which increased the cruising speed to 174 mph at 6,400 ft altitude and the max speed to over 180 mph. A new uniform taper (thin) wing was fitted, which incorporated a vacuum operated retractable undercarriage, vacuum operated retractable lift flaps and drag flap,

The M.28 Mk.IV, U-0243.   *[Air-Britain via Bert Clarke]*

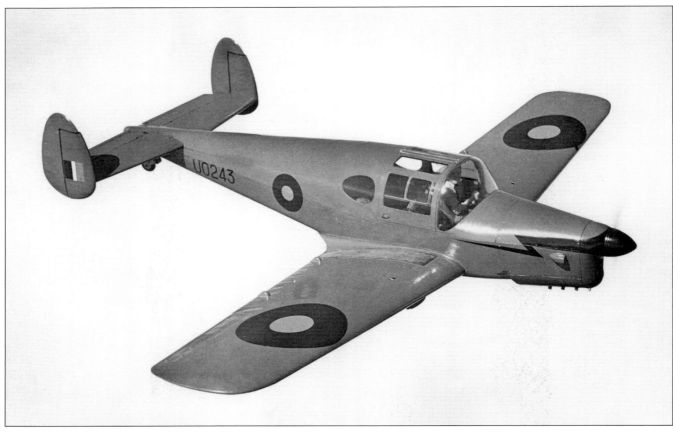

The M.28 Mk.IV, U-0243, after it had been repainted in PR blue.

as on the M.28 Mk.III and oval rear windows. Completed as a luxury taxi/tourer, to be also suitable for post war private use, the M.28 Mk.IV was allotted B' mark **U-0243** and camouflaged. First flown, by Hugh Kennedy, on 10th July 1944, it was later painted PR blue overall with red/blue roundels and fitted with a larger spinner.

M.28 Mk.5

This was a four-seat tourer, built by the Experimental Department, Liverpool Road, Reading in 1947. Fitted with a 150 hp Blackburn Cirrus Major III engine it was similar to the Mk.6 but had an improved undercarriage, normal stick control and square rear

windows. An unusual feature of the M.28 Mk.5 was its doors, which were hinged on the windscreen frame to open forward. Registered **G-AJFE** on 20th March 1947 to Miles Aircraft Ltd, Woodley, it was first flown, by George Miles, on 18th April 1947.

M.28 Mk.6

This was also a four-seat tourer, with single control, intended to be flown from the port side, with wheel control mounted on top of control column. Built by the Experimental Department, Liverpool Road, Reading in 1946, it was fitted with a 150 hp Blackburn Cirrus Major III engine with Fairey Reed fixed pitch metal airscrew. It had the uniform taper (thin) wing and undercarriage as

G-AJFE, the M.28 Mk.5.   *[GS Collection]*

G-AHAA, the M.28 Mk.6.   *[GS Collection]*

on the M.28 Mk.III and oval rear windows. First flown, by Don Brown, on 26th March 1946. Temporarily fitted with a third fin later for trials. Registered **G-AHAA** on 26th January 1946 to Miles Aircraft Ltd, Woodley.

Both economically and operationally, the M.28 was a big advance on contemporary aircraft as, with a DH Gipsy Major engine, it could easily carry four people; it had a top speed of nearly 160 mph; a still air range of 500 miles and would do over 20 miles per gallon of fuel. Unfortunately, owing to the urgency of other wartime commitments, the M.28 never went into production and only three further examples were built for civil use after the war had ended but for completeness all six M.28s built are covered in this chapter.

A note from PS15, giving details of: 'Applications during the past twelve months for the export of aircraft or the sale of licences for manufacture abroad', dated 3rd December 1943, stated, under Turkey, that:

Miles Aircraft Ltd applied for permission to sell the licence to manufacture the M.28 or M.38 but this was rejected because the necessary Gipsy engines could not be supplied. It may be revived if Lycoming engines can be fitted and obtained without detriment to the British supplies. De Havillands applied for permission to supply to Turkish Airlines the equipment and technical assistance necessary for the manufacture of Gipsy engines in Turkey. This was, however, refused owing to technical difficulties and the fact that the proposal did not have the support of the Turkish Government.

An early potential customer for the M.28 was Mr Rusi Mistri, head of a large group of industrial concerns in India and who, in August 1945, was in England in connection with post-war civil aviation development plans for his Asian Air Associates and Aeronautical Corporation of India. It was reported at the time of his visit that his company had ordered two M.28 Mercurys, two M.38 Messengers and four M.57 Aerovans from Miles Aircraft Ltd and that Asian Air Associates had planned to use the aircraft on charter operations as soon as possible. However, nothing further was heard of the venture, and the aircraft were not delivered. It must be assumed that either the finance was not forthcoming, or that export and import licences were not granted. Mistri similarly ordered a number of Percival Proctor Vs, most of which never reached India.

The National Archives holds some interesting correspondence concerning the proposed purchase of an M.28 for the use of Peter Masefield, the Civil Air Attaché in Washington, USA (N.A. Ref: T161/1366):

From Washington to Foreign Office, Earl of Halifax, dated 12th January 1946 (received 16th January 1946): *Your telegram No. 1478 Saving (of December 18th: Aircraft for the Civil Air Attaché).*

I recommend most strongly that authority be given . . . As applied to the Civil Air Attaché here, there is more in the argument in your paragraph 2(a) than meets the eye. Second only to the political questions which have recently tied him to Washington, it is of the highest importance for the intelligence and contact side of his work that he visit the aircraft manufacturers, aircraft research centres, attend "air meets" and travel over the air network. A private aircraft is the only way of reaching many of the airfields of the aircraft factories and research centres. It is obvious too that a man who flies himself has a much better entree into flying circles than one who does not. This latter point runs into the question of prestige and advertisement. If, as I understand, the Miles 28 is a good aircraft of its size, there is no doubt at all that the appearance of the Civil Air Attaché in a Miles at civil aviation centres and gatherings will keep alive the belief that the British aircraft industry has or will have something really good to sell besides its triumphant combat aircraft.

It seems to me therefore that the small sterling purchase price and the very small dollar running costs would be fully justified. Masefield thinks there will be no difficulty in selling the aircraft later in the United States for sufficient dollars to cover all previous dollar expenditure. He is hoping to arrange for free maintenance service in return for similar facilities for the American Civil Air Attaché in London.

Then, in a letter dated 20th February 1946:

Dear Evans, (C A Evans of the Ministry of Civil Aviation - PA).

With reference to my letter of the 17th December to Davis and to our recent telephone conversation, I send you herewith a copy of the telegram which has been received from Washington in reply to the telegram sent to Washington on the 18th December at our request about the proposal to provide a Miles M.28 Mercury aircraft for use by the Civil Air Attaché, Washington, in carrying out his duties. As I explained on the telephone, the enclosed telegram, although it appears to have been received in the Foreign Office on the 16th January, did not reach me until the day before yesterday.

In view of the recommendation contained in the enclosed telegram, we can now give you the authority asked for in Davis' letter of the 24th November to proceed with the purchase of a Miles M.28 Mercury aircraft for the use of Mr Peter Masefield at an estimated cost of £8,250 including spare engine, spares, radio and instruments, but excluding packing and transport.

Yours sincerely, W L GORELL-BARNES (Gorell-Barnes was in the Treasury - PA).

Although nothing came of the proposal to supply Peter Masefield with a Miles M.28 (he was in fact supplied with Percival Proctor V G-AHGN in June 1946), a Miles M.65 Gemini Mk.1A was later ordered by the Ministry of Supply under Contract 6/Aircraft/224/CB.10 - Supply of Gemini aircraft and spares - for the use of the Civil Air Attaché (Mr Peter Masefield) in Washington, U.S.A. (N.A. Ref: AVIA 15/1971 and AIR 3176).

OY-ALW, the modified Miles M.28 Mk.6, is the only M.28 to have survived to this day. Based at Stauning, Denmark it is owned by Hans Kolby Hansen, who has his business in the UK but keeps it in airworthy condition and flies it occasionally when he returns to Denmark.

For a summary of Miles M.28 production see Appendix 27.

SUMMARY OF SPECIFICATION AND PERFORMANCE

Engines:	130/140/145 hp DH Gipsy Major I/II/IIA/III; 150 hp Blackburn Cirrus Major III; see individual aircraft histories for details of particular installations
Dimensions:	span 30ft 8in; length 24ft 0in; height 8ft 4in; cabin width 4ft 0in; wing area 160 sq ft; aspect ratio 5.8; wing section, root NACA 23018, tip NACA 2412.

Weights: DH Gipsy Major III/Blackburn Cirrus Major III engine:

	two seat trainer aerobatic category	three seater	four seater
Tare	1,460 lb	1,460 lb	1,460 lb
Fuel (24 gall)	180 lb	180 lb	180 lb
Oil (3 gall)	27 lb	27 lb	27 lb
Pilot	170 lb	170 lb	170 lb
Passengers	170 lb	340 lb	510 lb
Parachutes/luggage	60 lb	200 lb	80 lb
Total	2,067 lb	2,377 lb	2,427 lb
Wing loading	12.92 lb/sq ft	14.86 lb/sq ft	15.17lb/sq ft

Weights: DH Gipsy Major III S Engine with constant speed airscrew:

	two seat trainer aerobatic category	three seater	four seater
Tare	1,540 lb	1,540 lb	1,540 lb
Fuel (20 gall)	150 lb	(24 gall) 180 lb	(24 gall) 180 lb
Oil (3 gall)	27 lb	27 lb	27 lb
Pilot	170 lb	170 lb	170 lb
Passengers	170 lb	340 lb	510 lb
Parachutes/luggage	40 lb	200 lb	70 lb
Total	2,097 lb	2,457 lb	2,497 lb
Wing loading	13.11 lb/sq ft	15.36 lb/sq ft	15.61 lb/sq ft

Weights: DH Gipsy Major I/C or V Engine:

	two seat trainer aerobatic category	three seater	four seater
Tare	1,400 lb	1,400 lb	1,400 lb
Fuel (24 gall)	180 lb	180 lb	180 lb
Oil (3 gall)	27 lb	27 lb	27 lb
Pilot	170 lb	170 lb	170 lb
Passengers	170 lb	340 lb	510 lb
Parachutes/luggage	60 lb	200 lb	80 lb
Total	2,007 lb	2,317 lb	2,367 lb
Wing loading	12.54 lb/sq ft	14.48 lb/sq ft	14.79 lb/sq ft

Performance: DH Gipsy Major III S Engine with constant speed airscrew:

	two seat trainer aerobatic category	three seater
Max level speed at rated alt 7,000 ft	183 mph TAS	180 mph TAS
Cruising speed at rated alt 6,400 ft	173 mph TAS	169 mph TAS
Initial rate of climb	1,300 ft/min	1,080 ft/min
Stalling speed	42 mph	46 mph
Ultimate range on 24 gall	490 miles	480 miles
Take-off run (5 mph wind)	330 ft	480 ft
Landing run (5 mph wind)	300 ft	360 ft

Performance: DH Gipsy Major III/Blackburn Cirrus Mahor III with fixed pitch airscrew:

	two seat trainer aerobatic category	three seater
Max level speed at sea level	160 mph	157 mph
Cruising speed at sea level	141 mph	139 mph
Initial rate of climb	1,070 ft/min	890 ft/min
Stalling speed	42 mph	46 mph
Ultimate range on 24 gall	420 miles	410 miles
Take-off run (5 mph wind)	480 ft	675 ft
Landing run (5 mph wind)	300 ft	360 ft

Performance: DH Gipsy Major I/C with fixed pitch airscrew:

	two seat trainer aerobatic category	three seater
Max level speed at sea level	155 mph	152 mph
Cruising speed at sea level	137 mph	135 mph
Initial rate of climb	900 ft/min	750 ft/min
Stalling speed	42 mph	46 mph
Ultimate range on 24 gall	430 miles	410 miles
Take-off run (5 mph wind)	525 ft	750 ft
Landing run (5 mph wind)	300 ft	360 ft

Performance: DH Gipsy Major III with constant speed airscrew:

	two seat trainer aerobatic category	three seater
Max level speed at sea level	163 mph	-
Cruising speed at rated alt 3,600 ft	159 mph TAS	155 mph TAS
Initial rate of climb	1,200 ft/min	1,000 ft/min
Stalling speed	42 mph	46 mph
Ultimate range on 24 gall	490 miles	480 miles
Take-off run (5 mph wind)	420 ft	600 ft
Landing run (5 mph wind)	300 ft	360 ft

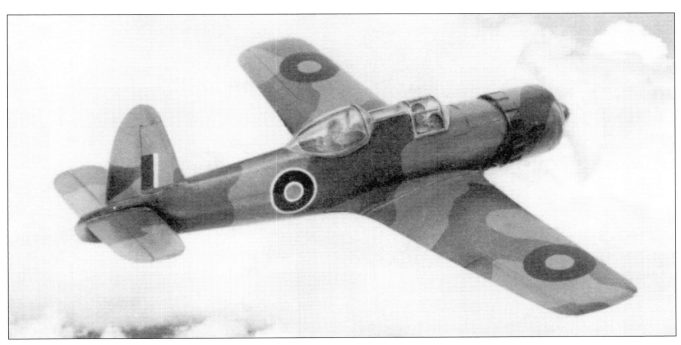

An artist's impression of the M.29 Master Mk.V.

Chapter 20
Miles M.29 Master Mk.V Advanced Trainer, Miles M.29 (Developments) Target Towing for RAF, Miles M.29 (Developments) Target Towing and Camera Marking for Army and Navy, and Miles M.29A (Developments) Singled Engined High Speed Target Towing Aircraft

In 1940, Miles decided that the Master should be replaced with a high-performance advanced trainer with a raised rear cockpit for the instructor. This would enable the instructor to obtain the necessary forward view without having to raise his seat for take-off and landing. Miles felt that with the forthcoming introduction of the larger and heavier fighters and bombers into service with the RAF, the advanced trainer should also be correspondingly heavier in order better to reproduce the handling characteristics of these new operational types.

The new project, the M.29, was known as the Master Mk.V and the intention was that it should bear the same relationship to the Hawker Typhoon as the Master had to the Hawker Hurricane and Supermarine Spitfire. The engine proposed for the new advanced trainer was either the 1,600 hp Bristol Hercules or the Wright Cyclone GR-2600A5B of corresponding power, according to their availability.

A mock-up of the proposed M.29 trainer with a raised, teardrop cabin for the instructor and with a rear fuselage and fin and rudder similar to that of the M.20, was built as a private venture but no further work on this promising design was undertaken. A photograph, taken after the M.29 trainer project had been abandoned, shows this mock-up stored between two wooden huts on Woodley Aerodrome.

In November 1941, a provisional specification for a target-tower was issued by Lt Cdr Pelley, RDN.1 and various preliminary discussions took place, the result of which was that a twin-engined scheme should be developed.

However, in view of DTD's statement that the possibilities of a single-engined aircraft should be fully explored, it was considered worthwhile investigating the possibility of utilising the basic structure of the M.29 for the purpose of target towing.

Private development work on the new design was put in hand in August 1942 and a new mock-up of the fuselage and tail of the M.29A Target Towing Aircraft was built. This bore little

The mock-up of the M.29 Master Mk.V seen between the wooden huts to the right of the Repair & Service Department at Woodley.

relationship to the original M.29 design, but the concept was later taken over by the MAP. A photograph of the Miles M.30 'X' Minor under construction in the Experimental Department, shows what was almost certainly the mock-up of the M.29A, with a single radial-engine and a very long fuselage.

In September 1942, a meeting was held at the MAP with the Air Ministry, the Admiralty and with RAF personnel to discuss the suitability of the provisional designs which had, in the meantime, been issued by the firm for a single-engined target-tower to replace the Martinet. Miles, however, remained unconvinced that a single-engined aircraft could meet the demanding requirements, and calculations soon showed that no single-engined aeroplane could provide the performance required for a high-speed target towing aircraft. Miles felt that a twin-engined design would be essential in order to provide the room, view, and comfort necessary for the crew to carry out their duties efficiently. The Ministry also eventually realised that no single-engined aircraft would meet the requirement and later issued Specification Q.9/42 to Miles Aircraft Ltd, which called for a twin-engined target towing aircraft and in due course became the M.33 Monitor.

Other available photographs show side-view drawings of three different single radial-engined, two-seat machines based on the M.29. They catered for three different requirements but all had fuselages similar in shape and length to that of the M.29A mock-up. Unfortunately, none of the photographs were dated but they were titled, as follows:

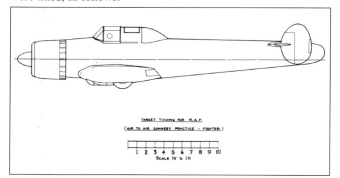

Above: Drawing of M.29 (Developments) Target Towing for RAF (Air to air Gunnery Practice - Fighter). Note: this version had twin fins and rudders.

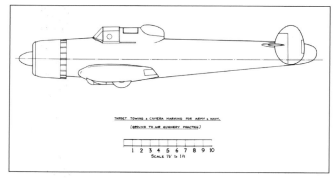

Above: Drawing of M.29 (Developments) Target Towing & Camera Marking for Army & Navy (Ground to Air Gunnery Practice). Note: this version had twin fins and rudders.

SPECIFICATION AND PERFORMANCE DATA

Engine:	1,600 hp Bristol Hercules or Wright Cyclone GR-2600A5B air-cooled radial
Dimensions:	Based on a scale drawing of one further version with twin fins and rudders and with what appeared to be an astrodome behind the pilot's cabin; span 40 ft 8½ in; length 34 ft 2½ in.

No further details are known.

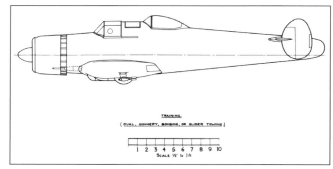

Above: Training (Dual, Gunnery, Bombing, or Glider Towing). Note: this version had twin fins and rudders.

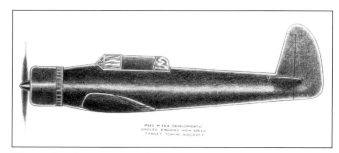

Above: Drawing of M.29A (Developments) Singled Engined High Speed Target Towing Aircraft. Note: this version had a single, tall fin and rudder.

Note: each of these versions had a different shaped rearward facing canopy for the operator/observer.

Two further drawings (showing the M.29 with twin fins and rudders) depict a gun turret aft of the cockpit and also a prone position operator for the target towing equipment.

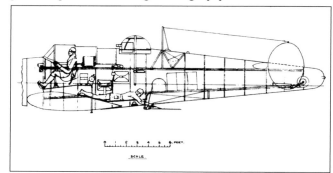

Above: Drawing showing a gun turret (unmanned), pilot and prone position operator.

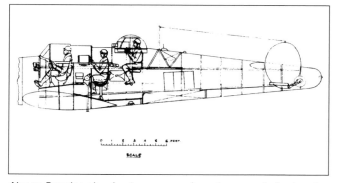

Above: Drawing showing two crew and an air gunner in the turret.

In 1945, the M.29 Advanced Trainer design was resurrected and developed into the M.37 Advanced Trainer, based on the M.25 Martinet. The original Miles idea for a raised rear seat for the instructor was later adopted by Supermarine for a trainer version of the Spitfire and later became the norm for conversion training.

An artist's impression of the M.31 Master Mk.IV.

Chapter 22
Miles M.31 Master Mk.IV Advanced Trainer

In late 1940, Miles suggested to the MAP that, if it was intended to keep the Master in production, a number of modifications and improvements based on service experience with the earlier marks could well be incorporated. Included amongst these improvements were a modified centre section and tailplane but most importantly, Miles suggested, once again, that the rear cabin be raised to give the instructor the necessary field of view for take-off and landing without first having to raise himself through the roof of the cabin, as had been necessary on the standard Masters.

Although this improvement had first been suggested with the M.29, nothing had come of it, but Miles felt that serious consideration should now be given to this improvement in the light of experience gained with the Master. However, by that time, a considerable number of Masters had been supplied to the RAF, and these were considered adequate to meet the needs of the service for the foreseeable future. As the MAP were about to ask Miles for a target-towing version of the Master at the time, the projected M.31 Master Mk.IV Advanced Trainer was, of necessity, abandoned.

There is still some confusion surrounding this project however, as for many years it was thought that the first production M.19 Master Mk.II, T8886, may have been completed as the M.31 Master Mk.IV, with some of the suggested improvements and modifications incorporated. These, however, did not apparently include the raised rear cabin. Don Brown recalled that; *'Master T8886 was a Master II with modifications'*, but unfortunately, he did not state what the modifications were.

Other, later reports referred to T8886 as a 'Master Mk.IV' but no photographic evidence has been found to confirm that it was ever fitted with the raised rear cabin of the projected M.31. However, it has been discovered that the fuselage of the M.31 was actually built and was stored at Woodley until at least January 1941, much earlier than had been thought.

The first production M.19 Master Mk.II, T8886, which was retained by the makers, was first flown, as a Mk.II, by Hugh

Kennedy, on 4th June 1941, on an 'air cleaner test', some two months after the second production Master Mk.II, T8887, which was first flown, also by Hugh Kennedy, on 8th April 1941.

I am therefore, of the opinion that, although modifications were undoubtedly made to the basic airframe, it was not modified to M.31 Master Mk.IV standard with the raised rear cabin, as all photographs of T8886 show it in standard M.19 Master Mk.II configuration.

T8886 was built with full span wings but photographs of the M.19 Master Mk.II, G-AHOB, which it later became, show it to have been retrospectively modified to have the short span 'clipped' wings.

Delivered to 'A' Performance Section A&AEE Boscombe Down on 22nd October 1941, it was on the strength of ETPS Boscombe Down between 1943 and 1944 (although listed incorrectly as a Mk.I in the book: 'The History of the Empire Test Pilot's School').

Hugh Kennedy records some interesting comments in his flying log book which further add to the confusion surrounding the history this aircraft. Test flights and flights to the A&AEE Boscombe Down and South Marston in T8886 made between June 1941 and February 1943 were recorded as Master Mk.II, then in March 1943 as a Master III. 'Master' and 'Master II' in April 1943; Master Mk.III and Mk.II in May and Mk.II in August 1943!

T8886 was acquired by the makers in 1944 and given 'B' mark **U-0246**, the first use of this mark being recorded by Walter Capley, who flew Master Mk.II, 'U-0246', from Heston to Woodley on 26th July 1944 with Don Brown as passenger.

One thing is certain though, externally it resembled the Master Mk.II but it was never a Mk.III. Hugh never recorded T8886 as a Mk.IV, although he later recorded a flight in U-0246 as a Master IV. The record card states that T8886 was a Master Mk.II, retained by the makers until being SOC on 31st January 1945.

Don also recorded 'U-0246' in his log book, as a 'Mk.II with a 840 hp Bristol Mercury 25 engine'. Hugh Kennedy recorded just one 'Instruction' flight, of 1 hr 45 min duration in the 'Master IV U-0246', on 21st August 1944 and Don Brown flew Master Mk.II, U-0246, with a 840 hp Bristol Mercury engine, on 13th September 1944 with George Miles as passenger.

There is no record of any subsequent flights being made as 'U-0246' but the mystery Master II/IV was refurbished by the Repair & Service Department between 29th January 1946 and May 1946 and given the 'new' c/n 6434. Painted in the cream and red 'house colours' of Miles Aircraft Ltd, it was allotted the 'B' mark **U5**, although there is no record of it carrying this 'B' mark.

Registered **G-AHOB** (CofR 10224, later 2574), on 13th May 1946, as a Master II, to Miles Aircraft Ltd, Woodley. Hugh Kendall made its first recorded flight as G-AHOB on 20th August 1946. G-AHOB took part in the flypast of Miles aircraft during the last

Miles 'At Home' day held at Woodley on Sunday 20th July 1947, flown by Sqdn Ldr Samuel E Esler, who recorded it as a Master II. Its last recorded flight was made by Hugh Kendall on 13th August 1947.

Photographs confirm that G-AHOB was definitely a Master Mk.II, with a Bristol Mercury engine and the 'clipped' wings of modified and later production Masters. No CofA was issued but it was sold and registered 15th June 1949 to Robert Alan Short, Thornton Heath, Surrey (although it remained at Woodley), where it was scrapped in 1950.

An interesting aircraft with a hidden secret.

SPECIFICATION AND PERFORMANCE DATA

No details known.

G-AHOB, previously T8886, the first production Master Mk.II, was often flown by Flt Lt Hugh Kennedy. However, he never recorded it as a Master Mk.IV until he flew it with 'B' mark Y-0246 in August 1944, after it had been acquired by Miles Aircraft Ltd. For the record, the difference between a Master Mk.II and a Mk.IV has never been established, but T8886 was registered G-AHOB as a Master Mk.II in 1946, and it is seen here at Woodley soon after in the Miles house colours of cream with crimson trim.

JN668, the second prototype M.37 Martinet Advanced Trainer. Although nothing came of the M.29 Master Mk.V Advanced Trainer project study of 1940, or the later projected M.31 Master Mk.IV Advanced Trainer, eventually the M.37 was designed and built to meet the preliminary requirement OR.215 for Spec. T.7/45. This called for the conversion of the M.25 Martinet into an Advanced Trainer, to be used in the interim until such time as a new advanced trainer, to Spec. T.7/45 Issue II, with a propeller-turbine engine, could be produced.

An artist's impression of what is believed to have been the first thoughts on the M.32 Glider proposal. Note the rearward facing machine gun behind the cabin.

Chapter 23
Miles M.32 Glider and
Miles M.32 Twin Engined Powered Glider

In 1938, Phillips & Powis Aircraft Ltd put forward a series of proposals for specialised freighters designed for rear loading which, at the time, were mainly centred on a project capable of carrying 150 armed troops, 50 light armoured motor cycles or 9 howitzers and crews.

Miles' views on this subject became more firmly entrenched in 1940-41 when he disagreed energetically with the official policy of building large numbers of heavy gliders. He then put forward a series of alternative designs for cheap relatively low-powered freighters, which were to have full depth/full width, front and rear loading facilities. These proposals covered a big field and ran from a 300 hp twin-engined aircraft capable of carrying one small utility vehicle or equivalent load, to a six-engined strategic freighter with a payload of 36,000lb and a range of 2,000 miles.

All these aircraft were designed for cheap construction from non-strategic materials and utilised obsolescent engines, mostly available in quantity, which were not required for operational duties. The two smallest projects were based on a layout which enabled them to be used either with or without engines but, when operated as gliders, the powered version could be used as a tug.

This was designated the M.32 and in the glider configuration it complied to Specification X.26/40, dated 29th January 1941, which called for a glider capable of carrying 25 paratroops with equipment. This specification was issued to Airspeed Ltd on 6th February 1941 and ultimately resulted in the Airspeed AS.51 Horsa.

However, Phillips & Powis Aircraft Ltd had previously been given a Ministry Development Contract, No.29063/39 dated 11th October 1939, for their M.32 glider project, which was designed to accommodate either 25 troops with 50lb of equipment each or the equivalent weight of vehicles or ordnance.

Right: Three-view G.A. drawing of the M.32 Glider.

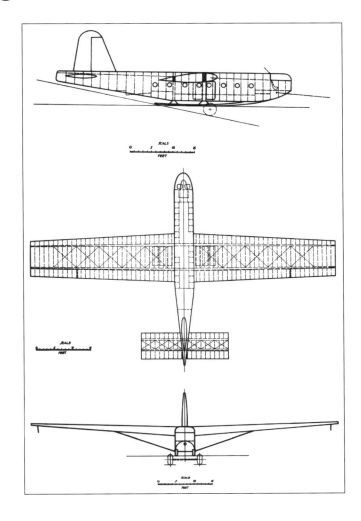

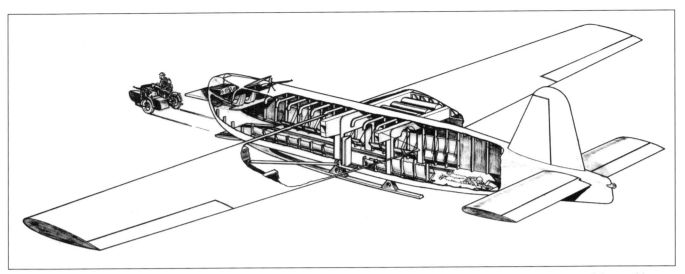

A partial cut-away drawing of the M.32 Glider showing a motor-cycle and sidecar with machine gun, exiting from the nose and the machine gun behind the cabin. Note also the prone machine gunner on the floor at the rear of the fuselage. A jettisonable trolley was to be used for take-off but landing would be made on pneumatically sprung ash skids.

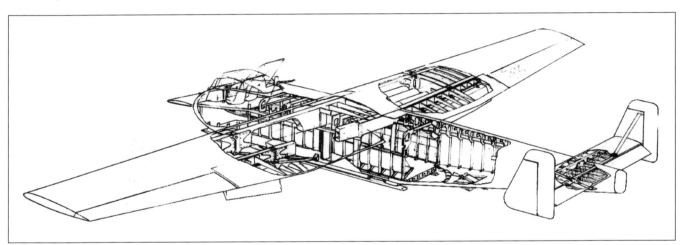

A partial cut-away drawing of the second version of the M.32 showing it to have twin fins and rudders. A jettisonable trolley was to be used for take- off but landing would be made on pneumatically sprung ash skids.

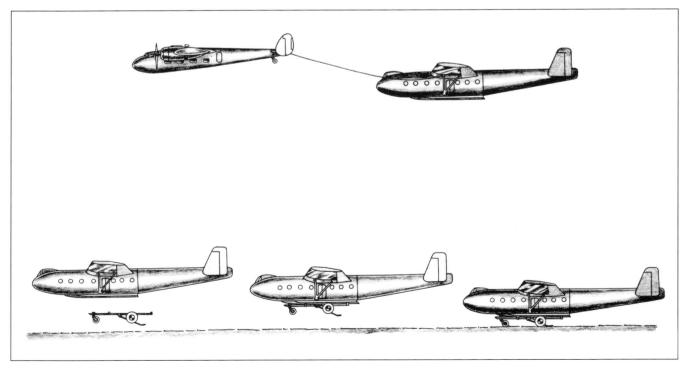

Drawing showing the take-off sequence with the jettisonable trolley.

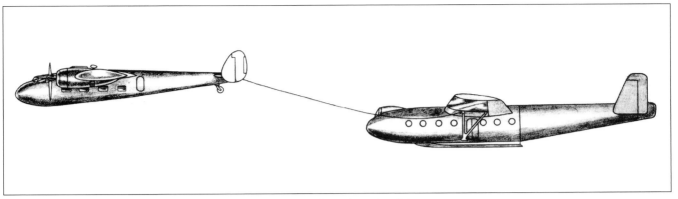

Above: Drawing showing the M.32 being towed from wing mounted attachments points.

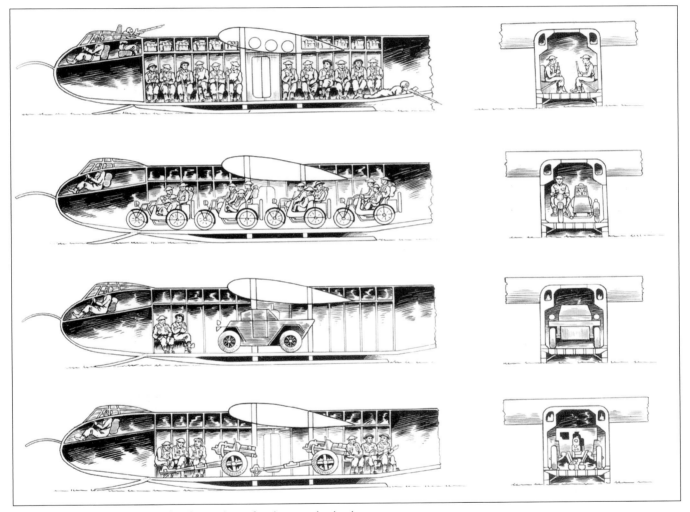

Above: Cut-away drawings showing the carriage of various service loads.

Undated Phillips & Powis photographs, simply titled 'M.32', show three-view drawings and a cut-away drawing of what is believed to have been their initial thoughts on the subject. This project was similar in shape to that of the well publicised M.32 glider but the pilot's cabin was situated high in a very 'blunt' shaped nose, with the forward opening door in two sections, the top part being hinged below the cabin floor and opening upwards, while the bottom part dropped down to be used as the loading/unloading ramp. It had a single fin and rudder, reminiscent of the prototype M.18, 24 inward facing seats (12 each side) with two doors amidships, staggered one of either side of the fuselage, two retractable defensive gun positions, one on top of the fuselage immediately behind the cabin and one prone position in the bottom of the fuselage just below the leading edge of the fin, and carried six cylindrical canisters (three each side) in the inner wings, presumably for further supplies.

The final version emerged with twin fins and rudders and the cabin mounted on top of the forward fuselage, with a one-piece drop down ramp in the nose to facilitate loading and unloading. It also had two retractable defensive machine guns as in the earlier project and it was this version which could also be fitted with two engines.

During this period George Miles put forward a paper for official circulation advocating such 'powered gliders' and prophesying that, as a result of operational experience, the Germans would abandon their glider policy and develop this type of transport. This prophecy was amply justified shortly afterwards by the appearance of the Gotha Go.244 and the Messerschmitt Me.323.

Meanwhile the British glider policy came desperately near to disaster because of the shortage of suitable tugs with which to carry out large-scale operations.

M.32 Twin Engined Powered Glider

In December 1941, Phillips & Powis Aircraft Ltd produced a booklet on the M.32 Twin Engined Powered Glider reproduced below:

PROVISIONAL SPECIFICATION FOR TROOP CARRIER

PURPOSE

To transport military equipment and/or personnel under the aircraft's own power or as a glider similar to Specification X.26/40.

DESIGN - GLIDER

High Wing Monoplane fitted with a ramp to the fuselage to allow vehicles etc to be driven straight in, thereby obtaining rapid loading and disembarkation on the ground. Parachute exits are fitted under the wings for paratroops, close to the centre of pressure. Pneumatically sprung ash skids for landing on which may be mounted a jettisonable trolley for take-off and training.

DESIGN - TWIN ENGINE

Converted quickly from above without structural alterations, except the removal of a 4 ft flap bay on both sides in way of

Above: An artist's impression of the M.32 Powered Glider with a motor cycle combination being loaded on board via the front ramp.

Above: Drawing showing fitters attaching the self-contained engine pod, complete with twin-wheel undercarriage, to the underside of the wing of a M.32 Glider.

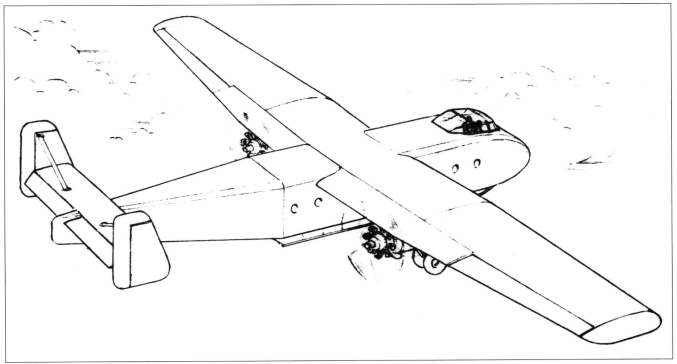

Above: Sketch showing the M.32 Powered Glider in flight.

nacelles. Any engine of from 800 to 1,000 hp can be used, with airscrew up to 11 ft 6 ins in diameter. In order to keep the controls and installation simple it is proposed to use wooden airscrews, fixed gill, automatic mixture control etc. The engine nacelles will be slung complete with chassis and fuel tanks under the ends of the centre section.

CONSTRUCTION

Almost entirely of wood - Grade B and C spruce, lime and commercial ply is used wherever possible. The few metal fittings are of mild steel. The aircraft is divided up into components which can be packed into standard shipping size cases (34 ft x 8 ft x 10 ft). The control circuits are all by wire and lever method (no pulleys).

EQUIPMENT

Restricted to the barest necessities, only ASI, altimeter, compass and watch holder, are intended to be fitted as standard, but space will be left for the mounting of a blind flying panel. When engines are fitted, the revolution counter and oil temperature gauge will be on the nacelle visible to the pilot.

MILITARY LOAD

As a glider the following alternative loads can be covered in addition to the pilot:-

(a)	2 paratroops with 6 containers	6,720 lb
(b)	4 motor cycle combinations and 12 men	4,872 lb
(c)	Scout car and 2/3 men	6,480 lb
(d)	2 Howitzers Mk.IV P/L or Mk.III/L and 16 men (approx)	6,880 lb
(e)	2 in and 3 in mortar sub sections and containers	6,480 lb
(f)	900 gallons of fuel and container	6,800 lb
(g)	680 gallons of water	6,900 lb
(h)	Any other stores or ammunition up to	6,900 lb

As a twin engine aircraft, all the above cases can be accommodated with the addition of 2,000 lb as an overload case. This brings the wing loading up to 21 lb/sq ft. The overload case would allow 40 men at 170 lb plus 50 lb each of equipment to be carried in addition to the pilot.

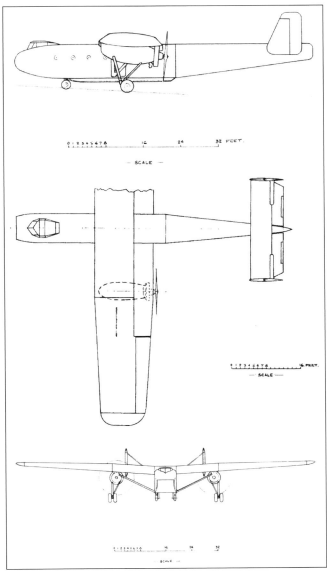

Above: Three-view G.A. drawing of the M.32 Powered Glider. Note the twin mainwheels.

C.G. POSITION AND NEUTRAL POINT

It has been calculated and checked by the RAE that the neutral point of the glider is .36C. It is necessary to have the c.g. of a towed glider at .15C in front of the neutral point (see RAE Report of meeting on 29th January 1941). Therefore the c.g. of the glider is arranged at .21C (which figure is not satisfactory for normal powered aircraft). It is estimated that for reasonable stability and control of a powered aircraft the c.g. should be at .33C. This is convenient as by using the pusher type of installation not only is the desired figure obtained but also it is then possible to arrange the fuel directly on the c.g. and so avoid any change of trim during flight. This means:-

The glider is satisfactorily balanced with full load.

The glider is slightly nose heavy with one pilot and no other load.

The powered aircraft is satisfactorily balanced with full load in the same stowage positions as for a glider.

The powered aircraft is satisfactorily balanced with overload on .33C.

The powered aircraft without load requires in the nose two pilots at 200 lb plus 175 lb ballast.

From the above it is seen that it is not convenient to drop the military load by parachute or other means from the powered aircraft.

In addition to that stated in the brochure, Don Brown recalled that the complete engine nacelles could be jettisoned in flight and the aircraft landed as a glider, with sufficient tailplane area and adjustment being provided to cope with the c.g. movement change. He also said that although the Bristol Pegasus engines were of sufficient power to maintain cruising speed, a tug would still have been required for take-off and climb to operating height, but the engines would have provided sufficient power for take-off at light load for ferrying purposes (Note: this was not mentioned in the booklet).

For towing purposes, the c.g. of the glider should ideally be further forward than that of a powered aircraft so it was therefore proposed that pusher power-plants be used on the powered version. Although the c.g. of the engines was aft of that of the glider, the difference was just sufficient to bring the c.g. of the powered version into the desired position.

The Ministry eventually carried out some rather belated and half-hearted experiments with a powered General Aircraft Hamilcar heavy glider and although a contract, believed for the construction of a mock-up of the M.32, was issued to Phillips & Powis, it was not ordered in either configuration.

Throughout the war, Miles continued to develop and enlarge on this concept but the complete lack of official interest led him to a private venture programme, albeit somewhat unofficially (in so much as he never got around to informing the Ministry that he was building it!), starting in 1944 with the construction of the smallest of the projects under consideration. This later became the M.57 Aerovan, which made its first flight, in the hands of chief test pilot Tommy Rose, on 26th January 1945.

A larger, four-engined development of this aircraft, the all metal M.71 Merchantman, was completed in 1947 and this was capable of carrying a 5,000lb payload to full ICAO Transport Category 'A' performance standards, on 1,000 bhp.

George Miles sent a letter to the technical editor of the American magazine *Aero Digest* in October 1951, in which he noted the striking similarity between the M.57 Aerovan, and the proposal for a twin-engined 'Utility Command' aircraft, which had been advocated in the 11th December 1950 issue of *Aviation Week*.

Other projects, which were developed from the original 1938 proposals included the M.57, M.61, M.62, M.68, M.71 and M.72. Details of these will be found in the next volume.

PERFORMANCE

Glider

Gliding angle	1 in 13
Gliding speed	81 mph
Stall (flaps down)	45 mph
Tow speed (normal)	150 mph

Powered aircraft (Normal load)

Top speed	
(2 x Pegasus engines)	185 mph at 6,500 ft
Cruising	150 mph at 10,000 ft
Stall	66 mph
Range	1,350 miles

WEIGHTS

	lb	Wing Loading (lb/sq ft)
Tare weight of glider	8,000	
Military load and pilot	6,900	
AUW as glider	14,900	12.4
Fuel (540 gallons)	2,200	
Engine nacelles	6,060	
AUW as powered aircraft	23,160	19.3
Overload	2,000	
AUW overload conditions	25,160	21.0

LEADING PARTICULARS

Span	95 ft
Length	64 ft
Height	18 ft

WINGS

Gross area	1,200 sq ft
Section	NACA 230
Root chord	13 ft 6 ins
Tip chord	10 ft 6 ins
Centre section T/C	18 per cent
Tip T/C	9 per cent
Root incidence	5°
Tip incidence	3°
Dihedral (measured on TE)	4°
Aspect ratio	7.7

AILERON

Type	Frise (hinge at .26C)
Area	111 sq ft
Volume	.06

SPOILER (for use with the glider case).

Area (total projected)	13.4 sq ft

FLAPS

Type	Irving
Area	140.2 sq ft

TAILPLANE & ELEVATOR

Span (fin centres)	24 ft
Chord	8 ft
Area	176 sq ft
Volume	.43
Section	NACA 0012
Tailplane area	111.8 sq ft
Elevator area	64.2 sq ft
Elevator volume	.47
Elevator hinge	.280
Elevator tabs	6.4 sq ft

FIN & RUDDERS

Area (total)	115.5 sq ft
Volume	.084
Section	NACA 0012
Fin area	65 sq ft
Rudder area	50.5 sq ft
Rudder volume	.035

The first prototype M.33 Monitor TT Mk.I NF900.

Chapter 24
Miles M.33 Monitor Target-Tower
Mk.I and Mk.II to Spec. Q.9/42

In November 1941, a provisional specification for a target-tower was issued by Lt Cdr Pelley, RDNI and various preliminary discussions on this specification took place. As a result of these discussions, a twin-engined scheme was developed.

At this time Miles was considering a new aircraft to replace the Master for training purposes and a mock-up of this, the M.29, had already been partially completed. In view of the Directorate of Technical Development's (DTD) statement that the possibilities of a single-engined aircraft should be fully explored, it was considered worthwhile investigating the possibility of utilising the basic structure of the Master replacement aircraft for the purpose of target towing. Work was put in hand in August 1942 and a new mock-up of the revised M.29 (apparently made of metal) was built to meet the target towing requirement.

Miles, however, was unconvinced that a single-engined aircraft would meet the requirements of the specified target towing role and in view of the high-performance required, soon proved that a twin-engined design would be required. This would also provide the room, view and comfort necessary for the crew to carry out their duties efficiently. In September 1942, a meeting was held at the Ministry of Aircraft Production with the Air Ministry, the Admiralty and RAF personnel to discuss the suitability of the provisional designs, which had, in the meantime, been issued by the firm. The meeting was told by DTD that in view of the shortage of engines a twin could not be considered, although it was pointed out that a single-engined aircraft fell short of the required performance. The single-engined mock-up was duly completed and Miles invited DTD to visit the works to convince himself that their criticisms regarding room and comfort for the crew were fully justified. This was agreed and authority was given on the spot for further investigation of the twin-engined version and to build a suitable mock-up.

The first design conference for an aircraft to meet the requirements of Specification No.Q.9/42 was held under the direction of the Technical Director, George Miles, in October 1942 but rather surprisingly, the actual Specification No.Q.9/42 Twin Engined Target Tower, wasn't dated until 15th April 1943. It was issued to Phillips & Powis on 27th April 1943 and extracts from this Specification are reproduced below:

GENERAL

This Specification is issued to cover the design and construction of a high-speed twin-engined target towing aircraft and gives only the particular requirements for the type in amplification of the general requirements stated in Specification No. DTD 1028 (Issue 4) and:

(a)   AP 970 with amendments up to and including AL No. 19.

(b)   ADMs current at 1st March 1943.

(c)   SIS current at 1st March 1943.

and these requirements shall be completely fulfilled except where varied by this Specification or where the prior concurrence of the DTD has been obtained.

DESIGN REQUIREMENTS

Design for Production. While this specification is intended to cover the design and construction of Prototype aircraft only, it is essential that the requirements of production be borne in mind and that the whole design be suitable for quantity production under war conditions.

Engine Installation. The aircraft shall be fitted with two Wright Cyclone R2600-9 Power Plants and the installations shall be suitable for operation under temperate, tropical, desert and sub-arctic conditions.

Glider Towing. Provision is to be made from the initial design stage for the towing of gliders.

EQUIPMENT

Equipment shall be fitted or provided for in accordance with the Appendix "A" to this Specification. The prototypes shall be delivered, one in RAF role and the other in the Naval role - each aircraft to be complete with equipment to convert from one role to the other. Requirements for any new type or range of equipment other than that stocked already by DGE should be brought to the notice of the Ministry of Aircraft Production and the Air Ministry as laid down in paragraph 8 of the Appendix "A" Memorandum of Instructions.

APPENDIX "B" Naval and Air Staff Requirements for a High Speed Target Towing Aircraft.

INTRODUCTION

This document describes the combined Naval and Air Staff requirements *(OR.119 - PA)* for a high speed target towing land plane. Any requirement which is peculiar to the Royal Navy or to the Royal Air Force is annotated "NS" (Naval Staff), or "AS" (Air Staff). Where there is no annotation the requirement is common to both Staffs, although there may be a quantitative difference. Where it is considered necessary for any such quantitative difference to be recorded the two requirements are separately defined.

The aircraft is required for the following duties.

   (i)   Target towing for ground to air firing practices by day or night.
   (ii)   Target towing for air to air firing practices by day or night.
   (iii) Cine marking of ground to air firing practices by day (NS)

The aircraft must be able to carry equipment for (i) and (iii) simultaneously (NS). The aircraft is to be capable of operating in any part of the world.

Speed.   The speeds required for the various operations which the aircraft will undertake are:

   (i)   A continuous cruising speed as close as possible to 300 mph TAS (260 knots) when towing a flare target with 6,000 ft of wire at 10,000 ft (NS)

   Note: The Air Staff requirement is the maximum possible continuous cruising speed for towing at 3,000 ft and at 25,000 ft, but it is considered that the Naval Staff requirement is the best that is likely to be obtainable.

   (ii)   A continuous cruising speed of 300 mph, TAS (260 knots) on cine marking duties (NS).

   (iii) A continuous cruising speed of 200 mph, TAS (174 knots) when towing (a) a 3 ft self-inflating "Y" type sleeve with 1,200 ft of wire at a height of 1,500 ft (NS); and (b) a 5 ft 5 in flag at 12,000 ft with 7,000 ft of wire (AS for ground to air firing by Anti-Aircraft Units).

Towing Gear. The aircraft is required to carry a totally enclosed power-operated winch with single drum. It is considered that for simplicity and smoothness of control the winch should be operated by hydraulic power.

Crew Stations. A crew of two (pilot and drogue operator, or observer WT operator or navigator) is required for target towing and for marking duties.

Drogue Control. The drogue operator station is required to be designed so that the operator can stream the drogue without lying prone. The winch is to be controllable from this position.

Cine Marking. The cine-camera is to be suitably mounted in a movable dome or turret to cover the arcs required by paragraph 18 below. The observer must be able to use the W/T when in the cine-marking position (NS). A clear view from 4° before the beam through aft, each side, above the horizontal, and at such angles of depression therefrom as the structure permits. An angle of depression on the beam of up to 15° is required. The cine marking turret is to be removable in such a manner that there is no speed loss due to provision for the turret when the turret is removed. The turret shall be replaceable by a hatch in the Naval version and by a Perspex blister in the RAF version.

OTHER FEATURES

Flotation. The aircraft is to be so designed that it will not "nose under" if forced to alight on water, and it is to be capable of floating in a horizontal attitude long enough for the crew to launch and embark in their dinghies.

Diving. The aircraft is to be capable of diving up to an angle of 45° at a speed of approximately 350 mph TAS (without target but with cine-marking). This feature is required so that throw-off firing may be carried out at the aircraft when simulating dive-bombing attacks (NS).

Equipment:

Targets. Stowage for targets is required as follows:

   (i)   Twelve flares and four 3 ft type "Y" sleeves (NS).
   (ii)   Six flag targets; or
   (iii) Six sleeve type targets (AS).

Photographic. Provision is required for the installation of one cine camera and stowage for four spare cine camera magazines. Provision is required for the installation of a fixed forward G.45 cine camera gun required for the exercise described in paragraph 24 (Diving).

Dinghies. Two "K" type dinghies together with a Type "M" aircraft dinghy and emergency equipment.

The design team, under the guidance of George Miles, was led by 'Toby' Heal, who was responsible for the design of the M.33 as this large machine was not 'George Miles' sort of aircraft'. During subsequent discussions relating to the development of the mock-up, the firm was requested to design the cockpit arrangements on similar lines to the Westland Welkin, which had recently been approved. A navigator's station was positioned aft of the pilot with provision for compass bearings and look-out windows etc.

Details of the Miles M.33 Monitor TT Mk.II were given in *The Aeroplane* for 5th October 1945:

Construction

The Monitor was required urgently, and it was laid down that the complete all-metal mainplane and undercarriage of the Bristol Beaufighter should be used, but this plan was scrapped because of the increased use of the Beaufighter for night-fighter defence in Fighter Command. In order not to delay the production of the M.33 Monitor, Miles Aircraft Ltd, quickly designed, and had accepted, an all-wood, one-piece wing consisting of two main laminated spars with orthodox rib formation and stressed skin plywood covering. In order to simulate dive-bombing attacks with speeds of up to 400 mph, dive-brakes are fitted to the upper and lower surfaces of the wing, between the main spars, outboard of the motor nacelles. Hydraulically operated and mechanically locked, the dive-brakes travel through 90 degrees, being fully open when the connecting arms are in alignment.

With regard to the need for dive brakes, it should be mentioned that this was a Naval requirement and they would only have been fitted to the Mk.II version.

However, although Miles discussed the possibility of using the Beaufighter's mainplane and undercarriage with the Bristol Aeroplane Company early in November 1942, fears were expressed as a result of their investigations regarding the availability of the Beaufighter's wing and centre section. Miles also stated, categorically, that while they were prepared to fit these components if so instructed, they would take no responsibility if the performance and handling qualities of the aircraft, particularly at target launching speed, were adversely affected. Miles also wanted to lower the centre line of thrust relative to the wing, not only due to the aerodynamic advantages but, as the aeroplane had to be of the high wing type to meet the ditching requirements, he wished to shorten the undercarriage as much as possible.

It can be seen, even at this early stage that delays in reaching agreement on how the aircraft should be built were beginning to make themselves felt. These 'Ministerial' problems were to continue to dog the Monitor throughout its production and, on reflection, it would undoubtedly have been much less time consuming and far simpler if the firm could have just been given a free hand in the design of the aircraft, without continually being side-tracked into wasteful schemes of trying to utilise existing parts from other aircraft.

Contract/Acft/2668/C.23(c), DTD Req.4335/RDT1, with the Instruction to Proceed (ITP), dated 5th December 1942, was placed by MAP for the construction of two prototype aircraft on 'the highest priority', at an estimated cost of £60,000. The two prototype aircraft were NF900, a TT Mk.I for the RAF and NF904, a TT Mk.II for the RN.

Since the use of a tricycle undercarriage would have required a cut-away for the nose wheel, which, in turn, would have made the skin discontinuous and therefore dangerous when alighting on water, a normal tailwheel undercarriage was considered to be acceptable, and in December 1942, Miles agreed to use as many parts of the Beaufighter's undercarriage as possible. Although the top of the main undercarriage had to be extended by several inches in order to obtain the necessary clearance for the larger propellers, at least the unmodified Beaufighter's tailwheel could be used on the Monitor.

In January 1943, it was finally decided to abandon the use of the Bristol Beaufighter wing, and it was then agreed that the Monitor's wing would be designed by Phillips & Powis and constructed of wood, while the fuselage, tail unit and all control surfaces would also be designed by the firm, but manufactured of metal. The Monitor thereby became the first Miles aeroplane to use metal construction on a large scale.

Don Brown recalled that the original intention was to fit the wooden wing with the Miles external aerofoil flap, which had proved so successful on the M.28 but a further requirement demanded that the aircraft, when dismantled, should be capable of being accommodated in certain standard packing cases. In order to comply with this, it was necessary to fit conventional slotted trailing edge flaps.

On 22nd March 1943, the ITP for the production of the Monitor was issued to the firm, at an estimated cost of £500,000, but the number of aircraft required was not apparently specified at that time. Contract/Acft/2831/C.23(c) dated 27th March 1943 was placed for the manufacture of 200 M.33 Monitor Mk.I and Mk.II to Prod Spec Monitor TT Mk.I/P1 and Prod Spec Monitor TT Mk.II /P1 aircraft. Although the exact numbers to be produced of each mark has never been established, the value of this production contract was believed to have been approximately £5,000,000 (although the ITP only gave an estimated cost of £500,000), and if so, this would have given a cost per aircraft of £25,000. An ITP for 'Q.9/42 Test Specimens', dated 23rd April 1943, gave an estimated cost for these of £10,000.

On 3rd May 1943, Specification No. Q.9/42 was received by Phillips & Powis and this covered the requirements of both the Air Staff and the Royal Navy. By this time, considerable progress had been made with the construction of the mock-up with the general form of the aircraft and positioning of the equipment having been more or less decided upon. Development work had also commenced on the design of the power-operated winch with a single drum, which, for simplicity and smoothness of control, was to be operated by hydraulic power and also the launching arrangements to suit the various targets required.

A 1/7th scale model was built for test at the National Physical Laboratory wind tunnel and this was fitted with airscrews driven by an electric motor with gearing supplied by the NPL.

The Monitor TT Mk.II was specifically designed to enable the observer to launch targets with the minimum effort and, to this end, the old-fashioned external wooden windlass which had been used on target-towers for many years was replaced by a new 10 hp hydraulic winch, designed by Miles Aircraft, and operated by power from the starboard engine. Whereas the old windlass was incapable of effective operation at speeds over 150 mph, the newly designed Miles winch could deal with 7,000 ft of towing cable at speeds in excess of 300 mph.

A high-wing layout was proposed and the machine was to be powered by two Wright Cyclone R-2600-9 radial engines (later replaced by two 1,750hp R-2600-31 14-cylinder, two-row air-cooled radial engines). The crew consisted of one pilot and one drogue operator or observer/wireless operator, or navigator and these were to be provided with the best possible view. The drogue operator was able to stream the drogue without lying prone and to be able to control the winch from that operator station.

In the end, the Monitor TT Mk.I was not delivered to the RAF because of the greater need of the Navy for the Mk.II which could also simulate dive-bombing attacks on ships of the Fleet. Apart from the dive-brakes, the two marks differed only in internal accessories, such as wireless equipment, although the RAF was to have had a dorsal Perspex observation blister, reminiscent of that on the Beaufighter, in place of the manually operated cupola.

In order to facilitate the launch and change-over of targets while over the firing area, a new hydraulic winch was designed by Miles and this, together with a conveyor-belt system to facilitate the launch and recovery of the three different types of targets, would certainly have made life easier for the drogue operator who, in the Monitor TT Mk.II, would have sat in the manually-operated dorsal cupola.

A full-scale wooden mock-up, built in great secrecy in the Experimental Department, was completed in time for the Mock-Up Conference held at Woodley on 10th June 1943 and during the course of this conference a number of potential snags were identified and 'ironed out'.

An undated drawing entitled 'M.33C Twin Engine High Speed Target Tower (RAF Version)' shows, along with many photographs of the actual mock-up, a Monitor with a somewhat 'flattened' cupola, which was lower at the front than at the rear, in the mid upper position. The significance of the designation 'M.33C' is unclear but the 'C' may possibly have referred to the Mock-Up 'Conference'.

It is recorded that the hydraulic installation was fitted to the prototype aircraft on 10th November 1943 and the flexibility of the British aircraft industry in general, and Miles Aircraft Ltd in particular, was well illustrated by the fact that no serious hold-up was experienced at Woodley when the Monitor was put into production. In fact, the experience gained by Miles Aircraft in the production of all-wood, high-speed trainers was turned to good account in the planning of the Monitor assembly line.

On the 11th June, the day after the Mock-up conference, George wrote to Mr W Lappin of Rolls-Royce Ltd, with an interesting suggestion:

On these two pages are five photographs of the mock-up of the M.33 Monitor.

Dear Mr Lappin,

Very many thanks for your letter of the 7th inst, enclosing data on the Griffon RG.14 SM and 61 engines.

The Q.9/42 is primarily intended as a very high-speed target towing aircraft; as you know, the target towers at present in service have a very low performance indeed and the anti-aircraft and

combat training which is carried out with their assistance is of very doubtful value due to the low towing speeds which are possible.

This machine has been designed to tow a target at speeds up to 300 mph and you can imagine that to obtain such a performance with the drag of several miles of cable and a target involves the use of rather an outstanding aeroplane.

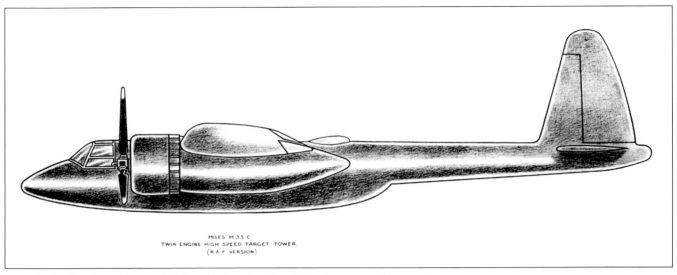

An early drawing of the Miles M.33C Twin Engine high Speed Target Tower (RAF version).

The wooden wing for the first prototype Monitor under construction in the Experimental Department. Note the Tricycle undercarriage M.18 and the M.39B Libellula in the background.

Another view of the large wooden wing for the Monitor under construction.

In this respect it occurs to us that by substituting Griffon engines for the 1,700 hp Cyclones which we are fitting to the prototype it would make a very useful high-speed bomber; in this form the performance would be equivalent to that of the Mosquito while carrying a very much heavier bomb load.

Should you be passing Reading at any time, I should be very pleased if you would look in and see the mock-up and prototype which is now fairly well advanced.

Yours sincerely,
George Miles

Just 15 months after agreement had been reached on the basic design, the prototype Monitor Mk.I, NF900 was ready for testing but, with the aircraft jacked-up for undercarriage retraction tests, an unexpected snag occurred - the undercarriage would not retract!

The Monitor pilot's cockpit.

The first prototype Monitor TT Mk.I, NF900 in April 1944 about the time of its first flight.   [MAP RTP Photographic Section]

For two days the staff worked feverishly to rectify the fault but without success. The Monitor had originally been designed to have no hydraulic lines in the cockpit area, the system being electrically controlled by a series of solenoid valves near the wing spar.

It was at this juncture that, characteristically, Miles appeared on the scene and calmly announced his intention of investigating the problem, although he freely admitted that he did not profess to be an expert on hydraulics. However, as he pointed out - the 'experts' had had their chance to solve the problem and failed, so for better or worse, he would try his luck!

The team were not sorry to be relieved of the task and there were apparently some good natured smiles at the sight of the Chairman of the company removing his jacket and getting down, single-handed, to investigate a system, the details of which were quite unfamiliar to him. Miles' line of attack centred on 're-plumbing' the system, replacing the solenoid valves with conventional pilot-operated manual valves. Miles worked all that afternoon and evening and right on through the night and by the next morning the undercarriage was retracted successfully and the Monitor was ready for its first flight - the effect on the morale of the workers could be imagined.

An incidental result of the hydraulic problems was that the dive brakes fitted to the first prototype Monitor Mk.I were never made operational. Dive-brakes were not fitted to the second prototype either, nor were they to be fitted in any subsequent production Monitor Mk.II aircraft, as this once urgent requirement was apparently subsequently cancelled following the end of the war with Japan in August 1945.

Another by-product of the hydraulic problems experienced on the first prototype was that the tailwheel was, initially, unable to be retracted. The prototype Monitor Mk.I turned out to be somewhat of a hybrid aircraft, with the (inoperable) dive brakes of the Mk.II,

but without its cupola. The Mk.I was also originally intended to have had a streamlined blister at the location of the cupola but this was not installed for its initial flights and was probably never fitted. No photographs have been found of the second prototype NF904, so it has not been possible to confirm whether this was, in fact, fitted with a dorsal cupola.

Just before the prototype Monitor first flew, however, a second order, to Spec. No. Monitor TT Mk.II/P.1 on an extension to Contracts/Acft/2831/C.23(c) dated 27th March 1944, was placed for the manufacture of 300 Monitor Mk.II for the RN.

The prototype Monitor, NF900, given the RAF Experimental Aircraft No.213 for identification purposes, was an exceptionally clean, sleek and sharp looking aeroplane, which looked 'right' in every respect. First flown, by Chief Test Pilot Tommy Rose with Assistant Test Pilot Hugh Kennedy also on board, from Woodley on 5th April 1944, the 35 minute flight confirmed that the new machine showed no swing on take-off, was docile and satisfactory to fly and gave no tendency to drop a wing at the stall. During the subsequent flight testing which followed, it was found that the aircraft had a maximum speed of 360 mph and could cruise comfortably at 300 mph, and the firm considered that no major modifications to the basic design were necessary. This meant that the Monitor was, in effect, probably the fastest piston engined, non-operational aircraft in the world at that time.

The resulting higher loads of the lengthened undercarriage necessitated the use of dual retraction cylinders (the Beaufighter only had one per side) and while Hugh Kennedy was making his third flight in the prototype just a couple of weeks later on 19th April 1944, a retraction rod failure in one of the cylinders caused a major problem, as the remaining one was not sufficiently powerful to raise or lower the undercarriage completely. The hydraulic system thereby demonstrating that it was not 'fail-safe' in this respect and in consequence, only one leg could be made to lower.

Although Hugh tried all means at his disposal, including the emergency system, to get the recalcitrant leg to lower, it was to no avail and he was left with no alternative other than to attempt a belly landing back at Woodley. Dennis Bancroft, the Chief Aerodynamicist, happened to be on the airfield filming some other trials at the time of the incident and he captured Hugh's faultless ensuing belly landing on film. In fact, Hugh made such a good job of the belly landing that the aeroplane was hardly damaged, there was no fire and he was able to get out of the cockpit with no difficulty.

Fortunately, the Monitor static test fuselage was sufficiently advanced in construction to allow the removal of its lower fuselage assembly and following the replacement of the damaged portion with this, the prototype was soon flying again, with Hugh Kennedy taking it off for a 25 minute flight on 26th July 1944.

A very interesting 'commentary on certain features of the Monitor', was written by Major Tommy Rose to George Miles on 28th April 1944. The last sentence suggests that certain problems needed urgent rectification before further flight testing was carried out!

As suggested, I am setting down for your consideration, a commentary on certain features of the Monitor. I have given a great deal of thought to the matter and I know you will make allowance for the fact that whilst my practical experience is considerable, my technical knowledge is not.

Rudder - This is very heavy at low speeds and gets progressively lighter as the speed increases. At 280 IAS it was very light indeed and it seems likely that we shall run into very serious trouble when we go higher. There is a certain amount of stiffness in the control statically which might account for some of the heaviness at the lower range. Possibly the lightness at the other end is caused either by the servo tab being too large (or overgeared), or by overbalancing, or both.

Trim - The fore and aft trim on the glide is unusual, inasmuch as with the CG in the forward position the aircraft is landed comfortably with the elevator trim tab central. With the CG extended aft or even aft it would seem that the approach will be made with the tab about ½ way between central and fully forward.

The aircraft flies very starboard wing low with the control column free and requires practically full aileron tab to maintain level flight laterally. From experience on former types this is probably due to the warping of the ailerons although it may also be influenced by the rigging.

The throttles do require redesign. They should be completely rigid. At the moment they flex considerably and as they are also a little stiff in operation they produce a stiffness and even bruising in the left hand of the pilot operating them.

Stability - You have received a confidential verbal report from Kennedy as to the instability, climbing, flaps and undercarriage fully down. As he had full fuel tanks the CG would be in approximately the mid way position. Although I am of the opinion that the aircraft is stable in level flight at cruising boost with the CG forward, I have a hunch that this may not be so at the extended aft or even aft position. I hope to goodness the hunch is a stumour, but I do think you will be well advised to take such steps as will put you in a position to remedy this in the shortest possible time should it turn out that way.

The undercarriage is such a headache to Miles and yourself that I will refrain from comment save to say that is seems to be so bloody-minded that it is not impossible that one day one leg will stick up and the other immovably down. Under this condition unless there was a very strong wind and ample time to use up all the fuel the pilot might decide to abandon the aircraft. Even if a landing was carried out the result would probably be a write off.

A copy of this will not be sent to Central Filing. Signed T Rose, Chief Test Pilot

The Monitor was then made available to the A&AEE Boscombe Down in order to satisfy an urgent request by the Director of Research and Development (Aircraft), (DD/RDA), Ministry of Aircraft Production that the aircraft should be flown by A&AEE pilots to confirm the good impressions gained by the Contractors' Test Pilots. Two pilots were detailed to make brief handling flights in the aircraft, in accordance with a letter dated 4th August 1944 from the Chief Technical Officer, Boscombe Down, to the Officer Commanding Performance Test Squadron. They were Flt Lts W R Morris and Alfred D Miller and, during the morning of Tuesday, 8th August 1944, they flew a Stinson Reliant from Boscombe Down to Woodley in order to undertake the assignment.

Flt Lt Miller had previously made his first flight in the prototype Monitor NF900 on 4th August and, on 8th August, Flt Lt Morris made his first flight, a 30 minute solo local, landing back at Woodley at 12.30 hrs. He reported that the flight had not been a problem and that he had found the aircraft to be easy to fly,

showing no undesirable tendencies, apart from undue noise and vibration which he experienced, but he did request that trimming cord adjustments be made to both ailerons in order to correct an out-of-balance aileron trim.

The aircraft was then refuelled, oiled and inspected before Flt Lt Miller was to make his second flight in the Monitor, later in the day, but this time he was accompanied, for the first time, by the civilian technical observer, Peter Ainsbury. Miller took off at 15.00 hrs, little knowing that this flight was to end tragically after just 30 minutes in the air, and as he was approaching to land.

There have been many theories put forward as to the cause of this tragic loss, but Service Accident Report No. W.1952, issued by the Accidents Investigation Branch on 6th October 1944, set out the findings of the accident investigation, as follows:

Aircraft:	M.33 Monitor NF900 (Prototype)
Engines:	Wright Cyclone R.2600-31: Port No:183054/41–28212; Stbd No:52122/41-29649
Owners:	CRD, MAP.
Pilot:	F/Lt Alfred D Miller, A & AEE, Boscombe Down - Burning injuries.
Crew:	Technical Observer - Mr Peter Frank Ainsbury BSc, A&AEE, Boscombe Down - Killed.
Place of Accident:	1 mile west of Wokingham.
Date & Time:	8/8/44 at 1533 hrs.

Notification: By telephone on 8/8/44 from Miles Aircraft Ltd and by signal from AID Hawk, Reading, received at 0900 hrs on 9/8/44. The scene of the accident was visited on 8/8/44.

Circumstances of the accident: DD/RDA had requested that the aircraft should be flown by A&AEE pilots to confirm the impressions gained by the Contractors' Test Pilots. Two pilots were therefore detailed to make brief handling flights in the aircraft in accordance with letter reference AM.80 dated 4/8/44 from the Chief Technical Officer, Boscombe Down, to the Officer Commanding Performance Test Squadron.

The pilot in question had flown the aircraft once before on 4/8/44 for approximately 55 minutes in compliance with these instructions. The aircraft was flown by his colleague on the morning of 8/8/44 for 30 minutes and the flight finished at 1230 hrs. In the interval between the morning and afternoon flights trimming strips were fitted on both ailerons, the wing fuel tanks and oil tanks were topped up and one side panel was removed from each engine cowling in order that an inspection of the interior could be made.

In the course of the final preparations for the afternoon flight a pilot type parachute was produced for the observer and the method of operating the two levers for the dual purpose entry-exit escape hatch was explained to him. Before the aircraft was taxied away, the observer was seen to be wearing his parachute which appeared to be properly fastened. The aircraft took off normally at 1500 hrs and during the next half hour general handling tests were carried out.

At 1530 hrs, the pilot prepared to land and the following extract from his statement describes subsequent events:-

"I put my wheels and flaps down early on the circuit to ascertain the amount of engine required to maintain height under these conditions, but before I could make any assessment of this there was a very faint smell of petrol, so slight as to be dismissed as not out of the ordinary. Shortly afterwards, at about 1,500 ft and at a speed of about 120 mph I felt a sudden blast of fire from behind. I immediately turned to Mr Ainsbury and told him to bale out, not releasing my seat back to give him a clear exit. He acknowledged my signal and bent down towards the exit, out of my sight. I waited

several seconds to make quite sure he had gone. By this time, the fire was so intense I could not reach the extinguisher buttons.

We were then at 800 ft, I pulled the aircraft round to the left, away from cottages; by this time I did not have full control. I then jettisoned the hood, baled out, striking the turret and tail en route. My parachute opened just before hitting the ground. On looking round I could not see my colleague, so dashed over to the crash and attempted to enter the fire again in case he should not have been clear, but this was of no avail. I have no idea what caused the fire or in which engine it originated, if any."

Other points referred to by the pilot were:

(a)   That flames appeared to fill the whole of the fuselage.

(b)   That the acknowledgement of his instructions to bale out were given verbally and visually.

(c)   That flames prevented him seeing his instruments other than the top of his blind flying panel.

Statements by witnesses on the ground established that:

Flames and smoke came from the port nacelle at the same time as the pilot became aware of the fire.

Immediately afterwards the sound of an engine or engines faltering was heard. The explanation for this could have been that the throttles were closed momentarily while the pilot told his observer to bale out.

The observer's hatch fell from the aircraft just before the pilot was seen to bale out.

The crash occurred not more than sixty seconds after smoke and flames were seen.

The aircraft dived out of control after the pilot had baled out. The pilot landed eighty yards from the crash. The observer's remains were found in the main wreckage; his parachute pack was unopened and the quick release mechanism indicated that all four straps were attached.

Further details:

(a)   Monitor NF900 was a high wing twin-engined monoplane designed for target towing (see photograph). It was constructed by Miles Aircraft Co Ltd at Woodley, Berks. The mainplane was of one-piece all wood construction while the fuselage was made of metal. The pilot's seat was situated in the front of the fuselage and the observer's seat was placed behind it on the port side. Both seats were forward of the line of the wing leading edge. The aircraft's total flying time amounted to 9 hours 5 minutes. A belly landing had been made after 4 hours 5 minutes flying time due to undercarriage trouble. Following this, the undercarriage was modified and two new engines and a new propeller were fitted. The engines were built by the Wright Aeronautical Corp, Paterson, New Jersey, USA., and were modified by Field Consolidated Aircraft Service Ltd in June 1944. Both had a total running time of 10 hours 50 minutes. Each was fitted with a Stromberg carburettor, type PT 13.E2.

(b)   Weather at the time was described by witnesses as clear with bright sunshine from a cloudless sky. RAF White Waltham, situated a few miles away, reported the weather as follows:

At 1450 hrs - Visibility 5 miles; 8/10 cloud at 2,500 ft; wind west 5 mph; ground temperature 77.2°F.

At 1550 hrs - Visibility 5 miles; 6/10 cloud at 2,500 ft; wind west 10 mph; ground temperature 75.6°F.

(c)   On inspection at the scene of the accident it was found that the aircraft had struck the ground at fairly high speed in an almost vertical attitude and was destroyed by impact and ground fire. Both propellers had their blades broken at the root, except one blade of the port propeller which was broken approximately 3ft from the root. Two of the starboard propeller blade leading edges were pitted, suggesting that this propeller was under some degree of power at the time of impact.

The observer's escape hatch was found 150 yards back from the scene of the accident, while the pilot's ditching hatch was found three-quarters of a mile back. The former was undamaged apart from a slight impact mark, but the latter, which was intact, was found to have the rubber sealing at the edges burnt at intervals round the whole seating, while soot marks were apparent between the burnt rubber and the bolts on the inside of the hood.

Several components from the port engine accessory bay were thrown clear of the ground fire area on impact. None showed any indication of the existence of a fire during flight in the accessory bay.

Owing to evidence obtained from witnesses on the ground, attention was concentrated on the port power plant. Examination of the port engine showed that the articulating assembly in both banks had been intact and evidently in good condition before the crash. The engine had been badly impacted and its rear cover was destroyed together with the entire installation. All exhaust stubs were accounted for.

The possibility of the exhaust cabin heater system being responsible for the fire was considered. It was found that the system had not been completed.

Steel blanking caps were fitted near the exit duct of the heat exchanger in order to prevent hot air reaching the remainder of the system. These caps were found intact.

(d)   Examination of the six fuel cocks found, confirmed that outer tanks only were in use and that both cocks to the centre tank were turned off. The balance cock was not found. Most of the copper fuel piping was recovered but was too badly damaged to provide any useful information.

(e)   The pilot's face, hands and forearms were burnt. He was wearing war service dress, leather helmet and goggles but no gloves. His jacket was severely scorched on the right arm, right breast and left hand side and near the collar at the back. His shirt collar was burnt at the back, just above the stud position, where it would project above his jacket. His trousers were scorched on the right leg. The goggles' strap at the back was slightly scorched. The leather helmet showed no evidence of heat, nor did the parachute or its harness when examined several days later, although the odour of singeing could still be detected.

Observations:

(a)   Fuel leak as source of fire. All the evidence in this accident points to the leakage of fuel in the port wing or engine nacelle being responsible for the fire. The engine showed no evidence of mechanical failure. The small throttle opening at the time of the outbreak of fire eliminated the possibility of boosted mixture being responsible. The suddenness and extent of the fire tends to rule out lubricating or hydraulic oil as the source.

(b)   Fuel tank vent pipe. This passes through the bottom of the outboard tanks and thence via a short length of Flexatex pipe to the tank panel below which it projects. The lower end of the Flexatex pipe was secured to the bottom panel. Relative movement between the fuel tank and bottom panel would tend to fracture the end connections resulting in any fuel spilled collecting in the tank bay. It is believed that had the Flexatex pipe failed most of the fuel spilled would have drained away through holes provided for that purpose and any that remained would be insufficient to maintain a fire of the intensity experienced.

(c)   Possibility of leak from the main fuel feed pipes. The fact that the engine did not cut or splutter immediately the smell of fuel was noticed by the pilot suggests that if the leak occurred in the main fuel line, the break could not have been a complete one initially, i.e. some fuel must have continued to pass through to the engine. In favour of the argument for a main fuel feed pipe failure, is the condition of the two propellers which suggests that the starboard engine was under a greater degree of power than the port engine. It is, of course, possible that flames around a fuel pipe would aerate the fuel inside and cause vapour locking and consequent loss of power.

(d)   Possibility of leaks from subsidiary fuel pipes. The pipe venting the Stromberg carburettor back to the wing tank and the priming pump feed were considered. The latter is situated in the fuselage and a leak would be unlikely to cause an extensive fire in the port nacelle. The carburettor vent pipe may feed back several gallons of fuel per hour. Assuming an excessive return of 10 gallons per hour, only one sixth of a gallon would be returned in 60 seconds, the probable maximum time between the pilot smelling fuel and the crash. It is unlikely this would cause such a sudden and extensive fire unless the leak had been present for some time causing fuel to collect in the engine accessory bay, the wing leading edge or the port tank bay. In this event, the pilot might have been expected to notice fumes earlier.

(e)   Plywood wing leading edge - ignition by exhaust fumes. The wing leading edges near the engine nacelles were protected from exhaust fumes by a light alloy plate. It is thought that had the leading edge been ignited first a distinctive smell of wood charring would have been apparent to the crew. As the fuel pipes in the vicinity were of copper and fuel cocks of light alloy bushed with brass an appreciable time would be required for them to be affected by fire.

(f)   Fire from any of the sources mentioned could only have reached the fuselage via the open end of the tunnel formed by the leading edge and front spar. As the cockpit side windows were open an area of negative pressure would be created inside the cockpit in the vicinity, causing the flames to be drawn forward and upward.

(g)   Cause of ignition. Individual short stub exhaust pipes were fitted on the engines. This design meant that the effluent was discharged all round the engine immediately aft of the shoulder cowl. Any fuel leaking in the accessory bay, wing leading edge or in the engine nacelle behind the bulkhead would almost certainly be ignited by the exhaust flames. The distance between the wing leading edge and the exit of the nearest exhaust stub was only eleven inches.

Emergency Exits:

The reason for the observer failing to bale out is obscure. The dual purpose entry-emergency hatch was conveniently situated, of ample size and was observed to drop from the aircraft just before the pilot baled out. Two levers were provided adjacent to the hatch on the starboard side of the cockpit. It is possible the observer wasted a few valuable seconds by operating the wrong lever first.

NOTE: In view of this, Miles Aircraft is, in Monitor No.2, modifying both levers so that initial movement of either will open the hatch whilst use of full travel will jettison the hatch.

Conclusions:

1.   This accident was caused by an outbreak of fire in flight.
2.   Evidence of the sole survivor and of witnesses on the ground establishes that flames indicative of a petrol fire appeared simultaneously from the port nacelle and in the cockpit from behind the pilot.
3.   The pilot had no alternative but to abandon the aircraft owing to the intense heat.
4.   Although the exact location of the fire remains obscure, there is good reason to believe that free fuel in the vicinity of the port nacelle was ignited by exhaust flame. Fire in this area could only enter the fuselage via the inside of the leading edge.
5.   Possible sources of fuel leakage are discussed in paragraph 4, page 5.

Recommendations:

1.   The short length of Flexatex pipe joining the two copper pipes running from the outer tank booster pumps to the main fuel balance pipe and secured by two Linalite clips should be replaced by a longer flexible pipe with standard AGS end couplings. This could be connected from the booster pump to the existing forward connections immediately aft of the front spar.

2.   The fuel tank vents which project underneath the wings should not be rigidly attached to the lower wing skin.

3.   Adequate provision should be made in each wing for ventilation and drainage. The latter should be so arranged that any inflammable fluid which may collect can only escape at points remote from the exhaust system and gases.

4.   The wing leading edge tunnels should be effectively sealed against the passage of flames, smoke or free liquids. The sealing should be capable of preventing a fire in the engine nacelle entering the leading edge or a fire in the leading edge spreading rapidly to the fuselage. Fireproof bulkheads near the leading edge junctions with the nacelles and fuselage would be preferable.

5.   The lower exhaust stubs should be repositioned to minimise the risk of igniting any inflammable fluid which might leak from the accessory bay. Alternatively, the existing exhaust system might be retained and the engine cowlings designed to seal the necessary bay from the outer air and arranged to trap any leaking fluid and convey it to an exit remote from the exhaust flames.

6.   All apertures in the fireproof bulkhead should be effectively sealed. The possibility of strengthening the existing asbestos socks which seal the holes through which the engine mounting tubes pass should be considered, as vibration might cause these to perish prematurely.

Matters arising out of the investigation:

1.   While NF900 was fitted with a drain plug on the tank base, drawings examined showed that it was intended to provide a fuel tank drain with the plug seat secured to the tank panel and connected to the tank by a short length of Flexatex pipe. The possibility of the connection being broken consequent upon relative movement between the tank and tank panel renders this assembly unsatisfactory.

2.   The brush gear and commutator of the generator of each engine are protected by a strip of metal with relatively large perforations. These perforations will not prevent the ingress of fuel or the emission of flames. In Service Accident Report No. W1486 dated 23/6/43 and again in RAE report CH404 of August 1943, generators with this type of brush gear protection were referred to as a potential source of ignition.

Signed: Vernon Brown - Chief Inspector of Accidents.

By a strange coincidence, Flt Lt Miller was discovered at the scene of the crash, in shock and very distressed, by the Chief Fire Officer of Miles Aircraft Ltd, Capt G A Jewell, who just happened to be passing the site quite by accident. He immediately commandeered a local farmer's car and took the pilot back to Woodley for medical attention. Shortly after his very lucky escape, Miller was promoted to Squadron Leader and just eight days later, having only just returned to flying duties, Miller was forced to abandon another aircraft, also due to a fire.

On 12th August 1944, before the official accident report was issued, Miles Aircraft Ltd held their own independent investigation into the cause of the accident and their findings were to be confirmed later in the official accident report.

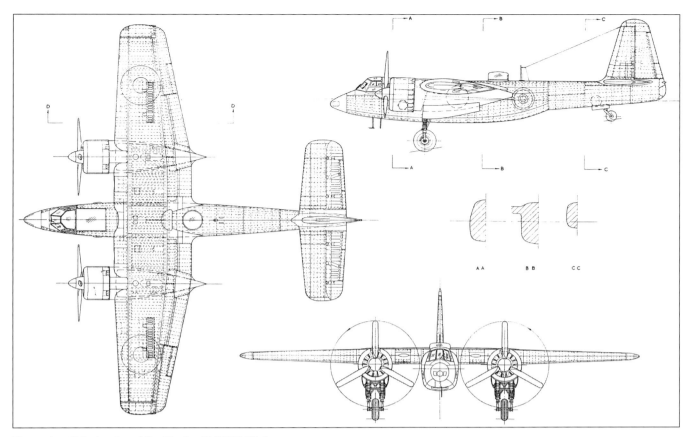

Three-view G.A. drawing of the Monitor M.33 TT Mk.II.

Miles wrote a letter to W Lappin of Rolls-Royce Ltd, Derby, dated August 21st 1944 regarding the Monitor crash, in which he stated:

Many thanks for your letter of August 15th. It is true that the Monitor crashed as a result of a fire in the port engine bay. There is as yet no concrete evidence as to the cause of the fire but our own theory is that it started as a result of a fuel leak between the bulkhead and the induction system. There seems to have been some trouble in America in connection with defective supercharger casings on Cyclone engines and although it is impossible to say whether this could have had any bearing on the Monitor accident I should be interested to know whether you have heard of any similar troubles with this installation.

I am enclosing one of our new pens and will send a further half dozen as soon as they are available. So far we have only had a few samples made up, but hope to get into production as soon as possible.

The airframe of the second prototype Monitor, NF904, which was completed as a Mk.II for the Royal Navy, was divided into five completed cross-sectional groups. By building the fuselage in five sections, instead of working on a complete airframe, a 40 per cent increase in output was gained and in this respect the Miles giant press also played a vital part. When these sections were 'married-up', it was found that no section was more than 50 thousands (i.e. 1/20th) of an inch out. The tail assembly, like the fuselage, was of all-metal, stressed skin construction, with balance tabs being incorporated on the elevators and rudder, as well as on the ailerons.

The undercarriage retracted backwards through 90 degrees into the engine nacelle and the self- centring tailwheel described a 90 degree arc forwards to retract into the rear fuselage. Like the slotted flaps, the undercarriage was hydraulically operated from three pumps, situated immediately behind, which derived their power from the starboard engine.

NF904 was first flown, by Tommy Rose, from Woodley, on 2nd December 1944, with Walter Capley acting as observer, for 20 minutes and, following maker's tests, it was delivered to the

A&AEE Boscombe Down on 27th July 1945. On 14th August, NF904 was being flown by A&AEE pilot Wing Cdr R L Smith (a recent graduate of the second Empire Test Pilots School course) when he experienced complete hydraulic power failure and was unable to lower the undercarriage for landing and yet another belly landing had to be made on the grass.

Reports differ as to whether this was executed at Boscombe Down or Woodley, and the confusion was probably caused by the fact that there are reports of another wheels-up landing being carried out at Woodley before the aircraft was delivered to Boscombe Down. Although the damage sustained in this accident was at first classified as Cat.5 (i.e. - write off), a replacement undercarriage, taken from the third production aircraft, was fitted to speed up repairs. A weakness in the design of the pilot's seat backrest was exposed during this belly landing, when the fittings on the fuselage which held the seat back in position failed. This caused the seat to collapse during the ensuing emergency landing, injuring the pilot. Unfortunately, no details of the ultimate fate of this aircraft can been found.

The M.33 Monitor TT Mk.I and TT Mk.II were ordered under Specification No. Monitor TT Mk.I/P.1 and Monitor TT Mk.II/P.1 respectively, both dated 8th September 1944. However, by then, the projected cost of the production aircraft had risen to approximately £40,000 each.

Air Publication 2607B Volume 1 - Monitor TT Mk.II - dated December 1944, gave full details of the production aircraft as follows:

The Monitor TT Mk.II aircraft is a two-seater high wing monoplane of composite construction, designed for high speed target towing duties. It is powered by two Cyclone air-cooled radial engines driving 3-bladed constant-speed fully-feathering propellers.

The fuselage is of metal stressed-skin construction comprising detachable nose, forward, aft and tail sections. The longerons are of

Monitors on the assembly line. Note the Martinets being assembled to the right of the line.

light alloy channel-section spaced by 44 light-alloy frames and radiused Z-section stringers. A manually-operated cupola can be fitted to the top of the fuselage forward section. Entrance to the fuselage is through a hatch just aft of the nose section. A target release hatch and observation window are fitted in the bottom skin aft of the cupola. A detachable bottom skin panel beneath the forward fuselage permits removal of the target winch for servicing. At the rear end two short tail plane spars are built in with two reinforced fuselage frames. These frames form the attachment points for the tailplane and the fin.

The main plane is a one-piece wooden structure consisting of two box-section spars with nose and centre ribs and detachable wing tips. The front spar is secured to reinforced fuselage frames, forward of the winch removal panel, through castings on the spar and tubular suspension members. The rear spar is bolted to the first oval-shaped fuselage frame. The engine mounting is secured to brackets on the front spars, and flush-fitting dive brakes are housed in the top and bottom surfaces of the main plane at each side of the fuselage. The ailerons are of conventional wooden construction; they are actuated through a sliding bar and triangulated differential operating hinge. An electrically-operated trimming tab, which also functions as a balance tab, is fitted to the port aileron, and a balance tab is fitted to the starboard aileron. Four slotted flaps, of wooden construction, are hinged to the main plane rear spar and extend to each aileron. The flaps are mechanically interconnected.

The tail plane is a metal stressed-skin structure in two sections, each section comprising two reinforced channel spars and flanged light-alloy ribs with a detachable tip. These sections are secured to the two fuselage tail plane spar members. The rudder, elevators and fixed fin are of similar construction. Electrically-operated sheet-metal trimming tabs are fitted to the rudder and elevators. Balance tabs are also provided.

The primary control surfaces are operated by push-pull rods from an "omega" type control column and an adjustable rudder bar in the pilot's cabin. The dive brakes are hydraulically operated and the upper and lower units are mechanically interconnected.

The alighting gear comprises two main wheel units, retracting rearwards and upwards into each engine nacelle, and a retractable articulated self-centring tail wheel. The shock absorbers of the three units are of oleo-pneumatic type, twin struts being provided for each main wheel unit.

The hydraulic system provides power for the operation of the undercarriage, flaps, dive brakes and target winch. Three VSG type pumps, driven by the starboard engine, circulate fluid from a reservoir to selector units and thence to the service required. A hand pump is provided for emergency and ground test operation. A Heywood compressor on the port engine provides compressed air to operate the main wheel and target winch brake units. The main wheel brakes are operated by a lever on the control column, differential control being effected by a relay valve connected to the rudder bar. A vacuum pump is driven from each engine, one pump operating the flying instruments whilst the other is in reserve; a change-over cock is located in the pilot's cabin. An oxygen system is provided, having supply sockets at the pilot's, navigation, and winch operation positions.

Fuel is carried in three tanks housed in the main plane between the engines. An electric booster pump controllable by the pilot, is fitted to each tank. The engine cylinder priming pump draws its fuel supply from the centre tank. Each tank is independently vented. The fuel cock controls are of Simmonds-Corsey type and operate plug-type cocks for each tank. Oil for each engine is carried in a tank mounted behind the fireproof bulkhead. The oil cooler is mounted in the main plane leading edge inboard of the respective engine. A reserve of oil is allowed for in each tank to operate the propeller-feathering unit.

The engine controls are mainly housed in a hand control box at the port side of the pilot's cabin. The controls in the forward portion of the box rotate sprockets which actuate chain and cable connections to the units concerned; those in the rear portion operate through Simmonds-Corsey connections.

Power for the electrical services is derived from a generator, driven from the port engine, which charges two 12-volt, 40 Amp hour accumulators connected in series. The generator output is controlled by a voltage regulator and an accumulator cut-out is provided to prevent feeding back from the accumulator. The aircraft is wired on the earth-return principle, the wiring being mainly housed in poly-vinyl-chloride conduits installed between junction boxes which are located at points suitable for distribution and dismantling purposes.

A main distribution panel is mounted on the starboard side aft of the pilot's seat. An external supply socket and Ground/Flight switch is included in the installation so that, with the switch at the

The DH Mosquito TT Mk.39 version by General Aircraft Ltd with large glazed nose for observer/camera operator. PF576 illustrated.

cancelled before any were built. Although 20 Monitors Mk.II from the original contract were built, it is possible that the last 3 of these, although completed, were probably not flown. Some were retained for maker's trials while others were delivered to the A&AEE Boscombe Down and to the AFEE Beaulieu for service trials.

Very strong rumours have prevailed over the years that Monitor Mk.II aircraft were seen at RNAS Dale but, although it is possible that they may have been earmarked to go there, as Dale was the FAA's twin-engine conversion establishment, there is no record that any actually went.

While a decision as to the fate of the Monitor was being discussed, some of the later ones produced were ferried to 113 Sub-Storage Depot, RAF Market Harborough, Leicestershire from about February 1946, as storage space at Woodley was by then at a premium. All remaining RAF personnel were withdrawn from RAF Market Harborough on 27th April 1947, although Monitors remained in storage there until at least 5th September 1947. Most of the surviving Monitors, including those which had been returned to Woodley after storage at Market Harborough, were broken up at Woodley during the latter part of 1947.

The Monitor therefore, just 'had to go' and 'in the interests of economy' (sick joke) as the need for a shore-based, high speed target tower was still patently obvious. However, as if the cancellation of the Monitor contract wasn't bad enough, General Aircraft Ltd, of Hanworth Park, Middlesex, were then awarded a contract to convert 24 Mosquito B Mk.XVIs into Mosquito TT Mk.39s, to Specification Q.19/45. This modification resulted in the most hideous looking machine with the necessity of having four people to operate it, as opposed to just two in the far more advanced Monitor, which I should remind the reader once again, had been designed specifically to fulfil this role.

Modifications to the graceful Mosquito included the fitment of an extremely ugly, heavily glazed nose (how could they have had the audacity to have done this to the graceful lines of the Mosquito?) and the addition of a dorsal cupola and winch gear. It pains me to have to include a photograph of this machine but, for completeness, see above.

However, the logic (if that is the correct word) behind such a stupid decision, reminds one of the 'savings' made by replacing the Miles M.52 with the unmanned Vickers remote-controlled, rocket-propelled models, which more than doubled the cost of completing the M.52 and finally proved, but far too late, that the concept of the M.52 had been correct..

These Mosquitos not only looked terrible but they were also intensely disliked by their crews and Cdr P C S Bagley, CO 728

Squadron, Hal Far from 4th February 1952 to 1954, had a very interesting letter published in the May 1980 issue of *Air Pictorial* regarding the exploits of 728 Squadron there, and I quote an extract from this: *When I took command on 4th February 1952, it was a chaotic composite outfit with Mosquito 16s, Sea Mosquito TT.39s Sea Hornet F.20s, Sea Vampire F.20s, two Firefly TT.4s, and two Expeditors - twenty-four aircraft in all, while in reserve at Kalafrana were eleven Sturgeon TT.2s. You will imagine my feelings on being informed by the Senior Pilot that the Mosquito TT.39 would not fly on one engine and that these aircraft were continually "falling to pieces". I soon confirmed his diagnosis with an air-test myself. After further troubles, we stripped a wing and found that the wooden structure was soft and spongy, having been exposed to continuous water and temperature variation while standing at dispersal. We promptly got rid of our Mosquito TT Mk.39s (by 1952 - PA) and re-equipped with (yet another conversion - PA) the Short Sturgeon TT Mk.2s.*

So, the unpopular Mosquito TT Mk.39s were 'promptly got rid of' by 1952 in favour of yet another conversion, this time in the form of the Short Sturgeon, about which I will refrain from comment!

I rest my case!

Footnote:

In the July 1997 edition of *Aeroplane Monthly* magazine, the late Wing Cdr Derek Collier Webb (a retired flight safety specialist advisor to the Director of Flying (PE), an HQ unit based at Boscombe Down charged with safety regulation and accident investigation), wrote of the Miles Monitor in the series entitled 'Tested & Failed - Flight-test accidents of the 1940s-1960s.' His findings, based on the 5th and 6th Reports No.A&AEE/832 Intensive Flying Trials and Engineering & Maintenance Appraisal, respectively, are reproduced below:

Despite frequent periods of unserviceability, NP410 was able to achieve 100 hours of so-called intensive flying by 17th May 1946. Trials of the target-towing equipment had not been possible, as the winch gear design had remained unapproved for the duration of the trial. Long before the trials had been completed, the view had been formed that the defects continually being exposed were caused by insufficient robustness in the design of several components, making overall reliability poor. Certainly the consensus was that the airframe structure was far too light relative to the engine power, particularly at full throttle, which accelerated the break-up of defective components. To make matters worse, the Wright Cyclone was also prone to rough running, and its spark plugs required careful attention at all times. Among other component failures, no fewer than 22 engine exhaust support brackets failed during the seven month period of the trial.

Engine changes were also something of an ordeal. When the port engine and starboard carburettor had to be changed on NP411, an Alvis working party took an unusually long 444 man-hours. Its disappointing construction, low reliability and difficult maintenance as reflected by the engineers aside, the aircraft was equally disliked by pilots and aircrews, mainly due to the excessive noise and vibration experienced. There were also uncomfortable draughts and water leakage into the cockpit that were not helped by the 'useless' heating and ventilation system. It was not a place in which aircrews would willingly want to spend up to four hours at a time in sheer sufferance.

Nevertheless, trials of the aircraft persisted. The winch gear design was finally approved and a trial installation made in NP406 in June 1946. The aircraft was despatched to the Airborne Forces Experimental Establishment at Beaulieu on 25th July 1946, for the requisite cooling and performance trials with the winch installation. On 22nd January 1947, while Flt Lt C Grannum was taxiing in after landing, a fuel leak from the port engine carburettor vent pipe was ignited by the exhaust efflux and the aircraft was engulfed in flames. Fortunately the station fire and rescue services were quick off the mark and had the flames rapidly under control; the aircraft was written off, but the pilot remained healthy.

That was about the last event to occur to a Monitor in flight test. Its time was up. Despite its interest, the Navy had had its fill of this innovative but troublesome, difficult and inherently dangerous aircraft, and changed its allegiance to the Mosquito TT Mk.39 to alleviate its target-towing needs.

The last paragraph of his article stated: *What a total waste of time, money, effort and expertise the Monitor was, during a period when new and innovative aircraft were all-important for the survival of the nation.* A somewhat damning indictment of what was otherwise

generally considered by most to have been a very promising aeroplane, the first to have been designed from scratch for the highly demanding role of high-speed target towing.

The introduction to Derek Collier Webb's article in *Aeroplane Monthly* written by the editorial staff, stated: *The handsome lines of the Miles Monitor target tug, concealed a Pandora's box of problems which made it unpopular with pilots, aircrews and ground crews alike. In his continuing series on accidents during flight test and development, Derek Collier Webb tells its tragic tale.* In my opinion, this introduction was ill warranted.

Having discussed my arguments with the Wing Commander at some length before he died, without success, we finally agreed to differ on the qualities of the Miles M.33 Monitor. However, despite the somewhat peculiar circumstances surrounding the background to the design of the Monitor, it was a new and very advanced high-speed target towing aircraft and like all new and innovative aircraft, it undoubtedly had its faults, *in the beginning*, but these would undoubtedly have been corrected in due course and the Monitor should have had a long and useful life in its specialised role.

For the record Wing Cdr Webb's criticisms were not borne out by the very reports used in the compilation of the story.

In conclusion, I must just reflect on an old aviation saying - 'if an aeroplane looks right - it is right' and in my considered opinion, the Monitor certainly 'looked right'.

For details of M.33 Monitor production and individual aircraft histories see Appendix 28.

(N.A. Ref: AVIA 5/26; AIR 2668; AIR 2831 and SB26520).

A photograph of six rather pensive-looking Monitors at Woodley awaiting their fate.

SPECIFICATION AND PERFORMANCE DATA

Miles M.33 Monitor Mk.I

Not known.

Miles M.33 Monitor Mk.II

Engines:	2 x 1,750 hp Wright Cyclone R-2600-31, 14-cylinder, two row air-cooled radial
Dimensions:	span 55ft 3in; length 46ft 8in; height tail up 18ft 4in, tail down 13ft 9in, one airscrew blade vertical 14ft 3in; wing area 500 sq ft; aspect ratio 6.3; aerofoil section, root NACA 23021, tip NACA 2412
Weights:	empty 15,723lb (Mk.I 15,850lb); fuel (480 gal) 3,504lb; oil (32 gal) 288lb; crew 400lb; military load 1,033lb; AUW 21,056lb (Mk.I 21,075lb); wing loading 42.15lb/sq ft
Performance:	max speed 360 mph at 18,000ft; 330 mph at 15,000ft; max cruising speed 280 mph; cruising speed 265 mph at 15,000ft; rate of climb 2,480ft/min; time to 10,000ft 5 min; time to 15,000ft 6.4 min; time to 20,000ft 10.1 min; service ceiling 29,000ft; run to unstick 1,305ft; distance to 50ft 2,430ft; stalling speed at an AUW of 21,056lb, 90 mph; max range 2,750 miles; max duration on 480 gal fuel 5 hrs at 200 mph.

An artist's impression of the proposed M.34.

Chapter 25
Miles M.34 Long-Range Low-Level Attack Fighter/ High-Speed Target-Tug

A project design for a twin-engined aeroplane intended for alternative roles and to be powered by two Rolls-Royce Merlin engines, was begun in 1941. The first role was for a long-range, heavily-armoured, low-level attack-fighter with four 40 mm cannon, a heavier armament than carried by any other contemporary aircraft. This would undoubtedly have made it a most formidable proposition for such duties as tank busting and submarine attack. Further project studies in this connection, designated M.42, M.43 and M.44 were also submitted during the summer of 1942.

The second role envisaged was for a high-speed target-tug, in anticipation of Air Ministry Specification Q.9/42, which was issued the following year and fulfilled by the M.33 Monitor.

The M.34 was envisaged as a mid-wing monoplane with the wing having a pronounced taper and large root fillets, and it was to be fitted with twin fins and rudders. The engine nacelles were to be mounted such that the thrust-line was approximately level with the leading edge.

The narrow fuselage housed a crew of either one or two according to the role of the aircraft, and a tailwheel undercarriage was to be fitted with the main units retracting rearwards into the engine nacelles.

However, owing to pressures of other work, notably on the specialised M.33 Monitor target-tug, the M.34 project was not completed and in retrospect it was unlikely that the Ministry of Aircraft Production would have approved the use of Rolls-Royce Merlin engines in a non-operational aircraft such as a target-tug.

Unfortunately, no photographs and no details of the specification and performance for the M.34 have survived.

The M.35 Libellula U-0235.

Chapter 26
Miles M.35 Libellula

During 1941, the Fleet Air Arm was plagued with aircraft which were ill-suited to the demands of landing on aircraft carriers and as a result, was collecting an unenviable deck-landing accident rate. Improvised shipborne fighters, such as the Sea Hurricane and Seafire, which were then being introduced into service, had both originally been designed as the land-based Hurricane and Spitfire fighters, a role in which they were eminently suitable being as good as, or better than, anything available at the time.

In addition to these problems, large numbers of relatively inexperienced pilots with few flying hours to their credit arriving at the units, made it inevitable that flying accidents would occur. This was not helped by using aircraft for a purpose for which they were not designed. The Spitfire was later modified to have folding wings but the Hurricane was not and had, perforce, to stay on the carrier's deck, exposed to all weathers.

The installation of wing-fold mechanism also meant either increasing the weight of the aircraft or reducing the amount of fuel or ammunition which could be carried. Capt Eric Brown was later moved to write: *The essential requirements for a good carrier borne aircraft were view, a robust undercarriage and a small wingspan to enable it to be transported to the ship's hangar on a lift and then stowed in the small hangar.*

At about this time, George Miles was giving serious thought to a layout which would overcome all these problems and on 18th November 1941, he flew to the A&AEE Boscombe Down in a Master Mk.III to pick up Don Brown, who was then working in London for the Ministry of Aircraft Production but who must have been on a visit to the A&AEE. While at Boscombe Down, George noticed the Westland Delanne, a modified Lysander with an extra-large tailplane and a Boulton Paul gun turret mounted in the rear of the fuselage. This was undergoing flight trials and although the aircraft was destined to remain a one-off prototype, it did enable

the c.g. to be much further aft than would otherwise have been possible in an orthodox aircraft, without incurring serious longitudinal instability. In fact, the c.g. in this particular aircraft was at 0.58c, and although the modified Lysander was still in effect an orthodox aircraft with an extra-large tailplane (as were the Peyret glider of 1922 and the Mignet 'Flying Flea' of 1936), it caused George to wonder whether a true tandem-wing layout might not be the solution that he was seeking.

The tandem wing layout meant that both horizontal surfaces would be true lifting surfaces, with each bearing a substantial proportion of the all up weight and with the c.g. lying amidships somewhere between the two. Such an arrangement, if it were feasible, would also provide a neat solution to the problems associated with the shipborne fighter, where the pilot could be located in the nose with a perfect, unobstructed view, while the engine could be located in the tail driving a pusher propeller and the armament and fuel carried amidships.

Furthermore, having two wings, the span could be kept to the limited dimensions of the hangar lift without recourse to the weight and expense of wing-folding. The weight and drag of a tailplane would also be saved and high-lift devices could be fitted to both wings, which being on either side of the c.g., would also be used to their maximum effect without to some extent being offset by the downward load of the tailplane necessary on an orthodox aircraft to achieve stability. Other advantages from an aircraft with such small overall dimensions would be increased manoeuvrability, decreasing the target area and the more efficient co-efficient of lift from both wings. The only unknown factor was whether such an aircraft would fly and be controllable.

We now have to move forward in time to the 1st July 1945 as a document, prepared by Don Brown with that date, obviously in preparation for the Investigation at Miles Aircraft Ltd by the

Three different views of the M.35 Libellula prototype U0235

Industrial Advisory Panel on 4th and 5th July 1945, not only throws new light on the origins of the Miles M.35 Libellula but also summarises the considerable problems that the firm had experienced with the MAP over the proposals for their new and unorthodox tandem wing aeroplane.

Nothing was known about this document until May 2012, when an anonymous donor deposited a packet of Phillips & Powis/Miles Aircraft correspondence and documents with The Museum of Berkshire Aviation, Woodley.

The substance of this document is quite astonishing because, until now, it has always been believed that the M.35 Libellula project was built in the utmost secrecy by the Experimental Department at Liverpool Road, without the knowledge of the MAP, witness Don Brown's previous writings:

The M.35 was built in secret at Liverpool Road, because it was decided that the Ministry of Aircraft Production should not be notified of their intention to build it as they would almost certainly not have given their authority to proceed with its construction! In wartime, the MAP were the only customer for the aircraft industry and no work was supposed to be undertaken without their knowledge and authority. Failure to comply with this directive could lead to the withdrawal of all materials and the consequent closure of the firm.

Although the Ministry of Aircraft Production maintained a Resident Technical Officer, with an office in the main factory at Woodley, it was felt that if the aircraft were to be built at Liverpool Road, away from prying eyes, it would have to be accepted as a fait accompli when it arrived at Woodley for flight tests, and the firm might then just 'get away with it'!

However, it can now be revealed that, not only were the MAP, the Admiralty and other official departments being kept fully informed of the progress with the M.35, but that this Private Venture aircraft was actually being inspected by representatives from all of these departments at various stages throughout its construction!

Thanks to Jean Fostekew I am now able to reproduce this noteworthy document in its entirety:

Libellula

During the latter part of 1941, Mr George Miles was giving considerable thought to the design of a ship-based fighter. At that time considerable difficulties were being encountered owing to the introduction of the Hurricane and Spitfire as shipborne fighters.

The principal difficulties encountered were two-fold. First, the lack of forward view for the pilot when making a deck approach and, secondly, the fact that neither of these aircraft had folding wings. The poor forward view was resulting in a high casualty rate among naval pilots.

Mr Miles was, therefore, endeavouring to evolve a machine in which the engine should be at the rear end of the fuselage in order to give the pilot the widest possible field of vision. He was also seeking to reduce the overall size of the machine so that it could be accommodated on the lift of an aircraft carrier without the necessity of folding the wings.

It was quite evident that this desiderata could not be made with an orthodox aeroplane and it was, therefore, necessary for Mr Miles to undertake the task of evolving an entirely new layout. After viewing the various unorthodox designs hitherto produced, Mr Miles decided to try out a design in which the wings were in tandem and this subsequently became known as the Libellula layout.

Having made preliminary drawings of this layout and its adaption to the design of a ship based fighter, Mr Miles showed these to Cmdr Spragg at the Admiralty on the 16th January 1942. Cmdr Spragg advised him to get into touch with Captain John, ADRDN

at MAP. It was evident that if the problem was to be solved quickly the time necessary for a full and scientific investigation of the feasibility and characteristics of the Libellula layout could not be attempted and Mr Miles decided to embark forthwith upon the construction of a small machine, the M.35, the sole purpose of which was to establish by actual flying trials whether or not the Libellula layout was a feasible proposition.

The construction of this machine was started on the 25th February 1942 and at the same time a small glider model was built and with this a certain amount of useful information was obtained regarding the proportions of the two wings and the probable behaviour of the machine.

On the 25th February 1942, Messrs F G and G H Miles attended a meeting at MAP with Captain John ADRDN and Lt Cmdr Paddy, RDN1 at which the proposals for a Naval Fighter were to be put forward. At this meeting Captain John expressed the opinion that in view of limitations of the width and overall dimensions of ship based aircraft it would only be possible to obtain further improvements in performance and movability by completely breaking away from the orthodox aeroplane. He, therefore, welcomed the Libellula attempt and suggested that the M.35 should proceed as a P.V. job and, if successful in its trials, that it should be submitted to DTD.

On the 2nd March 1942 Lt Cmdr Paddy sent us two draft specifications, one for a shipborne fighter and one for a shore-based TBR aircraft. By this time considerable official interest was being displayed in the Libellula and on the 18th March, Messrs Relph and Naylor of the NPL visited Woodley and discussed the M.35 which was then under construction. They were favourably impressed and could see no difficulties associated with the design.

On the 8th April 1942, Dr Roxee Cox, who was then DDSR, visited Woodley together with Mr Vessey of RDT4 and inspected the M.35 which was then nearing completion.

On the 18th April, the construction of the M.35 was completed, the time taken being just 7½ weeks. During the next fortnight fast taxiing trials and short hops were made by Mr Miles and on 1st May he made the first flight in this machine. Apart from some longitudinal instability no undesirable handling difficulties were accounted and on the 4th May Mr Miles advised Lt Cmdr Paddy at MAP that the Libellula layout was clearly a feasible proposition.

On the 6th May Mr Miles visited Lt Cmdr Paddy and found that the Libellula design already been discussed with DTD and the Technical and Naval Staffs at MAP.

On the 14th May, Major Green of SME Department RAE discussed the Libellula with Mr Brown and said that it was evident that this layout provided the possible solution to the C.G. difficulties then being encountered by the application of two jet units to orthodox aeroplanes.

Major Green was at the time evolving a tail first design the object of which was to solve this problem. On the 18th May Major Green visited Woodley, inspected the M.35 and said that he was going to ask M.A.P to place a contract with us for building his tail first aeroplane.

On the 21st May 1942 DTD telephoned Mr F G Miles asking him to release ten draughtsmen and expressing the opinion that we were wasting our time on such projects as the M.35.

On the 23rd May Major Green telephoned us and said that he had urged DTD to place a contract with us for the construction of his tail first aeroplane but that DTD had wished to place the contract with another firm.

On the 4th June Mr Farren, DRAE.visited Woodley together with Group Capt Wheeler and Major Green and inspected the M.35. They were most favourably impressed and complimented the firm on its initiative in this pioneering work. Mr Farren mentioned that nearly all the designers in the country were trying to solve the C.G. problem associated with the use of two jet units. In view of this it was decided to prepare a Libellula design to utilise either two orthodox engines or two jet units.

On the 6th June Mr Serby, DTRDA, and Captain Rithrope, DTD1, visited Woodley and inspected the M.35. In spite of the previous unfavourable comments of DTD they agreed that it was a promising development job and Mr Serby suggested that a layout for a high performance bomber of about 25,000 lbs AUW should be investigated. He added that there was no point in attempting to develop a naval fighter as one was not required.

On the 18th June Wg Cmdr Odbert and Sqdn Ldr Hancock of DOR visited Woodley to inspect the M.35 and to discuss the application of the Libellula layout to various operational types. They displayed great interest in the design and expressed the opinion that it would be a great pity if we discontinued work on the fighter projects as suggested by Mr Serby. They said that the latest development in air combat showed the extreme importance of providing a much better view, of installing the guns centrally and many of the other features which could be achieved with the Libellula layout.

On the 18th June Mr Brown was at MAP and was shown Mr Serby's report on his visit to Woodley. This report complimented the firm on their courage in connection with this project but described the M.35 as being "like an Exaggerated Delanne" thereby showing that he had clearly failed to grasp the basic purpose of the design.

On the 6th July, Mr G H Miles gave Mr Serby the specification for the M.39 Projected Bomber together with the design for the M.39B which was a 5/8 scale model of the M.39.

On the 10th August Mr G H.Miles visited Messrs Handley Page at the request of Major Green in order to give them advice regarding the hitherto unsuccessful attempts to fly their pterodactyl tail-less Monoplane

On the 12th August Miss Lyon of RAE visited Mr G H Miles and gave him to understand that a contract was about to be placed for further flight trials of the M.35.

On the 21st August a letter was received from Mr Serby saying that he had not yet had time to look into the specification of the M.39 which had been sent to on the 6th July 1942.

On 23rd September, Mr F G Miles visited Air Marshal Linnell and discussed the Libellula. After the interview Air Marshal Linnell wrote commenting favourably on the Libellula layout both as regards view and gun installation.

On the 8th October 1942 Mr Vessey wrote saying that the question of flight tests on the M.35 had been discussed by DDSR1 and DDRA and that they had decided no further work was required on this machine. Nothing whatsoever was added as to the reason for this decision.

On the 16th November Major Green informed Mr Brown that further developments on unorthodox aircraft were being left in the hands of Northrop and Curtis in the USA.

In the meantime, it was decided to go ahead with the construction of the M.39B although no official opinion, either favourably or adverse, had yet been received regarding the specification sent to MAP on the 6th July.

On the 17th May 1943, Captain Rithrope visited Woodley and was shown the M.39B which was nearing completion.

On the 22nd June 1943, Mr Brown reminded Mr Serby that we had still received no official comment on the M.39 project which had been submitted to him a year previously. Mr Serby promised that the matter would receive attention.

On the 22nd July Mr G H Miles made the first flight in the M.39B, the handling characteristics of which proved to be very satisfactory.

On the 26th August 1943, Colonel Hitchcock and Captain Logan of the Air Technical Section of the US Embassy called to discuss unorthodox aircraft and on instruction from CRD's private secretary, they were shown the M.39B and it was discussed.

On the 3rd September 1943, Mr F G Miles wrote to DTD again reminding them that no official verdict on the Libellula had yet been received.

On the 8th September CRD wrote to Mr F G Miles authorising the supply to the USA of all available information on the Libellula.

On the 13th September a further visit was paid by members of US Embassy who desired all possible information.

On the 16th September 1943 Messrs Serby, Garner, Morgan and Gates visited Woodley and it was agreed MAP should purchase the M.39B and award a small contract covering a series of flight trials on the result of which the possibility of a larger project would be considered. These trials are still being conducted at RAE.

In the meantime it is no exaggeration to state that the two small Libellula P.V. Aircraft have achieved a far higher degree of success than any of the various unorthodox aircraft being attempted both in this country and the USA despite the enormous large sums which have been and are being spent on these various officially sponsored projects.

Signed DLB

Returning now to 1941, with characteristic Miles courage and impetuosity, George decided that there was no time to start a programme of wind-tunnel tests but to actually build a simple wooden "flying mock-up" as quickly as possible. This would give immediate full-scale data, although possibly at the expense of some risk to the pilot making the first flight!

The "flying mock-up" was actually designed by Ray Bournon, under George Miles' direction, at Liverpool Road and given the designation L.R.2. It was also given the Miles designation M.35, and the new aircraft was of all wooden construction and was to be powered by a 130hp DH Gipsy Major engine mounted in the rear of the fuselage, driving a pusher propeller. The elevators were fitted on the forward wing, which was on the top of the fuselage immediately behind the cockpit and the ailerons were carried on the larger rear wing, which was attached to the bottom of the fuselage with twin fins and rudders fitted at the wingtips. Flaps were fitted to both wings and standard parts were used wherever possible, with the rudders, undercarriage legs and wheels from a Magister (which is why the legs protruded through the top of the rear wing!). The wingspan and length were about the same at 20ft.

The tiny aircraft which emerged was, as George Miles would go to great lengths to point out, a tandem-winged aircraft - and he was adamant that it was not a canard.

In the absence of any wind-tunnel tests and because of its unorthodox layout, it was deemed prudent, while the M.35 was under construction, to build and fly a large scale model in the hope that some indication of its handling characteristics might be obtained before the real thing had to be flown. Accordingly, a ¼ scale model was built and it was decided to tow this behind the prototype M.28 which had the necessary quick take-off and good control at low-speeds.

George Miles flew the M.28 while Don Brown hung out of the starboard window holding the towing line to which the model was attached. Ray Bournon held the model, hoping that it would be self-supporting by the time he could run no faster and as George gently opened the throttle, Ray started to run with the model. When Ray appeared to be reaching his limit, Don said 'Now' - George opened the throttle wide and the M.28 was airborne. So too was the model, which proceeded to climb more steeply than the M.28! In answer to Don's agonised cries, George climbed the M.28 to its limit but still the wretched model outstripped them and actually appeared to be catching them up! When it was nearly directly above them, Don released the line and the model promptly stalled and dived vertically into the ground, about 150ft below, with no sign of recovery! Since the purpose of the model test was to give an indication of the possible behaviour of the full-size aircraft, it was considered that this initial test was hardly reassuring!

As mentioned earlier, by 18th April 1942, the M.35 was complete and had taken just 7½ weeks to build. As it was only 20ft span and 20ft long, they decided to tow it through the streets early one morning from Reading to Woodley, before there were too many prying eyes. There was one worrying moment when it only just scraped through the railway bridge at Loddon Bridge and the lane leading to the aerodrome was found to be barely wide enough but all these hurdles were overcome and it eventually arrived safely at Woodley. However, the journey had caused considerable traffic problems and many of the employees arrived late for work at the factory!

When Tommy Rose, the Chief Test Pilot, saw it assembled for the first time, he was reported to have been heard to say: *'Surely you don't expect me to fly that?!'*

The strange craft was given the 'B' mark **U-0235** and was also given the RAF Experimental Aeroplane No.177 for identification purposes. Norman Angell (brother of Jack Angell), who was working at Liverpool Road at the time, recalled that he was responsible for installing the control runs from the throttle to the engine of the M.35. However, when he swung the propeller for the first time to start the machine, he was somewhat alarmed to find that the engine roared into life on full throttle! He rushed around to the cockpit to retrieve the situation and later found that the reason had been that a lever in the control run had been connected up the wrong way round! He told me, with somewhat wry humour, that he immediately corrected the fault and was pleased to find that nobody had witnessed the near disaster!

This cartoon, by an unknown artist, shows his ideas of the lengths they went to in the attempt to get the M.35 into the air, but please don't take it too seriously!

[From the George Miles archive via Jim Pratt]

George Miles usually carried out the first flights of his new aeroplanes, but his flying log books for this period have been lost, however, during the next fortnight he carried out the first fast taxi-ing runs and short hops and assistant test pilot Hugh Kennedy also made 'Straights and taxi-ing' runs in the M.35 on 29th April 1942. During the course of the early runs, the M.35 showed no inclination to leave the ground, not even for the shortest hop but George repeated the runs until the full length of the airfield was being used but it still showed no inclination to leave the ground. Don Brown then suggested, half in jest that the only thing to do now was to use a portion of the field adjacent to the final assembly hangar running at right angles to the main field in the form of an L. This meant starting the take-off run on the one leg of the L, coming round the corner at speed and proceeding down the length of the main field. Since there appeared to be no alternative, George elected to try just that with, as it turned out, surprising results. Having covered three-quarters of the length of the main field with still with no tendency to lift off, George hurriedly closed the throttle, having left himself only just sufficient length of field in which to pull-up. However, as he closed the throttle, the M.35 literally leapt into the air to a height of about 10ft and he only just managed to get it back on to the ground in time to avoid going through the boundary fence!

George immediately made a further attempt but this ended with the same result - the moment the throttle was closed, the M.35 became airborne. After two or three more attempts, he decided to risk opening the throttle again once the M.35 was airborne. This he did and to the surprise of the watchers below, he remained airborne - it had been an anxious moment - but all seemed well, so he continued straight ahead at a height of about 20ft and when some distance away, he started a gentle turn to port continuing in a wide circuit but still at the same height. A few minutes later he appeared over the far boundary and proceeded to land. As he taxied in he was surrounded by the small team who had produced the M.35, who were all anxious to know the results of this first brief flight. George said little, but it subsequently transpired that the aircraft was catastrophically unstable and that the brief flight had been a ceaseless battle to prevent a divergent oscillation in pitch. All this could probably have been predicted by wind-tunnel tests but these had been ruled out on the score of time. Subsequent wind-tunnel tests enabled the M.35 to be ballasted to the extent that the instability, while still present, was at least no longer catastrophic.

A fourth rear wheel was added aft of the main undercarriage, and under the engine, shortly after the first flight. This did not touch the ground when the aircraft was at rest and was fitted to prevent the propeller and rudders from striking the ground during a steep nose-up attitude while landing or take-off.

A very ingenious device was fitted to enable the pilot to bale out in an emergency without hitting the propeller which consisted of two lead-filled wooden arms attached to the fuselage which, when released, came into contact with the propeller, thus causing the blades to be broken off.

Although at first the M.35 was longitudinally unstable, the initial problems were successfully overcome and George Miles saw the way to continue with the development of other types of Libellula aircraft. On 11th May 1942, Hugh Kennedy carried out a 15 minute flight, with the 'Duty' unrecorded but when he next flew it, on 4th June, he recorded a 15 minute 'Stability test'. Hugh made just two more flights in the M.35, a 20 minute 'Handling' flight on 6th June and a 20 minute 'Stick position & Oil cooling test' on 11th June 1942.

Although the M.35 was considered by some to be 'positively dangerous', it was a means of quickly acquiring data to enable George Miles to proceed with a more advanced design for the M.39, a high-speed bomber to Spec. B.11/41. It had also clearly demonstrated the fact that there could be no fundamental objection to the tandem-wing layout.

Some thought was given to a generic name for this tandem-wing layout and at first, the name Dragonfly seemed appropriate but, as

An artist's impression of the M.36 Montrose Mk.I as an Aircrew Trainer. Note: this variant differs considerably from the M.36 Montrose Mk.I shown in the booklet reproduced below.

Chapter 27
Miles M.36 Montrose Mk.I
Flying and Aircrew Trainer and Light Glider Tug, Miles M.36A Montrose Mk.II Target Tower, Troop Carrier and Medium Glider Tug and Miles M.36B Montrose Mk.III Flying and Aircrew Trainer

By 1942, there seemed to be an increasing need for a new advanced aircrew trainer, especially in view of the forthcoming massive build-up of multi-engined bombers.

The Airspeed Oxford and Avro Anson had given yeoman service during the RAF's transition period from biplanes to monoplanes but with their low-powered engines and fixed pitch propellers they could scarcely be regarded as an appropriate introduction to the new types of operational aircraft shortly to enter service. Moreover, they did not make adequate provision for the simultaneous training of an entire bomber crew.

So, with these considerations in mind, Don Brown prepared a project design for the M.36 Montrose, a general purpose aircraft to be powered by either two 600 hp Pratt & Whitney Wasp S.3.H1 engines similar to those fitted to the North American Harvard trainer, two 870 hp Bristol Mercury XV engines or four 420 hp Armstrong Siddeley Cheetah XV engines.

In August 1942, Phillips & Powis Aircraft Ltd produced a booklet on the Miles Montrose variants, reproduced here, but it should be mentioned that these projects differ considerably from other three-view drawings with the same mark numbers, as will be shown later:

M.36 Montrose I - 2 Wasp S.3H.1 Engines

    Flying and Aircrew Trainer
    Light Glider Tug

M.36A Montrose II - 2 Mercury XV Engines

    Target Tower
    Troop Carrier
    Medium Glider Tug

M.36B Montrose III - 4 Cheetah XV Engines

    Flying and Aircrew Trainer

Montrose I - 2 Wasp S.3H.1 Engines

Owing to the increasing percentage of twin and multi-engined aircraft in operational use, as well as to the advent of the tricycle undercarriage on several types, it is evident that the production of a suitable training aircraft to give the wider specialised flying and aircrew training now necessary, is due for consideration.

The Miles M.36 has been designed with the idea to cover not only a diversity of aircrew training purposes, but also to provide the flying training and experience necessary to bridge the gap between the EFTS and the OTU, equipped with twin and multi-engined operational types. This gap is so wide that it has been no easy matter to provide in a single aeroplane the safety and ease of control necessary for the trainee fresh from the EFTS to the complexity of flying and operational equipment with which the whole crew must be conversant when they proceed to the OTU.

The following description enumerates the features incorporated in the Montrose I, in an endeavour to obtain the necessary compromise. Apart from the machine being readily convertible for use with either the orthodox or the tricycle type undercarriage, the fact that it is not a specialised operational type has made possible its ready adaption to a variety of other non-operational uses, namely:

> Navigational and radio training.
> Bomber and intruder aircrew training.
> Gunnery and interceptor fighter training.
> Glider tug.

Design and Construction

The machine is of stressed skin wooden construction throughout, and is designed for ease of manufacture both in this country and in Canada. Although the engine envisaged is the Pratt & Whitney Wasp S.3H.1, the reliability of which has been proved in the Harvard, various alternative engine installations such as the Wright Whirlwind R.975 E.3 may be substituted without difficulty. Rotol constant speed fully feathering propellers are fitted.

For flying training purposes only, the Cheetah XV may be employed, although this engine does not give sufficient power for the other more heavily loaded duties for which the machine is designed. The main structure is stressed to the following flight factors:

	lb
Structure weight	6,000
Fixed equipment	835
Tare weight	6,835
Solo & Aerobatic Training	
Fuel & Oil	970
Crew	200
Military Load	127
All-up weight	8,132
Rationalised Flight factor	2x5g
Normal Flying Trainer & Glider Tug	
Fuel & Oil	2,070
Crew	400
Military Load	127
All-up weight	9,432
Rationalised Flight factor	2x4.3g
Aircrew Training In Navigation, Gunnery & Bombing	
Fuel & Oil	2,070
Crew	1,200
Military Load	742
All-up weight	10,847
Rationalised Flight factor	2x3.75g

The maximum speed is 220 mph TAS at 7,000 ft, and the structure is designed for a maximum diving speed of 350 mph IAS.

The wing is in one piece, the root section being NACA 23018 tapering to 2412 at the tip. The flaps are 0.25c auxiliary aerofoil type fully retractable. From full scale flight trials on the Miles

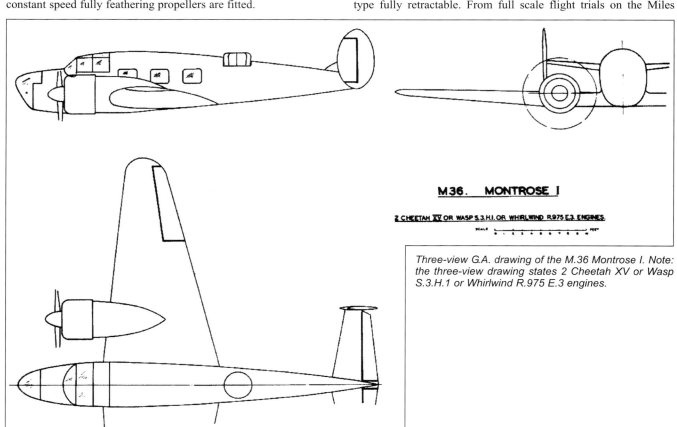

M36. MONTROSE I

2 CHEETAH XV OR WASP S.3.H.I. OR WHIRLWIND R.975.E.3. ENGINES.

Three-view G.A. drawing of the M.36 Montrose I. Note: the three-view drawing states 2 Cheetah XV or Wasp S.3.H.1 or Whirlwind R.975 E.3 engines.

M.28 this combination is found to give a remarkably high maximum lift coefficient, together with particularly good aileron control and stalling characteristics. Moreover the flaps are arranged so as partly to reproduce to a safe extent the marked change in longitudinal trim to which the pilot will have to become accustomed on many operational aircraft when the flaps are lowered.

From the accompanying drawings it will be seen that the pilot's cockpit provides an excellent view in all directions. Large sliding side panels are provided. Both the orthodox and the tricycle type of undercarriage are available, the necessary fittings for both types being provided. With the tricycle undercarriage the main wheels mounted on brackets attached to the rear spar, retract into the engine nacelles.

If an orthodox undercarriage is required, the machine is merely jacked up and the main wheel units are removed and re-attached to brackets mounted on the front spar, the operating jacks being simultaneously shifted to alternative mountings inside the engine nacelles, between the two spars. For both types of undercarriage, locks are provided whereby it cannot be retracted while the machine is on the ground, but the usual warning lights and horn are also provided for training purposes.

The fuel tanks are fitted with immersed fuel pumps, and have a maximum capacity of 250 gallons, which gives half an hour at maximum climbing conditions, together with 3½ hours cruising at maximum weak mixture conditions, or of course, considerably longer for economical cruising.

Flying Training

When the trainee from the EFTS is introduced to the Montrose, he encounters for the first time twin engines, constant speed propellers, cowling gills controls, and a retractable undercarriage. At this stage of his career no mention is made of the various additional controls with which he will have to become familiar as his training proceeds. He is flying the machine at a relatively light wing-loading, and when, after a few hours dual, he does his first solo on it, he is flying at a wing loading of only 19½ lb/sq ft with a power loading of 7½ lb/hp. At this loading the take off, climb and landing will be little harder than that to which he has been accustomed. The take-off in still air is only 150 yards, and the distance to clear 50 feet, 235 yards.

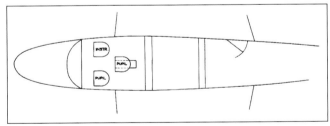

Above: Flying Training layout.

As his training proceeds, so he is enabled to gain further experience by acting as pilot for the various aircrews, whose training is proceeding concurrently with his own. In this way the loading at which he is flying is gradually increased until eventually prior to proceeding to his OTU he is acting as pilot to a full bomber crew. By this time, too he will have been trained in the use of the fuel system, the exhaust gas analysers, the operation of the bomb doors and the use of the automatic pilot. He will, further, have received instruction in both synthetic and actual instrument flying, in beam approach and in night flying, first of the synthetic sodium light type and later of actual night operations including the use of A.I.

The above will give some idea of the multiplicity of specialised equipment for which provision is made in the Montrose, and for the incorporation of which it is specially designed. Added to this is the fact that the above training can be carried out either with an orthodox undercarriage, or with a tricycle. An innovation is the

provision of a third seat, placed behind and above the two pilots' seats. This seat is for the use of a second pupil who can gain useful experience by observing the errors made by the pupils actually under instruction. Alternatively, it may be utilised by the instructor for checking up on the flying of two pupils.

Aircrew Training

Having gained some solo flying experience in conjunction with other pupil pilots, at wing loadings varying from 19½ to 23 lb/sq ft, the trainee pilot can then, under the supervision of an instructor, gain further experience at heavier wing loadings by acting as pilot on aircrew training flights.

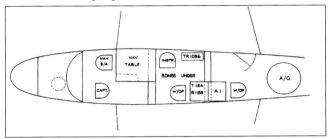

Above: Aircrew Training layout.

Gunnery and Interception:

For this duty the crew consists of instructor, pilot and 3 wireless operator-air gunners. The equipment comprises T1154, TR9F/R1155, R1124A, R3003, Beam Approach A.I. and Vickers gun and ammunition. With 250 gallons of fuel, the all-up weight is 10,695 lb, the wing loading at take-off being 26 lb/sq ft , and the power loading 9 lb/hp.

Navigation and Radio:

For this duty the crew consists of instructor, pilot and four pupils. The radio equipment is the same as for the Gunnery and Interception and in addition the Navigator's instruments and the F.24 camera are carried, but no Air Gunner, gun or ammunition. The all-up weight, wing loading and power loading are the same as for Gunnery and Interception.

Bombing:

For this duty the crew consists of Instructor, pilot, navigator/bomb aimer, flight engineer, and two wireless operator/air gunners. Full equipment is carried, comprising the following:

> Bomb Aiming. Automatic bomb sight Mk.II, Gyro Azimuth Mk.I, etc.
> Navigator Chartboard, sextant, CDC, F.24 camera, flares, smoke floats, etc.
> Radio T1154, R1155, TR9F, R1124A, R3003, A.I. and Beam Approach.
> Bombs 16 x 11½ lb practice bombs.
> Air Gunner Vickers gun, 500 rounds ammunition.

The all-up weight is 10,847 lb, giving a wing loading at take-off of 26½ lb/sq ft, with a power loading of 9 lb/hp. Even at this loading the still air take-off should be only 350 yards, and the distance to clear 50 feet about 550 yards. On completion of this training the whole of the aircrew are well equipped to pass to their OTU.

Aircrew Training Equipment:

Navigator/Bomb-aimer - The usual navigational equipment is provided. Sufficient headroom is provided in the nose for the bomb-aimer to take his sights in the seated position through a flat panel: alternatively a prone position may be used if required, as no dual flying controls are installed when the aeroplane is used for bomber aircrew training. The bomb-aimer's station is equipped with the automatic bomb sight Mk.II and with the usual selector

EQUIPMENT WEIGHTS

		MONTROSE I (WASP)						MONTROSE I				MONTROSE II		
		SOLO					BOMBING				SOLO		BOMBING	
BOMB & BOMB AIMER'S STATION.	AUTOMATIC BOMB SIGHT WITH ELECTRICAL RELEASE MECHANISM & INSTRUMENTS. 16 x 11½ LBS. PRACTISE BOMBS WITH 4 LIGHT SERIES CARRIERS	21·0	—	21·0	—	13·0	—	13·0	32·0	—	—	—	13·0	—	13·0 32·0
		11·0	—	11·0	—	11·0	—	11·0	134·0	—	—	—	11·0	—	11·0 134·0
FIRST & SECOND PILOT'S STATION	COMPLETE DUAL ENGINE FLYING INSTRUMENTS WITH R1124-A EQUIPMENT	140·0	50·0	140·0	50·0	140·0	50·0	140·0	50·0	140·0	50·0	140·0	50·0	140·0	50·0
NAVIGATOR'S STATION	COMPLETE SET OF NAVIGATIONAL EQUIPMENT INCLUDING CHART TABLE, ASTROGRAPH, SEXTANT & DOME, & DRIFT SIGHT WITH B.F. LOOP	82·0	—	82·0	—	82·0	30·0	82·0	—	REDUCED NAV.EQUIPT 22·0	10	82·0	10	82·0	—
W/T OPERATOR'S STATION	COMPLETE EQUIPMENT FOR THE FOLLOWING INSTALLATION. THIS R.1116 OR TR54 R.1155 TR.1196 R.3003 A.I.	45·0	—	45·0	100·0	45·0	100·0	45·0	—	—	—	45·0	—	45·0	—
		4·0	—	4·0	50·0	4·0	50·0	4·0	—	4·0	30	4·0	—	4·0	—
		12·0	27·0	12·0	27·0	12·0	27·0	12·0	27·0	—	—	12·0	27·0	12·0	27·0
		50·0	—	50·0	100·0	50·0	—	50·0	100·0	—	—	50·0	—	50·0	100·0
GUNNER'S STATION	GUN TURRET WITH VICKERS GUN & AMMO.	144·0	—	144·0	58·0	144·0	—	144·0	58·0	—	—	144·0	—	144·0	58·0
FLARE POSITION	FLARES MARINE DISTRESS SIGNAL, FLAME FLOATS & LAUNCHING CHUTE.	16·0	—	16·0	95·0	16·0	95·0	16·0	95·0	16·0	95·0	16·0	—	16·0	95·0
ELECTRICAL CONTROL PANEL	CONTROL PANEL COMPLETE WITH SUPPRESSORS SWITCHES ETC. & ACCUMULATOR 24 V.	150·0	—	150·0	—	150·0	—	150·0	—	150·0	—	150·0	—	150·0	—
DINGHY	DINGHY WITH EMERGENCY PACK	5·0	—	5·0	60·0	5·0	60·0	5·0	60·0	5·0	120·0	—	—	5·0	—	5·0 60·0
MISCELLANEOUS	NIGHT FLYING EQUIPMENT INCLUDING LANDING, IDENTIFICATION, NAV. & CABIN, LAMPS OR COMPASS, SANITARY CLOSET & OXYGEN BOTTLES.	45·0	50·0	45·0	50·0	45·0	50·0	45·0	50·0	45·0	50·0	45·0	50·0	45·0	50·0
CAMERA STATION	COMPLETE F.24 CAMERA INSTALLATION FOR VERTICAL & OBLIQUE PHOTOGRAPHY	10·0	—	10·0	—	10·0	—	10·0	32·0	—	—	—	—	10·0	—	10·0 32·0
POWER PLANT	GENERATOR, STARTER, FIRE EXTINGUISHER ACCESSORIES ETC. ALL EQUIPMENT MOUNTED IN POWER PLANT.	100·0	—	100·0	—	100·0	—	100·0	—	100·0	—	100·0	—	100·0	
TARGET TOWING GEAR	WINCH COMPLETE WITH FLARE, TARGET OR CAMERA & CUPOLA.	—	—	—	—	—	—	—	—	120·0	450·0	—	—	—	—
	FIXED & REMOVABLE EQUIPMENT.	835·0	117·0	1035·0	590·0	835·0	462·0	835·0	742·0	500·0	765·0	475·0	160·0	835·0	117·0	1035·0 742·0
CREW		800		1200		1200·0		1200		400·0		460		800		1200
FUEL & OIL		970		2070		2070·0		2070		2070·0		2070		970		2070
STRUCTURE WT.		6000		6000		6000·0		6000		6150·0		6250·0		6000		6000
A.U.W.		8632		10635		10567		10847		9565		13405		8632		11204

Above: Equipment Weights.

and fusing switches. Provision is also made for the F.24 camera. The bombs are slung beneath the cabin floor, between the spars on standard light series carriers. The bombs cannot be released until the bomb doors have been opened by the pilot. The usual means of communication between bomb-aimer and pilot is also provided.

Wireless Operator - Provision is made for two wireless operator/air gunners, and a large number of alternative sets can be accommodated. IFF and a DF loop are fitted, together with either fixed or trailing aerials as required. In addition, Beam Approach and A.I. equipment is carried.

Flight Engineer - At the Flight Engineer's station the following instruments are duplicated: Engine Speed Indicators; Boost Gauges; Exhaust Gas Analysers; Cylinder Temperature Gauges; Oil Temperature Gauges and Fuel Pressure Gauges. In addition, the gills controls are duplicated, and the carburettor air intake heat controls are in charge of the Flight Engineer, as well as the tank fuel cocks, the pilot's cockpit containing master cocks only. The Flight Engineer trainee may also be made responsible for starting up and testing the engines and propellers from the pilot's cockpit.

Air Gunner - The power driven gun turret is situated just aft of the cabin, and is readily accessible during flight. It is fitted with one Vickers gas operated gun, and four drums of ammunition are slung within comfortable reach of the gunner.

Glider Tug

The Montrose I is admirably suited for a tug for the Hotspur glider. When used for this purpose, a crew of two is carried, together with TR9D, R1124A and Beam Approach. The all-up weight is 9,400 lb, giving a wing loading of 23 lb/sq ft with a power loading of 7.8 lb/hp. Adding the loaded weight of the Hotspur gives a total power loading of 10.8 lb/hp, similar to that of the Master Tug.

Montrose II - 2 Mercury XV or Taurus VI Engines

The Montrose II is basically the same aeroplane as the Montrose I, the only alterations being the substitution of the Mercury or Taurus for the Wasp engines and the deletion of the gun turret. The functions of the Montrose II are four-fold, namely: Target tower; Glider Tug; Troop carrier or Paratroop trainer. *(Note: the following functions were quoted in the introduction: Target Tower, Troop Carrier, Medium Glider Tug - PA).*

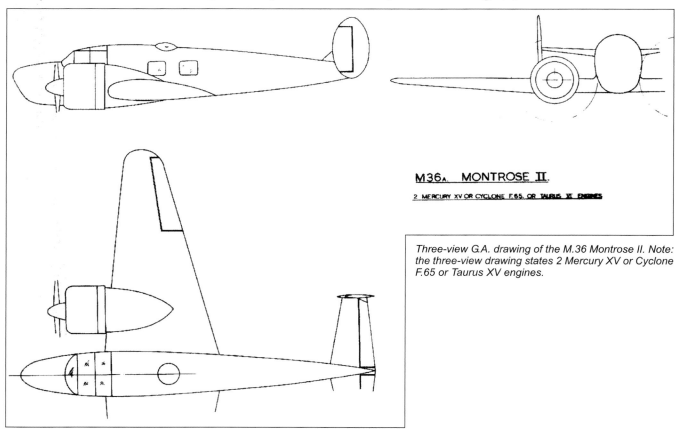

M36ₐ MONTROSE II.

2 MERCURY XV OR CYCLONE F.65. OR TAURUS VI ENGINES

Three-view G.A. drawing of the M.36 Montrose II. Note: the three-view drawing states 2 Mercury XV or Cyclone F.65 or Taurus XV engines.

Design and Construction

The main structure is stressed to the following flight factors:

	Target Towing	Glider Tug	Paratroop Training or Troop Carrying
	lb	lb	lb
Structure weight	6,250	7,000	6,250
Fixed equipment	500	500	475
Tare weight	6,750	7,500	6,725
Fuel and oil	2,070	2,070	2,070
Crew	400	200	200
Military load	765	350	4,110
All-up weight	9.985	10,120	13,105
Rationalised flight factor	2 x 4g	2 x 4g	2 x 3.1g

The maximum speed is 295 mph TAS at 14,000 feet, and the structure is designed for a maximum diving speed of 350 mph IAS. A moulded acetate blister on top of the fuselage amidships gives the Observer an unrestricted view aft for towing purposes.

The fuel tanks are fitted with immersed fuel pumps and have a maximum capacity of 250 gallons, which gives half-an-hour at maximum climbing conditions together with 2 to 2½ hours at maximum weak mixture cruising conditions. The engines are fitted with constant speed fully feathering propellers.

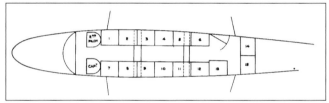

Troop Carrying layout.

Glider Tug

With Mercury engines it should be possible to tow up to three fully loaded Hotspurs, the power loading being then 12½ lb/hp with a wing loading of 24.8 lb/sq ft. With Taurus engines, a fully loaded Horsa may be towed, the power loading being then 12.2 lb/hp with the same wing loading.

Troop Carrier

Accommodation is provided for fifteen fully-equipped troops. Allowing a weight of 265 lb per man, this gives a wing loading at take-off of 32 lb/sq ft coupled with a power loading of 6½-7¾ lb/hp according to the engines used. The still air take-off run under these conditions would be of the order of 300 yards and the distance to clear 50 feet about 500 yards.

Numerous racks and stowages for light arms of all sorts are provided in the cabin. All seats are made quickly detachable and removal of the centre six seats provides access to a large loading hatch in the floor, between the spars. This hatch is 4 feet in diameter and is therefore sufficiently large to enable motor cycles

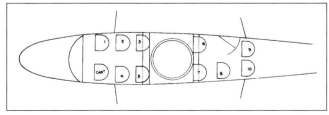

Paratroop Training layout.

and various military equipment to be loaded without difficulty. As already mentioned, the range provides for half an hour at maximum climb and 2-2½ hours at maximum weak mixture cruising conditions.

Paratroop Trainer

Accommodation is provided for ten paratroops, the equipment containers being slung on suitable racks beneath the centre section outboard of the fuselage on either side. The weight allowed is 380 lb per man and equipment. All seats face forward and are made to fold back flush against the sides of the cabin, leaving no projecting parts. The seats are equipped with Sutton harness.

The exit well is situated amidships between the spars, so that no appreciable change of trim is caused when the troops prepare to leave. It is 4 feet in diameter and is provided with the necessary strong points for the attachment of the static lines. The floor of the cabin both forward and aft of the well is completely unobstructed.

The entrance door to the cabin may also, if desired, be used for paratroop training. It is 30 ins wide by 4 feet high and, since it is about 15 feet ahead of and also below the tailplane, jumps may be made from it with perfect safety. The take-off and range are the same as given above for the troop carrier.

Montrose III - 4 Cheetah XV Engines

The Montrose III has the same fuselage, empennage, undercarriage and ailerons as the Montrose I and II *(shown in the booklet – PA)*. A different one piece wing, however, is substituted and carries 4 Cheetah XV engines *(this statement does not tie up with the previous drawings as the wing shown is the same as that used on the Mk.I and Mk.II in the booklet - but see later projects with the same Mark numbers - PA)*. The function of the Montrose III is as a four-engined flying and aircrew trainer.

Design and Construction

The main structure is stressed to the following flight factors:-

	Solo training	Bomber aircrew training
	lb	lb
Structure weight	8,000	8,000
Fixed equipment	835	835
Tare weight	8,835	8,835
Fuel and oil	970	2,070
Crew	200	1,200
Military load	127	742
All-up weight	10,132	12,847
Rationalised flight factor	2 x 4g	2 x 3.15g

The maximum speed is 240 mph TAS at 5,000 feet and the structure is designed for a maximum diving speed of 350 mph IAS. The fuel tanks are fitted with immersed fuel pumps and have a maximum capacity of 250 gallons. The engines are fitted with Rotol constant speed fully feathering propellers.

Equipment and Performance

The equipment both for the pilot and for the aircrew are identical with that described in detail for the Montrose I.

In January 1943, Phillips & Powis Aircraft Ltd produced a brochure entitled 'Miles Specialised Aircraft for Specialised Purposes'. Contained therein was a summary of a selection of Miles aircraft which had either been built or proposed up to then.

The M.36 was included.

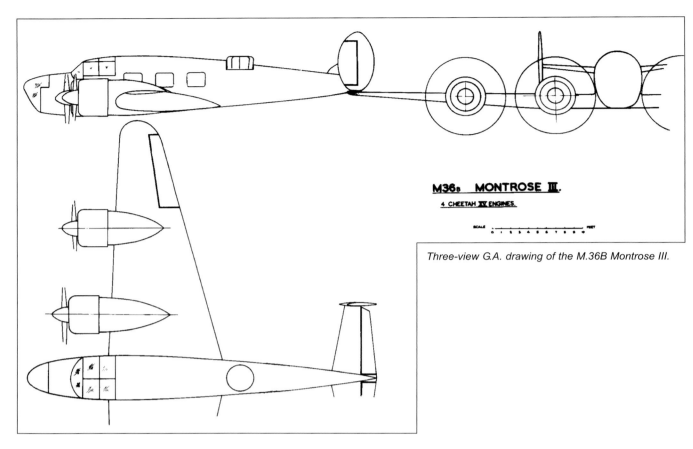

Three-view G.A. drawing of the M.36B Montrose III.

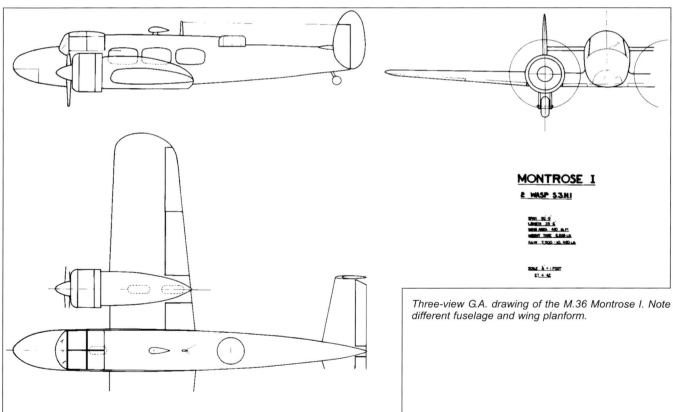

Three-view G.A. drawing of the M.36 Montrose I. Note different fuselage and wing planform.

M.36 Montrose Aircrew Trainer

The imminent enormous increase in the use of four engined aircraft makes the provision of a specialised air crew trainer almost an essential. For this purpose the Montrose has been designed to provide a complete course of training for every member of the bomber crew.

Span	60 ft 0 in
Wing area	500 sq ft
All up weight	12,800 lb
Engine	4 Cheetah XV
Max speed	240 mph at 5,000 ft

To add to the confusion surrounding the different proposed versions of the M.36 Montrose Mk.I and Mk.II, another series of surviving Phillips & Powis photographs show completely different versions of these two marks.

Montrose I - 2 Wasp S.3H.1 Engines

The following details of this version were given on the drawing:

Span	50' 0"
Length	39' 6"
Wing area	410 sq ft.
Weight tare	6,200 lb
AUW	7,500 - 10,450 lb
Scale	½" = 1 Foot
Date	27.4.42

Montrose II - 2 Mercury XV Engines

The following details of this version were given on the drawing:

Span	50' 0"
Length	36' 0"
Wing area	410 sq ft.
Weight tare	6,500 lb
AUW	9,300
Scale	½" = 1 Foot
Date	28.4.42

In due course the various M.36 Montrose projects were submitted to the MAP and while they were given sympathetic consideration, it was felt that the commitment of the entire aircraft industry did not allow for the production of a new non-

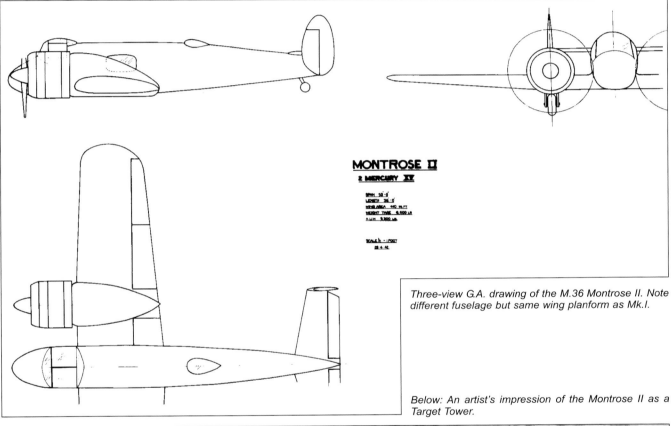

Three-view G.A. drawing of the M.36 Montrose II. Note different fuselage but same wing planform as Mk.I.

Below: An artist's impression of the Montrose II as a Target Tower.

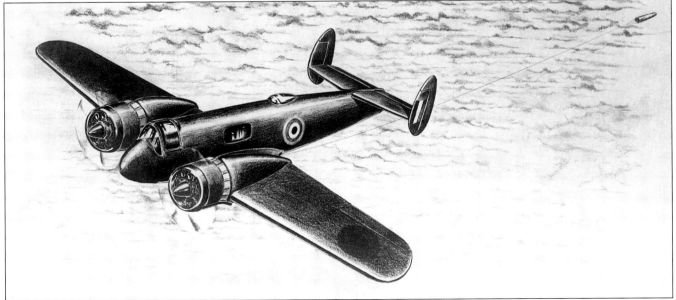

operational type at that time, however desirable it might have been. Thus the M.36 Montrose, in all its most interesting variants, did not progress beyond the drawing board and neither did the later projected Miles M.55 Marlborough, a projected larger four-engined aircrew trainer which succeeded it.

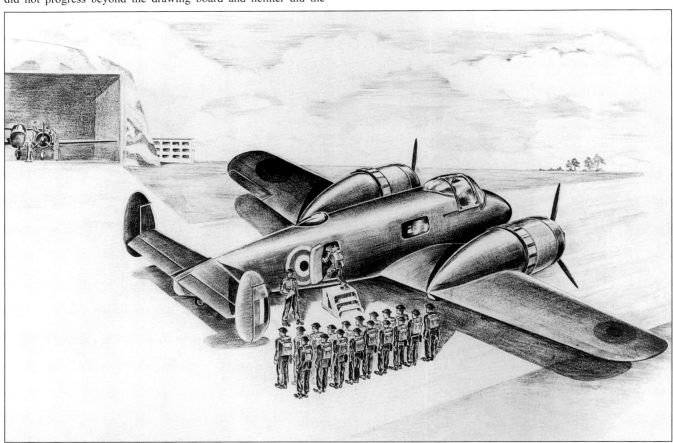

An artist's impression of the Montrose II as a Troop Transport showing 18 troops lined up, 1 entering the aircraft and 1 in charge. If this number were due to board then it is considerably more than the 15 troops catered for in the earlier version?

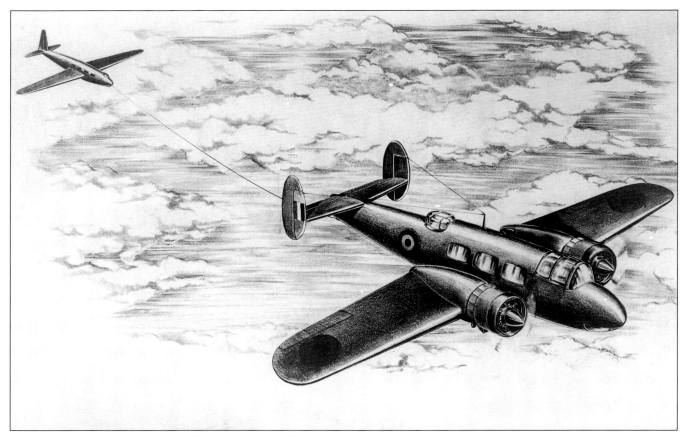

An artist's impression of the Montrose II in use as a Light Glider Tower.

JN275, the first prototype M.37 Martinet Advanced Trainer.

Chapter 28
Miles M.37 Master 5 (Master Replacement) and M.37 Advanced Trainer

Although nothing came of the M.29 Master Mk.V Advanced Trainer project study of 1940, or the later projected M.31 Master Mk.IV Advanced Trainer, Miles still felt that a number of modifications and improvements based on service experience with the earlier marks of Master could well be incorporated into a new design. Included amongst these suggested modifications was the rear cabin being permanently raised to give the instructor the necessary field of view for take-off and landing without having to manually raise himself through the cabin roof.

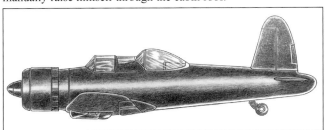

The M.37 Master 5 (Master Replacement).

The above drawing shows an undated side view of the proposed 'Miles M.37 Master 5 (Master Replacement)'. This was an advanced trainer concept very similar to that of the abandoned M.29 Master Mk.V but with Miles again envisaging a raised rear teardrop type canopy to the instructor's position and a modified rear fuselage, with the fin and rudder similar to that of the M.20. However, due to other more pressing production commitments, this project was shelved.

By 1945, the need for an improved trainer was finally recognised by the Ministry and the preliminary requirement OR.215 for

Spec.T.7/45 was issued. This called for the conversion of the M.25 Martinet into an Advanced Trainer, to be used in the interim until such time as a new advanced trainer, to Spec.T.7/45 Issue II, with a propeller-turbine engine, could be produced.

Miles tendered the M.70 (to be covered in the next volume) and three other companies, Avro, Boulton Paul and Blackburn also tendered.

In July 1945, Miles Aircraft Ltd produced a booklet, reproduced here, on what was ultimately to become the M.37 Advanced Trainer.

Martinet Advanced Trainer

In view of the probable shortage of advanced trainers both in the near future and until such time as the Experimental T.7/45 has proved successful and is available in production, an investigation has been made as to the feasibility of converting the standard Martinet into an advanced trainer. No serious difficulties are anticipated and such a conversion could be readily and relatively cheaply effected. Broadly speaking the conversion would entail the removal of the outboard fuel tanks and the installation of a revised cabin top and a second set of controls and instruments.

The accompanying drawing and illustration show clearly the type of cabin top envisaged and it will be noticed that the view provided for the instructor in the rear seat is greatly superior to that of either the Master or the Harvard. The proposed arrangement also completely overcomes the objection raised regarding these aircraft for gunnery training insomuch as reflector sights can be fitted in both cockpits.

The note on the drawing read:

The object of this conversion is to adapt a standard Martinet for trainer purposes and utilising the following standard parts to obviate additional tooling etc.

For conversion:
1 Standard seat installation as used on the Master II
2 Standard Martinet hand control box in rear cockpit interconnected with box in front cockpit
3 Standard Martinet flying control column and rudder bar assembly mounted in rear cockpit picking up main control system by a linkage system
4 Standard cabin top modified as shown on this drawing
5 Deletions - all target towing equipment etc
6 Outer wing fuel tanks

Note: All other components and assembly drawings and fixtures as standard Martinet.

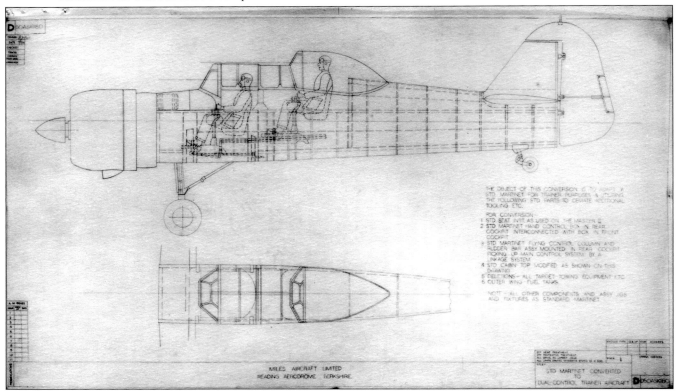

Drawing, dated 5/7/45, showing Standard Martinet converted to Dual Control Trainer Aircraft.

The photograph depicts the second production Martinet with an artist's impression of the teardrop cabin of the M.37 superimposed over the rear of the original Martinet canopy.

Analysis of Weights:	lb		Hydraulics	116
			Pneumatics	20
Mainplane and centre section	1,152		Electrics	180
Fuselage and seats	500		Services	316
Tail unit	122			
Landing gear	240		Furnishings	16
Controls	119		Misc Fixed equipment	161
Structure	2,133		Fixed equipment	177
Engine bare	1,103		Tare weight	4,511
Mounting and cowling	101		Signal pistol and cartridges	6.5
Engine cooling	25		First aid	3
Oil cooling	39		Radio TR9D and accessories	48
Oil in engine and cooler	19		Radio A.R.I.500 and accessories	31
Accessories and exhaust	194		Speaking tubes	2.5
Propeller and spinner	295		Blind flying hood	10
Power Plant	1,776		Crew and parachutes	400
			Crew and Removable equipment	501
Fuel tanks and supports	43			
Fuel system	30		Fuel 70 galls	525
Oil tanks and supports	20		Oil 7 galls	63
Oil system	16		Disposable load	588
Fuel Unit	109		AUW	5,600

A detailed weight analysis is included in the form laid down in MAP Form 2492 (see table above). From this it will be seen that the weight at take-off is 5,600 lb at which weight the corresponding ultimate load factor will be about 10.7. The maximum permissible diving speed at this weight will be 370 mph EAS, which is considerably faster than that of either the Master or the Harvard and almost equal to that of the Hurricane: while the CG remains within safe limits for the Martinet. Details of span, wing area, engine, etc, are not included as these are all exactly as on the standard Martinet.

The AUW of the M.37 was to be 1,150lb lower than the standard Martinet and at that weight, the maximum diving speed of 370 mph EAS made it 40 mph faster than the Master and the Harvard.

Before conversion of the first aircraft commenced, it was agreed to fit a mock-up rear canopy to a standard Martinet and this was carried out on HP413, which had been declared Cat.3 following an accident in 1945 and had been returned to Woodley for repairs on 19th September 1945. It was awaiting collection after repair on 23rd November 1945 but was transferred to Miles Aircraft for fitment of a mock-up of the raised rear canopy for preliminary aerodynamic and spinning trials. The modification was carried out by the Experimental Department at Woodley. HP413 was fitted with a Bristol Mercury 30 engine.

Following modification, Miles test pilot Ken Waller, made the first flight on 6th December 1945, and his Test Flight Report noted:

AUW @ take-off - 5,616.50 lb; CG Position - U/c down 25.4% AMC.

Preliminary handling and spinning report.

Take off - Trim tabs were set as for standard Martinet and the take off was found to be normal. The aircraft leaves the ground without being pulled off at approximately 70 ASI and climbs away steeply.

Climb - The climb was made at 140 ASI, 2400 rpm plus 2¾ lb. boost. All controls were normal, but it was noted that there is insufficient rudder trim to hold the aeroplane straight, feet off, below this speed.

Level speeds - Two level speed runs were carried out as follows:

Height.	RPM.	Boost.	ASI.
5,000	2400	Plus ½	192
3,000	2650	Plus 4¼	233

Martinet HP413 with mock-up rear hood for aerodynamic tests.

A view of HP413 at A&AEE Boscombe Down, note the Grumman Tigercat behind the propeller.   *[MAP RTP Photographic Section]*

A close-up of the mock-up rear canopy on HP413.

Stalling - With elevator trim fully back and with undercarriage and flaps up the aircraft glides at 120 ASI. There is very little warning of the stall which occurs at 75 ASI. At the stall there is slight buffeting and the nose drops, there is no tendency to drop a wing. With elevator trim fully back and with flaps and undercarriage down the aircraft glides at 105 ASI. There is very little warning of the stall which occurs at 50 - 60 ASI. The characteristics of the stall appear to be the same as with flaps and undercarriage up.

Sideslipping - At 120-140 ASI the aeroplane was sideslipped to right and left until full rudder was applied. There is no buffeting and no lightening off of the control.

Spinning - All spins were carried out with the cockpit hood closed and trimmers set in the neutral position. A sequence of spins were carried out as follows:

No of turns	No of turns to recover	Total Height Lost
1 left	½	1,500 ft
1 right	½	1,600 ft
2 left	½	2,300 ft
2 right	¾	2,100 ft
2 left	½	2,100 ft
2 right	1	2,000 ft
3 left	¾	2,500 ft
3 right	1	2,500 ft
5 left	¾	3,100 ft
5 right	1	3,000 ft

Diving - A dive was made to 320 ASI at 2,400 rpm plus ½ boost, the aircraft being trimmed to fly level at this condition. It was found to be unnecessary to re-trim during the dive, the forward pressure on the control column not being excessive. During the

dive all controls were moved through small angles, and were perfectly normal becoming heavier as speed increased.

Aerobatics - The following aerobatics were carried out, the trimmers throughout being set to the neutral position: Loop commencing at 240 ASI; Half-loop and roll out on top both to left and right, commencing at 260 ASI; Slow rolls to left and right; Half roll each way and dive out. During this test all controls were adequate and in every way normal, the aeroplane being very easy to manoeuvre. There is a slight tendency for the nose to drop when coming out of a roll or when half rolling off the top of a loop.

Approach and landing - The approach was made at 75 ASI and when engine was used a very slight vibration was felt on the elevator control. The hold-off and landing is normal, the aeroplane landing at 60 ASI.

It appears from these tests that the raised rear cockpit hood does not interfere in any way with the air flow over the empennage as the aeroplane handles in the same way as the standard Martinet.

One further test flight of HP413 to assess spinning characteristics was carried out by Ken Waller, on 8th December 1945, and his Test Flight Report on this flight reported:

Entry - On entry the aircraft rolls onto its back the nose falling steeply and then rising steadily during the first turn. The nose drops again during the first half of the second turn and then rises slightly as the second turn is completed. After two complete turns the aircraft settles into a steady spin. Considerable pressure is required on the rudder to hold the aircraft in the spin, particularly for the first two turns when the rudder kicks hard in the reverse direction to the spin.

Recovery - On applying anti-spin rudder and moving the control column forward the nose drops after which the aircraft recovers sharply and goes into a steep dive.

General remarks - Spins were also carried out with the front cabin hood open. The effect of ailerons during a spin was also investigated, full opposite aileron and aileron in the same direction of the spin appeared to have very little effect, recovery in each case being normal. Spins were also made with the elevator trim fully forward and full back. With trim fully forward the recovery from the ensuing dive necessitates a strong pull on the control column and with the trim full back there is a tendency to pull out of the dive too quickly with the consequent possibility of a stall.

Following these trials, HP413 was delivered to 'D1' Squadron, A&AEE Boscombe Down on 13th December 1945 for spinning trials. Following these, HP413 was returned to Woodley where it was subsequently scrapped.

Ken Waller's further test flight of HP413 to assess spinning characteristics included the following:

AUW @ take-off - 5,899 lb; CG Position - U/c down 30.93% AMC.

Height in Feet commenced	No of turns	Height Recovery	No of turns	Height out
Spinning Test CG normal - The following spins were carried out:				
8,000	3 Left	6,900	¾	5,900
8,000	3 Right	7,100	1	5,900
10,000	8 Left	7,000	¾	5,800
10,000	8 Right	7,200	1½	5,600
Spinning Tests CG Extended Aft - The following spinning tests were carried out:				
8,000	3 Left	6,900	¾	5,700
8,000	3 Right	7,000	1¼	5,600
10,000	8 Left	6,700	1	5,500
10,000	8 Right	6,900	1½	5,400

Two prototypes of the M.37 were then ordered by the MAP, both to be converted from standard Martinets. The first of these, JN275, which was issued to Miles Aircraft on 22nd October 1945, following a Cat.B Major Inspection, was chosen for conversion to be the first prototype M.37 on 17th December 1945.

It was stated in the Minutes of the 109th Meeting of the Executive Management Board (EMB) held on Monday 8th April 1946 with reference to the Martinet Trainer that; *This machine should be ready for flight on Wednesday (*10th April - PA), and at the 110th Meeting of the EMB, on Monday, 15th April 1946, it was recorded that; *This machine has now flown and appears to be satisfactory*, but the actual date of its first flight wasn't quoted. Don Brown however, records that the first flight of JN275 was made by chief test pilot Ken Waller on 11th April 1946, which would tend to agree with the Minutes.

The first recorded flight, which was probably its second, in the M.37 Test Flight Report file, was dated 11.00 hrs on 14th April 1946 and this is reproduced here:

AUW @ take-off - 5,407 lb; CG Position - 25.2% AMC.

Climb to 15,000 ft - The following readings were taken at 1,000 ft intervals (there followed a table of readings of Height; RPM; Boost; IAS; Oil Temp; Cylinder Temp; Time to 15,000 ft 10.33 min).

The next flight was made by Ken Waller at 12.00 hrs on 14th April 1946 and his Test Flight Report stated (figures in table below):

AUW @ take-off - 5,407 lb; CG Position - 25.2% AMC.

Level Speeds - The following levels were carried out at 4,000 ft, with cooling gills fully closed.

Ken Waller's next flight in JN275 was made at 12.30 hrs on 14th April 1946 and his Test Flight Report states:

AUW @ take-off - 5,407 lb; CG Position - 25.2% AMC.

Preliminary Dive Test - With the aircraft trimmed for level flight at 10,000 ft, 2400 rpm, 0 boost, (full throttle), the aircraft was dived to 330 IAS. During the dive and at limiting speed, all controls were moved through small angles, they became heavier as speed increased and there was no tendency to oscillate or flutter. The trimmers were not used during the dive, although a strong push is necessary on the control column at maximum speed.

Ken Waller's last recorded flight in JN275 was made on 15th April 1946, between 15.00 and 16.25 hrs and his Test Flight Report (signed off by Hugh Kendall) states:

AUW @ take-off - 5,685.50 lb; CG Position - 32.3% SMC.

Control and Stability at Stall - This test was carried out with both cabin hoods in the closed position.

Test 1 - With undercarriage and flaps up the stalling speed was found to be 74 IAS. When the aircraft was trimmed to glide at 1.2 times stalling speed (90 mph) the aircraft was longitudinally stable, the stick force required to stall the aircraft is light, the position of the control column being approximately half back from neutral. There is very little warning of the stall apart from the nose up attitude of the aircraft until some 2 or 3 mph, before the stall is

Time	RPM	Boost	Oil Temp	Cylinder Temp	IAS
Full throttle:					
1 min.	2650	+4¼	60	150	240
2 min.	2650	+4¼	61	155	239
3 min.	2650	+4¼	62	155	242
Maximum rich cruise:					
1 min.	2400	+2¾	62	160	229
2 min.	2400	+2¾	61	160	228
3 min.	2400	+2¾	60	160	230
4 min.	2400	+2¾	60	160	229
5 min.	2400	+2¾	60	160	226
Maximum weak cruise:					
1 min.	2400	+½	60	155	204
2 min.	2400	+½	60	155	203
3 min.	2400	+½	60	155	202
4 min.	2400	+½	60	155	203
5 min.	2400	+½	60	155	202

View showing the instrument layout for the instructor of the prototype M.37.

reached when a certain amount of buffeting occurs. At the stall, instability in roll develops, it being still possible to control this by use of ailerons only without use of rudder. With the undercarriage and flaps down, the stalling speed was found to be 55 IAS. With the aircraft trimmed to glide at 1.2 times the stalling speed (66 IAS) the aircraft was found to be stable. The stick force required to stall the aircraft is very light, the position of the control column being approximately a quarter back from neutral. There is little warning of stall apart from slight buffeting which commences some 2 to

3 mph, before the stall is reached, the characteristics of the stall being similar to that with flaps and undercarriage up.

Test 2 - With flaps and undercarriage up, the aircraft was trimmed at 1.2 times stalling speed and the aircraft was then glided at 1.1 times stalling speed (82 IAS). The aircraft maintained straight and level flight with the rudder and aileron held fixed. Having disturbed the aircraft from level flight, it can be regained by use of (a) ailerons only, the rudder being held fixed (b) rudder only, ailerons being

JN275, the first prototype M.37 at Woodley taken about the time of its first flight.

Photograph showing the safety tripod to the instructor's cockpit. Note a Monitor fuselage under construction in the background.

held fixed (c) both rudder and ailerons together. With flaps and undercarriage down, the aircraft was glided at 1.1 times stalling speed (60 IAS) and the same test was carried out. The behaviour of the aircraft is similar to that of flaps and undercarriage up, but greater movement of the controls is necessary to regain level flight.

Test 3 - With flaps and undercarriage up, the aircraft was trimmed to glide at 1.2 times stalling speed, and from a steady glide at 1.1 times stalling speed the control column was then eased slowly back as far as possible. The aircraft can be trimmed down to about 1.3Vs

or Vaf. When the aircraft is stalled, it becomes unstable in roll but control can be maintained by coarse use of ailerons, rudder held fixed. Control by this means becomes less effective as the stick is pulled further back. With the stick fully back, or nearly so, the machine flicks with simultaneous roll, yaw, and pitch (nose down). With rudder still fixed central, stick fully back and full opposite aileron, after, typically, ¼ to ½ turn in yaw, the aircraft steadies, hangs momentarily, and usually flicks the opposite way. There is no tendency to spin. Recovery is immediate on applying contra-spin controls. There is no significant difference in behaviour with flaps and undercarriage up or down.

Test 4 - With flaps and undercarriage up, and trimmed to glide at 1.2 times stalling speed, the aircraft was put into 30° gliding turns. The minimum speed at which a turn could be maintained was 85 mph both to the left and to the right. Below this speed slight buffeting commences and difficulty is experienced in maintaining a steady air speed. When the aircraft stalls in a left-hand turn the left wing and nose drops sharply, in a right-hand turn the aircraft tends to come out of the turn and falls away to the left. There is no tendency to spin. The behaviour and control of the aircraft during all turns and recoveries was normal, it being possible to recover from a turn by ailerons alone, rudder being held fixed. The same test carried out with flaps and undercarriage down, the minimum speed for a sustained turn of 30° being 65 IAS both to the left and to the right. The behaviour of the aircraft at the stall is similar to that with undercarriage and flaps up.

Throughout the above tests, no differences between behaviour with front hood open or shut could be detected.

Hugh Kendall also flew JN275 as follows: 'Handling Trial' on 15th April 1946; Demonstrations 18th, 24th and 29th 1946 and from Woodley to Hullavington on 18th April 1947.

The M.37 was generally considered to be 'delightful on the controls' and this was confirmed by Don Brown, who recorded a flight with Ken Waller on 'Spinning trials' in JN275 on 16th April 1946. Don vividly remembered these trials as they included spins in both directions and in every possible configuration, followed by a high-speed dive, a half roll in the inverted position at a height of 100ft and an inverted climb, during the course of which the undercarriage and flaps were lowered, upwards(!) and another half roll was then followed by a sharp sideslip and touchdown! Don considered that this manoeuvre was as much testimony to the handling qualities of the Martinet Trainer as to the pilot's skill.

On 17th April, Don was taken on his second flight in the M.37, this time with Hugh Bergel, an ex ATA ferry pilot turned test pilot who undertook sales demonstrations and test flying for Miles Aircraft Ltd when required. JN275 was seen, by the late Gordon Swanborough, at Woodley on 8th January 1947, who noted that it was fitted with two .303 machine guns but this is the only record of the M.37 having been fitted with any armament.

Martinet JN668 was modified to the second prototype M.37 and its only recorded 'Test' flight was made by Ken Waller on 25th June 1947, but it was displayed statically at the last Miles Aircraft 'At Home' day, held at Woodley on 20th July 1947.

From late 1943, formal meetings were held (usually on a weekly basis) of the Executive Management Board (EMB) and some copies of the Minutes have recently been discovered. Unfortunately, the Minutes from Meetings 1 to 87, 97, 126, 133, 151 et seq are missing but the following comments, which relate to the Martinet Trainer are of sufficient interest to be reproduced here:

17. 9.45	90th	It was reported that France is desirous of purchasing from 100 to 150 of this type of trainer, whilst there was some word that the Ministry is requiring 200 off with Cougar engine. Mr Hackett was authorised to quote a firm price to France for this aeroplane.
24. 9.45	91st	A letter had been received stating that the Ministry would not be requiring Martinet Trainers or M.18s, but the French Government were extremely interested in the purchase of the Martinet, and were now talking of 200.
8.10.45	92nd	No word yet of the French order.
15.10.45	93rd	French Order - Mr Hackett stated that he did not think he would hear further for ten days. Egyptian Order - Mr Hackett was asked to immediately take steps to try and obtain an order. Irish order - Here again Mr Hackett was asked to take immediate steps to try and obtain an order. It was agreed that Mr Parsons should accumulate a set of components so that a prototype high speed trainer could be constructed.
29.10.45	94th	French order. Awaiting Mr Hackett's return. Egyptian order. Awaiting Mr Hackett's return. Irish order. Awaiting Mr Hackett's return. Mr Parsons stated that he was trying to negotiate with the Admiralty to obtain through DTD one Martinet for conversion. This matter must be followed up urgently by the Sales Department.
5.11.45	95th	French Order - No news as yet. Egyptian Order - Mr Hackett says Mr Chick has gone to Egypt and he is awaiting his reply. Irish Order - Mr Hackett is awaiting news from Mr Powis.

JN668, the second prototype M.37 at Woodley.　　　　　　　　　　　　　　　　*[GS Collection]*

With reference to getting a Martinet for conversion G/Capt Bandidt is endeavouring to set this up.

12.11.45	96th	It was reported that the Martinet Trainer had now become a very real possibility with the RAF and that Group Captain Bandidt was pressing for a machine to be allocated in order that Trial Installation could be installed. French Order - No news as yet. Egyptian Order - Mr Hackett is still awaiting news from Mr Chick. Irish Order - Mr Hackett is awaiting news from Mr Powis.
3.12.45	98th	RAF Order - This was awaiting flying tests and then would be followed by the usual design conference.
10.12.45	99th	No minutes taken.
31.12.45	100th	Mr Hackett stated that he felt certain we would be receiving an order for these from MAP and from the French.
14. 1.46	101st	No mention of Martinet Trainer.
28. 1.46	102nd	Mr Parsons to give details as to when first and second prototypes will be ready to fly. It is considered most important to press these on as fast as possible.
4. 3.46	103rd	It was reported that the first prototype would be ready by the end of March; the second, two to four weeks thereafter.
18. 2.46	104th	Mr Parsons stated his promised date of end of March still stands.
25. 2.46	105th	Mr Miles asked that an urgent sales effort be made to obtain sales for the Martinet which had been cancelled. Mr Powis was asked to take action with reference to Southern Ireland.
4. 3.46	106th	No report was made with reference to the Martinet Trainer. Mr Miles had asked that an urgent sales effort be made to obtain sales for the Martinet which had been cancelled. Mr Powis was asked to take action with reference to Southern Ireland.
18. 3.46	107th	This is coming along nicely.
1. 4.46	108th	It was reported by Mr Parsons that this machine would be ready for flight this week.
8. 4.46	109th	This machine should be ready for flight on Wednesday.
15. 4.46	110th	This machine has now flown and appears to be satisfactory.
29. 4.46	111th	It was agreed that efforts should be made to get this machine away to Boscombe in order that handling trials can commence at the earliest possible moment.
6. 5.46	112th	Mr George Miles reported that Mr Walsh and G/Capt Bandidt felt that it would be unwise to send the first machine to Boscombe and that it would be better to wait for the second.
13. 5.46	113th	Mr Parsons stated that the second machine would be ready at the end of the month and Mr Bennett should watch the fact that the second machine contained a lot more than the first from a financial point of view.
20. 5.46	114th	Mr Parsons stated that the second machine would be ready at the end of the month.
27. 5.46	115th	It was reported that this was now flying *(JN668, the second machine - PA)* but awaiting Embodiment Loan Equipment.
3. 6.46	116th	Is proceeding satisfactorily.
17. 3.46	117th	Is proceeding satisfactorily.
1. 7.46	118th	It was reported that the final conference on this machine was held last week.
15. 7.46	119th	No further news.

22. 7.46	120th	Nothing to report.
29. 7.46	121st	Nothing to report.
19. 8.46	122nd	Certain mods are still being carried out on the existing machines, but information at the moment is that the Martinet Trainer is not wanted by the government. Sales: Martinet Sweden, Switzerland and Turkey. No news. France had definitely indicated that they do not want any aircraft.
26. 8.46	123rd	Sales: Martinet Sweden. An order had been received for five reconditioned aircraft. Turkey. Mr Hackett was looking into the matter. Switzerland - No news.
2. 9.46	124th	Sales: Martinet Conversion. No further News. Martinet Trainer. Mr Miles authorised Mr Clarke to proceed to see whether he could obtain a contract for the Martinet Trainer. Turkey. No report from Mr Hackett. Switzerland. No news.
19. 9.46		Extract from an Internal Memo from D L Brown to F G Miles, G H Miles, Sir William Mount, Mr Robinson, Mr Faulkner. Finally, I gather that, on arrival in Scandinavia, Bowman found the Martinet in a shocking condition and I have asked that he should let you have a detailed report.
23. 9.46	125th	Awaiting news from Mr Clarke as to the position of this machine. Sales: Martinet. Turkey. No report from Mr Hackett. Switzerland. No news.
	126th	Minutes missing.
21.10.46	127th	Still awaiting news from Mr Clarke as to the position of this machine.
11.11.46	129th	It was reported that the prototypes are practically ready, but there is no word yet of a production order
2.12.46	130th to 13.1.47 134th. Nothing to report.	
21. 1.47	135th	No mention of any type of Martinet at this or at any subsequent meeting.

Production summary

JN275 M.37 Advanced Trainer. First prototype; converted from M.25 Martinet Mk.I which had been declared Cat.B on an unrecorded date and had been returned to Miles Woodley for MI on 22.10.45. Although AW/CN on 17.12.45, it was not collected but instead was retained by Miles and converted to the first prototype M.37 Advanced Trainer. It is possible that a new c/n was issued to cover the conversion. First flown, by Chief Test Pilot Ken Waller, 11.4.46. Deld by Hugh Kendall to ECFS Hullavington for Service trials 18.4.47. To 27 MU Shawbury 4.11.48. To NEA at 27 MU Shawbury 2.7.51. Sold as scrap to Henry Bath & Sons 26.9.51.

JN668 M.37 Advanced Trainer. Second prototype; converted from M.25 Martinet Mk.I which had been declared Cat.Ac on 26.10.45 but re-Cat.B later before being returned to Miles Woodley 15.11.45. Although AW/CN on 14.1.46, it was not collected but instead was retained by Miles and converted to the second prototype M.37 Advanced Trainer. It is possible that a new c/n was issued to cover the conversion. First flight, probably made by Ken Waller, a few days before 27.5.46, On Miles Aircraft CSA 21.3.46. Sold 1.12.47 to L A Andrews. Regd **G-AKOS** (CofR 12105) 22.12.47 to Leonard Arthur Andrews, t/a Gloucester Flying Club, Cheltenham (based Staverton). Flown to Staverton but when and by whom is not recorded. CofA not applied for. Cld by the MCA 28.9.48. Probably not flown again after its ferry flight to Staverton and was noted derelict at Staverton by 1949. Scrapped later, its remains were taken to an orchard about 3 miles from Cheltenham, where they were abandoned.

These mouldering remains were re-discovered in the early 1980s, complete with the Bristol Mercury 30 engine, which had some small panels, once painted bright yellow but by then very faded,

with 'JN668' stencilled on them in black. The engine was recovered by Robin Day and other volunteers from the Berkshire Aviation Group and taken to Woodley. It was hoped that the engine could have been restored to static display condition by the Rolls-Royce Heritage Trust at Bristol but upon further examination it was found to be too corroded and it was returned to Woodley.

Above: JN668 at Staverton shortly after its arrival there.   *[Peter F Wright via Phil Davey]*

Below: The remains of JN668 in an orchard near Cheltenham. The engine and propeller were later recovered by Robin Day and taken to Woodley for The Museum of Berkshire Aviation.   *[Via Chris Mitchell]*

SPECIFICATION AND PERFORMANCE DATA

Engine:	870 hp Bristol Mercury 30
Dimensions:	span: 39ft 0in; length 30ft 11in; wing area 242 sq ft; aspect ratio 6.3; wing section; root, NACA 23024, tip NACA 23009; wing loading 23.2lb/sq ft
Weight:	empty 4,511lb; AUW 5,600lb; fuel (70 gal) 525lb; oil (7 gal) 63lb; crew 400lb; useful load 101lb
Performance:	max design diving speed 370 mph EAS; range 370 miles; duration 2.75 hrs

U-0223, the M.38/28 prototype Messenger at Woodley. MAP RTP photograph dated March 1944 shows the aircraft still in its original colours and markings which should have been changed by then as it was first flown on 12th September 1942. The photograph does, however, confirm that the engine was a Gipsy Major at that time.

Chapter 29
Miles M.38/28, M.38/28 Ambulance,
M.38 Messenger AOP/Communications Mk.I
Aircraft to Spec. A.17/43 and M.38 Mk.IIIB/M.48

The concept of a liaison aeroplane as a small, usually unarmed aircraft to be used by the army (Royal Artillery) as an Air Observation Post, or for transporting commanders and messages, had started to develop prior to the Second World War, particularly in the United States (with their Stinson Vigilant) and Germany (with their Fiesler Storch). However, with the outbreak of war in September 1939, the British army had access to just two types that loosely fell within this category - the Taylorcraft Auster Mk.I and the Westland Lysander. The Auster, with its 90 hp Cirrus engine, was, in no one's opinion, suitable for war and the pilots held very definite views on this, with which in this case, official RAF opinion concurred. The Lysander also failed as it departed from the fundamental principle of reconnaissance, whether on land, sea or in the air. That is to say, if you want to do reconnaissance (as opposed to Air OP work) you must either be prepared to go really fast, get your knowledge and return before you are caught, or else you must go prepared and sufficiently armed to fight for your information and if necessary fight to bring it home. As the Lysander fulfilled none of these requirements, it therefore failed in war.

Another view of U-0223.

Neither were the Auster nor the Lysander ideally suited to the role of transporting senior commanders. However, during late 1939, the army tried all available types of pre-war civil light aircraft at Old Sarum, Larkhill or High Post. These included: DH.60 Moth, DH.60G Gipsy Moth, DH.82 Tiger Moth, DH.94 Moth Minor, Taylorcraft Model D, Piper J-3 Cub, Arpin A-1 Mk.2, GAL.33 Cagnet, GAL.42 Cygnet and De Schelde Scheldemusch, etc, etc but it was the Taylorcraft, although lacking in many desirable characteristics, that came nearest to their requirements.

We have Lt Col H C Bazeley DSO, DSC (US), Royal Artillery, to thank for writing a manuscript, although a note at the beginning of this stated: *This short history is not for publication, but was written by me for the amusement and interest of my children, should they one day want to know what I did in the Second World War, It was written in October 1947 from my own diaries. It does not in any way pretend to be a detailed account of the difficult and weary months of struggle and frustration between June 1938, when the idea was first mooted, and November 1942, when the first Air OP Squadron won its spurs in Battle.*

A more detailed and technical history can be found in the archives of the Historical Section of the Air OP Officers' Association. This is merely my own story and should any reader complain that there is too much of the personal pronoun, I can only repeat that it was not written for general publication. (HCB).

However, his children recently agreed that this manuscript should be published and that Guy Warner should prepare the manuscript for publication. The finished booklet, entitled *The Air Observation Post - A short account of its birth, sickly childhood, adolescence and early manhood*, was launched at The Museum of Army Flying, Middle Wallop, on 22nd August 2012 and thanks to Guy, I was privileged to meet Lt Col Bazeley's daughter Sally there.

Sally very kindly agreed to me identifying her father, Lt Col H C Bazeley, as the un-named 'army officer' (not the 'certain army officers' mentioned by Don Brown in *Miles Aircraft since 1925*), who approached George Miles in 1942 with a view to designing an Air OP aeroplane for the army.

I am now pleased to be able to finally give Lt Col Bazeley the full credit that he so richly deserves and to quote relevant extracts from the booklet here:

During this spring my attention was drawn to the Miles M.28, a low wing light wooden aircraft, (which had been demonstrated to the School of Artillery at Old Sarum and Shrivenham on 2nd May 1942 - PA) and I visited George H Miles, the designer, at Reading. I explained what we wanted and he was most interested and in a very short time had produced a variant in the form of the M.38/28 which was the nearest approach to what we wanted we had so far seen. I recommended its adoption as the operational Air OP with all the force and vehemence I could and through every possible channel, official and unofficial.

This direct approach to an aircraft manufacturer was, of course, highly irregular as the approved procedure would have been to make their requirements known to the War Office who, if they thought fit, would pass them on to the Ministry of Aircraft Production who, again if they thought fit, would approach one or more manufacturers. All this would have taken months, if not years, and Lt Col Bazeley was more concerned with winning the war than with the observance of protocol. George Miles shared this view and agreed, unofficially, to produce a prototype, although he pointed out that production, if required, would have to be organised through official channels.

This was just the sort of challenge on which George Miles thrived and he promptly set about re-working his Miles M.28 Communications aircraft prototype, U-0232. The new aircraft utilised the fuselage, engine and tailplane of the prototype M.28 but was fitted with a new wing of six feet greater span and a fixed undercarriage. The new hybrid aircraft was known by the firm as the M.38/28 and was built by the Experimental Department at Liverpool Road, Reading as a private venture.

On 12th September 1942, just three months after the demonstration of the M.28 to the School of Artillery at Larkhill, Wiltshire, the prototype M.38/28, U-0223, was first flown, by George Miles, accompanied by Don Brown who recorded in his log book: '1st flight trials.'

No other aircraft which had been used for Air OP duties up to then surpassed the M.38/28's speed, range and short take-off ability, during which the tail is raised immediately and the aeroplane unsticks in just five to ten seconds, being pulled off at about 35 mph. A large tailplane was provided to cope with the pitching moment associated with the high-lift flaps and this was initially fitted with the two fins and rudders as on the M.28. However, on account of the M.38/28's exceptionally low stalling speed it was found necessary to add a third fin and rudder in order to maintain directional control at the very low speeds at which the aircraft was capable of flying. A large single fin and rudder was also tested but this was found to be less satisfactory than the three small ones, which then became the standard fit giving the subsequent Messenger its characteristic appearance.

Lt Col Bazeley continues:

There was, however, some malign influence at work which again defeated my efforts and Miles' effort came to naught, although a few M.38s, including that used by FM Montgomery, were used in an intercommunication role in Northwest Europe during 1944/45. Who was our enemy and what influence prevented our getting this aircraft as an Air OP I was never able to discover, though in the

autumn of that year I was able to pursue the project in Whitehall. Always I met with polite excuses and evasions and never once was I given a plausible reason for denying to Air OP pilots the best aircraft they might have had to fulfil their operational role. The Under Secretary of State for Air, Harold Balfour, himself flew the aircraft and I understand strongly recommended its adoption as an Air OP, but his efforts came to naught.

I have since heard it suggested that the official refusal to order its production for this purpose was due to the fact the Balfour was himself a shareholder in Miles Aircraft. He may well have been, but I can not believe this was the real reason for denying to pilots the best equipment for their purpose. To me this is still an unsolved mystery.

Don Brown wrote: *The final outcome to this private war was that the instigator was posted to North Africa. As a postscript it is interesting to note that, 12 years later, the instigator of this project was given a somewhat belated award of £1,000 for having conceived the idea of using light aeroplanes for AOP purposes.* However, neither of these statements have since proved to be correct.

Guy Warner elaborates on this part of Lt Col Bazeley's story:

In 1952-53 he applied to the Royal Commission on Awards for Inventors for an ex-gratia payment in respect of his work in the development of Air OP aircraft. In this he was unsuccessful, despite the support of Field Marshal Lord Alanbrooke. Sadly Charles Bazeley died before his time in 1955.

However, to return to the story of the M.38/28. The first recorded reference to the aircraft, later to become well known as the M.38 Messenger Mk.I, appeared on a three-view G.A. drawing dated 1st July 1942. A modification on this drawing also shows the wing with 'Auxiliary Airfoil Ailerons'. This entailed re-skinning the area where the original ailerons had been and fitting new ailerons aft of the original trailing edge to form a continuous line from the trailing edge of the existing flaps. However, it is not known if this modification was carried out. Another modification shown in faint chain-dotted lines on this drawing was the addition of outboard leading edge slats, which were fitted and flown as shown in the photographs here.

Above and below: U-0223 showing original configuration with two fins and rudders. Note also the lateral struts fitted to the undercarriage. These were dispensed with on the first true prototype and production aircraft.

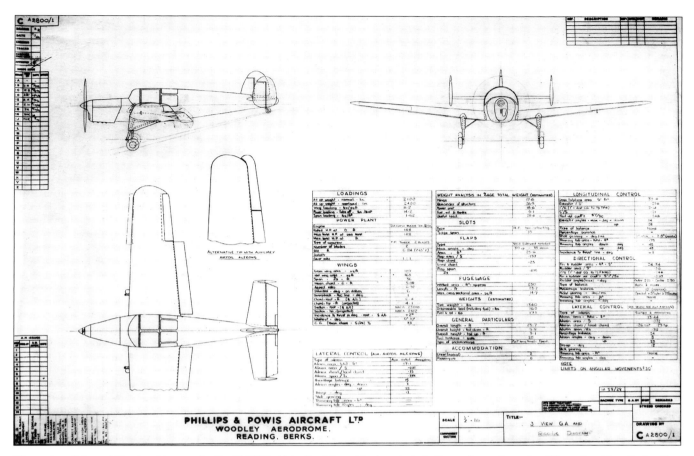

Three-view G.A. and Rigging Diagram for the M.38/28. Note the inboard-facing struts to the undercarriage; the 'Alternative Tip with Auxiliary Airfoil Ailerons, and, in faint chain dotted, the outline of the external leading edge slats fitted later for trials.

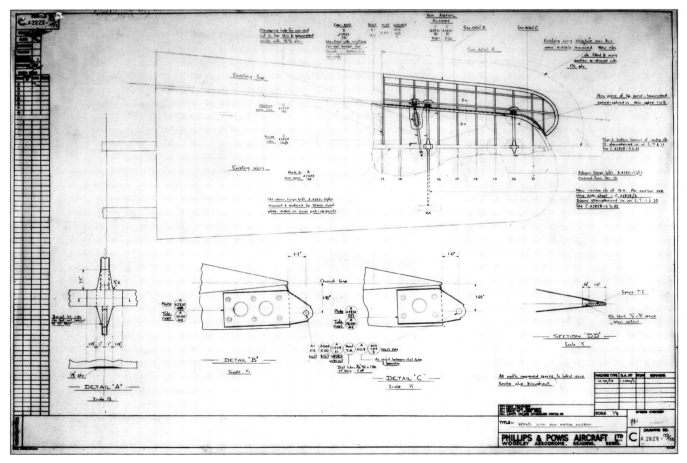

Drawing, showing Wing with Auxiliary Airfoil Aileron.

Above and below: The prototype M.38/28, U-0223, with outboard leading edge slats fitted for test purposes.

In September 1942, Phillips & Powis produced a booklet on the M.38/28 AOP Aircraft, reproduced here:

Preliminary Specification

The Miles M.38 has been designed primarily to meet the requirements for an AOP aeroplane. It is also adaptable to the following alternative uses:-

a) Two-three seater light communications aircraft;
b) Light ambulance aircraft carrying pilot, one stretcher case and one walking casualty or nurse;
c) Naval observation duties;
d) Light freight carrier.

The aircraft is of wooden construction and the design has been formulated with a view to operation in any part of the world. The protective treatment is based on our unique experience of the operation of wooden aircraft under varying climatic conditions. Waterproof synthetic resin glue is used throughout, and the structure has been made very robust to allow of quick handling under difficult conditions by unskilled personnel. Accessibility and servicing have received careful consideration, a good example being the tail-wheel shock absorber unit which is secured in a special mounting by a single nut and can be replaced with a new unit in about 30 seconds.

In view of possible short supply of engines, consideration has been given to the possible fitment of any of the following alternative power plants:

a)	Gipsy Major Series III	–	160 hp
b)	Cirrus Major	–	150 hp
c)	Lycoming 0.435	–	175 hp
d)	Warner Super Scarab	–	175 hp
e)	Gipsy Major I.HC	–	140 hp
f)	Gipsy Major Series II	–	140 hp
g)	Menasco D4B	–	160 hp

The prototype is fitted with a Gipsy Major Series II engine of 145 hp. Very special attention has been given to obtain an unequalled view in all directions. This is achieved by an exceptionally deep windscreen, fully glazed cabin and second backward facing windscreen for rearward view.

To achieve the exceptional take-off and landing performance which is required for AOP duties, large chord Miles auxiliary aerofoil flaps are fitted combined with drooping slotted ailerons. A fuselage flap is also fitted, which can be used either as a dive brake or to vary the approach angle while landing.

Leading Particulars

Type:	Two or three seater cabin low wing monoplane.
Duties:	AOP, communications, light ambulance duties, etc.

Principal dimensions:
Span	36 ft. 0 in.
Overall length	23 ft. 8 in.
Height overall (airscrew horizontal) (tail down)	7 ft. 3 in.
Width of cabin	4 ft. 0 in.
Wing area (gross)	187 sq. ft.
Flap area (including ailerons)	39 sq. ft.

Undercarriage:
Fixed, long stroke oleo-pneumatic levered undercarriage designed especially for severe operational conditions. Track: 9 ft. Brakes: Bendix mechanically operated with differential control from rudder bar.

In the unlikely event of there being insufficient suitable ground for a normal take off and landing, consideration has been given to a simple form of combined arrester gear and catapult which can, if desired, be carried in the aircraft. This consists merely of two short stakes and a length of "bunjee" cord. The aeroplane can fly over the landing area and drop this equipment to the troops below, who drive in the stakes and attach the "bunjee" cord, an operation taking only about five minutes. The aeroplane then lands just short of the arrester gear which engages in the tail wheel and arrests the aircraft in 25 yards in still air. This is clearly shown in the accompanying series of four photographs showing an arrested landing.

To enable the machine to take off in the same distance, the same gear may be used, the "bunjee" rope being pulled back by a lorry, scout car, or if no vehicle is available, by the troops. The machine is then catapulted off, the run to unstick being 25 yards in still air,

or even less if there is any wind. The unassisted take off and steep climb away is normally ample except under very exceptional circumstances and is illustrated by the accompanying photograph showing the machine after covering a distance of 100 yards in still air.

The equipment for AOP duties is as follows: Army No. 21 R/T set; Very pistol and cartridges; Armour protection for pilot as in the Spitfire; Syren; Rear view mirror; Parachutes - Seat type for pilot, Observer type for passenger; stowage for maps, glasses, revolver, helmet and gas mask; reversible observer's seat; Jacking pads; Picketing gears; normal flight instruments including Reid and Sigrist turn and bank indicator, Sperry horizon and directional gyro; and crash proof fuel tank.

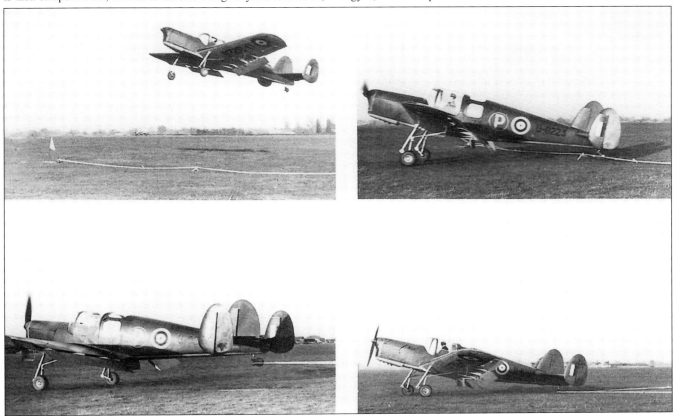

The prototype Messenger carrying out an arrested landing.

A close-up of the Messenger catching the arrester cable with the hook positioned immediately in front of the tailwheel.

Loading for AOP Duties (Gipsy Major III Engine)	
Tare	1400 lb
Fuel (18 gallons)	130 lb
Oil (2 gallons)	18 lb
Pilot and parachute	200 lb
Armour (as Spitfire)	45 lb
Radio and accumulator	69 lb
Miscellaneous equipment:	
Very Pistol and ammunition, Syren	30 lb
AUW for A.O.P. duties	1892 lb
AUW with above equipments	
- observer and parachute	2092 lb
Design all-up weight	2100 lb
Overload all-up weight	2500 lb
Performance with AOP Loading (Gipsy Major Series III Engine)	
Corrected run to unstick (5 mph wind)	60 yards
Corrected run to clear 50 foot screen	138 yards
Stalling speed with flaps down	28 mph
Cruising speed at 2200 rpm*	97 mph
Maximum speed at 2500 rpm*	105 mph
Initial rate of climb	1160 ft. per minute
Duration	3½ hours

* By sacrificing a small amount on the take-off and climb performance or by fitting a VP airscrew, the cruising and maximum speeds can be improved to approximately 120 and 140 mph respectively.

The prototype M.38/28 was given the RAF Experimental Aeroplane No.187 for identification purposes and was then handed over to Army Co-operation Command for its initial trials. While it was with them it was flown by everyone from the Air Officer Commanding-in-Chief, Army Co-operation Command (AVM Sir Arthur Barratt KCB, CMG, MC) to the latest pupil and their verdict was unanimous: *How soon can you let us have a hundred of these?*

Although Air Marshal Barratt stated in his letter (reproduced here) that the engine fitted to the prototype M.38/28 was a Blackburn Cirrus III, for its first flight at least it had a 130 hp DH Gipsy Major engine and seemed to retain this at least until March 1944. Engines were apparently changed regularly throughout the early lives of both the M.28s and the M.38/28 but a fine fixed-pitch two-bladed wooden propeller was fitted to give a very short take-off and steep climb, although this necessitated throttling well back in cruising flight to avoid exceeding maximum rpm.

On 1st October 1942, Air Marshal Sir Arthur Barratt, of HQ, Army Co-operation Command, RAF, wrote to The Under Secretary of State, Air Ministry, (VCAS), (with copies to the A.M. DMC and A.M. DGO):

Aircraft for:
(i) Air Observation Post Squadrons
(ii) Communication in the Field.
M.28/38.

Sir,

I have the honour to refer to the type of aircraft required for Air Observation Post Squadrons of my command, and for special communications purposes in the field.

At present, four Observation Post Squadrons are in being, and a total of 12 is envisaged. The Squadrons already formed are equipped with Auster aircraft (late Taylorcraft) and where these are insufficient they are supplemented by Tiger Moths. The Auster, however, was accepted for AOP work only as a temporary measure, and is by no means an ideal type for the work, as in my opinion, and in that of my Squadron Commander's, it lacks the necessary robustness for work in the Field, besides having poor performance and an insufficient field of vision. Originally intended as an interim

type, pending the arrival of Vigilants from the USA, the failure of the latter forced us reluctantly to agree to equip squadrons with Austers as a longer term policy.

I still hoped, however, that a more suitable aircraft might be found and the characteristics of an existing light communications aircraft; the M.28 of Messrs Phillips & Powis seemed to offer promise. The manufacturers were then asked by the School of Artillery to demonstrate the M.28, and subsequently, as a private venture, Messrs Phillips & Powis produced a prototype to AOP requirements. This has been named the M.28/38 (although known by the firm as the M.38/28 - PA).

I have now seen the M.28/38 perform, and have flown it myself, as have also members of my staff. In my opinion, it has very great possibilities both as an AOP and as a light communications aircraft.

In the recent report of my visit to the Middle East, I referred to the important uses to which light communication aircraft capable of landing and take-off from small areas could be put. The M.28/38 has a most impressive performance, combining a very quick take-off, rapid climb, and economical cruising speed of about 100 mph, and remarkably short landing run. In addition, it offers a first class field of vision. At present, powered by a Cirrus III engine of 90 hp, (it is generally believed that U-0223 was fitted with a 130 hp DH Gipsy Major engine at this time and, when first flown by George Miles on 12th September 1942 this engine was recorded in the log-book of his passenger Don Brown - PA), its performance can be still more improved if a slightly higher powered engine can be obtained. I understand that Messrs de Havilland have in production at present a Gipsy Mk.Ic engine, developing 145 hp, and that owing to a change of plan by the Canadians - for whom it was designed - (Note: the Gipsy Major Ic engine became available when many of the Tiger Moths in the BCATP were replaced by the Fairchild Cornell - PA) this can be made available to us, and deliveries beginning at once. Other possible alternatives are the Lycoming 175 hp or the Warner Scarab from the USA.

I strongly recommend that official notice may now be taken by Air Ministry of the M.28/38, and that if trials confirm my opinion as to its general suitability, the aircraft should be put into production in substitution of the current order for Auster aircraft and for communication purposes in the field.

signed Barratt
Air Marshall,
Air Officer Commanding-in-Chief,
Army Co-operation Command. RAF.

Although the Miles M.38/28 had indeed been built unofficially, George Miles was at pains to point out that any production, if approved, would have to be arranged through official channels!

Briefly, the aircraft was needed for use as an Air OP to operate from small areas of rough unprepared ground, often surrounded by trees and other obstacles, which necessitated a really exceptional take-off, angle of climb, steep approach and short landing run. In addition, for the Air OP role the aircraft was required to carry two occupants, radio transmitters and receivers, armour protection and other military equipment. Furthermore, it was required to be flown by Royal Artillery officer pilots of limited experience, to have an unequalled field of view in all directions, to be capable of being maintained in the field and be capable of being operated in all weather conditions. It was also required to seat three or four in the communications, light freighter or ambulance role.

Construction was of wood throughout, and the new single-piece wing of 6ft greater span than the M.28 (although the root and tip thickness for the M.28 and the M.38 were identical), with two continuous main spars passing through the bottom of the fuselage, was covered with plastic bonded ply skin panels. The fuselage was, like the M.28, built up from longerons, stringers and 'U' frames, in two main sections, which were connected at a transport joint just aft of the rear spar. The fuselage and tailplane were also covered with stressed plastic bonded plywood skin, with Phenol Formaldehyde heat and moisture resisting synthetic adhesive being used throughout the airframe for assembly of the components.

The Miles large-chord, non-retractable, external aerofoil flaps of symmetrical section were hinged on the trailing-edge ribs and were adjustable manually through 30º. Each aileron was connected to the adjacent lift flap so that the movement of these flaps, within their specified range, resulted in the aileron acting as an extension of the lift-flap area, thereby assisting take-off and improving the landing characteristics. An independent single drag-flap was mounted beneath the fuselage.

The fixed undercarriage consisted of two separate strut-braced support members secured in a casting on the mainplane front spar, with the landing loads being absorbed by a Miles oleo-pneumatic articulated suspension strut secured to the support member and to a lever hinged at the bottom of the support member. The self-centring tail wheel was mounted in a casting on the rear-most frame of the fuselage. The 'stalky' undercarriage provided a steep ground angle to enable take-offs and landings to be effected at high angles of incidence. Bendix cable-operated wheel-brakes were also fitted. The lateral strut bracing was deleted on later models. An early drawing showed the top of the undercarriage faired in to the wing following the line of the longitudinal strut, but there is no proof that this was ever fitted.

A large tailplane was provided to cope with the pitching moment associated with the high-lift flaps and this was initially fitted with the two fins and rudders as on the M.28. However, on account of the M.38/28's exceptionally low stalling speed, it was found necessary to add a third fin and rudder (all three rudders with horn balances) in order to maintain directional control at the very low speeds at which the aircraft was capable of flying. A large single fin and rudder was also tested but this was found to be less satisfactory than the three small ones, which then became the standard fit.

U-0223 fitted with the large single fin and rudder.

No other Air OP type had surpassed the M.38/28's speed range and short take-off, during which the tail is raised immediately and the aeroplane unsticks in 5 to 10 seconds, being pulled off at about 35 mph. The stall was very mild and occurred at 25 mph IAS with flaps fully down and 40 mph IAS with the flaps up. Motor-off approach could be made at any speed down to 40 mph IAS or a motor-assisted approach at 35 mph IAS to give a very short landing run.

The prototype M.38/28 was delivered to 'A' Performance Test Squadron, A&AEE Boscombe Down on 19th October 1942 to be assessed for Army observation and communications work. They reported that its handling was marred by the inability to trim in the glide at any speed, and ineffective ailerons near the stalling speed of 30-32 mph (flaps down), and that the engine was prone to over-speeding, even in level flight. The overriding comment, however, was that the aircraft was too fragile for army work, even with its AUW reduced to 1,965lb from the normal 2,110lb.

In January 1943, Phillips & Powis Aircraft Ltd produced a brochure entitled 'Miles Specialised Aircraft for Specialised Purposes'. Contained therein was a summary of a selection of Miles aircraft which had either been built or proposed up to then.

The M.38 was included.

M.38 Air Observation Post Aircraft or Light Ambulance

The M.38 is designed to provide an exceptionally short take-off, a steep angle of climb, an unequalled view in every direction, perfect control at low speeds and a short landing run. It is claimed that these desiderata have been combined to a degree never before attained. The machine may also be used as a Front Line Ambulance operating from unprepared ground, which would be impossible with a normal aeroplane. It is available with a variety of engines, both British and American.

Span	36 ft 0 in
Wing area	187 sq ft
Engine: Gipsy Major, Cirrus Major, Walter Scarab, Lycoming, Menasco	
All up weight	2,100-2,500 lb
Run to unstick	60 yards
Run to clear 50 ft obstacle	138 yards
Manoeuvring speed	45 mph
Stalling speed	28 mph

An interesting entry in 655 (AOP) Squadron Operations Record Book for 4th February 1943 read: *It was learned that the AOC in C had pressed AIR MIN to release the Miles M.38/28 for AOP trials with a Squadron. Major Dunlop (Air Min DMC) explained that his Directorate was not prepared to recommend the Miles M.38/28 as little, if anything, had been done since Boscombe Down trials of this type some 6 months ago. Although perhaps not the ultimate type this aircraft should be tried out by a Squadron. AIR MIN decision awaited.* (N.A. Ref AIR 27/2174)

There the matter rested, until 13th January 1944, when the MAP suddenly cancelled the contract for the M.38. Two letters from F G Miles to J E Serby (MAP) (N.A. Ref: AVIA 15/1968) on the subject of the cancellation of the M.38 are reproduced here:

January 17th 1944

Dear Serby,

Many thanks for your letter of the 12th instant, we are rather perturbed to learn about the cancellation of production orders for the M.38 since it has resulted in a great deal of difficulty in connection with our plans for Monitor production.

As you know, the all wood construction at the end of M.38 was ideally suited to dovetail into the difficult changeover period between the Martinet and the Monitor, and we are now forced suddenly to revise all our production arrangements at a time when our planning and progress staff are badly overloaded with preparations for the Monitor.

George's statement to you regarding the impossibility of utilising the labour off the prototype M.38s on the Monitor was absolutely correct, and the reason is very simple. As we have pointed out from time to time since we started the job, our more serious labour shortages have been entirely in connection with drawing office staff, panel beaters, skilled fitters and machinists.

The design of the M.38 has been based on the maximum utilisation of woodworkers and the few metal fittings on the aircraft are of the simplest kind and can be made almost entirely by semi-skilled labour. The only result, therefore, of putting the M.38 prototypes on the lowest priority would be to release woodworkers who will not yet be needed in connection with the Monitor. Although we shall need them badly later on.

Incidentally, I was given to understand (when the possibility of the cancellation of the M.38 contract was first rumoured) that the reason was the need for releasing the maximum number of men to the armed services. Since we now understand, however, that a new mark of Auster is to be produced in lieu of the M.38 - although it is acknowledged that it is not nearly such a good machine - this reason does not appear to hold water. It is a pity we can't use the better English design.

If we had been consulted when this matter was first discussed at M.A.P., we might have been able to clear up a lot of misconceptions.

With reference to your query regarding the magnitude of the work involved in connection with the two developments associated with the E.24/43, we have now almost completed the estimates and will forward them to you within the next few days.

Yours sincerely,
Sgd. F G Miles

January 28th 1944

Dear Serby,

Very many thanks for your letter of January 21st, confirming that the policy of dropping the M.38 was initiated and decided for production reasons.

Regarding your suggestion for putting part of the M.38 labour on to the Monitor specimen wing, I am afraid that this cannot be done since we already have as many woodworkers on this job as can be accommodated and the labour shortages in the factory are for quite difference classes of operatives than those which will be released by the cancellation of the M.38 contract. However, in order to reduce waiting time to a minimum pending the full flow of Monitor production, we have cancelled a sub-contract order for MAT's which had been placed on Slingsby Sailplanes and are arranging to put most of the M.38 section on to this work.

We have also agreed with DAP that for the time being we can manufacture Martinet wooden components in advance of programme and to this end Mr Warner is advising DGMP, that our allocation of materials should be increased to enable production of these components to remain at a suitable level.

I am sorry that I have not been able to let you have a statement of the work involved in connection with the special Falcon wing and Spitfire modification associated with the E.24/43 but as I explained before, our clerical staff has been severely overloaded with the work involved in the M.38 cancellation and I have not been able to press them for the other estimate. However,......(unfortunately, the next page is missing - PA).

Then started an inter-Ministerial war between the War Office and the MAP, a war of such bitterness that Don Brown recalled that the real war paled into insignificance against it! The Ministry was outraged that, once again, Miles Aircraft Ltd had built and flown an aeroplane without their knowledge or authority. As in the case of the M.35 Libellula, the design work had been done, under George Miles' direction, by Ray Bournon at Liverpool Road, where the prototype had also been built.

The '*History of the Messenger I (Miles M.38)*' can be seen in the more than somewhat biased Industrial Advisor's Report into Miles Aircraft (N.A. Ref: BT/28/1195), dated 30th May 1945, on the development work (private venture and official) which was carried out by Miles Aircraft Ltd during the war and which confirms Don's recollection of the inter-Ministerial war which raged at the time. This report will be reproduced in full in an appendix to the next volume but the relevant extract from this report is reproduced here for completeness:

History of Messenger I (Miles M.38)

This design has been pressed on the Ministry for various purposes since September 1942 as follows:

(a) *For Air Observation Post duties. The Army chose the Auster instead for artillery spotting* (did they get a choice? - PA)
(b) *For anti-submarine work taking off with depth charges from a cargo ship and landing into a net. This was turned down as impracticable through the Minister* (why - and what did he know about it anyway? - PA);

(c) *For communications purposes by the Navy from a carrier;*
(d) *For a light communications aircraft by Fighter Command and TAF; and*
(e) *For use by high ranking officers for communications purposes.*

In spite of opposition, the firm succeeded in (c) and (d) and, when these were cancelled, in (e). (d) was later revised. Details are to be found in Files SB.51742 - M.38 Technical Policy. DDRDA Folder 127 also deals with this matter. File SB.39914 deals with the attempt by Miles Aircraft Ltd. to supplant the Auster for purpose (a) (its original intended purpose - PA).

At Encl.3A it appears that an unauthorised visit by an Army deputation on 20.9.44 first placed the matter on an official footing, and DOR signified annoyance at the firm's invitation (unbelievable how childish this was all becoming - PA). *The matter was turned down after official trials proved that the Auster better met requirements.*

On reflection however, none of this rings true, as the Auster had been used in the absence of anything else, let alone better, since the early days of the war and it should not be forgotten that this 'deputation' had 'arrived' (at the firm's invitation?) in September 1944 but the Contract to build the Messenger had been placed in late 1943! This record also seems to be at variance with previous statements purported to have been made by Army deputations and shows beyond reasonable doubt that the Ministry would use any excuse to stop Miles from getting the contract for the Messenger, which had in fact been proven to be a much better aircraft for Air OP duties - see the letter above from Air Marshal Sir Arthur Barratt to The Under Secretary of State, Air Ministry.

I cannot help feeling therefore, that the author of this report was extremely biased against Miles Aircraft Ltd for some reason or other - probably due to the scant regard Miles had for bureaucracy - or perhaps he had some other kind of axe to grind as he does not seem to have marshalled his 'facts' in any reasonable order. He goes on:

Attempt (b) is recorded in File SB.51742, approach to the Ministry coming through the Minister, in January 1943. It was turned down on technical grounds shortly after. In April 1943, however, a demonstration was arranged at Reading, witnessed by AVM Joubert and later by the Minister, the aircraft flying into a net divided to leave room for the propeller. It was decided that this did not reproduce the turbulent air conditions found in the wake of a cargo ship, and no pilot could in practice guarantee to land with the accuracy required. (Min. 59 etc. SB.51742). (the authorities were, however, quite happy to have earlier allowed 'Hurricats', after their flights in defence of the convoys, to ditch in the sea! - PA).

As a result however of these trials, CMR was instructed by the Minister to arrange trials on a carrier for communications purposes, which obviously was a very different requirement. These were successfully carried out in April 1943 and when purpose (d) succeeded, the Navy were able to ask for some aircraft, on the strength of a report on these trials dated 25/6/43.

In May 1943, AM Trafford Leigh Mallory wrote to ACAS (TR) stating a requirement for a light communications aircraft and suggested the M.38. The Chief Executive then asked Fighter Command to test the M.38. DTD agreed to the technical suitability of the M.38 for this purpose. However, on 12th July 1944, DOR stated that they preferred the Auster for this purpose, as it was already in production, and at a meeting held by him on 5th August 1943 it was agreed to supply the Auster until the M.38, suitably modified, became available. ACAS (TR) expressed a preference for the Auster, but on MAP advice agreed reluctantly to the initiation of M.38 production. On 17th August 1943, DGAP called a meeting at which Miles Aircraft Ltd were notified that 190 M.38 aircraft would be required, some by Fighter Command, and some by the Navy.

On 29th September 1943 Contract Aircraft 3338/C23c (T.Req.4349D/RDT1) was placed for 2 prototypes (with the Instruction to Proceed, also dated 29th September 1943, at an estimated cost of £6,000 - PA), and on 1st October 1943 the Chief Executive arranged Contract SB.11716/C38 for 250 M.38 aircraft, subsequently placed as CA.3261/C23c (with the Instruction to Proceed dated 14th October 1943, at an estimated cost of £500,000 - PA).

On File SB.51742, minutes 129 and 130, dated 28th December 1943, is the decision to cancel M.38 production owing to interference with other more important work, the two prototypes only (probably RG327 and RG333 - PA) to remain on order. The firm were notified of this cancellation officially on 13th January 1944. No known requirement existed to cover the two prototypes.

Notwithstanding the Ministry's request to abandon the M.38 in favour of more important work, authority was given to the firm by contract, dated 6th May 1944 (source unknown), to construct 8 M.38 aircraft for the Dutch Government; in addition one on Air Ministry contract was placed at the disposal of General Montgomery (U-0245 - PA), and the two prototypes (RG327 and RG333 - PA) were earmarked for the personal use of Captain Balfour and Mr Lennox-Boyd, with apparent Ministry approval. (See file NS.74605, encl.2A). The Dutch subsequently preferred and were given Auster III aircraft as the M.38s were too expensive. Production of these 8 aircraft (later to become RH369 to RH376 - PA) is nevertheless proceeding at Woodley. General Montgomery's aircraft developed engine trouble in Normandy and was returned to the firm. The two prototypes were duly delivered with special fitments to personal requirements. One other has since been delivered for the use of the C in C Bomber Command (RH369 - PA), which was also fitted with a number of personal modifications. A further aircraft (RH371 -PA) was delivered for the use of ACM Tedder (later Marshal of the RAF, Lord Tedder - PA), recently and OA.5 state that the balance are similarly earmarked.

On 4th July 1944 ACM Leigh Mallory again demanded some M.38 aircraft (SB.25761/01) and stated that the Auster was not safe enough for use of senior commanders. This statement was rebutted by DTD. On 22/8/44 a contract was placed on the authority of the Chief Executive for the production of 40 M.38 aircraft to be made

in Northern Ireland (CA.4553/C23c.). It was not found possible to modify these aircraft to meet DOR's statement of his requirements. Production is proceeding notwithstanding this, and I now learn that these are for the ATA.

The Report went on to say, under (3) 'Unofficial development work, initiated by the firm without any known official recognition': M.38: Up to 29.9.43 all work on this type was private venture. At this date several completed aircraft existed.

However, this statement was not true either. Admittedly, the first (converted) prototype had made its first flight on 12th September 1942 but the second prototype, U-0245, the first true M.38 Messenger, was not to fly until 10th February 1944.

The first true M.38/II, U-0245, differed from the M.38/28 in having larger rear windows.

U-0245, which had been fitted with one of the firm's own 150 hp Blackburn Cirrus Major III engines, was first flown, by assistant test pilot Flt Lt Hugh Kennedy, on 10th February 1944 and this was later to become the personal transport of General, later Field Marshall Bernard Montgomery. Later still this machine became 'officially' the 'first production' aircraft as regards the RAF contract was concerned but not in the context of the manufacture of the following eight for the Dutch Government.

U-0245, the first true prototype M.38/II Messenger. Note the large rear windows with square corners. These were slightly reduced in size, with rounded corners, on production aircraft.

The first true prototype M.38/II Messenger, U-0245, under construction at Liverpool Road, Reading. The photograph shows this machine in the final stages of assembly in January 1944. It is in two unpainted sections, comprising the forward fuselage with engine and cabin mounted on the one-piece wing and the rear fuselage with complete tail unit.

George Miles flying U-0245.

U-0245 being flown from Woodley by F/O Trevor Martin, Gen Montgomery's personal pilot, probably on his first solo flight in it on 1st May 1944.

U-0245 with Gen Montgomery, F/O Trevor Martin and the RAF ground crew in France on 13th July 1944.   [IWM]

A close-up of Gen Montgomery with F/O Trevor Martin and U-0245 in France on 13th July 1944. *[IWM]*

RH368 at Woodley in late 1944, with 'U-0245' showing through under the paint. Note Gen Montgomery's four Stars on the central fin and the Invasion Stripes having been removed from the top of the fuselage.

While speaking with Norman Angell (Jack Angell's brother) recently, he mentioned that he was 'on the flight line' at Woodley at the time and well remembers also meeting with F/O Trevor Martin, who had been appointed as Montgomery's personal pilot and the General himself in the preparation of U-0245 for military use. Apparently this aircraft had been built with a few 'luxuries', including leather seats, carpet and ash trays etc but this was not acceptable to the General who demanded that these items be stripped out before he took delivery!

The first true prototype Messenger was U-0245, which later officially became the first production Messenger Mk.I, literally - 'in the field' - while it was being used by General Bernard Montgomery as his personal aircraft during the invasion of Normandy.

Full details of this episode in the life of this unique aircraft can be found in Appendix 29.

The prototype was then ready for war and from 12th June 1944, 'D'-Day + 6 it was used 'in the field' in Normandy, initially, and unbelievably, still with its 'B' mark U-0245, unique for a 'pseudo' service aircraft. U-0245 was flown throughout the invasion of Normandy by F/O Trevor Martin, Gen Montgomery's personal pilot with these marks but on 16th July 1944, Trevor recorded RH368 in his log book for the first time. He recalled in

U-0245 departing after the photo-shoot in France on 13th July 1944. *[IWM]*

conversation that the RAF ground crew responsible for its maintenance in the field had received instructions to paint out the 'B' mark U-0245 and replace it with RH368 forthwith! RH368 was originally allocated to the first production aircraft but as the completion of that aircraft was still some time away authority was given for its use on the prototype, which then officially became the first production aircraft (although with a different engine) - 'in the field'! At some stage in the development of the Messenger, a contract appears to have been placed for a 'Structural test specimen Messenger (wings and fuselage)' (N.A. Ref: AIR 3566) and although no further details of this have come to light, it could possibly account for a missing constructor's number.

An ambulance version of the M.38/28 was also proposed and this had provision for a stretcher along the starboard side of the cabin, with the pilot sitting on the port side and an attendant behind him facing to starboard. The cabin had a raised roof, hinged along its centre line for ease of access, and was fitted with a large single fin and rudder with end plates on the tailplane. A project drawing of the ambulance version showed the undercarriage to retain the lateral struts of the original M.38/28 and to have provision for alternative engine installations, including the DH Gipsy Major or Blackburn Cirrus Major, the Lycoming 0-435 and the Warner Super Scarab.

During the spring of 1943, Allied shipping losses in the Atlantic were reaching serious proportions and an idea occurred to George Miles that if a number of ships in each convoy could be equipped with a small deck on the stern, it might be possible to operate a slow-flying aeroplane like the M.38 Messenger from them. This machine would be capable of carrying depth-charges and maintaining anti-submarine patrols over a wide area and by operating relays of such machines, an unbroken patrol could be maintained throughout the hours of daylight over such a radius that enemy submarines would be unable to catch up with the convoy, attack and retreat to safety within the hours of darkness. If the aircraft failed to find a submarine, it would merely jettison its depth charges before landing on the small deck. Experience with the

RH368 at Woodley in late 1944. Note the HQ 21st Army Group Formation Sign on the cowling. For the record, the 21st Army Group was formed in the UK on 9th July 1943 to command the 2nd British Army and 1st Canadian Army for the invasion of NW Europe. 2+1 = 21 in army mathematics!

Messenger suggested that by the fitment of a very simple form of arrester gear it could probably be operated off a deck 60ft square and for full details of these trials see Chapter 30 Miles M.38A Mariner.

In spite of the initial attitude of the Ministry, an order was eventually placed for the construction of 250 Messenger Mk.I aircraft for the RAF, and a note in Appendix 'H' of a Confidential Report issued by the Ministry in 1945 into the wartime production of Miles aircraft, confirmed that: 'An order was received in 1943 for 250 M.38s - cancelled early in 1944; eventually 51 off were ordered'.

The original intention was, apparently, to manufacture 40 aircraft at Reading, to Contract Aircraft 3261, and 210 in Northern Ireland, to Contract Aircraft 4553. However, serial numbers were allotted for 42 and 208 respectively, which *implies* that a slightly different number of aircraft were to be built in the two factories. But, in January 1944, the requirement was cancelled altogether and only 20 production aircraft were eventually to be delivered, 10 from Woodley and 10 from Northern Ireland. The full story behind the order for these Messengers for the RAF has never been told, so in an attempt to finally clarify what is, at best, a very confusing state of affairs, it is also necessary to take the production order for the M.33 Monitor high-speed target-tower into account.

A study of the correspondence between the various Ministry of Aircraft Production Departments and Miles Aircraft Ltd shows that a considerable amount of activity was going on 'behind the scenes' in connection with both the Monitor and the Messenger contracts. By early 1944, it was obvious that the Ministry were getting concerned about the delivery programme of the M.33 Monitor high-speed target tower. The first prototype Monitor had yet to make its first flight and already fears were being expressed as to when it would be released to the services. It was therefore, decided to send somebody to visit Miles Aircraft Ltd to discuss the position. The problems with the Monitor were to have a profound effect upon the production of the Messenger and would also appear to have been causing some confusion in the Ministry as well. On

16th March 1944, Eric Mensforth of the MAP, wrote regarding his visit to Miles Aircraft at Reading the previous day when he met F G Miles, G H Miles and the Works Manager, Mr Parsons (who also discussed matters with Mr Gateskill, RAPO):

The primary object of this visit was to enquire into the position, as requested in your note of March 8th, on the M.38 aircraft, where in a letter to the Parliamentary Secretary of March 2nd Mr G H Miles suggested that work was so far advanced that it would help them to be permitted to complete 12 of these aircraft and sell them to the Netherlands Government. The opportunity was taken at the same time of seeing the general production position.

M.38. The original prototype of this aircraft (U-0223 - PA) is flying and in addition the first production prototype (this is the first intimation that U-0245 was known as 'the first production prototype' [but fitted with a Blackburn Cirrus Major engine and which later became RH368] - PA). *The company consider that the second production prototype (RG327 - PA) together with 10 additional aircraft* (some confusion here as the third 'production prototype' RG333 and RH369-RH378 - the 10 'additional aircraft' - would have made 11 aircraft in total - PA), *being the first production batch, are well advanced.*

It is not easy to check this statement as much of the manufacture is dispersed but a visit was made to one dispersal unit, that is to say Liverpool Road, Reading (which employs about 60 men and 50 women).

It would appear that the Company's statement could be substantiated but Mr Gateskill, RAPO was asked if he would be so kind as to see certain specified detail, as for example main spars, undercarriages, and report directly to DGAP; he mentioned that he was astonished to find that for example it was claimed that the 10th set of main spars were well advanced as he had understood the work had been stopped some weeks before, but the Company stated that on the contrary their arrangements with MAP had been to allow work to continue, otherwise waiting time would have occurred.

It appears that the majority of the detail is completed, e.g. 10 sets of ribs, engine mountings, while the assembly is proceeding on the 3rd wing and fuselage and aileron probably being the least advanced units with assembly proceeding on the 2nd only (it should be mentioned here that, on the RAF Messengers, the ailerons drooped as the flaps were lowered. The 'drooping' ailerons were deleted on the later Messengers for the civil market - PA).

Tooling quite adequate for the production, 40/50 aircraft of this type, seems to be available. 23 Cirrus Major engines, the property of the Company, are in stock and would be used (this statement is interesting because the M.38 Messenger Mk.I was ultimately to use the DH Gipsy Major engine - PA); *10 airscrews have been delivered and these are stated to be quite special to the aeroplane with a special coarse fixed pitch. A number of forgings were in question but the Company stated that for a small quantity of aircraft they would continue to use fabricated parts. Indeed the only major shortages appear to be blind flying panels as the airspeed indicators are apparently special and available and double tube for the undercarriages, where the designer stated that he would be prepared to sacrifice weight and use standard tube.*

If the firm were permitted to complete preferably 10 aircraft so that there would be no question of further set-ups being necessary then it would appear that another two could be completed by the end of May and probably the remainder by August (1944). (in fact RG327 was not to fly until 3rd July 1944 and it is not known when RG333 made its first flight, but RH369-RH378 made their first flights between 21st October 1944 and June 1945 - PA). *The amount of labour involved would probably not exceed 25/30 persons and as such would have little real effect on the gap which the Company foresee as a result of the cancellation of the main M.38 contract prior to the picking up of the Monitor* (the main contract was originally for 250 aircraft and 31 of these, which were to have been built at Woodley, were cancelled in January 1944 - PA). *As a result of this gap they state that they are very worried about their existing waiting time quoted as 6,500 man hours per week, roughly two-thirds of this is on women and the remainder on semi-skilled men; this is not particularly high but may increase.*

The major advantage of completing the aircraft would be the assistance to the morale of the people who have put enthusiastic effort into it and the fact that raw material certainly fully mortgaged on this particular aircraft would be converted into machines useful to a friendly government, maintaining or obtaining in this way a valuable post-war commercial contract.

In view of your remark that you would recommend that up to 10 aircraft should be completed if they are in a reasonably advanced stage and no great amount of material is required, it would appear that subject to any overriding political considerations and to the check by DGAP's officer that the impression I obtained of the degree of completeness being reasonably correct, this recommendation should go forward.

Other Work.

(a) Conveyor. Apparently there has been some suggestion that the remaining overhead feeder conveyor stated to cost about £15,000 was in abeyance, but that the Company had lately received a message that probably they were to proceed. It would be necessary to devote more time to this scheme to say whether they are absolutely essential but as the general re-equipment of this factory was stated to have already cost of the order £250,000 it would certainly be a pity to spoil any experiment in mechanisation for the last portion of the equipment, believed by the sponsors of the scheme to be vitally necessary.

(b) Press Shop. The firm stated that there is some question of their 5,000 ton rubber press not being made available to them until about September of this year and that this will unquestionably cause delay on the Monitor. Their Geco stamps are being delivered about May with foundation work proceeding. The suggestion is made, for DGAP's consideration, that it may be possible to allocate

to the firm so many hours per week on an existing press, say that at AW Swindon (Sir WG Armstrong Whitworth Aircraft, who had taken over the Short Bros facility at FS.2 on South Marston airfield by this time - PA)*, where they could try out tools and obtain initial production.*

(c) Monitor Programme. The Monitor prototype was seen fairly well completed and it was stated that it should fly this month (the first prototype Monitor, NF900 made its first flight on 5th April 1944 - PA). *The firm seem to think that as a result of the delay on their mechanisation scheme and on the presses, that the programme of production may be some months late. (N.A. Ref: AVIA 15/2044)*

On 17th May 1944, Mr G Bennett, Secretary of Miles Aircraft Ltd, wrote to N H Curzon of the Ministry of Aircraft Production:

With reference to your letter of the 3rd instant, we acknowledge the order for 10 additional M.38 aircraft together with the Company's PV pre-production machine (the 10 production aircraft were RH369-RH378, but this is the first time that Private Venture has officially been mentioned for U-0245, later RH368 - PA). *Regarding the two conditions of this order, we entirely agree with (1) and would mention that this does not affect the original arrangement in connection with the M.38, the priority of which was always far below the Monitor and Martinet in spite of the very short time allowed to get the aircraft into production. This was the reason why the aircraft was designed for manufacture entirely by small dispersal units and sub-contracting.*

With regard to condition (2), your request that we undertake to agree not to produce any further M.38s is one which we cannot readily accept. If we agree to your request we place ourselves in the position of being unable to compete commercially with any other firm, either British or American, without first obtaining the blessing of the Ministry.

Naturally we cannot do this because peace-time conditions may be upon us much sooner than we imagine. For this reason we suggest that your condition (2) be amended to read "No further M.38 aircraft shall be built by us for delivery to any member of the Air Ministry or Army without first obtaining permission of the Ministry of Aircraft Production."

This would leave us free to satisfy any commercial demands there may be for the aeroplane in future; the ordinary controls which the Ministry of Aircraft Production can exercise cover you, we feel, in regard to this aspect. We would also like to add to proviso (2) that we should be permitted to retain one aircraft for our own experimental and research work. This aircraft (probably the M.38 Mk.III U-0247 - PA) *will, of course, belong to us.*

The delivery programme for the remaining 10 aircraft is now being prepared, but it is considered that we shall be able to maintain the original programme less the deduction of the time between the cancellation of the original production contract and the placing of the reduced order.

(This tends to imply that the original contract was cancelled in its entirety and a new one raised for the 'additional 10 aircraft' but if this was the case, then the serials allotted to the original contract were used again for the 'remaining 10 aircraft'. It should also be noted that the M.65 Gemini prototype, G-AGUS was, according to a firm's document (also referred to later); manufactured in August 1945 by removing the engine from a Messenger and fitting two Cirrus Minor engines, one in each wing. The engine mountings were welded steel tubes and the undercarriage was fixed down.

The identity of this Messenger has yet to be discovered but its c/n 4701, is very close to the end of a batch of unconfirmed Messenger c/ns. George Miles however, had different views on the origin of the prototype Gemini and later wrote: The prototype Gemini was designed and built [largely using M.28 parts] at Liverpool Road - PA).

It is noted that no provision has been made for spares for these aircraft now being ordered and if these should be required we shall be glad if arrangements may be made to have the order issued at an early date so that our planning can be facilitated.'

Yours faithfully,
G Bennett,
Secretary

(N.A. Ref: AVIA 15/2044).

Hugh Kennedy made a flight in the 'M.38TC' (probably entered in error) on 2nd March 1944, with '35' entered in the serial column in his log book but this was probably the first flight of the sole triple control M.28 Mk.III. The significance of the '35' is not known but that particular M.28 was first given the 'B' mark U-0242, later the serial PW937 and details of it can be found in the chapter on the Miles M.28.

On 23rd June 1944, U-0223 met a dramatic end but even this accident demonstrated the safety of the aircraft. U-0223 had been loaned to an RAF Officer based at RAF Hendon and on that day he decided to give a demonstration of the aircraft's handling qualities to his CO. A strong wind was blowing but the pilot only taxied out a short distance from the apron before beginning his take-off, without bothering too much about the direction of the wind. Unfortunately, he elected to take-off almost dead cross-wind and although the Messenger was airborne after the customary short run, its low climbing speed coupled with the strength of the wind gave a very marked angle of drift towards a nearby hangar. Caught unawares, the pilot failed to take the necessary corrective action and the starboard wing hit the hangar just below the level of the eaves.

The impact broke the wing off and swung the aircraft around so that the engine hit the hangar and also broke off. The remainder of the aircraft then turned over and fell about 25ft to the ground. The cabin top and tail unit took the impact and the two occupants found themselves hanging head downwards, unable to open the cabin doors and unable even to remain upright. Another few inches and their necks would have been broken. Mercifully no fire ensued and they had to remain thus, with their heads bent to one side, until the wreckage was lifted and they were able to scramble out.

In September 1944, Miles Aircraft Ltd produced a booklet entitled:

The Miles Messenger

The Miles Messenger was designed for war duties but promised to be one of the most outstanding light aeroplanes for use in peacetime. It was originally produced at the request of the Army who required a specialised aeroplane for use as an "Air Observation Post". Briefly, the Messenger was required for use from small grass areas of rough unprepared ground close to the front line, often surrounded by trees and other obstacles. To be able to do this a really phenomenal take off, angle of climb and short landing run were essential.

In addition the machine was required to carry two occupants wearing parachutes, a large radio transmitting and receiving set, armour protection and various items of military equipment: furthermore it was required to be easy to fly, to have an unequalled view in all directions and to be capable of operation with the minimum of unskilled maintenance and under all weather conditions. A more appropriate and exacting specification could scarcely be devised for the private owner's or club aeroplane.

Exhaustive trials both by the Army and by the Royal Air Force proved that these requirements had been fully met and the Messenger went into production. Before doing so, however, some further trials were conducted at the factory to prove conclusively the robustness of construction and the load carrying capacity of the machine. A description of these tests may not be without interest to the prospective private owner.

First, U-0223 was mounted on a trolley equipped with two of the powerful rockets used for assisting the take off of heavily loaded fighters and bombers. The engine was started, the rockets fired and the little Messenger was fairly thrown into the air but sustained no damage whatsoever and was flown round and landed under full control. On 1st May 1943, U-0223 was flown with no less than six people on board, the time to take off under these conditions being only 8 seconds. Finally, in May 1943, came the most searching test - George Miles actually flew U-0223 straight into a net, the whole of the impact being taken on the wings before the machine dropped on to the ground.

The Messenger an instant before hitting the net.

After having been brought to rest by the arrester net.

The Messenger being examined for any signs of damage - but no damage was sustained.

It is improbable that any other aeroplane has ever been subjected to such a severe series of tests but such was our confidence in the Messenger, and in its construction, that the latter test was done, without previous rehearsal, before a large gathering of high officials from both the Admiralty and the Ministry of Aircraft Production, including the Minister himself. There can be little doubt then as to the serviceability of the Messenger and to its ability to withstand anything it may be called upon to do in the course of Club or private use.

Turning now to a few details of the machine, it is evident from the photographs that the view from the cabin is unexcelled - as indeed it had to be to comply with the requirements of the Army's original specification. The interior of the cabin, which is roomier than in any other similar type of aeroplane, is comfortably and luxuriously upholstered and soundproofed, and conversation may be carried on in a normal voice without difficulty. Several standard arrangements of seating are available and the machine can be supplied as either a two, three or four seater, with or without dual control.

A large number of alternative engines are available to suit both the home and overseas markets, examples being: 140 hp Gipsy Major Ic; 140 hp Gipsy Major V; 150 hp Cirrus Major III; 160 hp Gipsy Major III; 160 hp Menasco D4B; 175 hp Warner Super Scarab; and 175 hp Lycoming 0-435

The Messenger is of wooden construction and the design has been formulated with a view to operation in any part of the world. The protective treatment is based on our unique experience of the operation of wooden aircraft under widely varying climatic conditions, waterproof synthetic resin glue being used throughout.

Accessibility and servicing have received careful consideration as well as general robustness of construction.

Alternative uses of the Messenger are as an air taxi, a light freighter or an ambulance, carrying pilot, stretcher case and nurse. In the case of the freighter version, it is of interest to note that the machine is capable of carrying a complete spare engine.

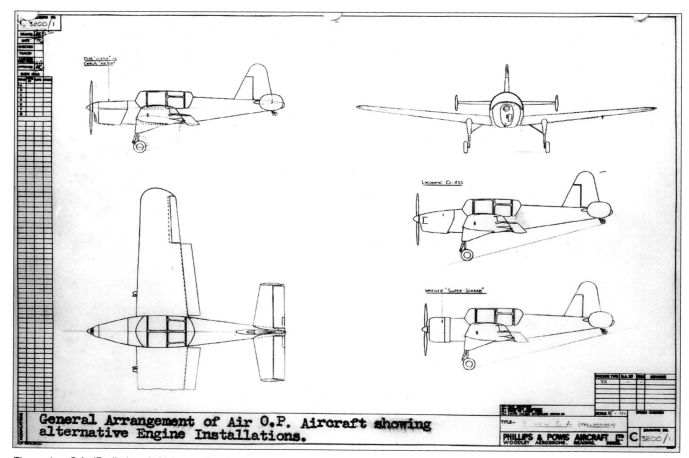

General Arrangement of Air O.P. Aircraft showing alternative Engine Installations.

Three-view G.A. (Preliminary). Notes on the drawing read: 1 - DH Gipsy Major or Cirrus Major; 2 - Lycoming 0-435; 3 - Warner Super Scarab.

Left: Sketch showing Air Ambulance version.

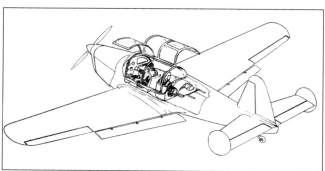

DIMENSIONS

Span	36 ft 2 ins
Length	24 ft 0 ins
Height	7 ft 6 ins
Wing area	191 sq ft
Track	9 ft 11 ins
Interior width of cabin	4 ft 0 ins

WEIGHTS

	lb
Tare weight	1,360
Fuel (18 gallons)	135
Oil (2 gallons)	18
Pilot	160
Passengers (2)	320
Normal AUW	1,993
Reserve for fourth occupant, luggage, radio, additional fuel, special equipment etc.	407
Design AUW	2,400

PERFORMANCE

The following figures apply to the machine when flown at the above normal AUW in a wind of 5 mph:

Run to unstick	60 yards
Distance to clear 50 ft	138 yards
Initial rate of climb	1,100 ft/min
Maximum speed	115 mph
Cruising speed	100 mph
Stalling speed	28 mph
Duration (Normal version)	2½ hours
(Long range version)	5 hours

Note - By sacrificing a small amount on the take-off and climb, or by fitting a VP airscrew, the maximum speed can readily be increased to 140 mph and the cruising speed to 120 mph.

Don Brown obviously used the details contained in this booklet for his article *Milestones No.62*, which appeared in the *Miles Aircraft Works Magazine* for May 1946:

As we have already described, the M.38 or Messenger was originally conceived during the war as an AOP aeroplane, the requirements for which necessitated a quick take off, low landing speed and exceptional range of view coupled with ease of maintenance. As the end of the war approached, it became obvious that the Messenger, with certain modifications, would make the ideal aeroplane for the private owner and flying club.

We took a Messenger and used it as a flying test bed for trying out a whole host of suggested modifications, the idea being to evolve the ideal Civil Messenger. Among the modifications we tried out were the substitution of a 150 hp Blackburn Cirrus Major III

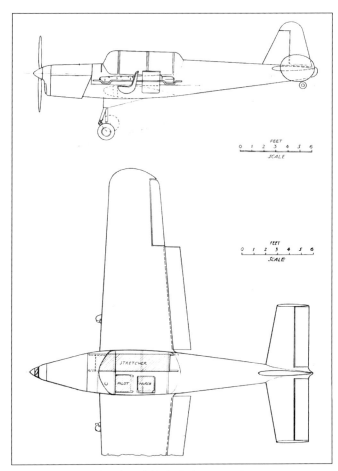

Above: Two-view drawing of Air Ambulance version.

engine for the 140 hp DH Gipsy Major, a coarser pitch propeller to give a higher cruising speed, retractable flaps operated by a Miles actuator (the trailing edge of the wing was in fact modified to allow the flaps to retract fully - PA), dual flying controls, increased tankage and the addition of a folding fourth seat

Below: U-0247 in flight.

The machine on which all these modifications were incorporated was called the M.48 (actually it was first just known as the M.38 Mk.III at the time and for some time after, but because of the vast number of differences from the standard M.38 it was really a new type, so it was later decided to re-designate it M.48 - PA) and it has been flown by all and sundry, receiving the bare minimum of maintenance. From the experience gained, much valuable information has been obtained. Some of the modifications have been found to be worthwhile, others of doubtful value. One thing is certain, however - the civil Messenger will be the ideal machine for the private owner. While retaining the ease of handling of the military version, the performance has been enhanced, as the following figures show:

	M.38	M.48
Maximum speed	*123 mph*	*135 mph*
Cruising speed	*97 mph*	*124 mph*
Distance to unstick in 5 mph wind	*65 yards*	*75 yards*
Landing run	*80 yards*	*80 yards*
Still air range	*230 miles*	*460 miles*

The first recorded flight of the M.38 Mk.IIIB, which was painted PR Blue overall with red/blue roundels and with 'B' mark U-0247, was made by Hugh Kennedy, on 14th November 1944 and Don Brown flew it on 16th November 1944, so it was almost certainly first flown, by George Miles (whose wartime log books are missing) sometime on or before 14th November 1944.

A view of the electrically operated retractable flaps on the Messenger Mk.IIIB, U-0247. Note the lack of hyphen in the marks as applied.

This photograph was stated to have been taken in September 1944 and shows the M.28 Mk.IV U-0243; the M.48, U-0247; RH369 the first production Mk.I; RH370 and RH368 (U-0245) with an unpainted cowling. To help date the photograph, RH368 was ferried from France to Woodley by F/O Trevor Martin on 8th September 1944 to be fitted with a DH Gipsy Major engine to bring it in line with the subsequent production Messenger Mk.Is for the RAF and the first record of RH368 being flown with this engine was when Don Brown flew it on 5th December 1944. However, RH369 did not make its first flight until 21st October 1944 so the photograph was probably taken in late 1944.

Although the M.48 offered a number of improvements over the M.38, no further examples were produced. An undated Miles Aircraft Ltd document stated that:

This aircraft was the first of the Messenger type to receive a CofA, and for that purpose it has become the Type aircraft. Its registration letters are G-AGOY, and it has now been sold to a Swiss company when its registration letters will be changed to HB-EIP.

Don Brown gave the reason for the Messenger Mk.IIIB later being re-designated M.48 as; *being due to the differences between it and the standard Messenger* but it has since been found that, towards the end of the war, Miles wanted to publish the existence of the Messenger Mk.III as an indicator of his post war plans, so he 'concocted' the designation M.48 as a Messenger variant which the Ministry could not control - whereupon the Ministry promptly took the Messenger off the secret list!

U-0247 was later used extensively by the firm on communications duties and like all Messengers, the Mk.IIIB/M.48 proved to be an extremely pleasant aeroplane to fly.

On 1st July 1944, Mr W F Jenkins, PDDC. of the MAP, wrote a note relating to the M.38:

Mr Miles did not attend the meeting with Parliamentary Secretary yesterday (30/6/44). He sent Mr Robinson and Mr Capley. They say there is complete misunderstanding about the price of £2,000 quoted to the Dutch. This is their figure for manufacture and sale to their own standards three months after hostilities cease. Their not too convincing story is that they can quote much less on a civil contract than on a contract for MAP since they are concerned with less exacting standards and are free of the expense of meeting our costing and accounting requirements, etc. One thing which helps them is that they have Cirrus engines in their own stock which they can use if free of our specification. But over and above this, they would be prepared to risk a considerable initial loss to get in on the market. The price quoted has no relevance to the existing 10 aircraft about which everything is abnormal.

They realise that their figures have put us in a difficulty with the Dutch, although they say this is due to misunderstanding and not to misrepresentation on their part. They are willing to write to the Dutch authorities putting their quotation in its proper perspective and removing any impression that they will be charging such a low figure to the MAP for the machines being made now. The draft of this letter will be sent to Parliamentary Secretary who will refer it to Second Secretary before replying.

The company would like an early accounting settlement on the present contract. I said we would examine their accounts as soon as they are ready and that DDC(2) would get in touch with them.

(They said they had "tooled up for 1,000 aircraft" and I indicated that they must expect difficulty in our accepting any expenditure charged to the reduced contract which was not reasonable).

DGAP stated that the Ministry now want 25 of these aircraft. He could not support any further manufacture at Reading, but Parliamentary Secretary indicated that the Minister was inclined to favour the company's project of manufacture in N. Ireland. The company's representatives said that they had had discussions with Sir Basil Brook who was strongly in favour of Miles Aircraft establishing themselves there with a view to providing post-war employment.

Miles are now using 30,000 ft of requisitioned space at Banbridge, Co. Down, where they are making torpedo tails and Stirling bomb doors. They say they can find labour there, adequate in numbers and suitable in skill for making the M.38 from beginning to end. They maintained that no assistance from resources at present applied to war needs would be diverted except spruce and "a little metal". No capital assistance would be required. (It may be thought desirable to verify these statements).

The possibility was seen, (i) of delivering the existing 10 M.38s to the Air Ministry as a first instalment of the 25 they now require; (ii) of ordering 15 for the Air Ministry for manufacture in N. Ireland. (It will probably be best to make this a new contract and not to mix it up with the existing abnormal contract, although there can be a transfer of jigs and tools) and (iii) to allow 10 to be made for the Dutch after the above 15 are delivered and under conditions which ensure proper priority for the RAF requirement. This need not be a contract with the MAP if policy permits a private contract with the Dutch.

It is to be borne in mind that if (ii) and (iii) of paragraph above are followed, the company ought to be able, from what they said in the earlier part of this talk, to quote a moderate fixed price for the 15 ordered by MAP. If this appears high for the airframe in relation to their estimated figure for manufacture (£2,000 in flying trim with everything supplied by the company), they ought to be made to give a more convincing explanation of the difference than paragraph 2 above provides.

Parliamentary Secretary will refer to the Permanent Secretary before any recommendation is made to the Minister on the above lines. PAS(R) drew attention to questions of higher policy involved in any present project of permitting civil orders to be accepted, and to the difficulty of giving preferential facilities to one aircraft firm. He asked the company whether they had given any pledge to Sir Basil Brook to carry on in N. Ireland after the war; they indicated that they had, but not necessarily in the aircraft field.

Parliamentary Secretary made clear to the company's representatives that no promise had been given to them, and that the outcome of the discussion depended upon policy decisions yet to be taken. (N.A. Ref: AVIA 15/2044).

The author considers that, with so many different civil servants and Ministries involved in the manufacture of aeroplanes during the war, each with their own ideas on how things should be done, it is quite astounding that anything was ever actually produced!

On 28th August 1944, Peter Masefield, who was by then with the MAP, also became involved in the M.38 debate and he wrote to Norman W Graham, Principle Private Secretary, MAP, as follows:

I enclose an extract from a letter which the Lord Privy Seal has received from Mr Ronald Tree MP. You will see that he raises a question on the supply of M.38 light communications aircraft to the Dutch Government. It seems unlikely that the position is quite as he suggests.

I should be most grateful if you could let me have, for the Lord Privy Seal's information, the true facts so that he can deal with the matter with Mr Tree. Apparently Mr Tree is thinking of putting down a Parliamentary question on the subject, and if we can give him an answer in this matter, it might save a lot of trouble.

The following extract from the letter from Mr Ronald Tree MP, who appeared to be very well informed, makes for very interesting reading:

There is a matter of aircraft supply which has caused me considerable anxiety. After the prototype of the M.38 had been built and flown, representatives of the Dutch Government in London inspected it and stated it was the exact aeroplane for which they were looking for use when Holland was liberated. They therefore asked that 20 should be delivered to them as soon as Holland was liberated in order that they might be used on the air strips there.

At that time the Miles Company had a contract from MAP for a large number of these aircraft for communication purposes. They have now been forced to cancel the Dutch order without any explanation, except that it had nothing to do with the reputation of the aircraft itself. The Dutch Government have been advised to purchase Taylorcraft Austers in their place, which as you know are an American type of aircraft (although the Taylorcraft Auster may have been based on an American design in the first instance, it was a British, not 'an American type of aircraft! - PA).

Apparently the Dutch representatives in this country have been most anxious to buy some Yorks for their immediate post-war requirements, but have now been told that they cannot have them and been advised to buy DC-4s. In other words these European countries closest to us, and who in my opinion should be encouraged in every way possible to fly British aircraft at the end of the war, are being pushed into the position of buying American aircraft.

It would seem to be extremely doubtful, once they had decided on American aircraft, that they will ever be willing to buy British. (How very right he was - PA). *I feel that this matter is so serious that it should be raised in Parliament at the earliest possible moment and I intend to put down a question, unless it would be contrary to the public interest to do so.* (N.A. Ref: AVIA 5/2044)

As if things weren't confused enough, they now really do start to get very complicated and Norman Graham tried to sum up the situation in his reply to Peter Masefield in a letter dated 2nd September 1944:

With reference to your letter of 28th August, enclosing an extract from Mr Ronald Tree's letter to the Lord Privy Seal on aircraft to the Dutch, the facts as regards the M.38 are as follows. Early in October 1943, 250 M.38 aircraft were ordered by MAP from Miles Aircraft Ltd. They were required by the RAF for communications duties and by the Admiralty as light reconnaissance and anti-submarine aircraft. We had at that time no knowledge of any requirement for the Dutch.

About the end of 1943 the manpower allocated to the aircraft industry was reduced and the Services decided, in order to maintain their supply of more important aircraft, to give up their requirement for M.38s. The contract was therefore cancelled in January 1944. (At last we now know the true reason behind the cancellation of the original contract - PA). *The firm exceeded, quite wrongly, the scale of production they were entitled to continue under the break-clause, and by March 1944,* (in addition to the prototypes and two pre-production aircraft, which were completed or practically completed - PA), *10 production aircraft had reached a stage at which it was more economical to complete than to scrap them. By then the Air Ministry had a new requirement for 3 M.38s and the Dutch were asking for 10.*

With the concurrence of the Air Ministry (who are responsible for the allocation of aircraft to foreign countries), the contract was reinstated in May 1944 to the extent of 11 aircraft in addition to the two prototypes (U-0245, RH369-RH378, RG327 and RG333 - PA).

Although it was the intention at that time to supply 10 of the aircraft to the Dutch, all the aircraft were ordered by MAP since the possibility was foreseen that the Air Ministry requirement would increase. Miles were never authorised to make any private contract with the Dutch. In the absence of any Government decision to subsidise the Dutch, we were bound to charge them the full cost of the aircraft to us, and, as the number now being made is small, the price is much higher than that quoted by Miles Aircraft Ltd. (without the knowledge of the MAP) in 1943 when the large scale production was contemplated. The Dutch, therefore, refused on price grounds to accept.

The Air Ministry requirement has now increased to 53. There has not been labour available in this country to do more than complete the 13 aircraft previously ordered, and the further production has been arranged in Northern Ireland, where labour is available. (Only 10 Messenger Mk.Is were ultimately to be built in Northern Ireland, of which the first few were completed at Banbridge with the remainder being completed in the new factory at Newtownards - PA). *Negotiations are now going on to supply Austers to the Dutch instead of M.38s, the number now being 20. These Austers would come from production in this country, not America.*

With regard to the Yorks, although foreign requirements are a matter in the first instance for the Air Ministry, I can tell you that the output which we have been able to arrange, having regard to the RAF requirements for heavy bombers, falls short of the Air Ministry requirement alone, and there are none available for other demands. In view of the Air Ministry's concern I have sent a copy of the correspondence to Dunnett. (N.A. Ref: AVIA 15/2044)

An interesting 'Top Secret' Telegram dated 18th November 1944 was sent from Washington to the Air Ministry in Whitehall, regarding the implications of the UK being allowed to export aircraft without upsetting the Americans over Lease-Lend, throws more light on this subject. In this telegram it was stated that a number of aircraft were required by the Netherlands Government and included within their requirement was one for 50 Austers:

Details of this case are given in AASC (44)20, attached hereto as Appendix 'B' and the case was reinforced orally by DDO(A) at the Air Assignment Committee on 25th August – AASC (44) 4th Meeting when he said:-..... the British Government was under a moral obligation to meeting this Dutch request, as early in this year Approval had been given to the Dutch placing an order for M.38 aircraft which, at the time, were not required by the Air Ministry. Production of this aircraft, however, was stopped and the Dutch were told that none would be available for them. Later a military request arose for M.38 aircraft and it was decided to start production in Northern Ireland where the manpower shortage was much less acute than in England. The first 50 to be produced, however, would be for the British Government and once again the Dutch requirement could not possibly be met in time. It had therefore been decided to offer the Dutch 20 used Auster IIIs subject to the approval of the Committee.

It is not generally known but, in fact, the Americans were causing the British Government a considerable amount of aggravation over the sale of British-built aircraft to foreign governments at this time, as they seemed to be under the selfish impression that they should be supplying all the foreign governments' aircraft needs themselves.

This was a typical case in point where the Americans were 'dragging their heels' to such an extent that the Secretary of the Committee suggested that, if there was further delay the Committee might simply record US dissent and proceed with the supply, adding that the CMAB sometimes took decisions in the face of dissent by the British Members.

The Americans then gave in and on the next day (9th September) General Crain wrote concurring in the transfer of the second 10, concurrence was stated to be based on the Dutch request being a military requirement. American compliance was not said to be based on expediency - in the first case, the Dutch were asked to choose and voted British, while in the second, American concurrence was specifically given on the grounds of a military requirement.

The Americans were even arguing over whether permission should be granted for us to supply of the odd Proctor and Dominie to foreign governments - it was indeed a very difficult time for the British.

A document detailing: 'Applications during the past twelve months for the export of aircraft or the sale of licences for manufacture abroad', from PS15, dated 3rd December 1943, included a note, under 'Turkey', to the effect that:

Miles Aircraft Ltd applied for permission to sell the licence to manufacture the M.28 or M.38 but this was rejected because the necessary Gipsy engines could not be supplied. It may be revived if Lycoming engines can be fitted and obtained without detriment to the British supplies. De Havillands applied for permission to supply to Turkish Airlines the equipment and technical assistance necessary for the manufacture of Gipsy engines in Turkey. This was, however, refused owing to technical difficulties and the fact that the proposal had not the support of the Turkish Government.

Another note in the same document stated, under 'Chile', that:

An application by Miles Aircraft Ltd to sell manufacturing rights of the Magister, M.18 and M.38 is under consideration. One difficulty in the way of the proposal, is that of finding a suitable local timber in substitution of spruce. Arrangements have been made for the Chilean Ambassador and Air Attaché and certain Chilean industrialists to visit the firm.

Then, on 1st May 1944, Mr N V Meeres, PS 17 at MAP, suddenly announced that the M.38 Messenger was to be built in South Africa. Miles had always been interested in producing his aeroplanes overseas and was especially interested in the potential that he felt that South Africa offered. News of this proposal first appeared in *The Aeroplane Spotter* for 25th January 1945 under the heading *African Messenger*:

According to the Johannesburg Sunday Times, the Miles "African Messenger" is to be produced in Southern Rhodesia. In a recent speech, Sir George Albu, Bart, Chairman of Miles Aircraft of SA (Ltd.), said that the "African Messenger" has been designed specifically for African use, but that the Union Government had turned down a proposal that it should be produced in the Union of South Africa.

The reason given by the Government was that it felt that wooden aircraft were unsuited to South African climatic conditions. This statement was made in spite of the great advances that have been made in the use of wood, and the successful performance all over the World of such aeroplanes as the Mosquito.

Sir George went on to say that it was only after the South African proposal fell through that the Southern Rhodesian Government was approached, and immediate assurance was given that every facility would be given to permit production of the "African Messenger". Speaking of the "African Messenger" itself, Sir George said that it was a single-motor aeroplane suitable for use by private owners and local Government departments as an air ambulance, light freighter or inter-communication aeroplane. See next volume for further developments on this story.

Today, there is just one ex RAF Messenger Mk.I surviving in airworthy condition, albeit now modified to become the sole Mk.4B, G-AKVZ (ex Northern Ireland built RH427), which regularly attends air displays and fly-ins, thanks to its dedicated and enthusiastic owners Shipping & Airlines Ltd of Biggin Hill. The fuselage of VP-KJL (RH371/G-ALAR) is in England (see Appendix 41 for the story of VP-KJL) and the remains of G-ALAH (RH377) are in Spain.

For a summary of M.38 Messenger Mk.I production and individual aircraft histories see Appendix 29.

For details of post-war civil variants of the M.38 Messenger see the next volume.

(N.A. Refs: AVIA 15/1971; AVIA 15/2044; BT28/1195; AIR 3261; AIR 3338 and AIR 3566).

SPECIFICATION AND PERFORMANCE DATA

Engine: M.38/28 first prototype 130 hp DH Gipsy Major and/or the 150 hp Blackburn Cirrus Major III
                             M.38 first true prototype M.38 155 hp Blackburn Cirrus Major III and later the 145hp DH Gipsy Major ID
                             M.38/II two pre-production prototypes, Mk.I & Mk.4A 145 hp DH Gipsy Major ID (the engine in the Mk.4A, ex RAF Mk.I, was also recorded as the 145 hp DH Gipsy Major 10 Mk.1 but the only difference between the two engines was that the latter ran on 80 octane leaded fuel)

For the record, the later, civilian and civilianised RAF Messengers had the following engines:

                             M.38 Mk.2A, Mk.2B & M.38 Mk.III (M.48) 155 hp Blackburn Cirrus Major III
                             M.38 Mk.4 145 hp DH Gipsy Major 10
                             M.38 Mk.2C & Mk.4A 145 hp DH Gipsy Major 1D
                             M.38 Mk.V 150 hp Praga E
                             M.38 Mk.5 180 hp Blackburn Bombardier 702

Dimensions: span 36ft 2in; length 24ft 0in; height 7ft 6in; wing area 191 sq ft; aspect ratio 6.81; wing section, root NACA 23018, tip NACA 2412

Weights: M.38 Mk.I: empty 1,518lb; fuel 135lb; oil 18lb; pilot 160lb; payload 69lb; AUW 1,900lb; wing loading 10lb/sq ft
                             M.38 Mk.2A basic equipment: tare 1,341lb; fuel (for 250 miles) 132lb; oil 22lb; pilot 160lb; three passengers 480lb; reserve for luggage etc 265lb; AUW 2,400lb; wing loading 12.6lb/sq ft
                             M.38 Mk.2A with standard equipment: tare 1,438lb; fuel (for 250 miles) 132lb; oil 22lb; pilot 160lb; three passengers 480lb; reserve for luggage etc 168lb; AUW 2,400lb

Performance: M.38 Mk.I: max speed 116 mph; cruising speed 95 mph; distance to unstick 64 yards; distance to 50 ft 193 yards; landing run 110 yards; landing over 50ft, 250 yards: rate of climb 660ft/min; time to 10,000ft, 30 min; range 260 miles; duration 3.5 hr; service ceiling 14,000ft
                             M.38 Mk.2A with standard airscrew, at 2,000lb AUW: max level speed 135 mph; max cruising speed 124 mph; distance to unstick in 5 mph wind 75 yards; distance to 50 ft in 5 mph wind 200 yards; landing run in 5 mph wind 80 yards; max rate of climb at sea level 950 ft/min; still air range with 36 galls fuel 460 miles; duration with 36 galls fuel 5.2 hours; indicated stalling speed 25 mph; service ceiling 16,000ft; absolute ceiling 19,000ft.

" — HOW CAN I, IF YOU WONT SLOW DOWN ? "
WITH APOLOGIES TO "THE AEROPLANE"

An artist's impression of an M.38A Mariner approaching the aft deck of a merchant vessel.

Chapter 30
Miles M.38A Mariner

During the spring of 1943, Allied shipping losses in the Atlantic were reaching serious proportions and an idea occurred to George Miles that if a number of ships in each convoy could be equipped with a small deck on the stern, it might be possible to operate a slow-flying aeroplane like the M.38 Messenger from them. This machine would be capable of carrying depth-charges and maintaining anti-submarine patrols over a wide area and by operating relays of such machines, an unbroken patrol could be maintained throughout the hours of daylight over such a radius that enemy submarines would be unable to catch up with the convoy, attack and retreat to safety within the hours of darkness. If the aircraft failed to find a submarine, it would merely jettison its depth charges before landing on the small deck.

Experience with the Messenger suggested that by the fitment of a very simple form of arrester gear it could probably be operated off a deck 60ft square, with a large net provided at the forward end of the deck to prevent the aircraft from flying into the superstructure of the ship in the event of failure to engage the arrester gear. A gap would be left in the centre of the net which would allow the engine and propeller to pass through and the impact to be evenly distributed along the leading edge of the wings.

The posts to which the net was attached were secured by bungee ropes so that at the moment of impact they could move through several feet, thus considerably lessening the magnitude of the impact loads. It just remained to see whether or not the idea was

feasible, so George Miles carried out some fast taxi-ing trials into a net erected on Woodley aerodrome using the prototype M.18, U-0222, although he did not actually fly the M.18 into the net.

In April 1943, George Miles carried out initial touch-downs some 20-30ft ahead of the impact point but he was so encouraged by these very satisfactory initial results, that he then flew the Messenger into the net while still airborne, simulating a 'missed-gear' landing, without any difficulty or damage to either himself or the aircraft. Having thus demonstrated the feasibility of the scheme, George Miles then submitted it immediately to both the Ministry of Aircraft Production and the Admiralty. A 60ft 'deck' was then marked out on Woodley aerodrome to demonstrate its feasibility to the Minister of Aircraft Production, Sir Stafford Cripps, Lady Cripps, Air Marshall Sir Philip Joubert de la Ferte, Commodore (later Rear Admiral Sir Matthew) Slattery, Professor P M S Blackett, the Hon J P Maclay and other officers and high ranking officials but on the day of the demonstration the wind suddenly and unexpectedly veered round 180° and George had to land the aircraft down-wind. No arrester gear was used and he flew it straight into the net, again with no difficulty or damage.

George Miles was moved to write about this in *Flight* magazine on 10th April 1959:

"I was interested in the photographs of the net landing on HMS Eagle and the reference to arrester nets at Gutersloh in your issue

of March 20. Enclosed are illustrations from a proposal for anti-submarine measures which I submitted to the Ministry of Aircraft Production and to the Admiralty early in 1943 (in one of these the artist has omitted the slot which was necessary for propeller-driven aircraft). These proposals appear to have been the origin of arrester nets and barriers of the type now in use and, to some extent, may have suggested the angled deck.

In April 1943 I carried out landings into a prototype net erected on the aerodrome at Woodley as a demonstration of the practical nature of the scheme before Sir Stafford and Lady Cripps, Air Marshall (note different rank from that quoted above - PA) *Sir Philip Joubert, Commodore Slattery, Professor Blackett, the Hon J P Macklay and other officers and officials. One test, partly to demonstrate that heavier aircraft than the Messenger could be arrested in this manner, was carried out down-wind. Subsequently, encouraged by the very satisfactory initial results, I flew into the net while still airborne; the previous touch-downs had been made some 20 to 30 ft ahead of the impact point.*

Unfortunately, the scheme was not put to use during the war, the official verdict being that it was impracticable! Our request to be permitted to rig a net for trials on a towed float or Naval vessel was refused and we consequently made arrangements with Mr Billmeir to carry out unofficial trials on one of his Stanhope Line freighters as a private venture. Under war-time regulations, however, official permission had to be granted and this we were unable to obtain".

The prototype Messenger, U-0223, was then fitted with a light arrester hook and re-named the M.38A Mariner for the trials.

In 1943, Phillips & Powis Aircraft Ltd produced a booklet which gave details of the prototype M.38/28 Messenger, U-0223, while temporarily modified into the M.38A Mariner and this is reproduced here:

The Miles M.38A Mariner

In view of the present urgent need for an effective anti-submarine weapon the following suggestion is advanced: A number of ships in each convoy should be provided with a small aeroplane or aeroplanes designed primarily with the object of being able to fly at a very low speed and having exceptional visibility and reasonable load carrying capacity. Such an aeroplane could be rapidly developed from the Miles M.38 Air OP Aircraft. Such an aeroplane could be very easily launched by a variety of means such as a simplified form of catapult or by means of a rocket assisted take-off from a light wooden platform.

The landing apparatus would consist essentially of a sprung net arranged at an angle from the stern of the ship, together with a very simple form of arrester gear which has proved satisfactory on test. The aeroplanes would operate in relays providing a constant patrol around the convoy over a large area. It would thus be impossible for a submarine pack to approach in daylight to within a considerable distance of the convoy without being sighted. If a submarine is detected the patrolling aircraft would drop its depth charges and simultaneously other aeroplanes could be launched to ensure the accurate placing of further depth charges much more quickly that could be effected by the convoying vessels. Moreover it would not be necessary for these vessels to leave the convoy.

Although at first sight the operation of such aeroplanes might appear to be fraught with some difficulty; as a result of preliminary trials with a machine of the type envisaged, it is felt that the launching and the alighting methods suggested have every chance of success. In any case the apparatus necessary is extremely simple and could quickly and cheaply be applied to a merchant vessel for practical tests. It is thought that the necessary modifications and flying to prove the practicability or otherwise could be completed in a few days if ordinary commercial practice is applied. Owing to

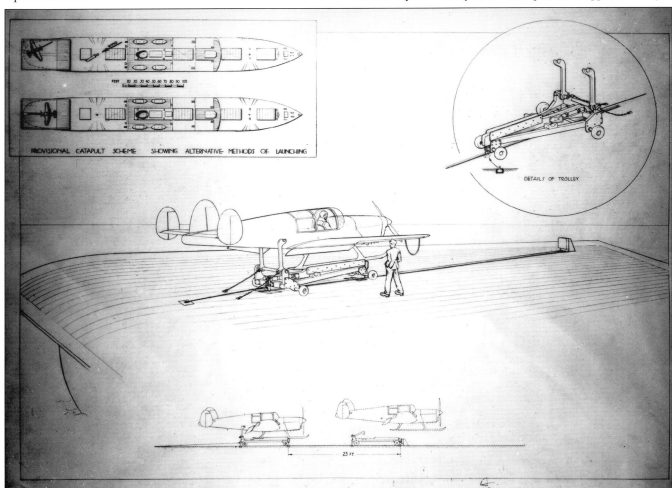

An artist's impression of an M.38A Mariner showing details of launching from the small deck of a merchant vessel.

An artist's impression of an M.38A Mariner landing into the arrester net of the aft deck of a merchant vessel. Note, the artist has omitted to include the gap in the centre of the net for the propeller but shows a skid hitting the net below and in front of it.

the very light weight of the aeroplane and the fact that it would be airborne at about 30 mph there is no doubt as to the ability of a very small light and simple type of catapult to launch it into the air as shown in the accompanying illustration.

With regard to the landing, the ship would for this purpose steam into wind so that the aeroplane could approach astern and alight at a very low relative speed on the afterdeck. If the approach has been accurately judged, contact will have been made with the arrester device and the net will not have to absorb the landing shock but great latitude is permitted for errors of judgment on the part of the pilot or the effect of air disturbances caused by the ship's superstructure. Even if the aircraft is still airborne at the moment of striking the net, tests have shown that no damage is likely to occur.

The aeroplane would be fitted with a single central skid so that in the event of a forced landing on the water it would 'hydroplane' until almost at a standstill, giving the pilot every chance to step out and inflate his 'K' type dinghy. It is not claimed that the foregoing provided a complete solution to the submarine menace since obviously it would be inoperable in times of fog. It is claimed, however, that such a scheme could be readily and quickly put into operation, would not involve extensive preparations or difficult modifications to the ships concerned and would make a very material contribution towards reducing the risks at present endured.

It is of interest to note that the prototype aeroplane which was designed for AOP duties illustrated has actually been taken off and landed with ease at an all-up weight 250 lb in excess of that when carrying two depth charges and that in this condition it could be comfortably flown under adequate control at an indicated airspeed of less than 40 mph. The illustration is pictorial only and certain features of the scheme have been intentionally omitted. The possibility of operation at night has also been considered and is believed to be feasible. In this event the aircraft would hunt in pairs, one carrying depth charges and the other a searchlight to illuminate the operations.

Loading for Patrol Duties:

	lb
Tare	1,400
Fuel for 4 hours patrol	150
Oil	20
Pilot, parachute and dinghy	210
All-up weight	1,780

Loading for Attack Duties:

Tare	1,420
Fuel	150
Oil	20
Pilot, parachute and dinghy	210
2 Depth charges	600
All-up weight	2,400

Note: If even longer patrol duties are considered desirable for any reason, it is, of course, obvious that up to 700 lb of fuel and oil could be carried in place of depth charges if tankage is provided.

Performance with Patrol Loading and Gipsy Major Series III Engine:
Corrected run to unstuck -
5 mph wind 60 yards - unassisted
Corrected run to clear 50 foot screen 138 yards - unassisted
Stalling speed with flaps down 28 mph
Cruising speed at 2,200 rpm* 97 mph
Maximum speed at 2,500 rpm* 105 mph
Initial rate of climb 1,160 ft/min
Duration (at cruising speed) 4 hours

By sacrificing a small amount on the take-off and climb performance or by fitting a VP airscrew, the cruising and maximum speeds can be improved to approximately 120 and 140 mph respectively.

The trials were to be carried out on the 60ft 'deck', by then fitted with a simple bungee cord arrester gear and thanks to the excellent handling characteristics of the Mariner, no difficulty was found in engaging the arrester gear and landing within the confines of the small 'deck'.

To prove that the aircraft would carry the weight of two depth-charges, Hugh Kennedy carried out a 5 min 'Overload take-off' flight on 1st May 1943 with 'human ballast', which comprised George Miles, Don Brown and three others and Don recorded in his log-book '6 up, 2,580lb, t/o 8 secs!'. Two light but powerful rockets of the type used by the Royal Navy for rocket-assisted take-off were then attached to the aircraft and these literally threw it into the air with a run of only a few yards. Hugh Kennedy recorded a 10 min 'Take-off (Assisted)' flight on 10th June 1943 and this must have been the first time that rocket assistance was used.

In spite of the success of the trials on land, the authorities still remained sceptical and it proved impossible to obtain official permission to conduct trials either on a towed float, a naval vessel or a merchant ship. Mr JA Billmeir, Chairman of the Stanhope Shipping Line, heard about the scheme and was so enthusiastic about it as it afforded the possibility of saving the lives of his crews, that he offered to provide, at his own expense, the necessary deck on the stern of one of his Stanhope Line freighters as a private venture to enable flight trials to be carried out. Under wartime regulations however, official permission to undertake the trials had to be granted and this Miles was unable to obtain.

Eventually, permission _was_ given to carry out some trials on an aircraft carrier at sea and Jeremy Miles relates the story of how George Miles flew the Mariner on to an aircraft carrier in the Clyde for a preliminary test. On the day of the flight however, George was told that the carrier would be moored alongside the jetty and that the flight would have to be abandoned. George was not to be put off by such trifles as 'no wind over deck' however, and replied that he was still prepared to come anyway. Upon his arrival he found that, although the carrier was moored alongside, the wind was blowing across the deck, so, undeterred, George promptly landed the Mariner into wind, across the deck! It can only be imagined as to what their Lordships at the Admiralty must have thought of the whole affair!

For the official trials, Hugh Kennedy flew the Mariner: 'Reading-Blackpool, Blackpool-Carlisle, Carlisle-Crail 18th June 1943; 'At Crail' 19th June 1943; 'Crail-Machrihanish' 20th June 1943. The sea trials were undertaken in heavy rain by a pilot who had never flown the aircraft before and who was required to land on the wet deck, without the use of arrester gear and with the carrier steaming across wind. However, even under these adverse conditions, he still managed to carry out a successful landing.

The pilot for the trials was in fact Cdr Eric Brown and he wrote of his experience with the Mariner thus:

While in the Service Trials Unit at Arbroath, I was suddenly asked to check out whether a light four-seat aircraft designed for army co-operation duties could be safely operated on an escort carrier on an ad hoc basis. The aeroplane proved to be the prototype Miles Messenger, U-0223, which was duly delivered to Machrihanish airfield, from which I was already conducting trials with a Grumman Martlet IV on the escort carriers Attacker and Hunter in the Firth of Clyde in mid-June 1943.

A quick check on the flaps-down stalling speed gave an absurd 28 mph. In consequence I decided on a carrier approach speed of 35 mph to allow sufficient control in the turbulent wake off the carrier's flight deck. When I arrived over Hunter on 22nd June the combined wind-speed over the deck (the carrier's speed plus the speed of the local wind) was 30 knots, and since this was equal to my intended approach speed I had no alternative but to open up the engine and drive the M.38 on to the deck at about 45 mph. Even then I felt I was never going to catch up with the carrier. When I cut the throttle the aeroplane sat down gently and literally stood still on the deck. The take-off was just as ridiculous. I ran the aircraft up to full power on the brakes and then released them, holding the stick well back, and the M.38 ran about its own length and then went up like a lift. Certainly for landing the lateral control left something to be desired, but even so this was the idiot's ideal deck-landing aircraft.

At the end of the sea trials, Hugh Kennedy flew the Mariner: 'Machrihanish-Blackpool, Blackpool-Reading' on 23rd June 1943. Unfortunately, despite the fact that the trials were a complete success, no further action was taken. The official verdict was that it was impracticable and George Miles was told that the official view was that helicopters could do the job better. However, this was in 1943 and the helicopter was still in its infancy and it was going to be a very long time before the helicopter would ever carry out operations of this, or any other, kind for that matter.

Meanwhile the brave merchant seamen and their valuable shipping with its equally valuable loads continued to be lost at sea in what was to become known as the Battle of the Atlantic, and to think how easily a lot of this wastage could have been avoided . . .

Upon completion of the trials the Mariner was returned to prototype M.38/28 Messenger configuration.

Mrs F G Miles (Blossom Miles) seated in the cockpit of what must be the prototype M.38 Messenger Mk.1, U-0223. The lateral struts to support the undercarriage were not fitted to later production. (via JM Collection)

An artist's impression of the Miles Glider Tug towing a glider.

Chapter 31
Miles Glider Tug or Target Tower

During the early days of the war British gliders were usually towed by obsolescent bombers, such as the Whitley but this arrangement had certain disadvantages, since a bomber, even when carrying no load, was much heavier than an aircraft which had been designed specifically as a tug.

Therefore, in 1942 Frank H Robertson, a young project engineer at Phillips & Powis, prepared a tail-first design with a tricycle undercarriage for use as a specialised glider tug or target-tower. He adopted this layout for two reasons: i) it allowed the towing attachment on the tug to be close to the centre of gravity, thereby minimising the effect on manoeuvrability and stability of the tug, and ii) it enabled a power-driven slipping winch to be installed to absorb the shock loads in the tow-rope.

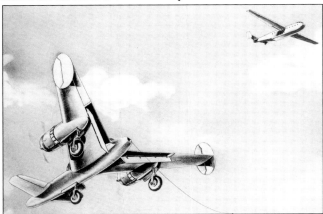

An artist's impression of the Miles Glider Tug coming in to land after having just cast off its glider.

Phillips & Powis produced an undated booklet on the Glider Tug (or Target Tower) (which was never given a Miles numerical designation) and this is reproduced here:

Glider Tug (or Target Tower)

The rapid development of the large, towed glider for troop and cargo transport makes the need for a specially designed "Tug" increasingly apparent.

The existing method of towing, that is to say from a hook at the extreme tail end of a bomber, introduces many disadvantages and is obviously most uneconomical. The chief drawbacks can be enumerated briefly as follows:

1. Manoeuvrability and stability of both glider and tug are adversely affected by the load applied by the tow rope.
2. A bomber, even when lightly loaded, is very much heavier than a tug of similar power need be.
3. The absence of a slipping winch means that other methods of absorbing shock must be devised and the tow rope must be jettisoned after each release.

The Phillips & Powis Tug has been designed specially to avoid these troubles. The adverse effect of the load from the tow rope has been minimised by using a tail first layout which allows for towing from a point close to the centre of gravity.

A power-driven slipping winch is carried which absorbs shock loads in the tow rope and allows the rope to be wound in after releasing the glider. The type of Tug illustrated and described in this booklet is designed to tow one fully loaded glider of the Horsa class. It is obviously desirable to standardise a Tug and it is thought that towing one glider with two or more tugs is a more practicable proposition than towing two or more gliders with one tug. Thus a glider of the Hamilcar class could be dealt with by two Tugs.

Phillips & Powis "Tug"

Brief Specification:

Type	Twin engined tractor monoplane - tail first.
Engines	Bristol "Mercury" (Standard Master II installations complete).
Construction	Wood.
Undercarriage	Tricycle - fixed or retractable.
Accommodation	Crew of two (armoured), slipping winch with 1000 ft of 5 ton cable and 417 galls fuel. (Plenty of room for guns if thought necessary).
Span	46 ft.
Length	34.5 ft.
Wing area	377 sq ft.
Tare weight	6,980 lb.
AUW	11,305 lb. See estimated weight analysis.
Wing loading	30 lb/sq ft.
Power loading	6.3 lb/hp. (with loaded "Horsa" 13.8 lb/hp).

Preliminary Performance Estimate:

Condition of Flight - Aircraft flying at AUW of 11,305 lb, and glider at AUW of 13,500 lb. Towing glider at 5,000 ft at 116 mph on an economical cruising power. This power gives a rate of climb of 100 ft/min for the combination. Return flight without glider at 187 mph on most economical cruising power.

Range - Allowing for warming up, take off and climb to 5,000 ft, aircraft can tow glider 520 miles and return to base. After release, glider can travel a further 10 miles in descending from 5,000 ft to 1,000 ft, making total range of 530 miles.

Target towing - When towing a 3 ft LD sleeve at 3,000 ft, the max continuous towing speed is 210 mph. Aircraft alone, at AUW of 9,300 lb, has speed at 4,500 ft of 265 mph.

Rate of climb:

Aircraft towing glider at AUW	24,800 lb.
Initial rate of climb at sea level	450 ft/min.
Continuous rate of climb at sea level	370 ft/min.

Aircraft alone at AUW	9,300 lb.
Initial rate of climb at sea level	3,180 ft/min.
Continuous rate of climb at sea level	2,915 ft/min.

Estimated Weight Analysis:

2 Mercury 870 hp engines and accessories	3,454 lb
Fuselage	400 lb
Wing	1,500 lb
Nose plane	100 lb
Elevator	35 lb
Fins	35 lb
Rudders	45 lb
Cabin top	118 lb
Undercarriage (Main)	400 lb
Nose Wheel	100 lb
Flight Controls	120 lb
Engine Controls	48 lb
Fuel System	350 lb
Oil System	75 lb
Fixed Equipment	200 lb
Tare	6,980 lb
Crew (2)	400 lb
Fuel (417 galls)	3,125 lb
Oil	300 lb
Winch	300 lb
Cable (1,000 ft of 5 ton)	200 lb
All up weight	11,305 lb

In January 1943, Phillips & Powis Aircraft Ltd produced a brochure entitled 'Miles Specialised Aircraft for Specialised Purposes'. Contained therein was a summary of a selection of Miles aircraft which had either been built or proposed up to then.

The Miles Glider Tug was included, as follows:

The obvious unsuitability of our medium bombers to act as tugs for the Horsa glider and of our heavy bombers to tow the Hamilcar glider has unfortunately been only too evident in practice and it has become increasingly evident that a specialised aeroplane was needed if the job were to be done efficiently.

The truth of this statement is abundantly clear when it is realised that the proposed tug, using only Bristol Mercury engines could perform a job which has been found impracticable hitherto, even with aircraft fitted with two Hercules engines: while two such tugs could achieve more than is possible as a tug by any existing four engined bomber.

The desirability of towing from the C.G. of the tug immediately suggested that an aeroplane designed for this one specific duty should be of the tail first type.

Span	46 ft 0 in
Wing area	230 sq ft
All up weight	11,300 lb
Engines	2 x Bristol Mercury
Cruising speed with Horsa	116 mph
Range with Horsa, returning alone	520 miles

Don Brown later recalled that the project was not proceeded with because the Ministry were reluctant to divert design and production manpower to anything other than an aircraft deemed as immediately essential for the war effort.

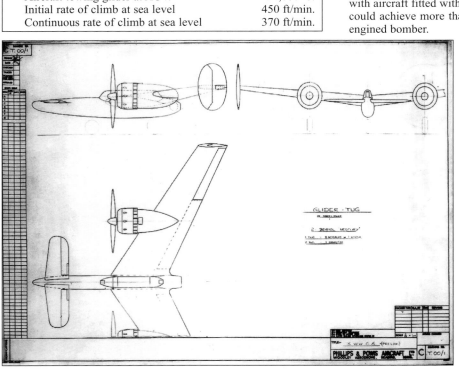

Left: Three-view G.A. (Preliminary) of The Glider Tug or Target Tower. Notes on drawing state: 2 x Bristol Mercury; 1 Tug, 3 Hotspurs or 1 Horsa; 2 Tugs, 1 Hamilcar.

Model of the M.39 High Speed Bomber.

Chapter 32
Miles M.39 High Speed Bomber to Spec. B.11/41, M.39A and M.39B Libellula Full Scale Flying Models and M.39C Libellula High Speed Bomber

In 1940, Hawker Aircraft Ltd tendered their design P.1005 for a High Speed Bomber with two Napier Sabre NS8SM (a high altitude development of the Sabre engine), or two Power Jets jet engines, and an AUW of 33,000 lb. Although the P.1005 did not quite meet the requirements of the specification, having an estimated range of only 1,500 miles at 329 mph, Hawkers were contracted to build two prototypes in 1941 and Specification B.11/41 was apparently later framed round this design to be issued to Hawker Aircraft Ltd on 3rd June 1942. In the event, since the development of the Sabre engines appeared likely to take some considerable time the Hawker project was not proceeded with.

About this time, Don Brown noticed in an RAE report on Specification No.B.11/41, dated 27th May 1942, which called for a 'High Speed Bomber Aircraft' to meet Operational Requirement OR.110. This requirement called for the design and construction of a high-speed bomber aircraft (which may fly either armed or unarmed), with a range of 1,500 miles at a height of 30,000 ft. with the defined military load which was expected to be a bomb load of 4,000 lb. The machine was to have a crew of two.

However, having been told about the specification, George Miles decided to submit the tandem-winged M.39 Libellula Bomber to the MAP.

The M.39 design proposal, which also envisaged the construction of a 5/8th scale flying model of wooden construction, was submitted to the MAP in July 1942 and wind tunnel experiments were put in hand, but at about the same time as the M.39 project was submitted to the Ministry, the contract to produce the Hawker P.1005 was cancelled. It is thought that the Ministry were obviously not prepared to order such an unorthodox machine as the M.39 but George Miles decided to proceed with the construction of the 5/8th flying scale M.39B anyway in order to prove the concept.

In June 1942, Phillips & Powis Aircraft Ltd produced a booklet on the Miles M.39 High Speed Bomber, which they submitted to the MAP in July 1942.

Miles M.39 High Speed Bomber

It is evident that the limit of performance with orthodox aeroplanes is rapidly being approached. Any further improvements can only be obtained at the cost of enormously increased power coupled with excessively high landing speeds and impaired manoeuvrability. The whole problem has been carefully reviewed with the idea of obtaining, if possible, enhanced performance and manoeuvrability without further increase of power and without increasing present landing speeds.

Of the many different layouts considered, the best solution appears to lie in a machine having, broadly speaking, a monoplane wing at either end of the fuselage, the engines being mounted on the rear wing. Such an aeroplane would not have the ordinary tail and empennage, and the centre of gravity would lie just aft of amidships between the wings. Unorthodox as the layout appears, it seems to possess a number of important advantages.

At first it might appear that the more usual tandem wing layout, as developed by Peyret around 1920 and later reintroduced by Delanne, might meet these requirements, but initial investigation shows that such a design would have very few advantages because of the inherent inefficiency of this arrangement and the very limited backward movement of the centre of gravity which can be attained in practice. The extended aft position of the CG is usually fixed on Delanne types at only about 50 - 60 per cent of the front wing chord, for reasons of stability. It can be seen, therefore, that only a relatively small improvement in layout can be obtained in comparison with an orthodox design. Other arrangements investigated were the tail-first type and the tailless aircraft. The disadvantages of these as compared with a conventional aeroplane are well known and may be briefly summarised as follows:

Tailless Aircraft

1. Low C_L max due to impossibility of balancing large C_p shift, caused by lift increasing devices.
2. Sensitivity to C_p shift.
3. Loss of efficiency resulting from large washout, which is essential for stability.
4. Large overall span.
5. Difficulty of providing effective landing gear.

Tail-first Aircraft

1. Restriction of view by front stabilising surface and supporting structure.
2. Sensitivity to C_p shift.
3. Excessive side area forward of CG.

Proposed Specification

It is, however, now understood that a high speed, lightly armed, high altitude bomber is of greater urgency, and the M.39 and M.39A projects have been based on this need. The essential characteristics envisaged are:

	M.39	M.39A
Bomb load	7,000 lb	4,000 lb
or 2 torpedoes	or 2 torpedoes	
Range in max weak mixture	1,600 miles	1,700 miles
at 31,000 ft.	with bombs	with bombs
or 2,500 miles	or 1,900 miles	
with torpedoes	with torpedoes	
Cruising speed at 31,000 ft	350 mph	380 mph

Rationalised flight factor - 2 x 2½ g.
Take off and climb to 50 ft in still air - Under 1,000 yards.

In the light of present knowledge, it would not appear to be possible to meet such requirements with a conventional aeroplane, but an investigation of a layout based on the Libellula principle suggests that such a specification may be fulfilled.

Principal Advantages of Proposed Design

The main advantages of this layout as applied to the purpose in question are:

(a) The saving in span as compared with an orthodox monoplane of the wing area and aspect ratio enables a very material saving in structure weight to be effected with a corresponding increase in military load.

(b) Not only is it possible that the advantages of both short span and high aspect ratio may be combined, but all horizontal surfaces are used for lift only. In this way the drag, weight and negative lift of the conventional tailplane are eliminated, and the structure weight, wing loading and wetted area correspondingly reduced.

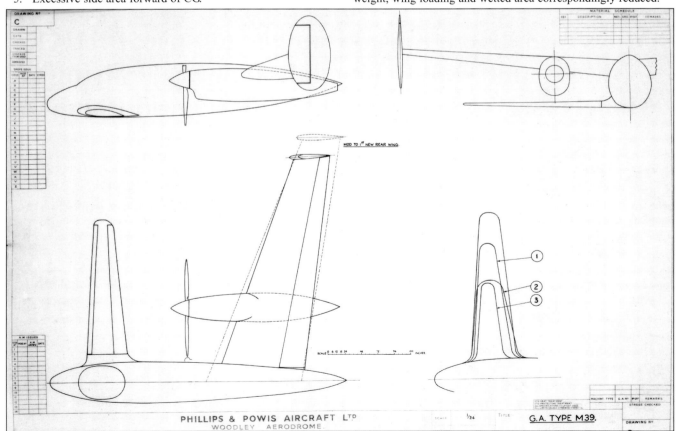

An undated three-view G.A. drawing of the Type M.39. Note twin fins and rudders and various front wing extensions. Note also Mod to 1st New Rear Wing.

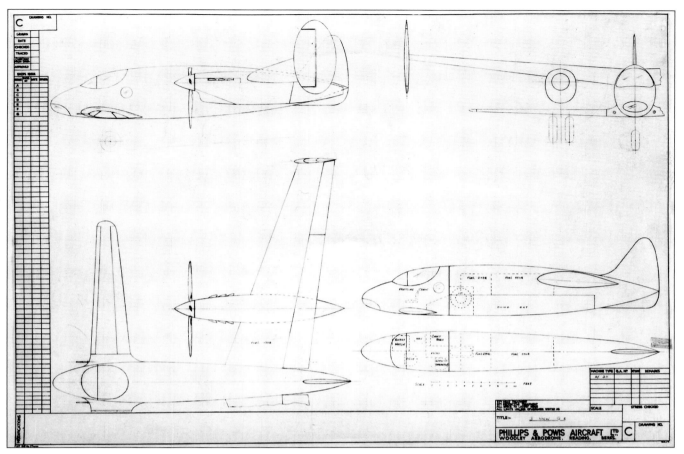

An undated three-view drawing of the M.39 showing three fins but only two rudders and twin main-wheel tricycle undercarriage.

(c) Due to the elimination of the conventional empennage the fuselage can be conveniently reduced in length, with corresponding further reduction in structure weight and wetted area.

(d) The reduction possible in overall dimensions not only effects a marked diminution in target area, but also promises to enhance the manoeuvrability for taking evasive action. Thus in the M.39, for approximately the same overall dimensions as the Blenheim, it appears possible to produce a bomber almost comparable in range and bomb load with the Halifax and having a greater top speed than the Hurricane.

(e) The proposed design provides an almost ideal layout for alternative means of propulsion in either one, two or three units, used either in combination with or independently from the orthodox power plants. It appeared, therefore, that in any endeavour to avoid these as well as many other disadvantages inherent in all previous types of aeroplane, it would be necessary to

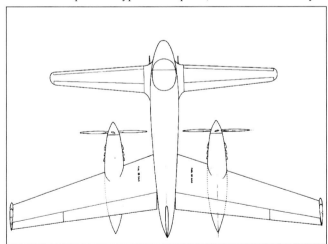

Above and below: Plan and front view of the M.39.

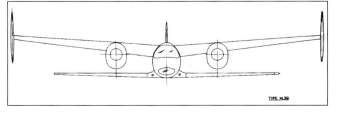

Side view drawings showing details of the M.39's pressure cabin with crew layout, fuel capacities and bomb bay. Note also two forward firing machine guns in the front wing root.

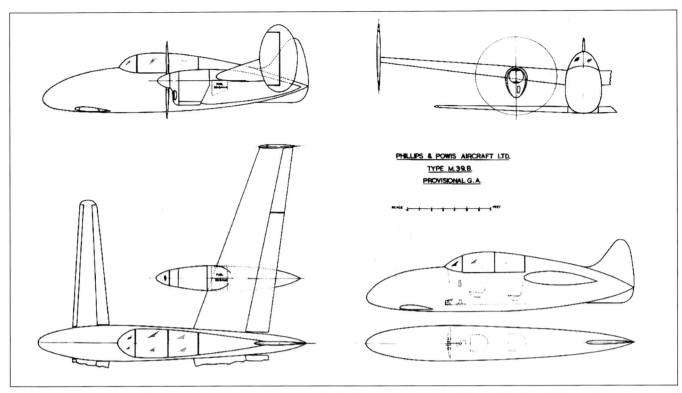

This Provisional three-view G.A. arrangement drawing shows the M.39B to have been powered by two DH Gipsy Major engines, to have had two seats in tandem in a cabin situated approximately midway along the fuselage and with three fins and rudders on the outer two fins only.

approach the problem from an entirely new standpoint. In the original conception of the Libellula layout, we were influenced by the problems of the Fleet Air Arm and the first projects were based on the special requirements of shipborne aircraft.

(f)   In conventional aeroplanes of this type the engines are almost inevitably sufficiently far ahead of the pilot to result in a serious restriction of his view sideways. This disadvantage is eliminated in the Libellula design and the view provided is as nearly perfect as possible on any aeroplane.

(g)   Owing to the short span, a very high percentage of the rear wing is covered by the propeller discs. In this way the "Crouch Bolas effect" becomes very marked and is of particular value during the take off at a high wing loading.

By virtue of the above advantages it is felt possible to attain a combination of speed, military load, range and take off, which would not be possible in an orthodox design.

Leading Particulars

	M.39	M.39A
Span	55 ft 0 ins	50 ft 0 ins
Length	35 ft 10 ins	35 ft 10 ins
Wing area	555 sq ft	450 sq ft
Engines	2 x Merlin 60 or Hercules VIII	2 x Merlin 60 or Hercules VIII
Tare weight	13,050 lb	12,300 lb
All-up weight	26,750 lb	22,500 lb
Range (at 31,000 ft)	1,600 miles at	1,700 miles at
Bomb load.	7,000 lb	4,000 lb
Estimated cruising speed (at 31,000 ft)	350 mph	380 mph
Wing loading at take-off	47.3 lb/sq ft	50.0 lb/sq ft
Power loading at take-off	10.1 lb/hp	8.65 lb/hp
Estd distance to unstick in still air	570 yards	550 yards
Estd distance to clear 50 ft in still air	950 yards	900 yards
Wing loading at landing	26 lb/sq ft	30 lb/sq ft

Construction

The airframe is of stressed-skin metal construction, with a tricycle undercarriage. The crew of three are accommodated in a pressure cabin in the nose. Due to the high speed, great operating height and good manoeuvrability which should result from the small size of the aircraft, the only armament provided consists of two fixed 20 mm cannon, mounted in the leading edge of the forward wing, close to the fuselage.

The bulk of the fuel is carried in the fuselage amidships, where it is protected by the engines on either side. A small quantity of fuel is also carried in the centre section of the rear wing. The bomb bay is amidships in the fuselage and is sufficiently wide to accommodate two 18" torpedoes.

Initial Development of Design

The Libellula layout, unorthodox though it appears, has recently been demonstrated as practicable by full-scale flight trials on the single-engined M.35. Although the data is as yet far from complete, these trials have shown the design to be well worthy of further investigation. Wind tunnel experiments on the M.39 are now projected and, parallel with the data to be so acquired, it is suggested that a wooden 5/8 scale flying model, the M.39B, should be built and flown to ensure that no time is lost in making available to the services any advantages which may result from the design.

This machine is shown in the accompanying general arrangement drawing, from which it will be seen that in every essential particular it is a faithful scale model of the M.39 *(Note: in fact the actual M.39B differed considerably from this initial design study - PA).*

For full details of the 5/8th scale M.39B Libellula, see the next chapter.

Meanwhile the detail design of the M.39 can be proceeding and by the time it is ready to go into production, the M.39B should have been completed and tested so that any improvements or modifications indicated could be incorporated in the design of the M.39 before the prototype is built.

Leading Particulars of M.39B

Span	35 ft 0 ins
Length	22 ft 6 ins
Wing Area	216 sq ft
Engines	2 Gipsy Major
All-up weight	3,200 lb
Wing loading at take off	14.8 lb/sq ft
Power loading at take off	12.3 lb/hp

The Specification was re-submitted to MAP in January 1944 as the Miles M.39C Libellula High-Altitude Unarmed Bomber:

Three-view G.A. drawings of the M.39C Libellula High Speed Bomber, all dated 8.10.43, show three different versions, all with twin fins and rudders and single wheel main undercarriage, as seen on this page.

Provision was also made for the M.39C to be fitted with 1,650 hp Bristol Hercules VIII very high-altitude engines but no drawings have survived to show this version.

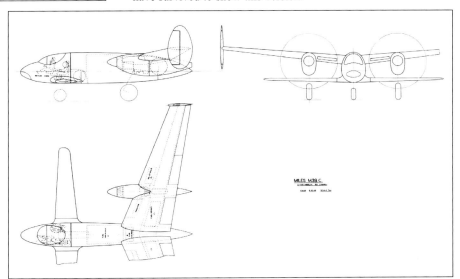

Right: The long range version, powered by two of the new 1,280 hp Rolls-Royce Merlin 68 engines, which had high-altitude performance. This had two fuel tanks installed above the bomb bay behind the cabin (the front tank 'A' holding 555.5 gallons and the rear tank 'B' holding 48 gallons), two fuel tanks ('Ci' and 'Cii', holding 88 gallons each) located in the wing between the fuselage and the engines, and two oil tanks ('D' holding 27 gallons each) which were positioned in the wings outboard of the engines. Two radiators were buried in the leading edge of the wings between the fuselage and the engines.

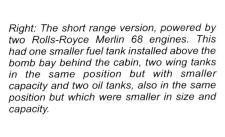

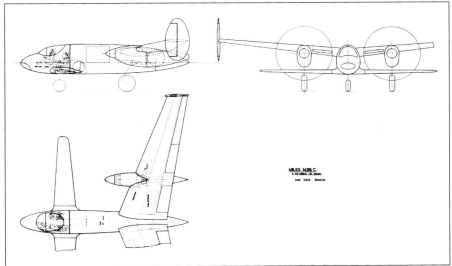

Right: The short range version, powered by two Rolls-Royce Merlin 68 engines. This had one smaller fuel tank installed above the bomb bay behind the cabin, two wing tanks in the same position but with smaller capacity and two oil tanks, also in the same position but which were smaller in size and capacity.

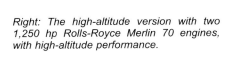

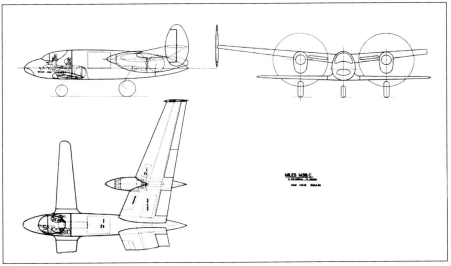

Right: The high-altitude version with two 1,250 hp Rolls-Royce Merlin 70 engines, with high-altitude performance.

Although the full programme of trials has not yet been completed, the results already obtained have been sufficiently encouraging to suggest that the estimated performance contained in the original submission was not optimistic. In fact it is noteworthy that the latest version of the specification has not needed alteration in any material particular. In the revised estimate submitted herewith the structure weights are assessed on the best available information relating to existing types, and the performance estimate is based on the preliminary results obtained in full-scale flights with the M.39B.

	M.39C	Mosquito IV	Douglas A-26
All-up Weight	26,750 lb	19,670 lb	31,709 lb
Gross Wing Area	556 sq ft	450 sq ft	540 sq ft
	(Both planes)		
Take-off Power (BHP)	2,480	2,600	4,000
Absolute Still Air Range	1,710 miles	1,710 miles	1,600 miles
Cruising speed	365 mph	290 mph	263 mph
and Height	27,000 ft	21,000 ft	13,500 ft
Corresponding Bomb Load	6,000 lb	1,000 lb	2,000 lb
Equipment Service Load	1,860 lb	2,420 lb	6,940 lb

The latter show a marked improvement in overall drag as compared with the orthodox aeroplane, and confirm the impression given by wind tunnel tests conducted by the NPL a year ago. The flight trials conducted to date have not revealed any adverse handling characteristics.

In the following specification, the loading assumed has been based upon the CG position which flight trials have shown to be practicable from the point of view of stability. It is possible that further trials may establish the possibility of moving the CG appreciably further aft. If this proves feasible, a very material increase will be possible in the disposable load, but for the purpose of this specification no such assumption has been made. A very brief overall comparison of the estimated performance of the M.39C, with those of two existing bombers is seen in the table above right.

These figures show that the M.39C shows promise of a very marked advance over the orthodox aeroplane both in regard to speed and disposable load. For instance comparing the M.39C with the Mosquito - which is generally accepted as being one of the best aeroplanes in service today - it is seen that, for the same range, the M.39C may offer a substantial increase of speed while carrying more than twice the disposable load.

Structural and Aerodynamic Data:

Areas	sq ft
Leading Plane	139
Main Plane	417
Fuselage, wetted	464
Fins and Rudders, wetted	74
Nacelles, wetted	262
CPF Factor	5

Weight Analysis	lb
Leading Plane	1,080
Main Plane	1,800
Fuselage and Pressure Cabin	1,800
Undercarriage	1,340
Fins, Rudders and Controls	500
Engine Mountings and Cowlings	555
Tanks (bare)	450
Structure Weight	7,525
Power Plant	5,350
Weight Empty	12,875
Crew and equipment	1,860
Fuel and Oil	6,015
Bombs	6,000
All-up Weight (lbs)	26,750

Drag Analysis	
Profile Drag in lb at 100 ft/sec	lb
Leading Plane	7.81
Main Plane	34.85

Fuselage	13.90
Fins and Rudders	6.25
Nacelles	13.43
Cooling	6.70
Leakage	6.70
	89.64
Interference	10.36
	100.00

Net Wing Area in Slipstream	233 sq ft

Transition point on area outside slipstream assumed as 40 per cent.

Aerofoil Data:
Wing section on both wings	NACA 66

Thickness Chord Ratio:	Root	Tip
Leading Plane	0.175	0.15
Main Plane	0.20	0.15

Performance
Maximum Cruising Speed at 27,000 ft - 365 mph (TAS)
Corresponding range - 1,710 miles
Economical Cruising Speed at 22,000 ft - 250 mph (TAS)
Corresponding range - 2,300 miles

Engine Data
Engines - 2 Merlin 70
Take-off Power - 1,240 BHP per engine
Maximum power at altitude - 1,475 BHP per engine
 at 23,300 ft
Maximum cruising power at altitude - 980 BHP per engine
 at 27,200 ft
Corresponding consumption - 79 gallons/hour
Economical cruising power at altitude - 700 BHP per engine
 at 22,000 ft
Corresponding consumption - 51.5 gallons/hour

The crew of three was situated in a pressure cabin; the pilot sat on the port side with the wireless operator behind him and the radio situated between him and the navigator, who sat behind the lower entry hatch on the starboard side facing aft towards his chart table.

Two fuel tanks were situated above the large bomb, the forward tank holding 275 gallons and the aft 550 gallons, and two fuel tanks were situated in the wings between the fuselage and the engine nacelles each holding 135 gallons.

The drawing also showed the two 20 mm forward firing cannons mounted in the leading edge of the wing to fuselage fairings.

In January 1943, Phillips & Powis Aircraft Ltd produced a brochure entitled 'Miles Specialised Aircraft for Specialised Purposes'. Contained therein was a summary of a selection of Miles aircraft which had either been built or proposed up to then.

The M.39 was included.

M.39 Libellula High Altitude Bomber

MAP Specification B.11/41 calls for an unarmed high altitude high speed bomber. For this purpose the Libellula layout is particularly suitable, so much so that in the M.39 it is possible to make the remarkable claim that it combines the speed of a Hurricane with the size and manoeuvrability of a Blenheim and yet carries the bomb load of a Halifax.

Span	55 ft 0 in
Wing area	555 sq ft
All up weight	26,750 lb
Engines	2 x Rolls-Royce Merlin 61
Cruising speed	350 mph at 31,000 ft
Range	1,600 miles
Bomb load	7,000 lb

Alternatively the same machine may be used as a long range torpedo bomber, in which case the range, when carrying two 18" or one 21" torpedo, is 2,500 miles.

The M.39 would have had a crew of three, who were housed in a pressure cabin, two in tandem on the port side and the third midway between the two, but facing aft, on the starboard side. The estimated cruising speed for the piston-engined version was 360 mph at 2,400ft, while that projected for the jet-engined version would have been 500 mph at 36,000ft. The M.39C, which would have been capable of carrying a bomb load of nearly 7,000lb, would have therefore combined the speed of a Spitfire with the bomb load of the Halifax, in an aeroplane of the same overall dimensions as the Mosquito!

Both de Havilland and Armstrong Whitworth also offered proposals to meet the requirement but in April 1942, they were informed that the Napier Sabre NS8SM engines would not be available. The high-speed bomber was never ordered and the requirement was cancelled on 3rd July 1942.

Although no details of a contract having been issued to Phillips & Powis Aircraft Ltd/Miles Aircraft Ltd for the manufacture of the M.39C have come to light, serial RR910 was allotted for one prototype M.39 aircraft on 12th November 1943, long after the requirement was cancelled. However, as it was also planned to install three jet engines in the M.39 when they became available, it is possible that the serial was allotted for the later version.

The RAE at Farnborough also appear to have looked into the possibility of a tail-first layout using two of the new and the highly secret turbojets designed at the Establishment by a team led by Hayne Constant (later to become Director of the National Gas Turbine Establishment) and then being built by Metropolitan Vickers, but I have not been able to find anything further on this project.

Don Brown was fired by enthusiasm for George Miles' Libellula tandem-winged layout, as it seemed to him that this design had distinct advantages, not only for his envisaged shipborne fighter but also for a bomber, particularly in view of the extended cg range and the reduction in target area that this layout offered. The idea of designing a high-altitude aircraft also appealed to Don because, in the small but closely knit team at Woodley, he had always been the one in favour of the high aspect ratio thin-wing, whereas Miles and George had always tended to favour thick low aspect ratio wings, on account of their undoubted structural advantages.

In the light of the data then being gained with the M.35, it appeared that the ratio of areas of the forward and rear wings needed revision, so this was reduced from the 1.2 of the M.35, to a value of 1.3 in the M.39. Don Brown also felt that the forward wing should be mounted low on the fuselage and the rear wing high so that the latter could be well clear of the downwash effect from the forward wing. This reversed the arrangement adopted in the M.35 and provided ground clearance for the propellers of the two engines, which were mounted on the rear wing.

George Miles always insisted that the M.39 was a true tandem-winged aircraft, hence the decision to name it the 'Libellula' - the Latin generic name for the Dragonfly. However, although this insect had genuine tandem wings, they were of *the same span and area*.

The ultimate version of the M.39 bomber was to be powered by three Power Jets W.2/500 jet engines, which were being designed by Frank Whittle and his team but this design was held back because the engines were not yet fully developed. It is of interest to note that the security surrounding the jet engine at the time was so effective that, had Don Brown not spent a year with the MAP before he joined the firm, they would have been completely unaware of its existence!

It was envisaged that, when these jet engines ultimately became available it would have been a relatively simple task to replace the piston engines with them; another advantage of the Libellula layout, as such a substitution would have been practically impossible in an orthodox aeroplane. In late 1944, the M.63 mailplane/bomber was in fact projected, to have been powered by either two or three jet engines and details of this will be found in the next volume.

The M.39 was to have been of all-metal construction, with a crew of three being accommodated in a pressurised cockpit, and a tricycle undercarriage. The armament was two 20 mm Hispano-Suiza cannon mounted in the wing root of the forward wing, and the wide bomb bay situated amidships could have carried either 7,000lb of bombs or even two 18" torpedoes. Wings of high-aspect ratio were used which gave a high wing loading by the standards of the day. Elevators were fitted to the inboard section of the forward wing and flaps fitted outboard, both being in the form of trailing edge flaps. The rear wing, which carried the two tractor engines, had flaps inboard and ailerons outboard, with fins and rudders at the wing tips.

However, it is also possible that the reason behind the cancellation of Specification B.11/41 was that production of the DH Mosquito

MILES M39 - 39A. DEVELOPMENTS.
HIGH SPEED BOMBER.
(ENGINES — MERLIN OR HERCULES.)

An early, undated, artist's impression of M.39-M.39A Developments. High Speed Bomber (Engines Merlin or Hercules). Note these had three fins and rudders.

was by then well under way, and it was considered that this aircraft would be more than capable of adequately fulfilling its requirements.

In the event, the M.39B was first flown, by George Miles, on 22nd July 1943 and it proved to have perfectly normal handling characteristics.

The firm also decided to take out a patent covering the tandem-wing layout and both George Miles and Don Brown spent many hours in the Patent Office in Chancery Lane, London, collaborating with a Patents Agent whose legal phraseology and jargon they did not really understand any better than he understood the technicalities of their idea which they were required to describe in his language!

To their disappointment nothing came of the Libellula project but many years later, the Avro Blue Steel stand-off bomb was produced and also the Swedish SAAB Viggen fighter, both of which were, in effect, tandem winged aircraft. The British and American authorities were also investigating various layouts for future supersonic aircraft and it seemed that the tandem wing layout might well be adopted for some of these.

On 5th November 1957, George Miles' original patents, Nos. 563,467 of 1942 and 578,978 of 1944 were extended to cover these possible applications and the new patent, No. 844,614 for a 'Tandem-Winged Aircraft', was taken out in the joint names of F G Miles Ltd, George Herbert Miles and Donald Lambert Brown and read:

It has been previously proposed to provide a tandem-winged aircraft with a forward wing structure in the form of a stabilising aerofoil which is mounted above and in front of the centre of gravity of the aircraft whereby the lift and drag applied to the centre of pressure of this wing have an appreciable moment relatively to the transverse axis through the centre of gravity, which tends to pull up the nose of the aircraft and consequently gives it a satisfactory pendula stability. It has also been proposed to control the lift of the forward wing of the aircraft by providing for the incidence of at least a part to be adjustable from the pilot's seat, and for this purpose it may be pivoted about a transverse axis passing through its centre of pressure. In contra-distinction from the object to be achieved by the above construction, which is adaptable only to aircraft of relatively low speed, the present invention is particularly concerned with high speed aircraft and, therefore, the introduction of any appreciable moment relative to the transverse axis passing through the centre of gravity is to be avoided. With continual increase of the speed and altitude performance of aircraft, designers are faced with the problem of providing greater longitudinal stability and control to overcome the difficulties arising from the displacement of the centre of pressure which occurs at sonic speed, &c., and the object of the invention is to provide an aircraft having improved longitudinal stability and control. The invention consists of an aircraft in which the forward wing is of less area than the rearward wing, the forward wing being mounted for restricted rotation about an axis transversal of the longitudinal axis of the aircraft to provide longitudinal control and is situated, when the aircraft is horizontal, close to the horizontal plane passing through the centre of gravity of the aircraft. It is preferred to make the area of the forward wing about one-quarter to one-third the area of the rearward wing. In the case of high-speed aircraft it is preferred to provide both wing structures with a low aspect ratio and a thickness/chord ratio not exceeding 7½ per cent, but in the case of low speed aircraft this would not be applicable. Also either or both wings may be fitted with lift increasing devices if desired, while the forward wing in particular may be arranged to incorporate means of controlling the flow of the boundary layer. 17th August 1960.

Since then, many variations of the tandem wing layout have been projected and actually used, such as the Rutan light aircraft of 1975 and the Beechcraft 2000 Starship 1 of 1986. Its use on the Blue Steel Stand-off bomb was the subject of litigation between George Miles and Don Brown on the one hand and the Ministry of Defence on the other for very many years over tandem wing patent infringement.

SPECIFICATION AND PERFORMANCE DATA
(Note: The figures from the brochure may differ in certain respects from the following due to the number of different projects).

Miles M.39 Libellula Bomber
Engines: 2 x Rolls-Royce Merlin
Dimensions: span, forward wing 39ft 3in, rear wing 55ft 0in; length 35ft 9in
Weights: not known
Performance: not known

Miles M.39-M.39A Developments. High Speed Bomber
Engines: Merlin or Hercules

Nothing further known.

Miles M.39B Libellula Flying Scale Model
Engine: 2 x 140 hp DH Gipsy Major IC
Dimensions: span, front wing 25ft 0in, rear wing 37ft 6in; length 22ft 4in; height 9ft 3in; wing area, front wing 62 sq ft, rear wing 187 sq ft; aspect ratio, front wing 10.1, rear wing 7.5; wing section, front wing root NACA 23018, tip NACA 2412, rear wing root NACA 23021, tip NACA 2415; sweepback on leading edge of rear wing 21° 48'
Weights: tare 2,405lb; fuel (25 gal) 188lb; oil (3 gal) 27lb; pilot 180lb; AUW 3,200lb
Performance: max speed 164 mph; stalling speed, flaps down 59 mph; rate of climb 1,100ft/min; run to unstick 435ft; distance to 50ft 855ft; landing run 495ft; landing run over 50ft 1,275ft

Miles M.39C Libellula Bomber
Engines: 2 x 1,280 hp Rolls-Royce Merlin 68 or 70; or 2 x Power Jets W.2/500 jet engines
Dimensions: span, front wing 37ft 6in, rear wing 55ft 9in; length 35ft 10in; wing area, front wing139 sq ft, rear wing 417 sq ft; aspect ratio, forward wing 11.1, rear wing 7.25; wing section, both wings NACA 66; thickness/chord ratio, forward wing, root 0.175c, tip 0.15c, rear wing, root 0.20c, tip 0.15c
Weights: empty 12,875lb; fuel (585 gal) 4,210lb; oil (90 gal) 810lb; crew 600lb; military equipment 1,255lb; defined military load, unarmed 5,769lb, armed 6,836.5lb; AUW 26,750lb
Bomb load: 6,000 lb
Performance: weak mixture cruising speed at 24,000ft (Rolls-Royce Merlins) 360 mph (with jet engines 500 mph at 36,000ft); max range with 6,000lb bomb load 2,900 miles; range at 360 mph 1,750 miles

The M.39B Libellula 5/8th flying scale model under construction in the Experimental Department at Liverpool Road, Reading.

Chapter 33
Miles M.39B Libellula 5/8th Flying Scale Model

Following the early flight tests of the M.35, George Miles decided to design an aircraft of the tandem wing type to meet the requirements of Spec B.11/41, which called for a high-speed bomber. However, in order to flight test the principle and feasibility of his revised tandem winged design (it should be mentioned that George Miles used to get annoyed when it anyone referred to it as a Canard but I have no idea of what he must have thought of the RAE's definition of it as a 'tandem biplane'!), he decided first to build a 5/8th scale flying model of the proposed M.39 High Speed Bomber. This became the M.39B Libellula and in 1943, Ray Bournon (under George Miles' direction) began preparing the design, which was built by the Experimental Department at Liverpool Road, Reading and given the designation LR.3. It was of wooden construction and was powered by two 140 hp DH Gipsy Major IC engines. The layout of this new design differed from the M.35 in having a low forward wing at the front of the fuselage with the rear wing, which carried the two engines and twin-fins and rudders at the tips, mounted near the top of the fuselage.

The aircraft industry was notified by the MAP that Dr F W Lanchester had been retained as a consultant and that his services were available to any firm. This remarkable man, then 74 years of age, was a true combination of scientist and engineer. His basic scientific knowledge was profound, as evidenced in a lecture in Birmingham in 1894 when he put forward the concepts which, many years later, were recognised as the basis of the theory of lift and drag. This theory, which revolutionised practice in the fields of aircraft and propeller design was also discussed by him in two volumes, published in 1907.

The availability of Dr Lanchester's services was very welcome and, since the tandem-wing layout was such a new concept, Don Brown flew to Castle Bromwich in Monarch G-AGFW on 7th June 1943 to consult him. Shown the drawings of the M.39B, the Doctor's first question was, 'Why on earth should anyone want to build an aeroplane of this layout?' This question was easily answered and a long and interesting discussion ensued on the problems involved. Throughout the subsequent flight trials, Lanchester asked to be kept fully informed of the results obtained and, in fact, right up to the time of his death three years later, he never lost interest in the development of the Libellula.

Upon completion, the M.39B was taken by road to Woodley where, during the initial taxiing trials, George Miles managed 'to knock the nose-gear out' but this was soon repaired and Don Brown

The M.39B, U-0244, photograph probably taken about the time of its first flight as this Miles Aircraft Ltd print was dated 28th July 1943.

U-0244 in flight showing its clean lines.   *[Miles Aircraft Ltd photograph via T R Judge]*

records that it was first flown, by George Miles, with 'B' mark **U-0244**, on 22nd July 1943. A 1947 report in *The Aeroplane Spotter* stated that its first flight was 10th July 1943 but although George Miles' log books are missing for this period, it is more likely to have been the 22nd July 1943.

Assistant test pilot Hugh Kennedy made a 'Handling' flight later on 22nd July, which tends to confirm that this was the day of its first flight. Hugh then made ten further flights in U-0244 as follows: 'Handling' 7.8.43 and 16.8.43; 'PE (Position Error)' 19.8.43; 'Local' 20.8.43; no duty recorded 24.8.43; 'Local' 7.12.43; 'Handling' 4.1.44, 5.1.44 and four on 14.1.44; 'Local' 16.1.44.

Unlike the M.35, the M.39B proved to be perfectly stable over a wide range of centre of gravity positions and entirely normal in its handling characteristics. The permissible range of cg movement was found to be much greater than that normally obtainable with any other type of aeroplane. In fact its permissible cg range was so wide that the forward limit was only determined by running out of elevator control and touching down nosewheel first; the aft limit was determined not, as is usual, by lack of longitudinal stability but by the position of the main units of the undercarriage.

The only snag encountered in the early flights was a structural one. Since the aircraft was a one-off experimental type, every effort was made to beat all records as regards structural weight but this praiseworthy aim was carried a little too far and it was found that the strength of the fuselage was barely adequate. Don Brown recalled that if a bump or slight turbulence was encountered, the front fuselage (containing the pilot!) oscillated laterally in a rather disconcerting manner. However, since the aircraft was of wooden construction, the fuselage was easily re-skinned in order to effect a cure.

As originally built, the front wing of the Libellula had slotted elevators inboard and slotted flaps outboard, and an unusual feature was in the use of the flaps. Since these were fitted to both wings it was possible, by small adjustments, to use them for trimming purposes and they were so effective that it was possible to trim the aircraft to fly straight and level with the control column in any position from fully forward to fully back. This feature necessitated an unusual addition to the pre-landing check list, namely that one had to look down into the cockpit when in the landing configuration and check that the aircraft was so trimmed that sufficient backward elevator movement was available for effecting the flare-out.

An interesting letter dated 7th October 1943 and marked SECRET, from George Miles to Col H G Bunker, USAAC, then based in West London, has been recently discovered by Jim Pratt, George Miles' son-in-law and this gave details of the M.35, M.39 and M.39B Libellula projects:

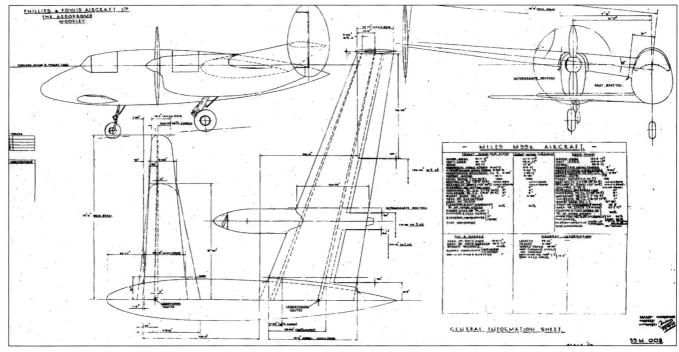

Three-view G.A. drawing of the M.39B. Note: this drawing shows the extended front wing but does not show the third, central, fin.

The M.39B which you have seen is a scale model of this aeroplane and, as you know, has now done a considerable amount of flying with most encouraging results. A dimensional three-view drawing is enclosed herewith.

Leading particulars of this aircraft are:-

Span - Front wing	*25 ft. 0 ins*
Span - Rear wing	*37 ft. 6 ins*
Length	*22 ft. 4 ins*
Wing area - Front wing	*62 sq. ft*
Wing area - Rear wing	*187 sq. ft*
All up weight	*3,200 lb*
Power plants	*2 Gipsy Major engines*
Airscrews	*Fixed pitch, wooden*

Performance tests are still proceeding with the aircraft which, as you know, is a single-seater and, although position error determination has been carried out over the high speed end of the speed range, I have not, as yet, been able to obtain reliable figures for the position error near the stall. The lowest indicated landing speed achieved so far is 48 mph ASI and if an adverse position error of 10 mph is assumed, it will be seen that the overall C_L compares quite favourably with orthodox types, particularly in view of the fact that as yet we have tried only the first of a series of front wings which has a comparatively simple form of flap. Later we propose to try out alternative front wings embodying more effective high lift devices which will be similar in design to those proposed for the full scale aircraft. This machine has not yet been stalled and the speed quoted above is at an incidence which seems to be fairly well below the stalling incidence.

The overall drag of the M.39B appears to be of the order of 63 pounds at 100 ft/sec. This I think is very promising since, although the aircraft is reasonably clean, it has been impossible to keep the engine nacelles down to the correct size for an exact scale model and the cabin and windscreen also are not quite as clean as they would be on the full scale job. The take-off has proved to compare very reasonably with an orthodox aeroplane of similar power and the climb is definitely better that we expected. Stability with controls fixed is satisfactory in all three axes over the cg range so far investigated and there is no reason to suppose that they will not be equally good with stick free.

The third fin, which you will notice on the photographs, was intended as a temporary appendage only and flight tests have been carried out both with it fitted and without it. The impression we have gained is that the handling characteristics of the aeroplane are improved with additional fin area although I think that the centre one is much larger than is really necessary. Probably a slight alteration in the lines of the rear end of the fuselage is all that is required to dispense entirely with the centre fin.

Now that our preliminary tests are completed we propose to dismantle the machine for certain structural alterations to the rear wing which flight tests have indicated to be advisable. This, however, was not unexpected since major design alterations were made half way through the construction of the aeroplane due to the non-availability of the type of engines originally specified, which resulted in a rather flexible rear wing and we had anticipated the possibility of trouble from this source. Small alterations will also be made to the ailerons and rear flaps since these were shown to be somewhat overbalanced on the first flights and although this snag was easily cured by the addition of trailing edge strips we propose to move the hinge points forward slightly.

We have a film, which I showed you, depicting the aircraft in flight and I am having a copy of this made and will send it on to you in due course. We have also made tentative proposals for a number of operational aircraft of generally similar layout and I shall be glad to let you have provisional information on these if you require it. In the meantime, however, I think the above information is fairly comprehensive and it is only necessary to add that the experience we have gained with these two aircraft has confirmed our belief

that the energetic investigation of unorthodox types is well worth while and that the Libellula tandem wing arrangement shows promise of possessing important advantages over the more usual tailless and tail-first arrangements.

The firm received the usual reprimand from the Ministry when the existence of the M.39B became known, despite the fact that in the submission of the original M.39 project it had been clearly stated that a flying scale model would be built! However, in late 1943/early 1944, the Ministry announced their intention to purchase the aircraft and continue the flight trials at the RAE Farnborough. George Miles pleaded to be allowed to complete the trials programme then in progress but permission was refused on the grounds that, with the superior facilities available at the RAE, the programme could be completed far more speedily.

The M.39B was allotted serial **SR392** in early 1944 and was also given the RAF Experimental Aeroplane No.217 for identification purposes.

It was duly delivered to the RAE Farnborough, but on 17th May 1944, Sqdn Ldr D D Weightman DFC of Aerodynamic Flight, RAE Farnborough was landing in heavy rain on his first flight in the type and was so concentrating on the flap setting, that he forgot to select undercarriage down! The warning horn did not operate either, because the throttles were insufficiently closed for landing and the damaged M.39B was duly returned to Miles Aircraft Ltd, Woodley for repairs.

Above: SR392 in flight.

The project pilot allocated to the M.39B at the RAE Farnborough was Cdr Eric Brown RN who had joined the RAE as an experimental test pilot with the Aerodynamics Flight in January 1944. He recalled later that it was kept in 'A' Shed, which was known as the 'Heinz Hangar' - because of its association with what seemed like the 57 different varieties of aircraft being kept in it! Eric Brown first flew the M.39B on 30th June 1944, after the two mishaps at Farnborough but he was concerned mainly with stability and control rather than performance, in order to prove the tandem-wing configuration. Eric Brown reported on the handling of the M.39B as follows:

I found taxi-ing very easy with the steerable nosewheel tied in with the rudder bar, although, because it could not be disconnected, it made for some problems with landing. The flaps were operated manually by two levers and both the front and rear flaps could be moved five notches. The front flaps had a very powerful nose-up effect on trim and were generally counteracted by the rear flaps, so it was normal to operate them in turn one notch at a time, there were no trimmers fitted.

The Aero Flight was particularly interested in the stalling characteristics of the tandem-wing layout, and carried out extensive tests in that region of the flight envelope, usually at a height of 5,000ft. I found that with no flaps the aircraft could not be stalled, but, with the front flap, stalls were, in general, gentle and straightforward, with the nose dropping increasingly sharply until an angle of 50° was reached at the 5/0 setting. Use of the rear flap, with the front flap at maximum extension (in order to retain enough backward elevator power to stall the aircraft), produced stalls with no warning and gave a sharp nose drop, but, as the rear flap setting increased, the ease of inducing any fore and aft porpoising motion got less until it was completely eliminated at the 5/3 setting. The height loss in the stall was a mere 100ft. At the 5/4 and 5/5 settings, the aircraft would not stall but settled into a stable descent at increasing airspeed as the rear flap setting increased.

Landing the Libellula was 'a very straightforward affair' with the approach being made engine assisted at 75 mph with a flap setting of 4/2. The view was superb and the controls, except the rudders (which I thought were 'sloppy'), effective. If corrective rudder was applied just before touchdown the nosewheel would contact the ground off-centre and the violence of the self-centring action could burst the tyre or give the pilot's ankles a good wrench on the rudder bar!

I thoroughly enjoyed flying this unusual aircraft because it was so much out of the ordinary run of conventional design, but I could never really see it as a serious test vehicle for a naval operational aircraft.

On 2nd November 1944, Hugh Kennedy made a 'Test' flight and on 9th November 1944, he made a 'Delivery Fight' (back to RAE Farnborough). Shortly after being returned to the RAE, it was parked unnoticed behind a larger aircraft whose engine was then run up, with the result that the M.39B was blown onto its rear fuselage, necessitating yet another return to Woodley for repairs, although this incident was not apparently officially recorded!

By this time George Miles was feeling sorely tempted to enquire whether this was what was meant by *completing the trials more speedily owing to the superior facilities available at the RAE!* However, it was probably just as well that he did not, because on 6th September 1945, Miles test pilot Ken Waller, having completed a test flight, landed with the undercarriage retracted! He had selected undercarriage down and although the lights remained red, and the warning horn sounded, he assumed that it was an electrical failure and did not check further!

The RAE published two reports on the results of their tests and these are reproduced here:

Technical Note No. Aero.1499 (Flight)

August 1944

ROYAL AIRCRAFT ESTABLISHMENT, FARNBOROUGH

Flight tests of the Miles Libellula (M.39B)
tandem biplane

Part I. Interim note on performance and
handling in the original condition

- by -

P Brotherhood, DLC
and
J R Evans, BSc, DIC

RAE Ref: Aero.1373/JRE/140

SUMMARY

The Libellula (M.39B) is a single-seat twin-engined tandem biplane built by Miles Aircraft Ltd to give data on tail-first aircraft. This note gives the results obtained from brief flight tests at RAE up to the time of writing.

Handling characteristics are normal for aircraft of this power and wing loading and do not differ from those of a conventional aircraft. The aileron control is rather sluggish at low speeds.

With the present amount of lift on the front wing it is not possible to use more than about 10° of flap on the rear wing for landing. It is obvious therefore that further development should aim at the provision of adequate high lift, in order to explore more fully the capabilities of the type.

The maximum level speed at sea level is 166 mph.

CONTENTS

1. Introduction
2. Description of the aircraft
3. Performance
4. Handling tests
   4.1 Stability and control
   4.2 One-control tests
   4.3 Single engine flying
   4.4 Ground handling, take-off and landing
5. Conclusions

1. Introduction

The M.39B "Libellula" is a tandem biplane designed and built as a private venture by Miles Aircraft Ltd.

The programme of flight tests immediately projected on the aircraft with the present wing arrangement, covers brief performance, trim curves at three C.G. positions and handling tests. As the stalling and spinning characteristics of the type are unknown, it is not proposed to measure CLMAX until tail parachutes have been fitted.

This note presents the information so far obtained, and is not intended to represent the results of a complete programme of tests. At time of writing, the aircraft is undergoing a 30-hour inspection.

The M.39B was first received at the RAE on 17th January 1944. After three flights it was obvious that a more reliable undercarriage retraction system was required and this was incorporated by the firm. The aircraft was received back on 24th April 1944, instruments were fitted and flight testing commenced.

Three accidents have delayed the programme considerably:-

(i)   The aircraft was pushed into a crane, causing slight damage.

(ii) The pilot omitted to lower his undercarriage before landing - this damaged the propeller tips, and the under-surfaces of the fuselage and nacelles.

(iii) The aircraft was left tail to wind and this blew it backwards resulting in damage to the central fin and aft end of the fuselage.

      So far 16 hrs 20 mins flying has been made at RAE since the undercarriage retraction system was modified.

      The aircraft number is SR392.

2. Description of the aircraft

The M.39B is a single-seat, twin-engined tandem biplane of wooden construction, fitted with a retractable tricycle undercarriage. The engines are Gipsy Major Mk.IC, and drive fixed pitch airscrews. The aircraft is intended as a flying model of a larger aircraft.

A 3-view general arrangement drawing is given in Fig.1 and aerodynamic data in Table I.

The rear wing is swept back and fitted with plain flaps inboard and ailerons outboard. The front wing is fitted with elevators inboard and plain flaps outboard. The flaps on either wing may be lowered independently for test purposes; lowering the flaps on the front wing causes the elevators to droop, giving added lift.

Throughout this note flap positions have been quoted in the form "A/B" where "A" is the position of the front flap and "B" the position of the rear flap. These positions are measured in divisions from the flaps-up condition. A full calibration is given in Fig.2, but roughly one division of the front flap lever corresponds to a flap angle of 9° and a droop of the elevator of about 3°. One division of the rear flap lever corresponds to a flap angle of about 4°.

End plate fins and rudders are fitted to the rear wing, and a central fin is provided on the fuselage. No trimmers are provided on any control.

A noteworthy feature is that the centre of gravity is about 40% of the distance between the quarter chord points of the two wings forward of the quarter chord point of the rear wing. In normal flight the front wing is thus taking about 40% of the weight of the aircraft.

3.   *Performance*

3.1   Position Error

The pitot-static head is under the nose of the fuselage. Position error has been measured by flights over a 7½-mile speed course and the results are given in Fig.3. It will be noted that there is a positive correction of about 12 mph over the whole speed range.

3.2   Level speeds

Values of the maximum level speed, corrected in the normal way for temperature and position error are plotted in Fig.4.

4.   *Handling tests*

Throughout this paragraph speeds quoted our pilot's A.S.I. readings corrected for instrument error only and centre of gravity positions are in terms of percentage of the distance between the quarter-chord positions of the front and rear wings ahead of the quarter-chord point of the latter.

4.1   Stability and control

4.11   Longitudinal stability and control

Trim curves at a normal centre of gravity position (37.3%) are given in Fig.5 for two rear flap positions. They indicate that the aircraft is longitudinally stable in this condition.

Longitudinal control is satisfactory. The only means of trimming is however by means of elastic cord attached to the control column, and pilots preferred to lower the front flaps to give approximate trim. Thus at flap settings of 2/0 at cruising speed or 1/0 on the climb the stick was approximately trimmed.

The front flap is not powerful enough to balance the moment produced by lowering full rear flap. Thus a rear flap setting of 2 (8° down) was the most that could be used while still allowing sufficient stick moment for flattening out on landing, and a rear flap setting of 3 (12½° down) was the most considered desirable for use in flight.

It thus became obvious that there is insufficient lift on the front wing to balance the pitching moment due to lowering the flaps on the rear wing. A slightly increased incidence on the front wing would also be desirable to give zero elevator angle in the maximum speed and cruising speed conditions.

In flight, it is recommended to lower the front flap before the rear flap, and to keep it 1 to 2 positions further down than the rear flap. The elevators became less effective as front flap is lowered.

4.12   Directional stability and control

With the added central fin the directional stability is adequate. There is practically no change of directional trim throughout the speed range. Rudder control is satisfactory at all speeds.

4.13   Lateral control

The ailerons are effective at high speed, but become sluggish and ineffective below about 85 mph especially if the rear flap is lowered.

4.2   One control tests

4.21   Control by rudder

These tests were made in the cruising configurations:-

115 mph A.S.I.; 2,100 rpm; 3,000 ft
Flaps 1/0

When the rudder is displaced and freed, ailerons fixed, there is a small amount of swing, the aircraft banks quickly, and commences to turn.

Good turns are possible on rudder alone. Gentle application of rudder produces 1° - 2° of swing; sudden application of rudder produces 3° of swing, and in either case a correct turn is set up.

If the aircraft is held in a 30° turn with rudder, the aileron being fixed central, and the rudder is freed, the turn remains steady.

In none of the above tests was there any difference between port and starboard application of rudder.

The maximum steady rate of flat turn to port is 180° per minute, aileron being the limiting control. Full aileron cannot be applied as the stick comes against the pilot's knee; ¾ rudder is needed. To starboard rather more aileron can be applied (there is more space on this side of the cockpit), and this requires nearly full right rudder, giving a slight increase in rate of turn.

4.22   Control by ailerons

These tests were made at the following conditions:-

110 mph A.S.I.; 2,000 rpm; 3,000 ft
Flaps 1/0

When the ailerons are displaced fairly quickly and released, with rudder fixed, there is a small amount of yaw (about 3°) before aircraft banks. The stick returns to central, but the aircraft continues in the turn. Application of rudder with stick still free will bring the wing up. Behaviour to port and starboard is identical.

Sudden application of the ailerons causes more yaw, and the nose rises.

Good turns are possible with ailerons only, there being very little slip on going in or coming out.

4.23   Straight side slip

The aircraft was trimmed in a normal glide, flaps up, at 110 mph, and then put into a straight side-slip, (15° on the side-slip indicator). About 40° bank could be obtained, the rudder being the limiting control. Three-quarters aileron is required, and there is a small amount of nose-heaviness.

Behaviour to port and starboard is identical

4.3   Single Engine Flying

4.31   Effect of cutting one engine suddenly

The test was made from cruising speed in the following conditions:-

105 mph A.S.I.; 1,900 rpm; 3,000 feet
Flaps 1/0

On cutting the port engine suddenly, the aircraft immediately banks about 15° to port and swings fairly fast in the same direction with a rapid decrease of speed. The nose then begins to drop, bank increases, and a steep spiral commences if no corrective action is taken.

On cutting the starboard engine, the bank becomes about 25° and the swing is rather faster than to port. Otherwise behaviour is similar

4.32   Steady flight on one engine

Straight and level flight can be maintained with the port engine at full throttle (2,100 rpm) and the starboard engine throttled right back (850 rpm) at an airspeed of 85 mph at 3,000 ft. About 90% of full rudder travel is required and the force is large (this is in part due to the increase of rudder: rudder bar gearing near maximum travel).

With the starboard engine on (2,100 rpm) and the port engine throttled (850 rpm) the speed for straight and level flight is 80 mph at 3,000 ft, and full rudder is required

No aileron is required in either case.

Under the same conditions, but with the rudder fixed central it is possible to keep laterally level with nearly full aileron towards the live engine, but the aircraft is turning fairly quickly towards the dead engine.

Single-engined flight is unpleasant, because of the low speed (and bad aileron control) for level flight, and the large rudder load required. At the weight flown height could be maintained on one engine.

4.4   Ground handling, take-off, and landing

4.41   Ground handling

The steerable nose wheel operated off the rudder bar makes ground handling very simple, although the high tick-over speed of the engines makes fast taxying the rule. The possibility of landing with some rudder on (e.g. in a cross wind) so that the nose wheel was not pointing in the direction of motion at the instant touching down, was adversely commented on. This might lead to structural failure,

---

TABLE I

LIBELLULA (M.39B)

Aerodynamic data

GENERAL:		FLAPS: FRONT WING	
Mean weight during trials lbs	2,600	Type	plain
Engines (2)	DH Gipsy Major Mk.IC	Movement	44.5°
Max H.P. at sea level	140	Flap area sq ft	3.62
Wing loading: front lbs/sq ft	17.1	Flaps area/S'	5.87%
Wing loading: rear lbs/sq ft (Assuming centres of pressure at 0.33 chord)	8.2	Flap chord/local chord	30%
		Flap span/2 s'	33.6%
C.G. h (mean position) measured forward from rear wing quarter-chord point expressed as a fraction of distance between quarter-chord points of the two wings: (chassis up)	0.386	REAR WING	
		Type	plain
Airscrew diameter ft	6.5	Movement	21°
		Flap area sq ft	27.7
WINGS: FRONT WING		Flap area/S	14.78%
Area gross S' sq ft	61.7	Flap chord/local chord	30%
Area nett sq ft	51.0	Flap span/2 s	42.7%
Span 2 s' ft	25.0	LONGITUDINAL CONTROL	
Geometric mean chord ft	2.47	Area of elevators sq ft	8.75
Quarter-chord point aft L.E. at CL ft	0.92	Area of elevators/S'	14.2%
Aspect ratio	10.1	Elevator chord/local chord	30%
Dihedral on datum line	1° 15'	Elevator movement flaps up	(-19.5° (+26.5°
Taper ratio	0.436	Elevator movement flaps down	(-5.8 (+45°
Sweep back on L.E.	3°		
Incidence to thrust line (1.75' to CL)	3°	Distance between front and rear wing aerodynamic centres ft	12.6
Incidence to thrust line (12.5' to CL	2°		

or damage to the pilot's foot owing to the sudden kick given to the rudder bar by the nose wheel.

4.42 Take-off

Take-off is very simple, the steerable nose will making it very easy to correct any tendency to swing. So far no rear flap has been used for take-off, although it is proposed to measure take-off speeds with up to two divisions of rear flap.

The effect of front flap on take-off is as follows:-

Flaps 0/0: The aircraft requires to be pulled off the ground very firmly.

Flaps 1/0: A slight backward pressure on the stick is required to ease the aircraft off the ground.

Flaps 2/0: The aircraft will fly itself off with the stick held neutral at 80 mph.

This is the ideal setting for take-off.

4.43 Approach

The flaps are lowered by hand with very little effort.

When gliding with the flaps at 4/2 the pilot has an impression of sinking at 70 mph, and of diving at 90 mph. The normal approach speed would be 80 mph, but in order to obtain sufficient control for flattening out a minimum approach speed of 87 mph is recommended without engine, or 77 mph engine assisted. In gusty weather conditions, the sluggish aileron control requires that the approach speed should be kept up to about 82 mph. This corresponds to a true airspeed of 95 mph and this is very fast for an aircraft of this wing loading, even allowing for the fact that very little rear flap can be used. It is apparent that much higher lift is required on the front wing, so that a reasonable flap angle say (40°) can be used on the rear wing.

4.44 Landing

Landing is straightforward at the normal C.G. position. The optimum flap position is 4/2. With less front flap or more rear flap a large rearward stick movement is required to flatten out.

5. Conclusions

The conclusions drawn at this stage of the tests must necessarily be limited. One of the most interesting items of information will be the stalling speed and behaviour at the stall. It is not proposed to investigate this until tail parachutes have been fitted.

No peculiarities of handling of this aircraft have been noted as compared with a conventional aircraft of similar wing and power loading - in fact a pilot flying blind would be unable to detect the difference.

It is important of course to select the correct combination of flap settings in order to maintain trim. In a non-experimental aircraft the front and rear flap levers would be linked. At the moment the use the of rear flap is severely restricted by the lack of adequate flap on the front wing. A rear flap angle of 9° is the maximum for landing, and approach speeds are very high.

(N.A. Ref: AVIA 6/10616)

Technical Note No. Aero.1687   September 1945

ROYAL AIRCRAFT ESTABLISHMENT, FARNBOROUGH

Flight tests of the Miles Libellula (M.39B)
Tandem Biplane

Part II. Interim note on Stalling Characteristics.
Performance and Handling when in the
Original Condition

- by -

H G Aliston, MSc
and
P Brotherhood, DLC

RAE Ref: Aero.1373/171

SUMMARY

The Libellula (M.39B) is an experimental single-seat twin-engined tandem biplane built by Miles Aircraft Ltd, to give data on tail-first aircraft.

This note gives the results of flight tests done between August 1944 and February 1945. During these flights observations were made at the stall and records were taken which established the rate of climb, lift, drag, P.E. and longitudinal trim curves. At an all-up weight of 2,770 lb the minimum stalling speed is 59 mph Estimated Air Speed (EAS). corresponding to a CL of 1.24 based on the gross area of both wings. The neutral point was estimated to be 111.8 inches aft of the datum point, undercarriage down, both with engine on to maintain level flight and on the glide. The provisional normal C.G. limits are from 99.7 to 101.3 inches aft of the datum point, undercarriage down.

1. Introduction

This note describes the work done on the Libellula between August 1944 and February 1945. Details of previous work and a description of the aircraft are given in Technical Note Aero.1499(F).

The present flight tests have determined the behaviour of the Libellula at the stall, established curves of lift and drag and added to the information available on performance, longitudinal trim and position error.

2. Description of the Aircraft

The condition of the Libellula during the present series of tests was substantially the same as it was for the tests described in Technical Note Aero.1499(F). The only differences were as follows:-

(i)   A venturi pitot was connected to a special low reading A.S.I. and mounted at the end of a strut attached to the centre of the fuselage nose. The strut was 30 inches long and parallel to the aircraft datum. A new fuselage nose cap had to be made to take this attachment.

(ii)   A trailing static, which had 60 feet of rubber tubing to connect it to the low reading A.S.I. system was mounted below the fuselage. When the trailing static was not in use it was housed in a specially made streamlined plywood casing built beneath the fuselage. The casing was sealed with thin paper. By pulling a lever in the cockpit the pilot could release the trailing static for use; by pulling a second lever the static and tubing were jettisoned. A small parachute, attached to the trailing static tubing, was opened by the jettisoning lever and thus presented damaged in the static head due to impact with the ground.

(iii)   Two anti-spin parachutes were packed in the main wing, one aft of each engine. The total weight of the parachutes and their installation was less than five pounds. The only external fittings were the hooks, which projected slightly above the wing surface, and the external safety wire which connected the two parachutes and which was doped at its mid-point to the trailing edge of the centre fin.

Throughout this note coefficients of lift and drag have been based on total wing area and not on the area of the rear wing alone. This is because a considerable proportion of the total weight is carried by the front wing.

The position of the centre of gravity, k, is defined as the ratio of the distance of the C.G. forward from the rear wing quarter-chord point the distance between the quarter-chord points of the two wings.

3. Programme of Tests

A few flights were made on the aircraft after Technical Note Aero.1499(F) had been written and whilst the aircraft was still in the condition described in that note and before the modifications had been incorporated. This work consisted of further performance and longitudinal trim measurements.

The second part of the tests covered position error measurements with the trailing static, investigation of behaviour at the stall including determination of the stalling speed, partial glides to provide information for constructing the lift and drag curves, and a further short investigation of the longitudinal stability of the aircraft.

4. Results

4.1 Performance

A check was made on the level speeds whilst the aeroplane was in the original condition. This showed that the maximum speed at sea level was 164 mph, or slightly less than the original figure of 166 mph.

Partial climbs were done at 4,500 ft through a height range of 1,000 feet. The maximum rate of climb at this height is about 1,100 feet per minute at a true airspeed of 100 mph (95 mph EAS) for a weight of 2,800 lb.

4.2 Position Error

The position error had been determined during the previous series of tests by flights over a speed course. In order to determine the P.E. near the stall the aircraft was fitted with a trailing static and a venturi pitot. A special nose had to be built for this purpose which caused some alteration to the P.E. The correction varies from 20 mph at speeds below 85 mph E.A.S to 12 mph at 140 mph EAS. It has been applied to all results quoted in this note except where the contrary is stated.

4.3 The Stall

The behaviour of the aircraft at the stall was investigated two C.G. positions, first at the centre of the normal C.G. range where k = 0.387 and later two inches further aft where k = 0.373. A summary of the findings is given in Table.I (on page 309).

At the stall the nose drops and recovery is straightforward on easing the stick forward or raising the front flaps. The stall is not always easy to recognise for the manoeuvre is gentle and entails a loss of no more than 100 feet. At some flap settings it is masked by the fuselage tremor which produces the stall.

If, at the stall, the stick is held fixed or eased back pitching oscillations are set up which gradually increase in violence. For those flap settings in which the stall is preceded by a fuselage tremor the pitching oscillations are very readily induced. The oscillatory motion appears to be caused by the front wing stalling and the nose dropping followed by an increase in speed and the unstalling of the front wing.

Lift is regained and incidence increased until the front wing stalls again and in this case the stall will be dynamic due to the altitude of the aircraft. Then follows a more severe nose drop and eventually a still severer stall. The pitching oscillation can be stopped if the stick is pushed firmly forward or if the front flap is raised.

4.4 Lift and Drag

The tests were done on the glide with the engines throttled fully back, and with the flaps up, at a range of speeds between 90 and 150 mph EAS.

Measurements were made of forward speed, rate of descent, attitude (a-Y) and the engine speed and from these readings were deduced the values of the gliding angle Y, the incidence a, the total lift and drag coefficients CL and CD and the wind-milling drag of the propellers.

Values of CL are plotted against attitude and (a-Y) and against incidence, a. The total drag coefficient, CD, is plotted against incidence. The negative thrust of the windmilling propellers has been calculated and appears to be considerable. The slow running of the engines was occasionally adjusted between flights so that the rpm when throttled back also varied. It is estimated that the variation in the negative thrust coefficient at a given incidence was, for this reason sometimes as much as +/- 0.003. This is thought to account for some of the scatter of the CD curves.

4.5 Longitudinal Stability

The elevator angles to trim were measured at three C.G. positions on the glide at 5,000 ft. Corresponding measurements for cruising level condition were obtained while observing the position error and these are included as they give an indication of the effect of engine power on the longitudinal stability. The rear wing flap was up for all the flights and the front wing flap was up for the flights with the C.G. at k = 0.35 and k = 0.41. For the flight with the C.G. at k = 0.38 the front flap was set down nine degrees during the glide 18 degrees whilst flying level.

The slopes of the trim curves indicate that the neutral point, stick fixed, is at k = 0.31 on the glide. The value of k corresponds to 112 inches after the datum point, undercarriage down.

Trim curves with power on for level flight indicate that the engine conditions have a negligible effect on the neutral point. The increase in power up to full throttle would have very little more effect.

5. Discussion

5.1 Performance

The results of further flights suggest that the maximum level speed at sea level is 164 mph and not 166 mph. The figure of 166 mph is less than that measured by the firm so that the further drop in top speed suggests that either there has been a drop in engine power or an increase in drag due to the deterioration of the aircraft with time. The level speed measurements were made before the fitting of equipment.

The maximum rate of climb at 4,500 feet is about 1,100 feet per minute and occurs at 100 mph True Air Speed (TAS). for an all-up weight of 2,800 lb. This rate and climbing speed are what might be deduced from considerations of airframe drag based on the maximum level speed, the engine rpm and propeller efficiency

5.2 The Stall

The stall was investigated at two C.G. positions, k = 0.387 and k = 0.373, which were two inches apart. The minimum recorded stalling speed of 59 mph EAS occurred when the C.G. was at k = 0.373, the undercarriage up, the front wing flap fully deflected and the rear wing flap 13 degrees, or just over half, down. This speed corresponds to a CL of 1.24 based on the gross area of both wings or of 1.65 based on the gross rear wing area. The part of the lift provided by the front wing corresponds to a coefficient of 1.88 based on the gross area of the front wing; the remainder of the lift, assumed to be supplied by the rear wing, corresponds to a coefficient of 1.03 based on the gross area of the rear wing. It was not possible to obtain more lift from the rear wing at this, or more forward, C.G. positions owing to the maximum lift obtainable from the front wing being insufficient to enable the rear wing to reach a greater incidence. The aircraft has now been returned to the firm for the fitting of a high lift front wing.

There is no difficulty in controlling the aircraft when the front wing stalls if the stick is eased forward or the front wing flap raised. Failure to do this may result in pitching oscillations which successively increase in violence.

5.3   Lift and Drag

The drag and, to a lesser extent, the lift measurements show an appreciable amount of scatter.

The scatter in the drag measurements of the complete aircraft is expected because adjustments to the slow running of the engines between flights led to differences in windmilling drag when the engines were throttled right back. The windmilling drag was first estimated from the observed rpm and then subtracted from the drag of the complete aeroplane in order to provide an estimate of the drag of the airframe alone. This method of estimating windmilling drag is rough and the scatter of the airframe drag points is therefore not unexpected.

An independent check on the accuracy of the airframe drag measurements was provided by an estimate based on the measured maximum speed at sea level of 164 mph. For this purpose the propeller efficiency was taken at 64%, the total engine horsepower as 272 B.H.P., and the total weight was assumed to be divided between the wings in the ratio 2:3. The profile drag, allowing 4% for slipstream, was thus estimated to be 66 lb at 100 ft/sec.

5.4   Longitudinal Stability

From the curves the neutral point on the glide, stick fixed and flaps and undercarriage up, is calculated to be 114 inches aft of the datum. This is equivalent to 112 inches aft of the datum when the undercarriage is down so that the neutral point is well behind the normal C.G. limits of 99.7 to 101.3 inches aft of the datum point. This value of the neutral point holds for C_L less than 0.4 (EAS greater than 105 mph). Most of the trim curves were established before the stalling characteristics had been examined and for this

reason few low speed observations were made but there were sufficient to suggest that the stability is greater at high values of C_L than at low.

The destabilising effect of engines-on was found to be negligible which is in good agreement with the results of wind tunnel tests.

(N.A. Ref: AVIA 6/10802)

The M.39B had a somewhat hard life and even Miles managed to upset it onto its rear fuselage sometime later, with the wooden fairing again suffering considerable damage. Grahame Gates also recalled that it was damaged when 'it fell over in the hangar' at Woodley! Apparently one of the shop boys had been detailed to take the battery out of the nose for re-charging but the lead ballast, mounted on a plate in front of the battery, had to be removed first. Everyone else used to put the lead on the front wing but the youngster put it down on on the floor then removed the battery - and over it went! The fuselage tailcone, which was a very light wooden structure, in Grahame's own words, 'suffered 'orribly'!

On completion of the RAE trials, the aircraft was returned to Miles Aircraft Ltd, and at some stage, Contract No.C/Acft/3401, undated, was awarded to Miles Aircraft Ltd for the 'Supply of mods' for the M.39B, SR392. This could have been in connection with the front wing being rebuilt to improve the flaps-down elevator power. The outboard flaps became slotted elevators and the inboard wing was modified to have retractable auxiliary aerofoil elevators, or elevator-cum-flaps (i.e. similar to those fitted to the M.48).

This is illustrated in the photographs on page 310.

However, there does appear to be some confusion as to the terminology of the control surfaces on the front wing, as will also be seen in the RAE Report.

The flap mechanism incorporated an ingenious but very simple method of progressively coupling the flaps to the elevator motion. When the flaps were retracted they were not influenced by elevator movement but when they were extended they went up and down with the elevators to make them in effect retractable elevators.

Further experiments and data collecting trials were then undertaken throughout 1946 and the early part of 1947, and the cg range

TABLE I								Tech. Note No. Aero.1687
Attempt No.	k	Flap front deg.	Angle rear deg.	Stick Position	Stalling speed mph E.A.S.	CL max.	Height feet	Characteristics of Stall Warning	Characteristics of stall etc
1	0.387	0	0	fully back	-	0.68	5,000	-	Unstalled; descending steadily at 81 mph E.A.S.
2	"	9	0	fully back	-	0.79	"	-	Unstalled; descending steadily at 74 mph E.A.S.
3	"	18	0	almost back	69	0.92	"	None	There is a well-defined nose drop but the stall is straight forward and gentle.
4	"	27	0	5/6 back	67	0.96	"	None	The nose drops. A pitching oscillation tends to set up near the stall.
5	"	36	0	4/5 back	65	1.01	"	Low frequency tremor and lack of lateral control.	The nose drops with a slight wing drop. A pitching oscillation is readily induced near the stall.
6	"	45	0	3/4 back	63	1.07	"	Fuselage judder and greater lack of lateral control than at (5).	The nose drops. A severe pitching oscillation is easily induced. The controls all become progressively less effective as the front flap setting is increased.
7	0.373	45	0	1/3 back	63	1.09	6,000	Low frequency fuselage tremor.	The stall is not well defined unless approached very gently. A severe pitching oscillation is readily induced.
8	"	45	4	2/3 back	63	1.09	"	None	The nose drops but there is no tendency for a wing to drop. The stall is better defined than at (7) since the pitching oscillation is more easily avoided.
9	"	45	9	5/6 back	61	1.18	"	None	The nose drops more sharply than at (8).
10	"	45	13	fully back	59	1.24	"	None	The nose drops and about 100 feet of height is lost in recovery.
11	"	45	17	fully back	-	1.08	"	-	Unstalled; descending steadily at 63 mph E.A.S.
12	"	45	21	fully back	-	0.86	"	-	Unstalled; descending steadily at 71 mph E.A.S. The controls, particularly the elevator, become progressively less effective as the rear flap setting is increased.

M.39B, RAE stall test results

Above: View of modified front wing, with retractable auxiliary aerofoil elevator-cum-flap extending and outboard elevator neutral.

Above: View of modified front wing, with auxiliary aerofoil elevator-cum-flap retracted and outboard elevator partially down.

Above: View of modified front wing, with auxiliary aerofoil elevator-cum-flap and outboard elevator down.

Above: View of modified front wing, with auxiliary aerofoil elevator-cum-flap retracted and outboard elevator up.

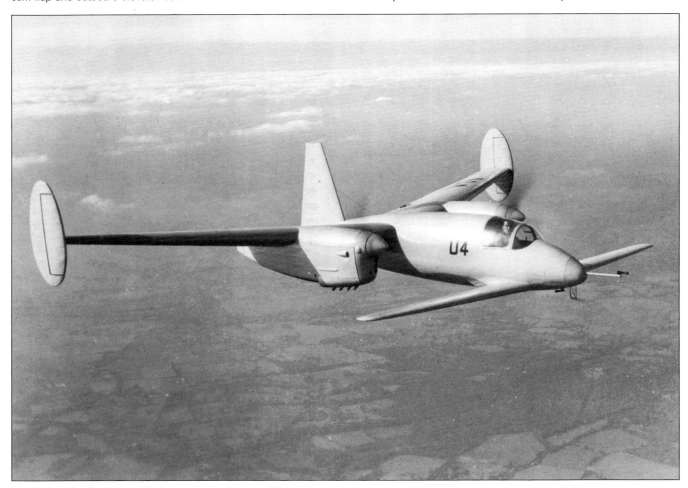

Hugh Kendall flying the M.39B in post war colours as U4.

(which had been limited to 1.6 inches during the RAE trials, although it is now known that this figure of 1.6 was not correct), was then explored, extending it to 12 inches, to give a 750% improvement. This necessitated modifications to the main undercarriage gear drag stays to move the wheels further aft and Grahame Gates recalled that, as assistant weights engineer at the time, he did virtually all the weighing and flight-test loadings associated with the programme.

Despite the numerous groundings for repairs and modifications which had to be carried out on the M.39B, a very considerable amount of very productive test flying was carried out, while the later modifications gave an appreciably higher coefficient of lift resulting in a shorter take-off and reduction in touchdown speed of some 6%.

A letter from Don Brown on the M.39B was published in the 29th June 1944 issue of *The Aeroplane Spotter*:

I was interested to read your article on the Libellula in your issue of June 1, but I would like to comment on the final paragraph. Possibly the provision of the central fin on the M.39B suggested that it was necessary for single-engined flight, but this was not actually the case. The fin was provided purely as an additional safeguard because when the machine was first flown, it was such an unknown quantity that we felt it would be wise to ensure as far as possible that it would be directionally stable.

In actual flight trials no difficulty has been found in maintaining control with one engine inoperative, and the machine has been flown in this condition down to speeds at least as low as would normally be possible on an orthodox aeroplane.

The very angular shape of the central fin, which was quite out of character with the generally elegant lines of the rest of the machine, was apparently originally fitted as a precautionary measure for its initial test flights, but it has also been suggested that perhaps the directional stability was not considered to have been good enough to have encouraged its removal!

Grahame Gates believed that he saw the M.39B make a flight one evening with the central fin removed but if he did then it was certainly back in place again by the following morning! This sighting was confirmed by John S Webb, who recalled that: *Although the aircraft was normally fitted with a large central stabiliser in addition to the wing-tip fins and rudders, it flew perfectly well without it, even in bad weather.*

In early 1946, the M.39B was painted yellow overall, with the post war 'B' mark U4, and Hugh Kendall made sixteen test flights in it between 29th May 1946 and 22nd May 1947.

I will never forget the beautiful display that Ken Waller gave in U4 during the last 'Miles Aircraft Open Day', held at Woodley on Sunday 20th July 1947 and just four days later, on 24th July 1947, it was to make its last flight, in the hands of Don Brown. The M.39B was dismantled in October 1947 and the 'cockpit-less shell of the fuselage' was later given to the Reading Sky Observers' Club branch of the British Association of Aviation Clubs. It was their original intention to make it presentable and display it alongside their Ju 52/3m fuselage but this never materialised and just the outboard fins and rudders and the central stabiliser were salvaged to hang in their clubroom at Woodley.

Unfortunately, nothing further is known this project.

Above: U4 at Woodley in readiness for a display.
[GS Collection]

The ignominious end of U4, seen scrapped on the dump at Woodley on 11th April 1948. Note the Junkers Ju 52/3m on the left. [Via Phil Jarrett]

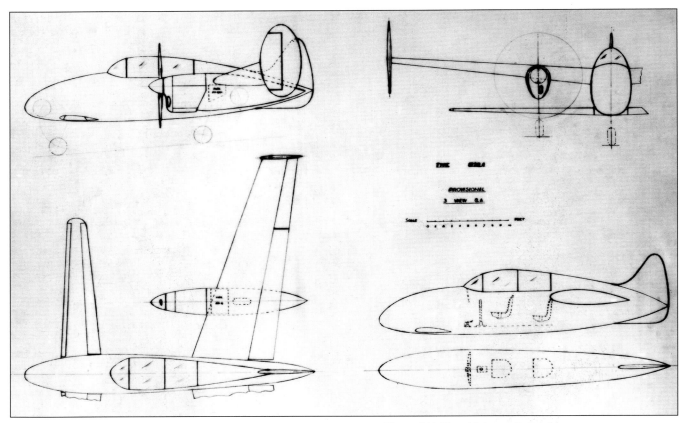

A provisional, undated, three-view G.A. of the two-seat M.39B Developments with two DH Gipsy Major engines.

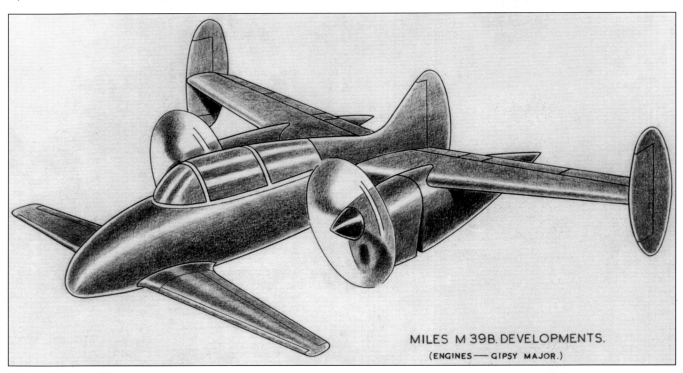

MILES M 39B. DEVELOPMENTS.
(ENGINES — GIPSY MAJOR.)

An undated artist's impression of the two seat M.39B Developments.

SPECIFICATION AND PERFORMANCE DATA

Engine:	2 x 140 hp DH Gipsy Major IC
Dimensions:	span, front wing 25ft 0in, rear wing 37ft 6in; length 22ft 2in; height 9ft 3in; wing area, front wing 61.7 sq ft, rear wing 187.5 sq ft; aspect ratio, front wing 10.1, rear wing 7.5; wing section, front wing root NACA 23018, tip NACA 2412, rear wing root NACA 23021, tip NACA 2415; sweepback on leading edge of rear wing 21° 48'
Weights:	tare 2,405lb; fuel (25 gal) 188lb; oil (3 gal) 27lb; pilot 180lb; AUW 2,800lb
Performance:	max speed 164 mph; stalling speed, flaps down 59 mph; rate of climb 1,100ft/min; run to unstick 435ft; distance to 50ft - 855ft; landing run 495ft; landing run over 50ft - 1,275ft

An artist's impression of the M.40 Specialised Transport in flight.

Chapter 34
Miles M.40 and M.41 Specialised Transports

Among the 1938 proposals for specialised freighters with rear loading put forward by Miles, was one capable of carrying 150 armed troops, 50 light armoured motorcycles, or 9 howitzers with crews, and by early 1942 the need for such a large military transport for the carriage of troops and equipment was becoming evident.

Unfortunately, Miles was unaware of the fact that, soon after America declared war on Germany, Winston Churchill had entered into an agreement which gave the Americans the responsibility for the provision of all transport aircraft, while Britain would concentrate on the production of fighters and bombers. This turned out to be one of Churchill's few very bad decisions as the Americans were no fools and this agreement gave them the opportunity to develop their two existing four-engined transports, the Douglas C-54 and the Lockheed C-69, into the DC-4 and

Constellation respectively, in preparation for the demand from airlines in the immediate post war years.

This was to have a far reaching effect on the fortunes of the British aircraft industry and one from which it was never to fully recover.

However, in 1942 Miles, in ignorance of all this, prepared project designs for two large specialised transports, the four-engined M.40 and the six-engined M.41 to fulfil the role for large military freighter aircraft. Both aircraft were to have been of simple wooden construction so they could be produced in Britain and Canada to help conserve the limited supplies of metal alloys, which were more urgently required for the construction of operational types.

The two transport aircraft were designed for immediate large-scale production with the minimum of simple jigs and utilising semi-

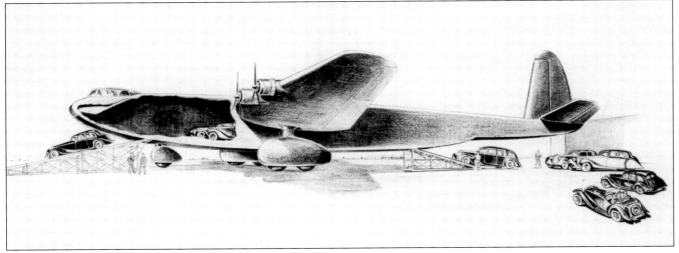

Later, with the end of the war in sight, Miles envisaged a post war use for the M.40 as a car transporter (thereby beating the design for the much smaller Bristol Freighter by a considerable margin) and an artist's impression of the M.40 showed a busy scene at an airport with private cars being loaded and off-loaded.

skilled labour. Front and rear loading ramps were employed to enable loading and unloading to be carried out simultaneously and they were to have been fitted with a simple fixed, large spatted, tricycle undercarriage.

The larger M.41 featured two freight compartments each of 36ft x 10ft x 9ft, giving a total capacity of 6,480cu ft and it was to have been powered by either Bristol Hercules or Wright Cyclone GR-2600 A5B engines.

Although neither project was ordered, it is interesting to note that four years later, a year after the war had ended, Spec C.3/46, dated 10.7.46 was issued for a Heavy Freighter Aircraft. On 19th July 1946 this spec was issued to General Aircraft Ltd who, over the next few years, built the GAL.60 Universal Freighter at Hanworth in Middlesex.

On 1st January 1949, GAL amalgamated with Blackburn Aircraft Ltd and the nearly completed Freighter was taken to Brough for its first flight, which was made on 20th June 1950, some eight years after the M.40 and M.41 could have flown. The metal GAL.60 (later developed into the Blackburn Beverley) was designed to carry 11 tons in a 'box' 36ft x 10ft x 10ft over 500 nautical miles but the comparable M.40 would have carried 12.5 tons in a similar sized 'box'. The GAL.60 needed four 2,850 hp engines to propel its bulk, whereas only four 1,600 hp engines were envisaged for the M.40.

Other projects, which were developed from the original 1938 proposals included the M.32, M.57, M.61, M.62, M.68, M.71 and M.72 and details of these can be found in the appropriate chapters in this and the next volume.

Above and below: Artist's impressions of the M.41 as a large military transport.

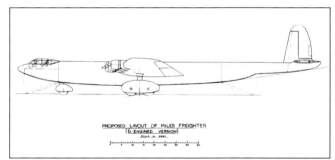

A side-view drawing of the M.41 Transport.

SPECIFICATION AND PERFORMANCE DATA

Miles M.40

Engines: 4 x 1,575 hp Bristol Hercules XI or 4 x 1,600 hp Wright Cyclone GR-2600-A5B
Dimensions: span 112ft 0in; length 75ft 0in; height 27ft 6in; wing area 2,000sq ft; aspect ratio 6.3; wing section, root NACA 23018, tip NACA 23009
Weights: empty 35,000lb; max payload 28,000lb or 120 troops; AUW 70,000lb; wing loading 35lb/sq ft
Performance: max speed 220 mph at 3,000ft; cruising speed 150 mph at 3,000ft; take-off run to unstick 1,500ft

Miles M.41

Engines: 6 x 1,575 hp Bristol Hercules XI or 4 x 1,600 hp Wright Cyclone GR-2600-A5B
Dimensions: span 142ft 0in; length 138ft 0in; height 33ft 6in; wing area 3,360sq ft; aspect ratio 6.0; wing section, root NACA 23018, tip NACA 23009
Weights: empty 60,000lb; max payload 48,200lb or 180 troops; AUW 117,000lb; wing loading 34.9lb/sq ft
Performance: cruising speed 180 mph; range 300 miles

An artist's impression of the Libellula B.1 Heavy Bomber.

Chapter 35
Miles Libellula Heavy Bomber (Two Projects)

Shortly after the M.35 had been conceived and concurrently with the submission to the MAP of George Miles' proposal for a tandem-winged shipborne fighter, Don Brown suggested that the same layout could be also used to advantage in the role of heavy bomber. Since the forward wing was not a mere stabiliser but a lifting surface carrying up to 40% of the all up weight of the aircraft, it meant that for approximately the same overall dimensions as existing bombers and with the same crew, a Libellula Heavy Bomber could carry a vastly increased bomb load. Thus, although the project submitted to the MAP was primarily for a shipborne fighter, a few pages were included describing Don Brown's proposal.

The fuselage of the Libellula B.1 resembled that of the Short Stirling but with two engines mounted on the low forward wing and four on the high rear wing. Rudders were fitted only on the outboard of three fins and three gun turrets were fitted, in the nose, tail and amidships on top of the fuselage. A note on the artist's impression stated: '6 Centaurus 3SM. Bomb Load 23 tons'.

In January 1943, Phillips & Powis Aircraft Ltd produced a booklet in which was a summary on the Libellula Heavy Bomber B.1:

The advantages of the Libellula layout are by no means confined to small aircraft and, in evidence of this, the Libellula B.I heavy bomber has been designed. For little more that the same overall dimensions than were specified for the existing heavy bombers

the Libellula layout has rendered possible a machine of greatly increased capacity. Carrying a bomb load of 23 tons, a squadron of 25 of these machines is equivalent to 300 Wellingtons. Apart from the greatly reduced target which such a bombing force would represent, the saving in crews would be enormous, 200 being required as compared with 1,800 in the case of the Wellingtons.

The Libellula Bomber aircraft would have been powered by six of the new Bristol Centaurus 3SM sleeve-valve air-cooled radial engines, which were then under development and which were designed to give double the horsepower of existing power-plants. The aircraft, of approximately 80 tons all up weight, would have had a normal bomb load of 51,000lb with a range of 1,330 miles. This was more than ten times the bomb load of the Wellington then in use.

In May 1943, about a year after the proposal was submitted to the Ministry, the Royal Aircraft Establishment, Farnborough published a report analysing a large number of project designs for a bomber very much larger than anything which had so far been envisaged. These project designs had clearly been by invitation of the Ministry and had come from five leading manufacturers: Avro, Bristol, Handley Page, Shorts and Vickers. The actual date of the invitation is not known but it must have been later than 1941 since the B.8/41 proposal submitted by Shorts was for a much smaller aircraft than that which was now envisaged.

These companies between them submitted no less than fifteen project designs for bombers with all up weights ranging from 170,000lb to 220,000lb and were, with one exception, all powered by piston engines. The proposal submitted by Avro had no less than ten engines in separate nacelles!

In the event, none of the proposals, or the Libellula Heavy Bomber B.1, were taken any further, probably for two reasons, i) because it was anticipated that the war would be over before they could have been brought into service, and ii) that it would be better to continue to rely on the Avro Lancaster for which massive production plans were already well in hand.

Second Libellula Heavy Bomber Project

Plans for an eight-engined Libellula Heavy Bomber were later prepared by George Miles and Ray Bournon. This was to be powered by either 2,300 hp Rolls-Royce P.I.26 or 2,500 hp Napier Sabre engines and was a much more elegant looking machine with a very 'flat' streamlined fuselage. It had a straight front wing carrying two engines and a swept rear wing carrying six engines in four nacelles (two engines being installed in each of the two inboard nacelles) but no mid-ships turret.

However, nothing came of either of these projects.

SPECIFICATION AND PERFORMANCE DATA

Miles Libellula Heavy Bomber B.I - First proposal - by Don Brown

Engines:	6 x 2,400 hp Bristol Centaurus 3SM
Dimensions:	span 115ft 0in; total wing area 2,700 sq ft
Weights:	AUW approx 150,000lb; bomb load 51,000lb
Armament:	10 x 0.303 Browning machine guns in four turrets
Performance:	max speed 310 mph at 21,000ft; cruising speed 240 mph at 24,000ft; range (normal) 1,330 miles with 51,000lb (max) bomb load; 2,000 miles with 37,000lb bomb load

Miles Libellula Heavy Bomber - Second proposal - by George Miles

Engines:	8 x 2,300 hp Rolls-Royce P.I.26 or 2,500 hp Napier Sabre

No further details known

Further Libellula Projects

In the next chapter, more Libellula projects are discussed. Seen here is an artist's impression of a twin-engined, two seat Libellula attack aircraft.

"Do not make the mistake of confusing this with an ordinary plane."

A cartoon taken from the booklet on Libellula Projects!

Chapter 36
Miles Libellula Projects – A New Basic Design

On 17th March 1942, Phillips & Powis Aircraft Ltd produced a booklet on the Libellula projects, reproduced here:

It is evident that the limit of performance with orthodox aeroplanes is rapidly being approached. Any further improvements can only be obtained at the cost of enormously increased power coupled with excessively high landing speeds and impaired manoeuvrability. The difficulties, moreover, are increased considerably in the case aircraft designed to operate from aircraft carriers, owing to the restrictions on size, weight and landing speed. Such aircraft are being placed at a rapidly increasing disadvantage in comparison with the land based aircraft which they have on occasion to meet in combat.

The whole problem has been carefully reviewed with the idea of obtaining, if possible, enhanced performance and manoeuvrability without further increase of power and without increasing present day landing speeds; such a solution if practicable, being of particular value to carrier based aircraft.

Of the many different layouts considered, the best solution appears to lie in a machine having, broadly speaking, a monoplane wing at either end of the fuselage, the engine(s) being at the rear. Such an aeroplane would not have the ordinary tail and empennage and the centre of gravity would lie roughly, just aft of amidships, between the wings. Unorthodox as the layout appears, it seems to provide a number of important advantages, which are described in more detail hereafter.

So promising do these advantages appear, particularly as applied to Service aircraft, that they have been thought to justify considerable thought and research in the hope that the conception will prove

practical and no time will be lost in making available to the Service the advantages which it is hoped the flight trials will prove to be attainable. At the same time, a number of layouts on these lines are being prepared for different functions. The apparent advantages in the proposed design are manifold and may be briefly summarised as follows:

The engine(s) being aft, the pilot has an unrestricted view ahead when taking-off and landing and also a windscreen free from the accumulations of oil and dirt which invariably obscure the windscreen of the normal single-engined aircraft. The position in the nose and the clear windscreen should prove of particular advantage when approaching for a deck landing.

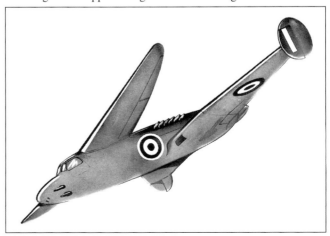

A Libellula project based on the M.35.

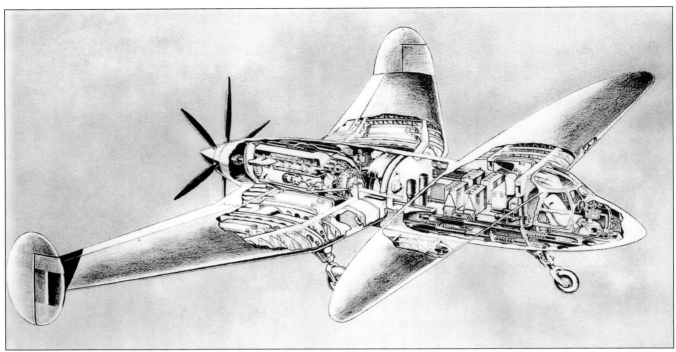

Cut-away drawing showing a Libellula ship-borne fighter project.

Both the wing span and length are considerably less than those of a corresponding orthodox aircraft, which it is hoped, will enhance the manoeuvrability of the machine, while at the same time effecting a material reduction in structure weight and a saving in the hangar space required. The reduction in overall size enables not only a greatly increased performance to be obtained, but also a marked reduction in target area. An example is afforded by the case of a fighter which, with an estimated top speed 100 mph faster than the Spitfire and armed with 6 cannon, would actually be smaller in overall dimensions than the Spitfire.

Of particular interest in connection with Naval requirements is the fact that such a machine would comply with the weight limitations for ship-borne aircraft. Moreover, the low aft position of the centre of gravity, combined with the use of the tricycle undercarriage, should prove particularly well adapted for use with arrester gear and should offer many advantages over the orthodox aeroplane with a relatively high forward position of the centre of gravity and normal undercarriage. Again, for the special purposes of the Navy, the layout can be so arranged that the aircraft can be stored with alternate wings overlapping, this simplifying handling. By this means and without having to resort to the delay, weight and complication of folding wings, more aeroplanes can be stored in a given hangar space than is possible with orthodox aircraft with their wings folded.

The diagrams shown here illustrate the advantages possessed by the Miles "Libellula" type of aircraft. Ten machines are shown housed in a representative section (100 ft x 62 ft) of an aircraft carrier hangar against seven orthodox aircraft of a lower military load capacity. Moreover the "Libellula" type permits a clear gangway down the centre of the ship.

Manoeuvrability may be still further enhanced by the fact that this wing arrangement enables all the heaviest loads to be situated close to the centre of gravity of the aircraft. All variable loads, such as bombs, torpedoes, fuel and ammunition can be concentrated close to the centre of gravity and thus the undesirable changes of trim, encountered during an operational flight in an orthodox aircraft, will be minimised. In addition to this, the design should allow much greater latitude with regard to the position of the centre of gravity than is possible with orthodox aircraft.

One of the greatest problems in connection with Service aircraft, and one to which no really satisfactory solution has as yet been found, is in the provision of a diving brake which does not interfere with the control of the machine. The proposed design, however, permits the incorporation of dive brakes which cause no change of trim and consequently no interference with control. The aft position of the engine(s) enables the fixed cannon to be housed amidships in the fuselage, where they can be readily reloaded during flight. In addition, in the single and three-engined layouts, it is possible to utilise the mass of the engine to absorb directly the reaction forces of firing the cannon.

The proposed design provides an almost ideal layout for either one, two or three engines. In the case of the single and three-engined

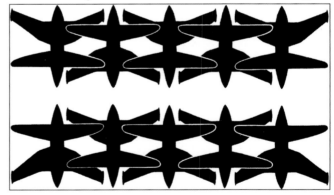

Above: Drawing showing 10 Libellula fighters housed in a representative section of an aircraft carrier's hangar.

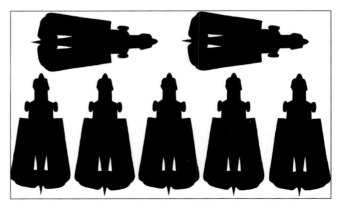

Above: Drawing showing 7 orthodox fighters housed in the same representative section of an aircraft carrier's hangar.

layouts, the disadvantages encountered in orthodox aircraft, such as poor view and low propeller efficiency, are avoided. While in the twin-engined layout the view is, if anything, rather better than anything achieved hitherto. In addition to the foregoing, there are a number of equally important but more technical advantages associated with the new design. These are as follows:

In connection with the many devices employed in the past for the purpose of increasing lift of a wing, the difficulty has always been that the increase in lift gained has invariably been accompanied by a marked movement of the centre of pressure, which in turn causes a considerable change of trim of the aircraft. One of the most effective devices known for increasing lift is the auxiliary aerofoil type of flap, but this flap has, unfortunately, met with little application owing to its being one of the worst offenders with regard to CP movement; and the more effectively the flap is used, the greater is the movement of the CP, and the more difficult does it become to control the resultant change in trim.

In an orthodox aircraft, the only way to overcome the difficulty has been to apply an opposite pitching moment by means of elevators. Thus, at the moment when the maximum lift is required, the wings and tail surfaces are necessarily acting in opposition to one another: and to such an extent as to preclude the employment of the flaps to their greatest effect. The proposed design, however, provides the ideal arrangement for the utilisation of these flaps to their maximum effect; for by fitting flaps to both wings, the increased pitching moments about the centre of gravity are, of course, in opposite directions and the operation of the flaps can readily be arranged so that the pitching moments balance out, leaving the trim unaffected while permitting full use to be made of the flaps. In this way, all horizontal surfaces are used for lift only and the drag and weight of horizontal stabilising surfaces are eliminated entirely. Moreover, the deletion of the tail loads inherent in the orthodox aircraft should enable a material saving in structural weight of the fuselage to be effected. Finally, for any given wing loading, it should be possible to obtain a much lower landing speed than has been attainable hitherto.

Although, as already mentioned, the proposed design permits all variable loads to be concentrated at or near the centre of gravity, yet, in the case of a bomber carrying a large load of bombs, it is inevitable, from considerations of space, that a number of these should be carried at some distance from the centre of gravity. A simple and powerful means of adjusting the aircraft for trim, both

before and after dropping the bombs, may be provided by differential use of the flaps, which virtually places the position of the centre of pressure under the control of the pilot, an advantage never hitherto possessed by any aircraft yet built.

Another feature which it is hoped the design may provide is that of combining the advantages of both short span and high aspect ratio. In this way high stresses are avoided, structure weight is saved and manoeuvrability is enhanced without sacrifice of aerodynamic efficiency. In multi-engined designs, owing to the short span, a very high percentage of the surface of the rear wing is covered by the propeller disc; in this way the 'Crouch-Bolas effect' becomes very marked indeed and is of particular value in assisting the take-off of a heavily loaded machine and in further reducing the landing speed, especially in the case of deck landings, where a 'power approach' is always made.

A most important feature peculiar to the design is the almost ideal layout provided for alternative means of propulsion in either one, two or three units used either in combination with or independently from orthodox power plants and without the CG difficulties encountered in a conventional aeroplane. By virtue of the above advantages, it is felt that the proposed arrangement appears to be not only a very material advance over the orthodox aircraft, particularly in the case of Service aircraft, but also shows promise of giving as high an all round performance as is attainable in the light of present-day knowledge.

Above: An artist's impression of an M.35 type Libellula fighter on the deck of an aircraft carrier. Below: A three-view provisional G.A. drawing of the Type M.39B.

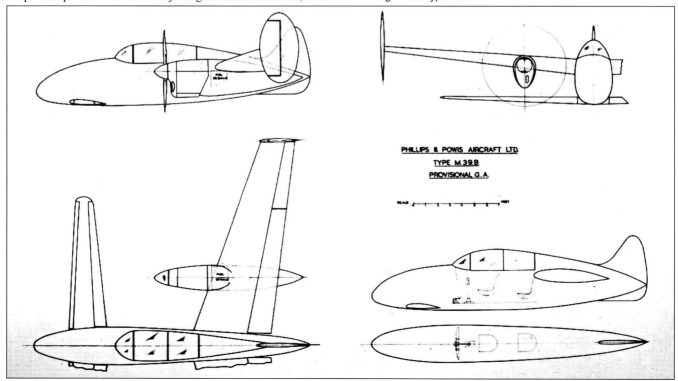

PHILLIPS & POWIS AIRCRAFT LTD.

TYPE M.39.B

PROVISIONAL G.A.

Above and opposite: Two artists impressions of the M.26J X.9 Scheme CX Passenger version, described in this chapter.

Chapter 37
Miles M.26J X.9, X.9 Scheme B, X.9 Scheme CX and X.9 Scheme BX, Mod. X.9, Miles M.26J X Troop Transport, Miles M.26A ½ Scale Flying Model of the X.9, Miles X Junior and M.26K X.10 Transport

It seemed obvious to Don Brown, despite the lack of interest shown by the MAP in the autumn of 1942 in the M.40 and M.41 short haul military transports, that there would soon be a need for a long range transport aircraft for use in the Far East. With the concurrence of the Miles brothers, the X.2 project of 1936 was revived and the M.26J X.9 was designed to fulfil the alternative requirements for a four-engine 74-seat troop-transport or glider tug with a crew of three.

The engines to be used in the M.26J X.9 were designed by George Miles and a small team in a dispersed drawing office at Binfield Manor and when the first engine was complete it was installed in a test house on the south west edge of Woodley airfield (building No.142 on AM Drawing No.418C/45) in May 1942 for ground running tests. However, in the event of the 'Miles' engine being unacceptable, or if an interim model of the aircraft was required, an alternative layout using four of the new 1,740 hp Rolls-Royce Griffon II engines was also proposed as the M.26J Scheme BX. The 'Preliminary Design Specification - Miles X.9' stated, with regard to the use of the Rolls-Royce Griffon engined version, that 'this, of course, would have a lower performance'!

In January 1943, Phillips & Powis Aircraft Ltd produced a brochure entitled 'Miles Specialised Aircraft for Specialised

Purposes'. Contained therein was a summary of a selection of Miles aircraft which had either been built or proposed up to then. Brief details of the M.26J 'X' Troop Transport were included and these are reproduced here:

One Service type which has hitherto been entirely neglected in this country and one which will become of increasing importance in the comparatively near future is the troop transport. The existing heavy bombers are manifestly unsuitable for this purpose while the policy of utilising the Hamilcar glider towed by a heavy bomber is almost prohibitively inefficient.

The M.26J has therefore been laid out on the well known Miles 'X' principle enunciated some years ago, and provides a troop transport having a range and capacity unequalled by any landplane in production today. It is, moreover, but a scaled down version of an even larger troop transport now being designed and having an all up weight of 130,000 lb.

In accordance with the firm's policy of acquiring full scale flight data on all unorthodox design advanced, a small flying mock-up has been built *(the Miles M.30 'X' Minor - PA)* and with it a considerable amount of flying has been done and data acquired.

Span	116 ft 0 in
Wing area	1,485 sq ft
All up weight	66,000 lb
Engines	4 x Rolls-Royce P.I.26
Max speed	360 mph at 16,000 ft
Cruising speed	250 mph at 10,000 ft
No of troops	74 (with 100 lb of equipment per man)
Range	1,500 miles.

Alternatively the machine may be used as a tug for the Hamilcar glider and when used for this purpose it carries 34 troops and has a range of 1,000 miles.

Another drawing, dated 31st March 1943, showed the M.26J X.9 to have a rear loading ramp, and three alternative military loads as follows:

47 troops	8,460lb
Arms and equipment	3,736lb
Total	12,196lb
17 motorcycles	7,650lb
17 riders	3,060lb
Arms and equipment	1,486lb
Total	12,196lb
2 scout cars	11,640lb
2 drivers	360lb
Arms and equipment	196lb
Total	12,196lb

The 'Preliminary Design Specification - Miles X.9' was undated but the backs of the drawings No. C2600/11, C2600/12, C2600/14 and C2600/15, shown here were stamped with the date 29th July 1943, so it must have been issued sometime after that date. This Specification gave extensive details of the X.9 transport aeroplane in all its various projected forms and is reproduced here.

The X.9 has been designed to fulfil the alternative requirements for a troop transport or glider tug (it would obviously also make a good freighter or passenger transport). The illustrations following this text are practically self-explanatory, but there are several points of interest in the design which are worthy of note.

Power units - It is proposed that the design of the engines be laid down in conjunction with the design of the aircraft. A great deal of attention has been paid to aerodynamic efficiency in the layout and it is considered highly desirable that the engines should be buried in the wing. There is no existing engine of the necessary proportions to fulfil this requirement so it has been assumed that special engines would be built to suit the job by Phillips & Powis.

The use of such engines, of course, would not be confined to the X.9 but would fill a long felt need. They would be of approximately the same power and weight as the Rolls-Royce "Griffon" but would have the cylinders arranged in two banks horizontally opposed, and would have direct injection with compression ignition. In the event of the engine project being unacceptable or of an interim model of the aircraft being required, an alternative layout using "Griffon" engines has been done. This, of course, would have a lower performance.

Structure - The X.9 would be of all metal light-alloy construction and would follow orthodox large aircraft practice except in the method of joining the wings to the fuselage. It was considered vitally important that the cabin in such a machine should be entirely free from obstruction, and, therefore, it was decided not to continue the spars through the fuselage but to attach them to a strong ring in the fuselage.

A considerable amount of stress investigation has been done on this scheme and it turns out to be quite economical provided that the spars are made to take full advantage of the depth of the root fillet.

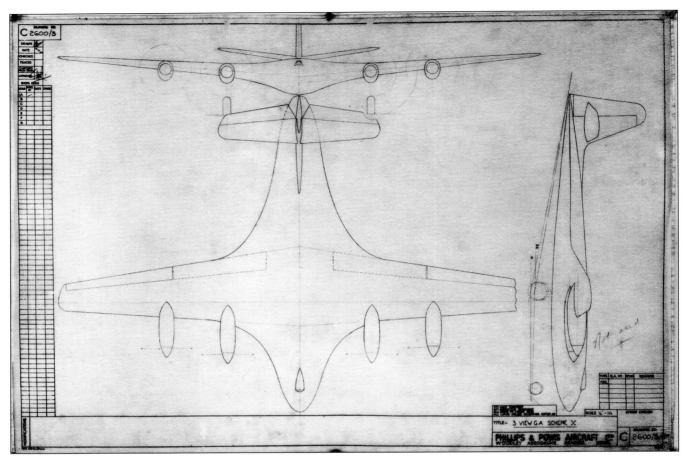

Three-view G.A. drawing, No.C2600/3, possibly dated 16.12.40, entitled M.26 '3 view G.A. Scheme X'. Note teardrop cabin for single pilot and single fin and rudder.

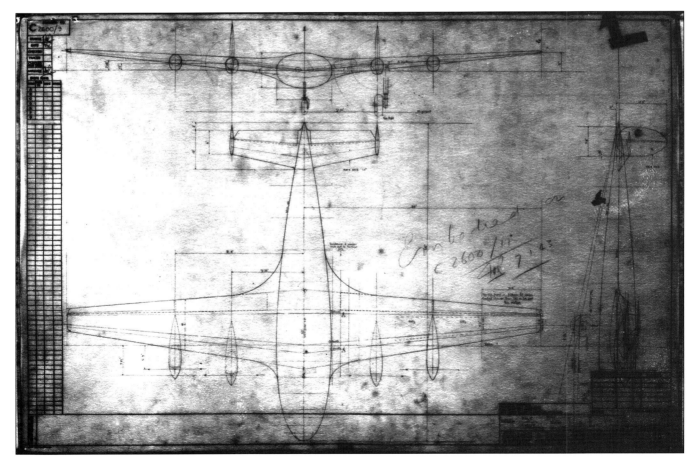

Three-view G.A. drawing, No.C2600/9, entitled 'Basic Layout M.26 Scheme BX', possibly dated 29.4.40, shows four engines installed in nacelles, twin fins and rudders and a single main-wheel tricycle undercarriage. Dimensions on the drawing gave a wingspan of 116 ft.

CHAPTER 37: MILES M.26J X.9, X.9 SCHEME B, X.9 SCHEME CX AND X.9 SCHEME BX . . .

323

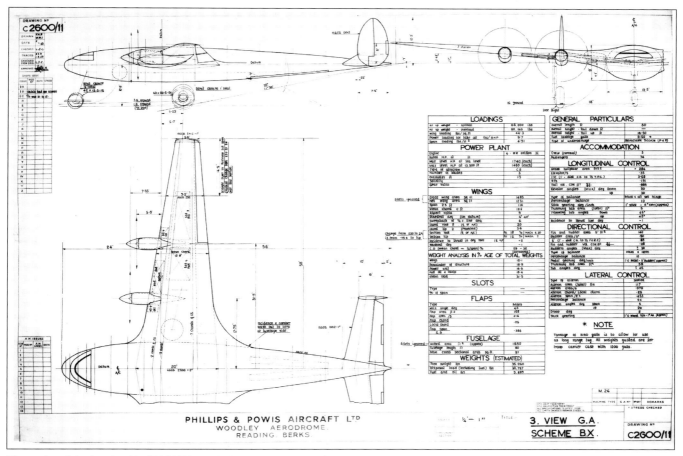

Three-view G.A. drawing No.C2600/11, entitled M.26 '3 view G.A. Scheme BX', dated 2.1.43, showed the four 1,740 hp (at sea level) Rolls-Royce Griffon II engines mounted in normal nacelles and with a wingspan of 116 feet.

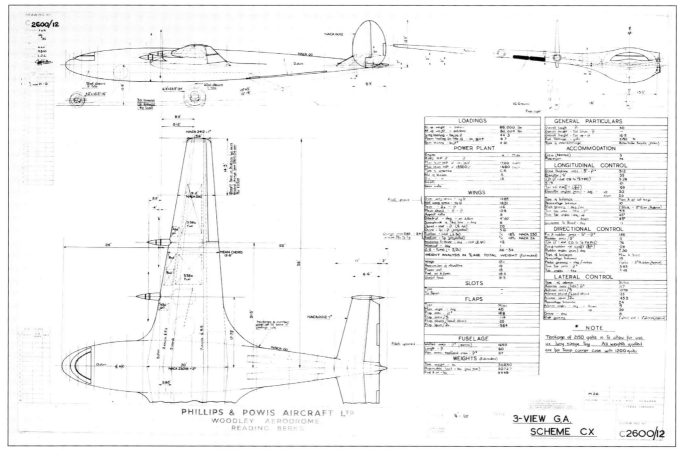

Three-view G.A. drawing, No.C2600/12, entitled M.26 '3 view G.A. Scheme CX', dated 26.1.43, showed the four 1,740 hp (at sea level) 'Miles' engines buried in the wings driving propellers through shafts and with a wingspan of 116 feet.

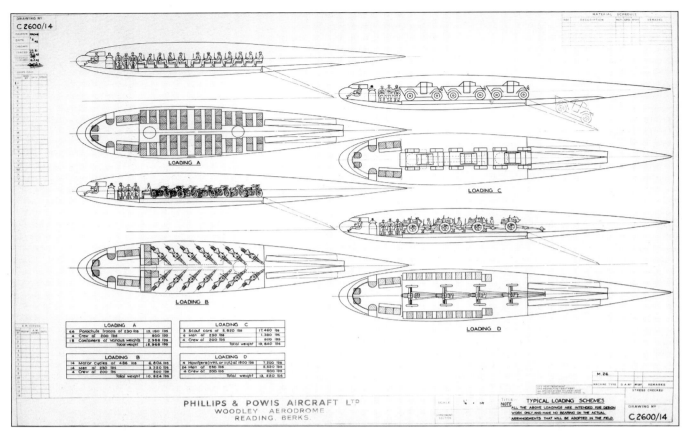

Drawing No.C2600/14, entitled 'Typical Loading Schemes', dated 1.2.43, showing the rear loading M.26J X.9, gave the following details of carrying capacity: A - 64 parachute troops, 4 crew and 18 containers of various weights, total wt 18,960lb; B - 14 motorcycles, 14 men and 4 crew, total wt 10,624lb; C - 3 scout cars, 6 men and 4 crew, total weight 19,640lb; D - 4 howitzers, 26 men and 4 crew, total weight 13,520lb.

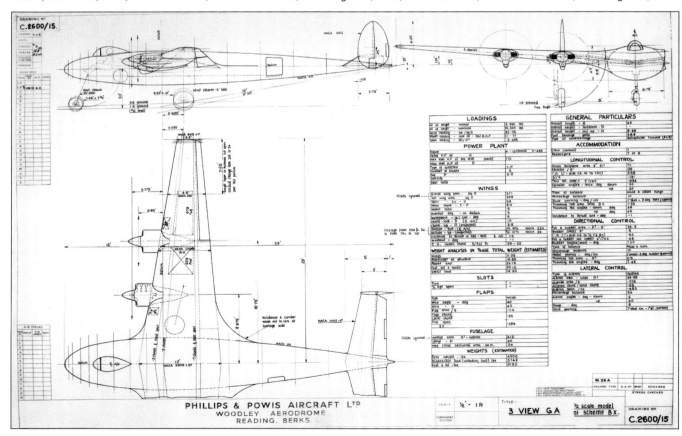

Three-view drawing, No.C2600/15, entitled M.26A '3 view G.A. ½ scale model of Scheme BX', dated 6.2.43, showed it to have four 175 hp horizontally opposed Lycoming 0-435 engines installed in clean nacelles blended into a mid-wing to give a buried effect (Note: an earlier three-view G.A. drawing of the M.26, No. C2600/7, entitled '3 view G.A. (Preliminary) Scheme B', possibly dated 4.12.40, showed the ½ scale model of the M.26 with the wings not blended into the fuselage and with the trailing edges of the wings at right angles to the centre line of the fuselage). The ½ scale model had a single pilot and provision for 7-8 passengers (although no windows were shown on the drawing), twin fins and rudders and a single main-wheel tricycle undercarriage.

Loading - To allow of rapid loading and unloading of almost any sort of vehicle, a power operated ramp would be provided which, in conjunction with the tricycle undercarriage layout, allows vehicles to drive straight in to their "loaded" position without any manoeuvring. This is a big improvement over the orthodox side door which, however large, always necessitates the vehicle being turned after entry.

Services - Flaps, aileron droop gear, trimming tabs, undercarriage, loading ramps etc. would all be operated electrically from a main supply. This supply would come from a self contained I/C - electric generator unit which would be quite independent from the main engines and would also be used for starting the latter.

Aerodynamics - The aerodynamic efficiency of the aircraft would be of a considerably higher order than is usually associated with transport aircraft and the resulting estimated performance is high. It is strongly recommended that, if the use of gliders is to be continued, a new type of glider be introduced with aerodynamic cleanness to match this tug.

With any of the existing glider types, which are extremely dirty, the overall efficiency of tug and glider would be seriously affected.

It is proposed that a half scale model of the X.9 should be built as soon as possible to verify the flying qualities and performance of the project.

Performance - with Phillips & Powis Engines	
Troop Transport – No data available	
Glider Tug – No data available	
Performance - with Rolls-Royce Griffon Engines	
Troop Transport (from RDT.1)	
Max. speed at 3,000 ft	305 mph TAS
Max. speed at 16,000 ft	320 mph TAS
Cruising speed at 10,000 ft	211 mph TAS
Distance to clear 50 ft. (still air)	870 yards
Time to 10,000 ft	7.4 mins
Still air range (1,142 gallons)	1,200 miles
Service ceiling	27,600 ft
Glider Tug - No data available.	
½ Scale Model - No data available.	

Below left and right: Two artists impressions of the M.26 Mod. X.9.

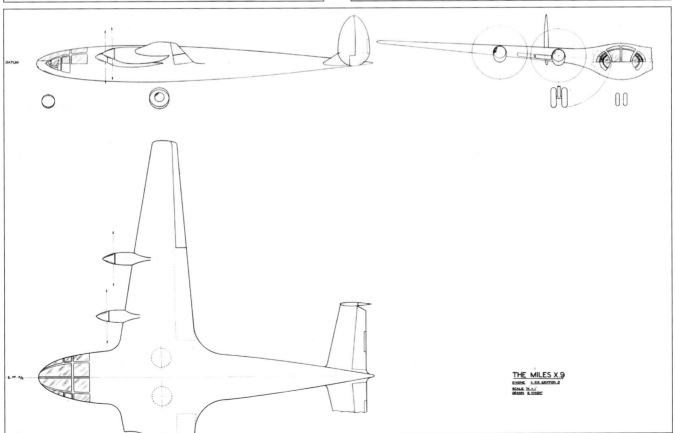

Three-view, undated, G.A. drawing of the M.26 X.9. Note the four Rolls-Royce Griffon II engines fitted in nacelles and the twin main and nose-wheels.

This sketch shows a full size, domestic, cooking stove installed in the galley, a work-bench with a full size engineering vice and a full rack of tools for the flight engineer.

The X.9's wings were laminar flow aerofoil section of high aspect ratio, with external aerofoil high-lift flaps. The X.9 had the fully glazed cabin in the nose, twin fins and rudders and, unlike the subsequent post-war British transport designs, it was fitted with a twin-wheel tricycle undercarriage, a very advanced feature at the time.

Details of the M.26 X.9. were submitted to the CRD at the MAP on 16th August 1943, at their suggestion, along with details of the X.14, another smaller proposed version of the X.11 and detailed structural and aerodynamic data for both designs was also supplied to Captain Liptrot's office in the MAP on 21st September 1943.

Despite the fact that they checked and agreed the estimated figures in respect of weight and performance and despite the fact that the leading particulars of the X.9 were to compare very favourably with those of the Avro Tudor (which did not appear until 1945), the X.9 was not considered, purely (as it transpired later) on political grounds. In fact, the Ministry had already decided to order the Avro York, which was just a simple four-engine transport using the wing and tail-unit of the Avro Lancaster.

It is not without interest at this point to compare the leading particulars of the X.9 with those of the Avro Tudor:

	Miles M.26J X.9	Avro Tudor
Span	116ft 0in	120ft 0in
Length	80ft 0in	80ft 0in
Wing area	1,485 sq ft	1,421 sq ft
AUW	76,000 lb	76,000 lb
Disposable load	32,300 lb	32,400 lb
Cruising speed	295 mph	290 mph

Sometime after 5th October 1943, Miles Aircraft Ltd produced an undated, A5 sized black plastic-covered booklet on the Miles X.9, reproduced here.

From time to time in the history of British aviation, an aeroplane has appeared which was a marked advance over any contemporary type. Notable examples have been the Bristol Fighter, the Fairey Fox, the Supermarine Spitfire and the Avro Lancaster. It was with the idea of effecting a worth-while improvement over the orthodox aeroplane, that the "X" layout was first conceived.

The "X" is no new idea - in fact the general layout was completed in 1936 and an article describing it appeared in *Flight* in April 1938. During the past seven years much painstaking research has been carried out, wind tunnel tests have been made, a flying scale model has been built and flown, from which we received confirmation of our theories and gained much valuable data. There is still much to be done, but it is felt that our present research can be extended and completed, concurrently with the building of the full-sized machine, by the construction of an exact one-third scale model described later.

The X.9 is intended primarily as the forerunner of a series of multi-engined airliners which will obviously be needed in the next decade to operate the Commonwealth air routes, linking together the widespread British Commonwealth of Nations. In war it can be used efficiently either as a bomber or as a Service Transport for the carriage of both men and equipment.

Much careful thought has gone into the preliminary layout of the X.9 which will be designed to be representative of the highest degree of aerodynamic efficiency attainable in the light of present day knowledge. Considerable effort has been expended in the preparation of a preliminary plan, whereby it is proposed to finish the whole undertaking within a reasonable time and to design and build the machine in stages so as to allow for revision in the light of any new discovery or knowledge that may become available. In view of its past achievements, this Company has no doubts as to the success of the design as such, while in view of its proud record of maintaining its production programme throughout the war, no apprehension is felt regarding the production of this machine.

General Design

The high performance and economy of the X.9 are due in no small measure to the low drag laminar flow aerofoil section employed. In addition, the manner in which the fuselage merges into the wing, which is an essential feature of the "X" layout, not only enhances aerodynamic efficiency by reducing interference drag but also provides a greater space for accommodation of passengers and freight than is possible on any orthodox aircraft of similar size. The machine will be of all metal construction with special attention to external finish.

The flaps are of the Miles patented extensible type. This type of flap has been extensively tested on actual flight trials and by this means it has been found possible to achieve a maximum lift coefficient of more than three, without adverse effects on the longitudinal control. In the layout of the pilot's cabin, the two main objects aimed at have been perfection of view and simplicity of control.

As will be seen from the illustration, the range of view provided is unequalled in any other type of aircraft, British or foreign. In addition the instruments have been limited to the normal blind flying panel, the Beam Approach instruments, two compasses and an outside air thermometer. The engine and fuel controls, instruments and the undercarriage control are all in charge of the Flight Engineer and are conveniently grouped at his station, the pilots being provided with master throttles and the flap control in addition to the normal flying controls and trimming tabs.

Leading Particulars of the X.9

Dimensions:	
Span	116 ft 0 in
Length	80 ft 0 in
Gross wing area	1,485 sq ft
Aspect ratio	9.1
Aerofoil	18 per cent - 15 per cent NACA laminar flow section
Power Plant	4 x Rolls-Royce Griffon
Weights:	
Loaded weight	76,000 lb
Wing loading at take-off	51 lb/sq ft
Performance:	
Cruising speed	295 mph at 8,000 ft
275 mph at 22,000 ft	
Run to take-off	800 yards
Distance to clear 50 ft	1,300 yards
Range:	2,150 miles against 50 mph wind.

The X.9 as a Civil Transport

The X.9 is designed for operation at any height from 8,000 to 22,000 feet and for any range up to 2,150 miles against a headwind of 50 mph. Luxurious accommodation is provided for 35 passengers in the maximum degree of comfort. This will be made possible by the exceptionally large volume available in the cabin and by the attention which will be given to pressurising, sound-proofing, air conditioning and lighting.

Conditioned air will be admitted to the cabin at the rate of 17 cubic feet per minute per person. A constant supply of fresh air can be admitted to the freight compartment for the protection of perishable goods.

All fuel will be carried in the wings and smoking can be permitted anywhere in the cabin. A large number of alternative seating arrangements are possible and the cabin may be sub-divided in a variety of ways to suit the requirements of the operator. When operated by night the machine can be arranged as a sleeper, bunks

and dressing rooms being provided for 30 passengers. Provision is made for a crew of four. Ample lavatory and luggage accommodation is provided.

Analysis of Weight of Transport

	lb
Weight, empty	36,700
Radio, automatic pilot, cabin furnishing and equipment	6,225
Crew	800
	7,025
Fuel (3,000 galls)	21,600
Oil	1,400
Passengers (35 at 180 lb)	6,300
Luggage at 55 lb	1,925
Food and water at 30 lb	1,050
	32,275
All-up weight	76,000

Imperial Air Routes - Some suggested routes for which the X.9 is suitable are shown below:

	Distance in Miles	Average time hours
United Kingdom to Newfoundland (Feeder services from Newfoundland to New York and Montreal)	2,350	8¼
Montreal to Vancouver	2,290	8
United Kingdom to Cairo	2,200	7¾
Cairo to Nairobi	2,200	7¾
Nairobi to Johannesburg	1,810	6¼
Cairo to Karachi	2,310	8¼
Cairo to Berbera	2,000	7
Berbera to Madras	2,100	7¼
Madras to Singapore	2,100	7¼
(Feeder service from Singapore to Hong Kong)		
Singapore to Perth	2,400	8½
Perth to Melbourne	1,900	6¾
Melbourne to Wellington	1,700	6

Note: On certain of the routes the payload would be somewhat reduced.

The X.9 as a Bomber

A long range version of the X.9 as a bomber is quoted below. After allowing the usual fuel reserve of 25 per cent the still air range is 2,000 miles, the corresponding bomb load being 5,500 lb. The suggested design includes a mid upper turret mounting two 20 mm Hispano cannon and a retractable mid under turret carrying two .5 machine guns.

Analysis of Weight:	lb
Weight, empty	39,500
Fixed equipment and military load and equipment	8,000
Fuel (3,000 galls)	21,600
Oil	1,400
Bombs	5,500
All-up weight	76,000

The X.9 as a Civil Freighter

The civil freighter version of the X.9 like its transport counterpart, has a range of 2,100 miles against a 50 mph headwind. Apart from its exceptional load carrying capacity, the large unobstructed space available in the fuselage would permit the carriage of large and bulky freight which could not possibly be accommodated in any orthodox aeroplane.

Analysis of Weight:	lb
Weight, empty	37,000
Fixed equipment	3,000
Crew (4)	800
Fuel (3,000 galls)	21,600
Oil	1,400
Cargo	12,200
All-up weight	76,000

The X.9 as a Troop Transport

The troop carrying version of the X.9 is well adapted for the transportation of a large variety of service equipment. In the paratroop version, six exits will be provided, two in each side of the fuselage and two in the floor. Some idea of the alternative loads which may be carried by the two versions is given by the following illustrative examples.

Alternative loads:	lb
Long range version (2,100 miles against 50 mph headwind):	
47 troops	8,460
Arms and equipment	3,760
Total	12,220
2 scout cars	11,640
2 troops	360
Arms and equipment	160
Total	12,160
17 motorcycles	7,650
17 troops	3,060
Arms and equipment	1,360
Total	12,070
Short range version:	
80 troops	14,400
Arms and equipment	6,400
	20,800
3 scout cars	17,460
14 troops	2,520
Arms and equipment	1,120
	21,100

Flying Scale Model

A most important item in the design and development programme is the construction of a representative flying scale model by means of which comprehensive flight trials can be made and data acquired during the actual design and construction of the full scale prototype. This machine would be a true half-scale model of the X.9 while the leading particulars given below show that the aerodynamic desiderata in respect of relative power, weight and wing loading are all accurately fulfilled. The machine would be of wooden construction and it is estimated that it would take about nine months to design and build, during which time the design of the full sized machine would be proceeding.

Main particulars:	
Span	58 ft 0 in
Length	40 ft 0 in
Gross wing area	372 sq ft
Aspect ratio	9.1
Aerofoil	18 per cent - 15 per cent
	NACA laminar flow section
All-up weight	9,500 lb
Wing loading at take-off	25½ lb/sq ft

Needless to say, approval for the construction of this flying scale model was not given.

An undated Phillips & Powis 'comparative silhouette' shows the Miles 'X' Junior, a scaled-down version of the X.9 designed to carry 50 passengers for 2,000 miles. The Miles 'X' Junior had four unspecified engines (but probably Rolls-Royce Griffon) buried in the wings, driving two airscrews through gearboxes and extension shafts. Its wingspan was 106 ft 0 in, it had twin fins and rudders and an AUW weight of 65,000lb.

Miles M.26K X.10

In 1942, a twin-engine, 30-passenger version of the X.9, with a 1,000 mile range was proposed. This was the M.26K X.10 and, although the engines were not specified, Don Brown recalled that they were to be mounted in nacelles on the wings 'due to the fact that in a transport of such modest size it was impossible to bury the engines in the wing in true X style.'

However, an undated Phillips & Powis 'comparative silhouette' shows the X.10 with buried engines, driving airscrews through extension shafts, and twin fins and rudders!

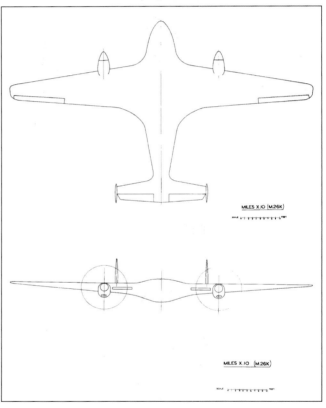

Above: Plan and front views of the M.26K X.10.

In a letter to the CRD dated 13th October 1943 concerning the final rejection of the X.11 Transport Project, Miles wrote that: *he presumed the adverse judgement applied to the X.11 only and not to the X.14 or X.9*, and almost as an afterthought after this final rejection of the X.11 he added: *Have you seen the X.9 and the X.14 with external Bristol engines?*

All of which just goes to show that Miles did not give up that easily!

Footnote

George Miles had a letter entitled 'You can't keep a good idea down' published in *Flight International* for 15th May 1975, in which he wrote:

I was interested to see, in Flight *for April 3, the sketch of the proposal for closer integration of wing and fuselage made by Clay and Sigalla at the 11th annual meeting of the American Institute of Aeronautics and Astronautics.*

The enclosed comparison of your illustration and the cross-section of the Miles 'X' design first proposed by my brother in the 1930s shows a remarkable correlation of ideas. The 'X' carried the principle even further than the 1975 model.

Miles Dufon Ltd, Shoreham Airport,
Shore-by-Sea, Sussex.
G H Miles

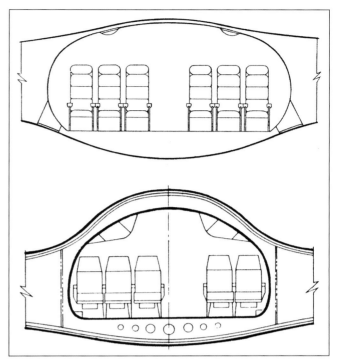

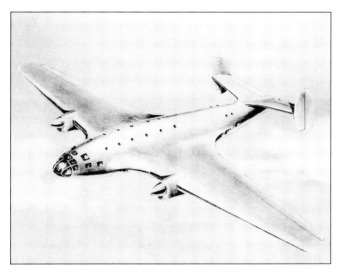

An artist's impression the twin engined M.26K X.10.

The remarkably similar integrated wing/fuselage designs mentioned in Mr G H Miles' letter on this page: the original Miles proposal is uppermost.

SPECIFICATION AND PERFORMANCE DETAILS

Miles M.26J X.9 and X.9 Scheme CX Troop Transport/Military Freighter/Glider Tug

Engines:	4 x 1,740 hp 'Miles', two banks horizontally opposed direct injection compression ignition
Dimensions:	span 116 ft 0 in; length 80 ft 0 in; wing area 1,485 sq ft; aspect ratio 9.06; thickness/ chord ratio, root 0.18c, tip 0.15c
Weights:	tare with 1,200 gal fuel 34,930lb; disposable load inc fuel 30,727lb; fuel (max 3,000 gal) 21,600lb; oil (156 gal) 1,404lb; crew 800lb; fixed equipment 3,000lb; military load 12,196lb; AUW normal 66,000lb, overload 80,000lb; wing loading normal 44.3lb/sq ft, overload 53.87lb/sq ft
Performance:	max speed at 3,000ft 305 mph TAS; max speed at 16,000ft 320 mph TAS; cruising speed at 10,000ft 211 mph TAS; distance to clear 50ft in still air 2,610ft; time to 10,000ft 7.4 min; still air range (1,142 gal fuel) 1,200 miles; service ceiling 27,600ft

Miles M.26J X.9 and X.9 Scheme BX Troop Transport/Military Freighter/Glider Tug

Engines:	4 x 1,740 hp Rolls-Royce Griffon II driving constant speed airscrews
Dimensions:	span 116 ft 0 in; length 80 ft 0 in; wing area 1,485 sq ft; aspect ratio 9.06; thickness/ chord ratio, root 0.18c, tip 0.15c
Weights:	tare with 1,200 gal fuel 35,260lb; disposable load inc fuel 30,727lb; fuel (max 3,000 gal) 21,600lb; oil (156 gal) 1,404lb; crew 800lb; fixed equipment 3,000lb; military load 12,196lb; AUW normal 66,000lb, overload 80,000lb; wing loading normal 44.3lb/sq ft, overload 53.87lb/sq ft
Performance:	max speed at 3,000ft 305 mph TAS; max speed at 16,000ft 320 mph TAS; cruising speed at 10,000 ft 211 mph TAS; distance to clear 50 ft in still air 2,610 ft; time to 10,000 ft 7.4 min; still air range (1,142 gal fuel) 1,200 miles; service ceiling 27,600 ft

Miles M.26A ½ scale model of Scheme BX (X.9)

Engines:	4 x 175 hp Lycoming 0-435
Dimensions:	span 58 ft 0 in; length 40 ft 0 in; gross wing area (fillets ignored) 371 sq ft, net wing area (fillets ignored) 308 sq ft; aspect ratio 9
Weights:	tare 4,502lb; disposable load (inc 268 gall fuel) 3,748lb; fuel & oil 2,190lb; AUW normal 8,250lb, AUW overload 10,000lb
Performance:	not known

Miles M.26K X.10 30 seat passenger derivative of the X.9

Engines:	2 x unspecified engines, but probably Rolls-Royce Griffon
Dimensions:	span 75 ft 0 in
Weights:	AUW 32,500lb
Performance:	not known

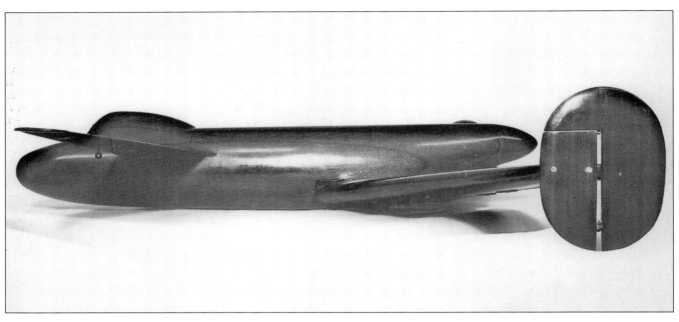

A wind tunnel model of the M.43 Libellula.

Chapter 38
Miles M.42 Libellula, M.43 Libellula (Tank-Buster), M.44 Single-Seat Low-Level Attack Fighter to Spec. F.6/42, M.42 Libellula Shipborne Torpedo Bomber and M.43 Libellula Shipborne Fighter

An Air Staff Requirement was issued during the summer of 1942 for a highly manoeuvrable single-seat low-level attack fighter for operations against land targets such as tanks and also shipping. This requirement was possibly intended to be a replacement for the Hurricane Mk.IID, which had originally been adopted as a stop-gap low-level attack aircraft but which had met with a considerable degree of success.

Specification F.6/42 called for a Single-Seat Fighter aircraft to be fitted with dive brakes and to have an armament consisting either of three 40 mm cannon or six rocket projectiles with two 20 mm

Three-view drawing of the M.42 Libellula.

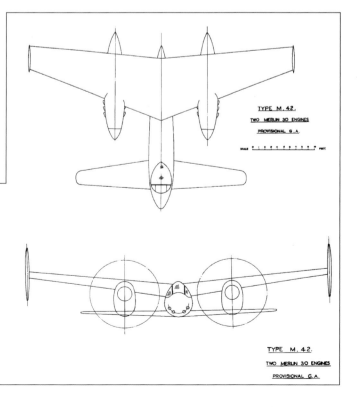

TYPE M. 42.
TWO MERLIN 30 ENGINES
PROVISIONAL G.A.

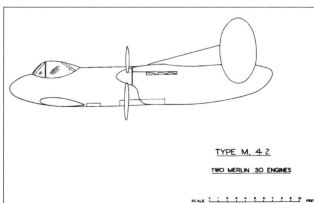

TYPE M. 42
TWO MERLIN 30 ENGINES

SCALE ⊢⊣⊢⊣⊢⊣⊢⊣⊢⊣ FEET

TYPE M. 42.
TWO MERLIN 30 ENGINES
PROVISIONAL G.A.

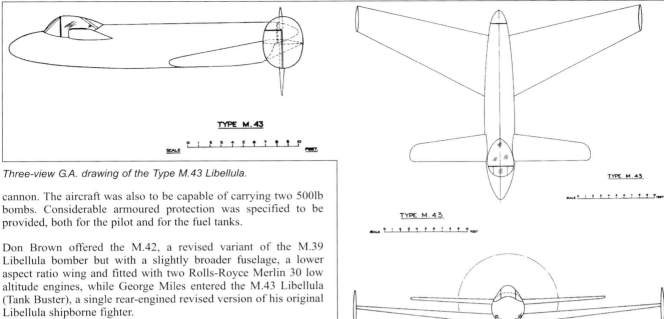

Three-view G.A. drawing of the Type M.43 Libellula.

cannon. The aircraft was also to be capable of carrying two 500lb bombs. Considerable armoured protection was specified to be provided, both for the pilot and for the fuel tanks.

Don Brown offered the M.42, a revised variant of the M.39 Libellula bomber but with a slightly broader fuselage, a lower aspect ratio wing and fitted with two Rolls-Royce Merlin 30 low altitude engines, while George Miles entered the M.43 Libellula (Tank Buster), a single rear-engined revised version of his original Libellula shipborne fighter.

In September 1942, Phillips & Powis Aircraft Ltd produced a booklet on the M.42 and M.43 Low Attack Aircraft, reproduced here:

Miles Libellula Low Attack Aircraft

M.42 - 2 Merlin 30 Engines & M.43 - 1 Griffon Engine

The Miles M.42 and M.43 have been designed to fulfil the Air Staff requirements for a highly manoeuvrable single seat low attack aircraft for operations against land targets, tanks and shipping. The need for such a machine had already been foreseen and some preliminary design and wind tunnel research work has already been carried out on some similar designs.

For the specialised duties called for, a primary requirement is to provide the best possible view for the pilot. In order to obtain this, to a degree unattainable in an orthodox aeroplane, the Miles Patented Libellula layout has, in each case, been employed. The feasibility of this unorthodox arrangement has already been demonstrated by actual flight trials of the M.35 and this was in fact, the purpose for which it was built. As can be seen from the accompanying illustrations, the pilot is seated in the extreme nose and thus enjoys an entirely unrestricted field of vision ahead and an excellent view in all other directions.

This, coupled with a high degree of manoeuvrability due to the small overall dimensions, should enable the pilot to sight on to the target immediately and without conscious effort.

Brief Particulars:	M.42	M.43
Engines	2 RR Merlin 30	1 RR Griffon
Span	42 ft 6 in	37 ft 0 in
Gross wing area	393 sq ft	300 sq ft
All-up weight	14,300 lb	11,400 lb
Normal range at max weak mixture power	750 miles	750 miles
Maximum range with jettisonable tanks	1,500 miles	1,500 miles
Estimated take-off in still air	350 yards	400 yards
Estimated distance to clear 50 ft	600 yards	650 yards

Construction - Either metal or wood construction may be employed and both machines would be designed for rapid production and ease of maintenance. If wooden construction is adopted the finish and protection will be suitable for operation in any part of the world.

Armament - The armament is fixed in one group amidships in the fuselage and fires through blast tubes which pass beneath the pilot's cockpit. In this way efficient screening from gun flash should be obtained, while the guns are readily accessible for removal and maintenance through an extension of the bomb doors and through detachable panels in the sides of the fuselage.

In the M.43, the recoil forces from the guns are transmitted directly to the engine bearers and thus absorbed by the inertia of the engine, eliminating the severe structural problems involved in the wing installation of the guns in orthodox single engine types. Provision may be made for five alternative armaments:

3 - 40 mm guns with 90 rounds of ammunition.
2 - 40 mm guns with 60 rounds of ammunition, together with 2 - 20 mm guns with 400 rounds of ammunition.
4 - 20 mm guns with 800 rounds of ammunition.
6 UP racks and 2 - 20 mm guns with 400 rounds of ammunition.
1.47 mm (3½ pounder) Vickers gun with 30 rounds of ammunition, together with 2- 20 mm guns with 400 rounds of ammunition.

In addition to the above armament, provision may be made for carrying bombs amidships within the fuselage, except in case 4 above, when they are carried on external racks beneath the fuselage. The alternative bomb loads are:

2 - 500 lb bombs.
2 - SBC's (Small Bomb Containers).
2 - 500 lb SCI Containers (Smoke Curtain Installation - also a euphemism for poison gas dispenser, although it could be used for either).

Protection - The pilot's cockpit is adequately protected on all sides and below with armour plate. In addition there are two sloping panels of armoured glass in front and behind his head, and inside the moulded Perspex cabin hood.

All fuel tanks would be of the self sealing type, paragraph 22 of the requirements being met by carrying 75 per cent of the fuel in the fuselage aft of the pilot, where it is largely protected by the armour provided for this protection. The remaining fuel is carried in the rear wing adjacent to the fuselage, where, in the M.42, it is largely protected by the engines.

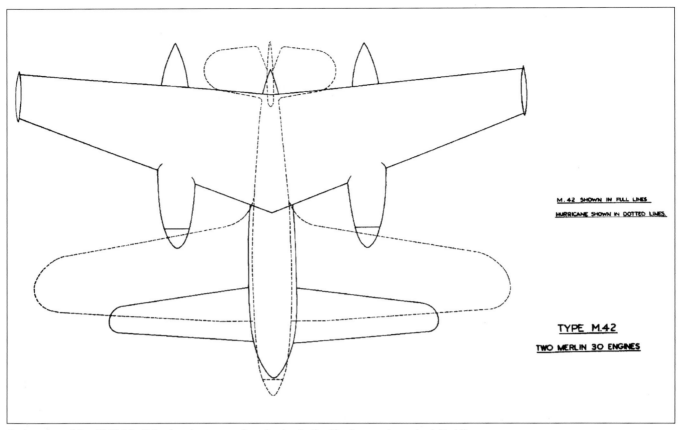

M.42 SHOWN IN FULL LINES.
HURRICANE SHOWN IN DOTTED LINES.

TYPE M.42
TWO MERLIN 30 ENGINES

A plan view of the M.42 Libellula showing comparison in size to the Hurricane, shown in dotted lines.

Emergency Exit - In addition to the jettisonable cockpit hood, the pilot is provided with a lever, the operation of which simultaneously allows the back of the pilot's seat to hinge backwards and jettisons the hatch in the floor of the fuselage behind the seat (Paragraph 24).

Equipment - VHF with BA and IFF would be provided. The equipment also includes ultraviolet lighting for the cockpit and provision for a K type dinghy.

General - The M.42, despite the fact that it is powered with two Merlin engines, is so small in size as to be comparable with a Hurricane. This is clearly shown on the accompanying drawing.

This, moreover, has not been achieved at the cost of excessive wing loading, the latter having, for the sake of manoeuvrability, and in view of the night attack requirements in para.7 been kept as low as feasible to afford the top speed specified.

The small overall size is one of the many advantages associated with the Libellula layout. Although slightly lower in performance,

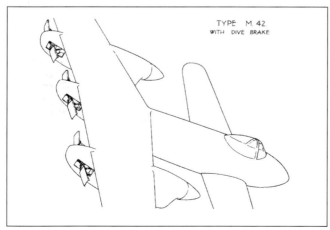

TYPE M.42
WITH DIVE BRAKE

A sketch of the Type M.42 showing dive brakes.

the M.43 is even smaller and both machines should therefore be highly manoeuvrable. Both could, moreover, be accommodated in the lift of an aircraft carrier without folding the wings, and should prove formidable anti-submarine fighters or ship based torpedo bombers.

Since the preparation of this Specification, instructions have been received that dive brakes are required. On the M.42, these would be arranged as shown on the accompanying illustration.

On the M.43, they would be incorporated in the rear wing and, since with the Libellula layout there is no tail, the difficulties encountered with an orthodox aeroplane will not arise.

Supplement to Specification of M.42 & M.43
Low Attack Fighters – The M.44

M.44 Low Attack Fighter

The Miles M.44 is an orthodox aeroplane intended to fulfil the same specification as the M.42 and M.43, which employ the Libellula layout. While the Libellula layout is considered almost ideal for the purpose specified, it is felt that a more orthodox type such as the M.44 might be regarded more favourably and could be considered as an interim type while the unorthodox but more favourable Libellula type was being developed.

Brief Particulars:	
Engines	2 RR Merlin 30
Span	48 ft 0 in
Gross Wing Area	425 sq ft
Aspect Ratio	5.5
All up weight	14,700 lb
Normal range at max weak mixture power	750 miles
Maximum range with jettisonable tanks	1,500 miles

The armament and equipment would be the same as that carried by the M.42 and M.43.

An artist's impression of the M.44 Low Attack Fighter.

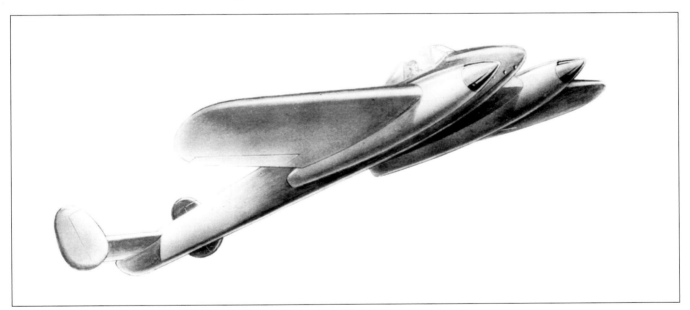

An unidentified and undated artist's impression of a possible variant of the M.44.

A photograph of a model depicting and possibly pre-dating the M.44.

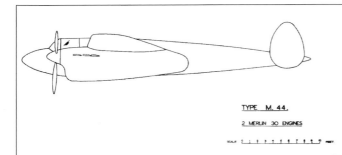

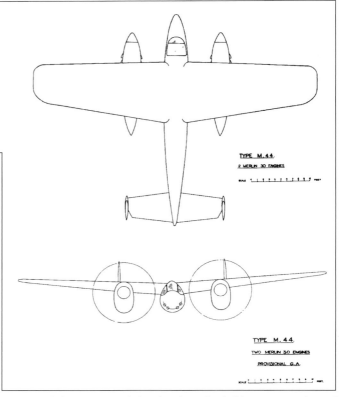

Three-view G.A. drawing of the M.44 Low Attack Fighter.

In January 1943, Phillips & Powis Aircraft Ltd produced a brochure entitled 'Miles Specialised Aircraft for Specialised Purposes'. Contained therein was a summary of a selection of Miles aircraft which had either been built or proposed up to then. Brief details of the M.42 Libellula Shipborne Torpedo Bomber and M.43 Libellula Shipborne Fighter were included and these are reproduced here:

M.42 Libellula Shipborne Torpedo Bomber.

The crying need for a high performance torpedo bomber is too obvious to need stressing. For this purpose the Libellula layout is singularly suitable in that by virtue of the small overall dimensions a high degree of manoeuvrability is ensured while, in addition, it is possible to design a twin engined torpedo bomber of such small dimensions that it can actually be accommodated on an aircraft carrier like a normal fighter: in fact the overall dimensions are comparable with those of a Hurricane.

Span	42 ft 0 in
Wing area	390 sq ft
All up weight	14,300 lb
Engines	2 x Rolls-Royce Merlin 32
Max speed	325 mph at 5,000 ft
Range	750 miles

M.43 Libellula Shipborne Fighter.

The limitations in respect of overall dimensions imposed upon a shipborne fighter, together with the exceptional view desirable for deck landing has led to the development of an unorthodox aeroplane in which these desiderata are successfully combined. In

view of the urgency of the situation, the bold step was taken of building a flying mock up as the quickest way of establishing the feasibility or otherwise of this departure from the orthodox. As can be seen from the accompanying photograph, the designers' hopes were amply justified.

Span	25 ft 0 in
Wing area	225 sq ft
All up weight	7,000 lb
Engine	Rolls-Royce Merlin 32
Max speed	330 mph at 5,000 ft
Armament	4 x 20 mm cannon or
	2 x 40 mm cannon or
	6 UP

The low attack fighter version has an AUW of 8,000 lb.

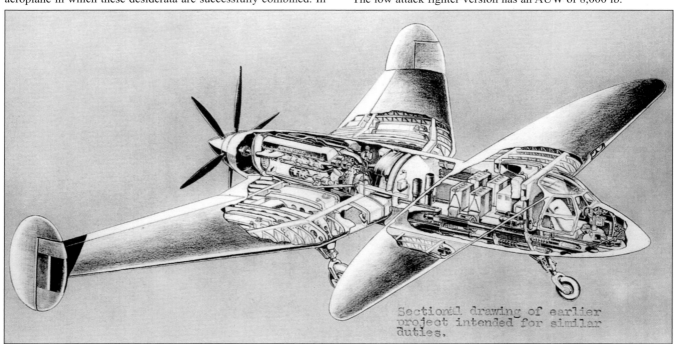

A cut-away drawing of the M.43 Libellula Shipborne Fighter.

A recently discovered Ministry document implied that a mock-up of the M.43 (Tank Buster) was made, and this has recently been confirmed by the very recent (May 2012) discovery of a Miles Aircraft document entitled 'Private Development', wherein it was stated in 1943; 'Mock-up of M.43 (For official invitation to tender for low attack fighter').

On this page are further photographs of a model depicting (pre-dating?) the M.44. Note three fins and rudders, bomb bay and the 'reversed tricycle' undercarriage.

A series of undated Phillips & Powis photographs depict an earlier model of an aeroplane very much resembling the later M.44. It had a flatter bottom to the fuselage, three fins and rudders, a 'reversed tricycle' undercarriage, four cannon installed in the underside of the nose, a bomb bay behind the gun installation and a round forward opening hatch behind the bomb bay, behind which the nose-wheel retracted into the fuselage.

The M.44 project did not appear until about early 1943, whereas the model was painted in the pre-war period RAF colour scheme of standard camouflage, with red/white/blue/yellow roundels on the fuselage and upper surfaces of the wings but with no tail-stripes. This implies that it had been projected before the outbreak of war, but it has not been possible to positively identify this project.

The unidentified and undated illustrations on this page show possibly yet another variant of the M.44.

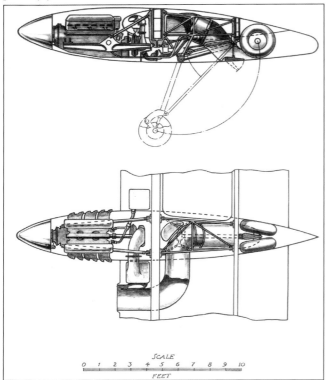

However, owing to the unqualified success of the Hawker Typhoon, which was by then in large-scale production, and the earlier tank busting Hurricane Mk.IID, the proposals for a new low-level attack fighter were dropped and none of the three proposed Miles projects were proceeded with.

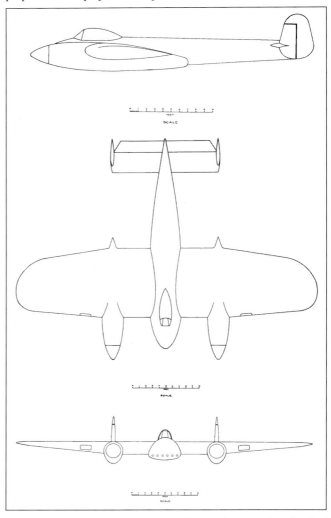

Above: Three-view G.A. drawing. Left: Drawing showing detail of engine and undercarriage installation.

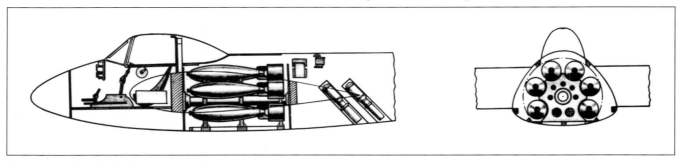

Drawing showing details of six bomb version.

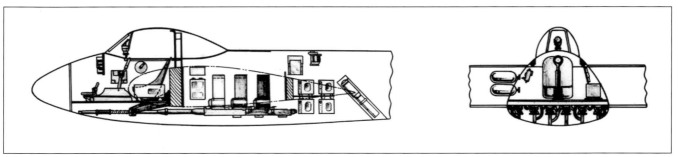

Drawing showing details of machine gun/cannon version.

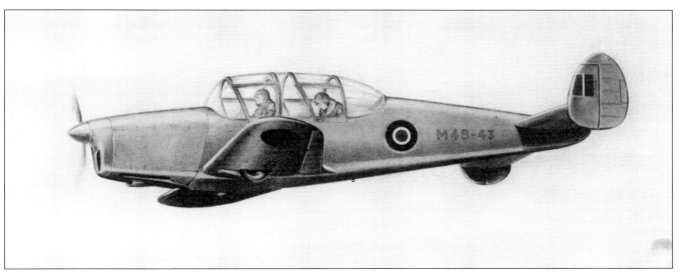

An artist's impression of the M.45 Trainer.

Chapter 39
Miles M.45 Trainer

George Miles, encouraged by the wide range of performance and ease of handling of the M.28, decided in early 1943 to attempt the design of a trainer aircraft which would combine the properties of an elementary trainer with the performance of an advanced trainer. If this were possible, as George believed it to be, it would replace the Magister, Tiger Moth, Master and Harvard then in service and would mean that only one type of aeroplane would be needed to train a pupil from *ab initio* right up to his introduction to operational types of aircraft.

The initial design work was carried out by Reginald J Fenner, under George Miles' direction (Reginald Fenner was a project engineer who was later to join the Air Registration Board). The M.45 was projected as a two-seat tandem cabin trainer and was fitted with a retractable undercarriage and retractable external aerofoil flaps. Don Brown recalled that the M.45 was to have been powered by a 250 hp DH Gipsy Queen 51 engine, but this engine (which actually developed 295 hp) did not appear until 1946. In fact, no Gipsy Queen engine developed 250 hp until 1946 so it is possible that he meant the Gipsy IV, which was an unsupercharged version.

However, the name of this was changed to Gipsy Queen 50 in June 1944 and this engine also developed 295 hp.

With an estimated maximum speed of nearly 200 mph and a stalling speed of 50 mph, the M.45 had twin fins and rudders and a tailwheel undercarriage. Although a considerable amount of design work was carried out on the project and a mock-up built, the design of the M.45 was never completed owing to the pressure of other work, both in the design office and the production department.

It was calculated that, had the M.45 gone into production, its performance would have been comparable with that of the Harvard, but on less than half of its power and without, so the Miles team hoped, the Harvard's tendency to ground loop!

Specification and Performance data

No details known.

Chapter 40
Miles M.46 Engine Test-Bed

By late 1942, Rolls-Royce Ltd was developing the new Rolls-Royce P.I.26 twelve-cylinder Vee, liquid cooled, compression-ignition, two-stroke engine. The P.I.26 was, in effect, a Diesel engine but the exhaust incorporated a turbine which necessitated a large diameter tail-pipe. This turbine could be either, i) geared to the engine crankshaft, ii) used to drive an additional propeller, iii) used to drive a supercharger, or iv) used to drive a ducted fan, thus giving very low specific consumption.

The design take-off power of the P.I.26 was 2,300 bhp and the engine was already running on the ground test bed at about half this power.

There was no suitable single-engined aircraft available which could have been adapted to take this engine, so Rolls-Royce approached

Miles with a view to constructing a single-engine aircraft for use as a flying test-bed. The M.46 was the result and in the interests of economy and to save time, it was decided to use the wings and undercarriage from a North American Mustang and to design a new fuselage to provide accommodation for a crew of two, together with very comprehensive test instrumentation.

Don Brown later recalled that the Mustang to be used was the one used by Rolls-Royce for development work in connection with the installation of a Merlin engine in place of its original American Allison engine.

A Phillips & Powis Internal Memorandum (reproduced here), written by Don Brown to George Miles, with copies to F G and Mrs Miles, dated 24th December 1942, stated that '*the Mustang wings have already been delivered to Rolls-Royce', which implied that a separate set of wings had been supplied and that the Rolls-Royce Mustang was not to have been 'cannibalised' for use in the M.46 after all:*

Mr J C K Shipp of DANA, MAP called yesterday to give us information regarding the Mustang in connection with the projected M.46 for Rolls-Royce. In the course of conversation a certain amount of interesting information on various matters was elicited and is given here:

Dr Roxbee Cox – Perhaps the most interesting was the fact that Dr Roxbee Cox, now DDSR1, is being appointed Director of Engine Development in charge of the development of jet propulsion power plants. There is little doubt that this appointment must have been envisaged for some time and, in view of this, the doctor's interest in the development of the Pterodactyl of his friend Handley Page becomes of greater significance.

American Production – Mr Shipp expressed the opinion that the recent rapid growth of aircraft production in the USA had not begun to be appreciated in this country even in official circles. He stated that in six months' time our production would be completely swamped by that of the USA and that heavy bombers would begin to pour in in unprecedented numbers. He said that, for instance, Ford was controlling 3 factories, each of which was turning out 24 Liberators a day. This statement, if correct, is certainly astounding.

Halifax – He said that it now appears probable that the recent movement in favour of discontinuing production of the Halifax will come into effect both on account of its being an inefficient machine and because of the forthcoming supplies from the USA (see the comparative figures and graphs in my report "a note on aeroplanes as freighters" dated 1/9/42). The English Electric Co, who have one of the factories producing large numbers of Halifaxes will, he stated, probably go over to the production of Mustangs with the Merlin 61 engine.

Marauder – He said the Martin Marauder (the successor to the Maryland and Baltimore) is now taking off at a wing loading of 60 lb/sq ft, the take off speed at this loading being 155 mph. The first trials at this loading were made at Salt Lake, Utah. There are 4 Marauders in this country for test purposes and 1,000 in the Middle East.

Mustang – The performance of the standard Mustang with the Allison engine is 375 mph at 15,000 ft. It is now proposed to increase the maximum permissible boost, which will increase the speed to 386 mph.

With the Merlin 61 engine and at several thousand feet below the full throttle height (for combat with the FW.190) the Mustang does 430 mph at 24,000 ft. (this is about 45 mph faster than the Spitfire IX at the same height).

Albemarle – The Albemarle, which unfortunately went into quantity production at Brockworth about 2 years ago, is now going to be employed as a tug (it has 2 Hercules engines). This, Mr Shipp said, was after an unsuccessful attempt to palm it off on to Russia together with the Airacobras, which were then regarded as unsatisfactory in this country!

M.46 – Mr Shipp has lent us the official handbook on the Mustang. He has promised to send us a copy of the type record of the machine if he can find a spare copy; if not, we can borrow the copy at RAE for long enough to get it photographed. He made a note of all outstanding information which we require and he is cabling forthwith to the BAC in Washington to obtain it for us. It is interesting to note that, according to Mr Shipp, the Mustang wings have already been delivered to Rolls-Royce.

The project design for the M.46, although approved by Rolls-Royce, was rejected by MAP possibly on the grounds that the initial flight tests of a new and experimental engine should not be conducted in a single-engined aircraft, although there were no twin-engined aeroplanes available capable of taking engines of over 2,000 hp at the time. Although the Rolls-Royce P.I.26 engine was running successfully on the bench, its further development was then abandoned.

SPECIFICATION AND PERFORMANCE DATA

Engine:	2,300 hp Rolls-Royce Crecy (P.I.26)
Dimensions:	span 40ft 3in; length 32ft 6in; wing area 265 sq ft
Weights:	empty 5,430lb; AUW 8,360lb; wing loading 31.5lb/sq ft
Performance:	not recorded

An artist's impression of the M.46 Engine Test-bed.

An artist's impression of the M.47A Radio Controlled Target Aircraft.

Chapter 41
Miles M.47/M.47A Radio Controlled Target Aircraft to Spec. Q.10/43, M.49 Radio Controlled Target Aircraft, and Conversion to M.28 Radio Controlled Target Aircraft

Towards the end of 1942, Phillips & Powis were officially approached regarding the possibility of replacing the existing radio-controlled target aircraft (the DH Queen Bee) by something with a considerably higher performance. Specification No.Q.10/43 was allotted for a Radio Controlled Pilotless Aircraft to Phillips & Powis but at that time no detailed specification was prepared. George Miles decided to submit two proposals, one based on rapid availability and the other, to appear later, with enhanced performance.

In January 1943, Phillips & Powis produced a booklet on these Radio Controlled Target Aircraft, reproduced here:

Miles M.47 and M.49

Further to the investigation now being conducted regarding the suitability of the Martinet as a Target Aircraft, the supplementary suggestion is made that an aeroplane specially designed for this purpose should be produced. It is understood that a speed as much as possible in excess of 200 mph at a height of 12,000 feet is required and that the aircraft must be capable of taking off and landing on normal aerodromes.

In view of the fact that the matter is of some urgency two proposals are submitted, one for an aeroplane which, by virtue of the fact that considerable use is made of existing components, could be available within a very short time: the alternative being a machine which would take slightly longer to produce but which would have a considerably enhanced performance. The engine assumed in each case is a simple and cheap engine developing 220 hp at 12,000 feet, which could be specially produced for this purpose, but in the meantime the DH Gipsy Six Mk.IV would be a satisfactory substitute.

	M.47A	M.49
Span	30 ft 6 in	21 ft 6 in
Length (Note: not shown on drawing)	24 ft 0 in	19 ft 6 in
Wing area	160 sq ft	70 sq ft
Tare weight	1,230 lb	900 lb
All up weight	1,800 lb*	1,550 lb
(*Note: the drawing had 1,870 lb)		
Max speed at 12,000 ft	230 mph	320 mph
Climb to 12,000 ft	6 mins	4 mins
Endurance	4 hours	4 hours

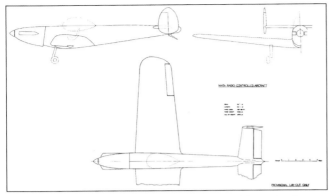

Three-view G.A. drawing of the M.47A Provisional lay-out only.

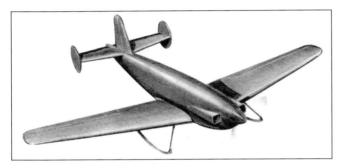

An artist's impression of the M.49 Radio Controlled Target Aircraft.

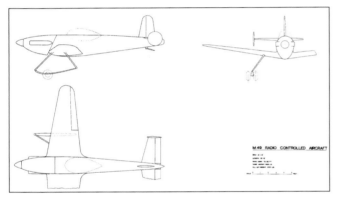

Three-view G.A. drawing of the M.49. Note single fin and rudder but also two tailplane endplates.

Conversion of M.28

Since the foregoing was written further discussions have taken place and a third alternative proposal is now submitted embodying certain features which are considered desirable. This envisages a conversion of the standard M.28 airframe to incorporate a DH Gipsy Six Mk.IV engine and a retractable tricycle undercarriage. The main wheel units of the undercarriage consists of standard M.28 components but reversed in direction and attached to the rear instead of the front spar.

Retraction and extension of the undercarriage and flaps would be effected automatically as described in proposals previously submitted to the Ministry. This would avoid the necessity for separate radio operated controls. A cabin is provided for initial

flight testing and adjustment by a pilot and his seat is arranged to be in line with the CG so that no change of trim is occasioned when, on completion of the test flights, the machine is flown as a pilot-less aircraft. An observer can also be carried if desired.

With the engine envisaged for the prototype the estimated top speed would be 225 mph at all heights between 7,000 feet and 12,000 feet. It should be noted that this proposal would involve very few alterations to the standard airframe to avoid delay in the construction of a prototype and the initiation of production.

The initial design, designated the M.47, was to have been powered by a simple, cheap, mass-produced engine giving 220 hp at 12,000ft. However, pending the production of a suitable power-plant, a 250 hp supercharged DH Gipsy Queen engine was substituted as a temporary measure and this was designated M.47A. No drawing of the M.47 exists but the 'Provisional Layout Only' of the 'M.47A Radio-Controlled Aircraft' shows it to have a fixed undercarriage with a tailskid, and with the wings and twin fins and rudders of the M.28.

The second alternative proposal, the 'M.49 Radio-Controlled Aircraft', was a smaller machine but powered by the same 220 hp engine as the M.47. The advantage of the M.49 was that it was designed to be 100 mph faster than the M.47 and Don Brown was of the opinion that anti-aircraft gunners trained on the M.49, flying at over 300 mph at 12,000ft, would have found the German V-1 Flying Bombs in June 1944 an easy target!

A few months after the M.49 project design was completed, and after further discussions with the MAP, George Miles put forward a third proposal, entitled 'Conversion of M.28'. All these projected designs were submitted to the MAP and the Admiralty but by then it had been decided to modify the M.25 Martinet to a pilotless radio-controlled target aircraft. This duly became the M.50 Queen Martinet and neither the M.47/M.47A, the M.49, nor the conversion of the M.28 were proceeded with.

In January 1943, Phillips & Powis Aircraft Ltd produced a brochure entitled 'Miles Specialised Aircraft for Specialised Purposes'. Contained therein was a summary of a selection of Miles aircraft which had either been built or proposed up to then and a brief note on the M.49 was included:

M.49 High Speed Target Aeroplane

The M.49 has been designed to provide for the need for a high speed target aeroplane. It is designed to be taken off and landed on ordinary aerodromes and for this purpose a special type of undercarriage is provided. This consists of a pair of skids resting on two pairs of small wheels. When the machine takes off the wheels remain on the ground and the machine lands on the skids, thus providing automatic braking. Although the engine is only of 220 hp the performance is comparable with that of a modern fighter. A new and improved type of radio-controlled pilot is also being developed for use with this machine.

Span	21 ft 6 in
Wing area	70 sq ft
All up weight	1,550 lb
Max speed	320 mph at 12,000 ft.

Below: Three-view G.A. drawing of the Conversion of M.28.

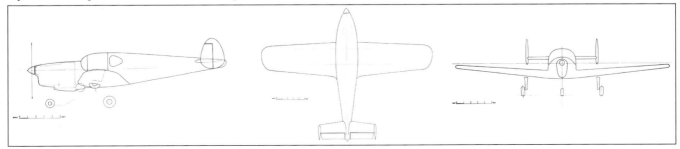

An artist's impression of the M.26L X.11.

Chapter 42
Miles M.26L X.11 Long Range 50 Passenger (Trans-Atlantic) Transport/Medium Range 100 Passenger Transport/Short Range Passenger Transport, M.26 X.11A 1/3 Scale Flying Model of the X.11, M.26 X.11 Heavy Bomber, M.26 X.11 Troop Transport and M.26 X.12 (?), M.26 X.13 (?)

Following seven years of painstaking research, wind tunnel testing and comparative flight testing with the M.30 'X' Minor, confirmation of the theories behind the 'X' design and much valuable data was gained. However, towards the end of 1942 it became known, although unofficially, that the MAP was about to issue a specification for a 50-passenger long range (trans-Atlantic) transport aircraft. This was to the recommendation of a committee which had been formed under the chairmanship of Lord Brabazon of Tara to consider and advise on the type of civil transport aircraft likely to be required after the war.

Several firms, including the Bristol Aeroplane Company, were anxious to tender designs based on this Civil Transport 'Brabazon I' Specification (later issued as Spec. 2/44) which, not unnaturally, re-awakened memories in the mind of F G Miles of the 'X' transport of 1936.

After an unsuccessful application to the Ministry for a copy of the specification, it was decided to go ahead with the M.26L X.11, a project design developed from the X.7 with the same dimensions and all up weight, but with twin fins and rudders and large single-wheel tricycle undercarriage.

The X.11 was based on what appeared to be the requirements for such an aeroplane, so Miles approached Sir Stafford Cripps, who had been appointed Minister of Aircraft Production on 22nd November 1942, informing him of his intention but, before embarking on the project, obtaining from the Minister the assurance that any design submitted would be seriously considered and either accepted or rejected, on the basis of its estimated performance.

Miles, encouraged by this promise, entrusted Don Brown with the task of preparing the project design to be submitted in competition with the Bristol proposal. The only condition he imposed was that the aircraft must conform to the general configuration of the X, which he regarded as the acme of aerodynamic refinement. In all other respects Don was given a completely free hand as regards size, weight, power and performance.

In view of the very strong headwinds encountered on the North Atlantic route, it seemed clear that a very high economical cruising speed was essential both to avoid a prohibitive duration of flight and also to ensure reasonable regularity of service. This entailed a relatively high wing loading coupled with a low power loading; in

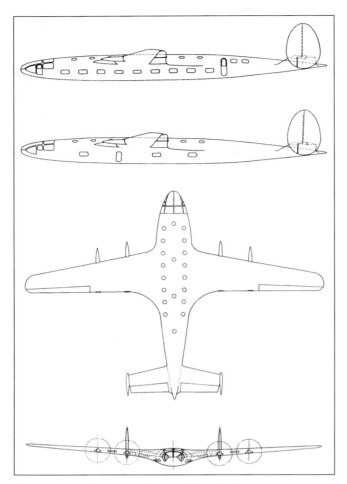

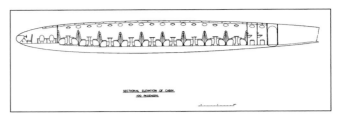

Above: Sectional Elevation of Cabin showing 100 passenger seating arrangement.

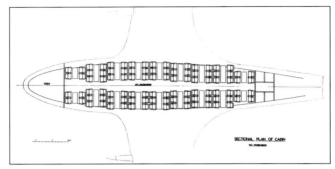

Above: Sectional Plan of Cabin showing 100 passenger seating arrangement.

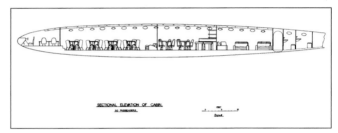

Four-view G.A. drawing of the M.26L X.11 100 passenger transport showing two different window and door arrangements in the fuselage.

Sectional Elevation of Cabin showing 50 passenger seating arrangement. Note bar in corner!

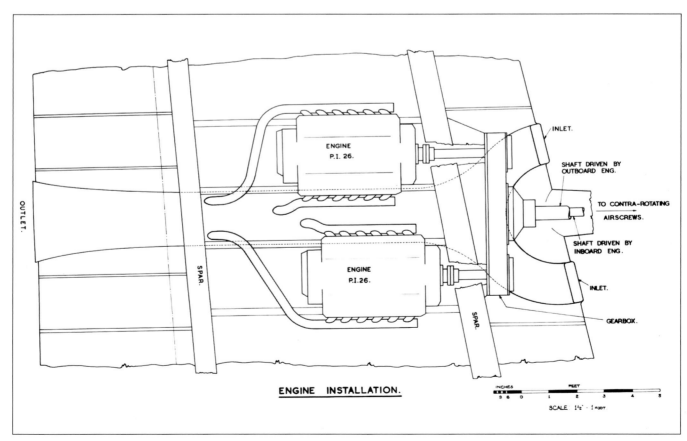

ENGINE INSTALLATION.

Drawing showing the installation of a pair of buried, coupled, Rolls-Royce P.I.26 engines and gearbox, driving contra-rotating propellers through two shafts.

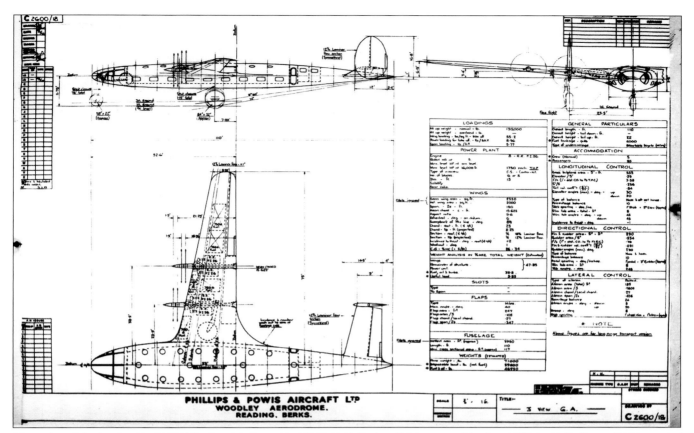

Three-view G.A. drawing No.C2600/18, dated 1.43, entitled M.26 X.11 '3 view G.A.', powered by 8 x 1,750 hp Rolls-Royce P.I.26 coupled engines buried in the wings driving 4 contra-rotating propellers through gearboxes and extension shafts. Wingspan 150 feet (Note trailing edge of wing at right angles to the centre line of the fuselage), length110 feet. Accommodation 50 passengers and 5 crew. AUW Normal 130,000 lb.

other words, what was required was a fast aeroplane of as small a size as was compatible with the necessary range.

The X.11 had an AUW of 165,000lb and was to be powered by eight 2,300 bhp (max take-off power) Rolls-Royce P.I.26 twelve-cylinder Vee, liquid-cooled, compression-ignition, two-stroke engines which were then under development. The exhaust system of the P.I.26 incorporated a ducted fan which necessitated a large diameter tail-pipe and as no existing single-engined aircraft could be adapted to take this arrangement, Rolls-Royce approached Miles with a view to constructing a single-engined aircraft for use as a flying test-bed. The M.46 was designed for this purpose and, for speed and economy, this project was to have utilised the wings from a North American Mustang which Rolls-Royce then had available. In the event, the construction of the M.46 was not authorised by the Ministry and the Rolls-Royce P.I.26 engine was not completed.

Had the P.I.26 engines been available, they would have given the X.11 a cruising speed of 350 mph.

In the X.11, the engines were to be coupled in pairs, buried in the wing driving four contra-rotating airscrews through gearboxes and extension shafts. The engines were designed to be removed for maintenance or replacement by simply lowering them through the under-surface of the wing. The wing of the X.11 was fitted with retractable external aerofoil flaps.

In January 1943, a Phillips & Powis brochure, entitled 'Miles Specialised Aircraft for Specialised Purposes' contained brief details of the M.26L X Post War Civil Transport, and these are reproduced here:

Although, as can be seen by the foregoing specifications, Service aircraft are regarded as of paramount importance until final victory is at last in sight, yet it is not too early to give some thought to the types of aircraft which this country will have to produce if it is to receive its rightful share in providing the aircraft which will inevitably be needed for operating the high speed lines of

communications between the scattered units of the far flung British Commonwealth of Nations. The machine envisaged would be a development of the large 'X' troop transport mentioned earlier under that heading.

Span	150 ft 0 in
Wing area	2,500 sq ft
All up weight	130,000 lb
Engines	8 x Rolls-Royce P.I.26
No of passengers	100
Max speed	400 mph at 20,000 ft
Cruising speed	250 mph at 10,000 ft
Range	3,500 miles

It was considered imperative that the design and development programme of the X.11 should also include the construction of a representative one-third scale flying model, in order to accumulate flight data during the construction of the full scale prototype. This model would have been of wooden construction and it was estimated that it could have been designed and built in nine months, during which time the design and construction of the full sized machine would be proceeding.

On 23rd December 1942, the Brabazon Committee was formed under John Moore-Brabazon, First Baron Brabazon of Tara, to investigate the future needs of the British Empire and Commonwealth's civilian airliner market.

The committee then drew up proposals for a range of airliners to which Miles, not unnaturally, tendered the X.11 as being an ideal contender to meet the Brabazon I Specification.

The leading particulars of the four contenders for the contract, one official and three uninvited were Bristol, who put forward their monster Bristol 167 project with an AUW of 240,000 lb; Shorts, who responded with an orthodox design and a tailless concept, the latter a Mk.VIII flying wing derivative of the Hill Pterodactyl powered by five Rolls-Royce 45H24 buried engines and Miles,

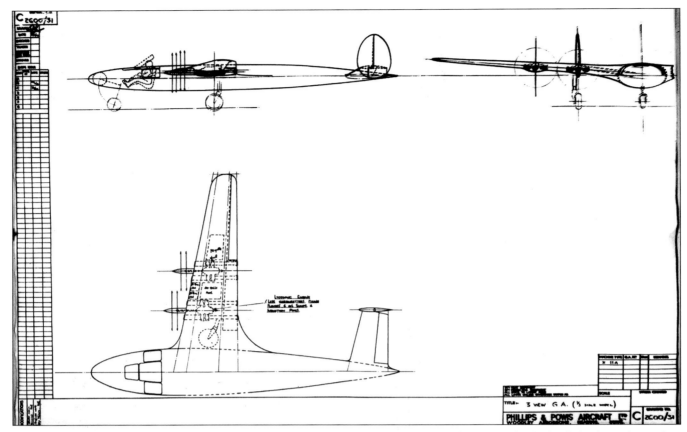

Three-view G.A. drawing No.C2600/31, dated 1.43, entitled M.26A '3 view G.A. (1/3 scale model)', powered by 4 x 4-cylinder, Lycoming engines buried in the wings, driving two bladed contra-rotating propellers through extension shafts. The pilot sat on the floor with a hinged transparent panel above his head to enable it to be used as a windscreen behind which he could raise his seat for take-off and landing.

who put forward their X.11, with an AUW of 165,000 lb, powered by 8 Rolls-Royce P.I.26 buried and geared engines, see the table below for more details:

Various Phillips & Powis sales brochures (marked Secret and Confidential) entitled *The Miles 'X'* were published prior to October 1943 and although they did not specify the particular 'X' model, these have since been found to represent various versions of the M.26L X.11. One, undated, had the No.1 in the top right hand corner of the front cover, and another was dated April 1943. They were both almost identical but with slight variations to the text and Illustrations. The illustrations were identical but with Fig.25 'Main

lounge cleared for dancing' in the undated edition deleted in the April 1943 edition, and Fig.16 'Drawing showing conversion of seats to bunks' added to the April 1943 edition.

On 9th June 1943, Don Brown paid a visit to the MAP and his report (with reference only to the Miles X) is reproduced in full here:

I saw Capt. Liptrot AD/RDT/1 and asked him whether any figures had yet been agreed regarding the power and fuel consumption of the P.I. 26. Capt. Liptrot immediately rang Major Ross who was not in, but he was informed that Major Ross was sending through a

	Bristol 167	Short Orthodox	Miles X.11	Short Tailless
AUW lb:	240,000	175,000	165,000	185,000
Wing area sq ft:	5,190	3,073	2,350	5,300
Wing loading lb/sq ft:	46.5	56.9	70.2	34.9
Engines hp:	8 x 2,500 Bristol Centaurus buried and geared	6 x 2,500 Bristol Centaurus in nacelles-pushers	8 x 2,300 Rolls-Royce P.I.26 buried and geared	5 Rolls-Royce 46H24 buried
Take off bhp:	19,200	14,400	18,400	16,500
Power loading lb/bhp:	12.5	12.15	8.96	11.2
W2/SP:	581	690	630	392
Span ft:	230	184	150	176
Aspect ratio:	10.1	11.0	9.55	5.85
Root t/c:	0.21	-	0.18	0.22
Estimated cruising speed mph:	270	259	350	287
Flight time against headwind of 60 mph, hrs	16.4	17.35	11.9	15.2
Firm's estimated profile drag at 100 ft/sec, lb	1,100	803	425	698
Seating capacity:	45	24	50	34

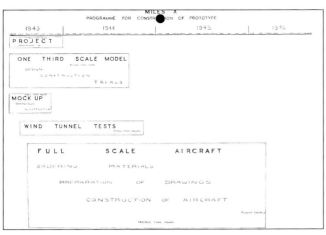

Miles X. Programme for Construction of Prototype.

Above and below: Artist's impressions of the M.26L X.11.

memo agreeing the figures quoted by Mr Wood of Rolls-Royce in his letter to MAP. Capt. Liptrot turned up this memo and the figures were as follows:-

Take-off power	*2,300 bhp*
Economical cruising	*1,660 bhp plus 90 thp*
Consumption	*0.48 pints/hp/hour calculated on 1,750 hp*
Installation weight complete with turbine	*3,250 lb*

Capt Liptrot urged that we should lose no time in the preparation of a revised project based on these figures and said that he was being pressed for a further report and could not keep the minister waiting indefinitely. I asked him what take-off you would be prepared to recommend and he suggested 1,400 yards to clear 50 feet. He added that he made this distance 1,000 yards on our original specification and this in fact was the figure for which we had aimed.

I then attempted to see Dr Roxbee Cox to seek his views on the gain in performance to be expected from 140 octane fuel, but unfortunately he was out. I left a message with his assistant saying that we were meeting F/L W E P Johnson next Tuesday.

I then saw Messrs Wright and Stansfield of RDE.1c regarding the effect of 140 octane fuel. They said that little or no information was yet available but they did not anticipate that any appreciable change in specific fuel consumption would be gained, although a marked increase in power obtainable from a given engine might be expected. They added that the transition from 87 to 100 octane fuel resulted in an increase in power of the order of 30%.

If a similar increase can be obtained by changing from 100 to 140 octane, the number of engines in the X can be reduced from 8 to 6.

Sometime after 5th October 1943, Miles Aircraft Ltd produced a booklet on the M.26L X.11 (with the introduction obviously based on the M.26J X.9). Some of the details contained therein differed slightly with those in previous brochures, so this may be taken to be the final version of the M.26L X.11 and it is reproduced here:

The X.11 is a development of the M.26J X.9 and M.26K M.10 projected multi-engined airliners which will obviously be needed in the next decade to operate the Commonwealth Air routes, linking together the widespread British Commonwealth of Nations. In war it can also be used efficiently either as a bomber or as a Service Transport for the carriage of both men and equipment.

Much careful thought has gone into the preliminary layout of the X.11 which will be designed to have a performance higher than anything yet attained and to be representative of the highest degree of aerodynamic efficiency attainable in the light of present day knowledge. Considerable effort has been expended in the preparation of a preliminary plan, whereby it is proposed to finish the whole undertaking within a reasonable time and to design and

build the machine in stages so as to allow for revision in the light of any new discovery or knowledge that may become available.

In view of its past achievements, this Company has no doubts as to the success of the design as such, while in view of its proud record of maintaining its production programme throughout this war, no apprehension is felt regarding the production of this machine.

General Design

The basic design may be adapted to cover the following three versions:-

1. The Long Range Version, having a practical range of 3,450 miles, allowing for a head wind of 50 mph the cruising speed being 350 mph.
2. The Medium Range Version having a practical range of 2,000 to 2,500 miles. *(2,100 miles, 100 passengers - PA)*
3. A Short Range Service Version with an operational range of 1,100 miles.

The manner in which the fuselage merges into the wing is an essential feature of the "X" layout and not only enhances aerodynamic efficiency by reducing interference drag, but also provides a greater space for accommodation of passengers and freight than is possible on any orthodox aircraft of similar size, the volume of the cabin being over 6,000 cubic feet.

The machine will be of all-metal construction with special attention to external finish.

Another advanced feature of the design of the X.11 and one which adds to in no small degree to the overall aerodynamic efficiency, is the housing of the eight engines, gear boxes, radiators, oil coolers, exhaust fans, and ducts completely within the wing.

For servicing purposes, large removable panels are provided over the whole of the power units while for replacement the engines may be lowered through the under surface of the wing, special built-in tackle being provided for the purpose.

To ensure that the strength of the wing is not impaired by the presence of these removable panels, a special design of stress-carrying panel will be employed.

The flaps are of the Miles patented extensible type. This type of flap has been extensively tested on actual flight trials and by this means it has been found possible to achieve a maximum lift coefficient of more than three, without adverse effects on the longitudinal control.

In the layout of the pilots' cabin, the two main objects aimed at have been perfection of view and simplicity of control. As will be seen from the illustration, the range of view provided is unequalled in any other type of aircraft, British or foreign.

In addition, the instruments have been limited to the normal blind-flying panel, the Beam Approach instruments, two compasses and an outside air thermometer. The engine and fuel controls, instruments and the undercarriage control are all in charge of the

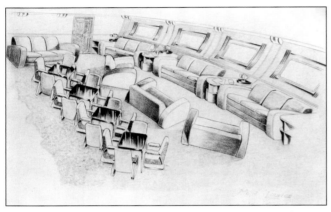

An artist's impression showing the forward cabin, or Main Lounge, with 34 seats.

Flight Engineer and are conveniently grouped at his station, the pilots being provided with two master throttles and the flap control in addition to the normal flying controls and trimming tabs.

Leading Particulars of the X.11

Dimensions:	
Span	150 ft.
Length	110 ft.
Gross wing area	2,350 sq.ft.
Aspect ratio	9.6
Aerofoil	18 per cent - 15 per cent NACA laminar flow section

(Note: in both an undated and the April 1943 brochures on the X-11, the Aerofoil was shown as 18% - 12% laminar flow section – PA).

Power Plant: Engines - 8 Rolls-Royce

Weights:	
Loaded weight	165,000 lb
Wing loading at take-off	70.2 lb/sq.ft.

Performance:	
Max. speed, Transport	425 mph at 16,000 ft.
Max. cruising speed (Transport)	350 mph at 16,000 ft.
Max cruising speed (Bomber)	400 mph at 16,000 ft.
Initial climb	1,500 ft. per min.
Run to take-off	900 yards
Distance to clear 50 ft.	1,350 yards
Range	3,450 miles against 50 mph wind at 350 mph at 15,000 ft.

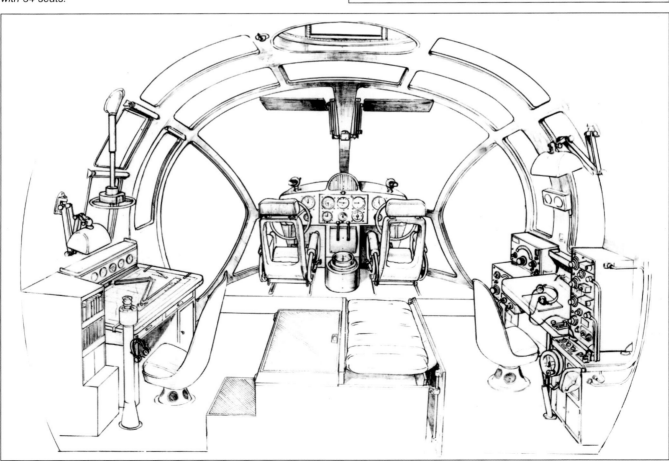

Drawing showing the pilot's cabin looking forward with the navigator's table on the left and the radio operator's radios and desk on the right.

The X.11 as a Civil Transport

The two civil versions are a long-range machine with a range of 3,450 miles against a headwind of 50 mph and accommodation for 50 passengers; and a medium range machine having a range of 2,100 miles against a headwind of 50 mph and with accommodation for 100 passengers. Both machines are designed for operation at any height from 8,000 to 22,000 feet.

Luxurious accommodation is provided and the maximum degree of comfort. This will be made possible by the exceptionally large volume available in the cabin and by the attention which will be given to pressurising, sound-proofing, air conditioning and lighting. The cabin is 16 ft. wide and 8 ft. high and has a volume of over 6,000 cubic ft. Conditioned air will be admitted at the rate of 17 cubic ft per minute per person. A constant supply of fresh air can be admitted to the freight compartment for the protection of perishable goods.

All fuel will be carried in the wings and smoking can be permitted anywhere in the cabin. A number of alternative seating arrangements are possible, some of which are shown in the illustrations. In the long-range machine the cabin may be sub-divided in a variety of ways to suit the requirements of the operator.

In one arrangement shown, three cabins are provided, the forward one being the main lounge holding 34 passengers, the mid-ships cabin being the dining and recreation room and the aft cabin being either a ladies room or a smoking room with accommodation for 16 passengers. An alternative arrangement shown in one of the illustrations *(below)* provides for a longitudinal partition in the centre with a ladies room on the one side and a smoking room on the other. When operated by night the machine can be arranged as a sleeper, bunks and dressing rooms being provided for 50 passengers. In the medium range machine the seats will be arranged in two rows of three on either side of a central gangway over 4 ft wide and some 60 ft long.

An artist's impression showing the aft cabin, or Ladies Lounge, with 20 seats.

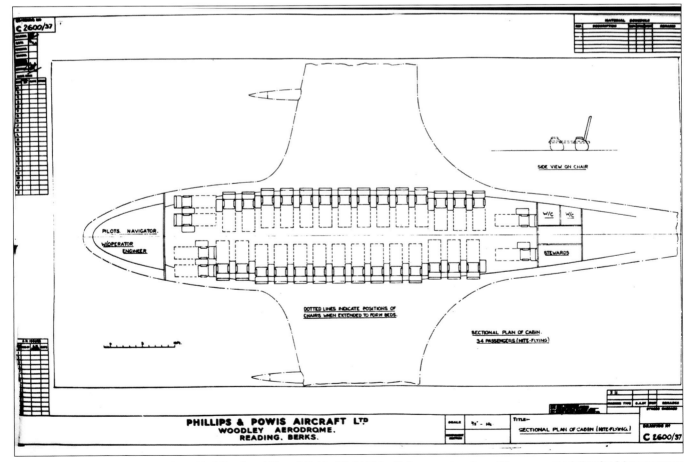

Drawing No.C2600/37, dated 1.43, entitled 'Sectional Plan of Cabin (Night Flying)' shows a plan view of the accommodation for 34 passengers for night flying. The positions show 28 seats extended inboard athwart ships (14 on either side), 4 extended forward and 2 extended aft, all to form beds for 'night-flying'. It also shows that the crew consisted of two pilots, navigator, wireless operator, engineer and stewards. Two toilets at rear of cabin.

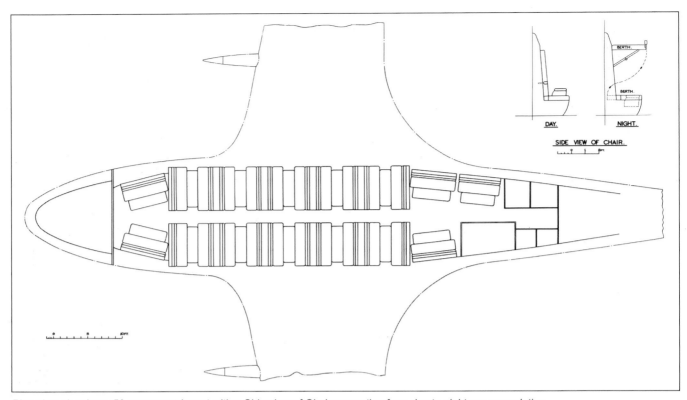

Plan view showing a 50 passenger layout with a Side view of Chair converting from day to night accommodation.

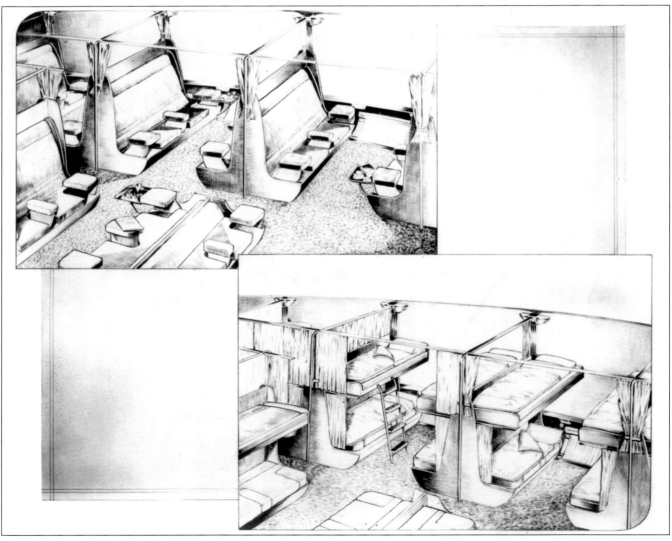

An artist's impression of the seating for day and conversion to night accommodation.

A cut-away drawing showing the buried, coupled engines, driving contra-rotating propellers through gearboxes and extension shafts and the interior fitted out for 50 passengers, with a bar in the corner.

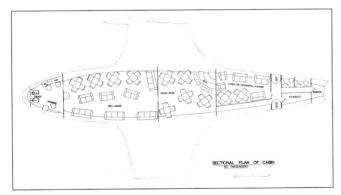

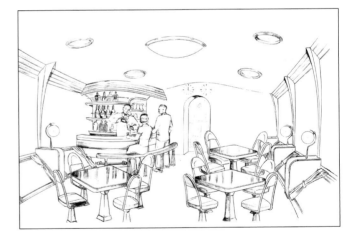

Above: Sectional Plan of Cabin for 50 passengers. Note the layout of the seats and the bar in the corner! Right: The bar in the corner seen in detail.

Analysis of Weight of Civil Transport

(a)	**Long range version**	lb.	(b)	**Medium range version**	lb.
	Weight, empty	75,800		Weight, empty	75,000
	Radio, automatic pilot, cabin furnishings and equipment	6,000		Radio, automatic pilot cabin furnishings and equipment	11,000
Crew (5)		900	Crew (5)		900
	Disposable load	8,500		Disposable load	17,000
	50 passengers			100 passengers	
	Luggage & freight	15,400		Luggage & freight	22,800
	Fuel	53,100		Fuel	34,800
	Oil	5,300		Oil	3,500
All-up weight		165,000	All-up weight		165,000

Assumptions as to World Air Routes:

The main air routes may be conveniently sub-divided into legs, the length of which corresponds closely to the two ranges available, thus:-

	Miles	Hours
UK to New York	3,450	10
UK to Montreal	3,250	9½
UK to Johannesburg		
UK to Lagos	3,120	9¼
Lagos to Johannesburg	2,800	8¼
or UK to Khartoum	3,200	9½
Khartoum to Johannesburg	2,900	8½
UK to Hong Kong		
UK to Cairo	2,200	6½
Cairo to Karachi	2,220	6½
Karachi to Hong Kong	2,980	8¾
UK to Wellington		
UK to Cairo	2,200	6½
Cairo to Karachi	2,220	6½
Karachi to Singapore	2,950	8¾
Singapore to Perth	2,400	7
Perth to Melbourne	1,900	5¾
Melbourne to Wellington	1,700	5
UK to Buenos Aires		
UK to Bathurst	2,860	8½
Bathurst to Natal	1,800	5½
Natal to Buenos Aires	2,500	7½

On these assumptions the two versions with ranges of 3,450 and 2,100 miles respectively cover the required distances excellently.

The X.11 as a Bomber

Preliminary arrangements for three versions of the X.11 as a bomber are given as illustrations, namely the long, medium and short range aircraft.

After allowing the usual fuel reserve of 25 per cent the ranges of the three types are 1,100, 2,200 and 3,400 miles respectively, the corresponding bomb loads being 26.9 tons, 17.3 tons and 6.5 tons.

The suggested design shows a mid-upper turret mounting two 20 mm. Hispano cannon and a retractable mid-under turret carrying two .5 in. machine guns. It will be seen from the drawing that the bomb doors are 40 ft. in length and it is of interest to note that the short range version can accommodate seven 8,000 lb. bombs. Even with this military load the initial rate of climb is 1,500 ft. per min., approximately double that of our existing heavy bombers, while the cruising speed is 380 mph at 18,000 ft.

(a)	Long range version	lb
	Weight, empty	84,000
	Fixed equipment	4,400
	Service load	3,600
	Disposable load:	
	Fuel	53,100
	Oil	5,300
	Bombs	14,600
	All-up weight	165,000
(b)	Medium range version	
	Weight empty	80,000
	Fixed equipment	4,400
	Service load	3,600
	Disposable load:	
	Fuel	34,800
	Oil	3,500
	Bombs	38,700
	All-up weight	165,000
Short range version		
Weight empty		77,000
Fixed equipment		4,400
Service load		3,600
Disposable load:		
Fuel		18,000
Oil		1,800
Bombs		60,200
All-up weight		165,000

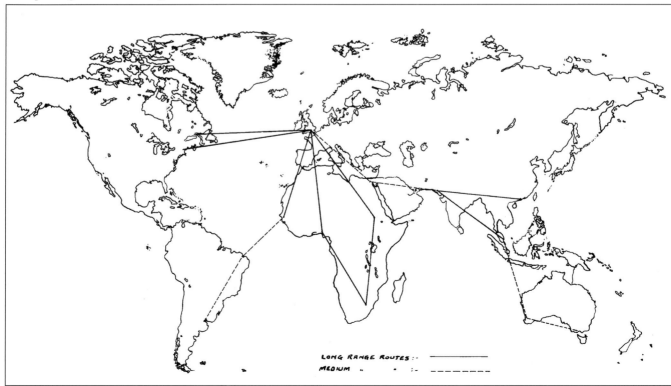

Map showing Long and Medium Range Routes.

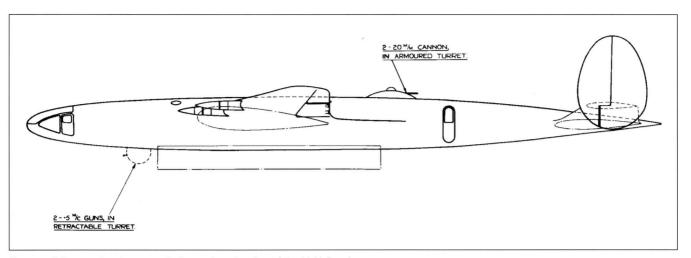

Seen on this page is a larger scale three-view drawing of the X.11 Bomber.

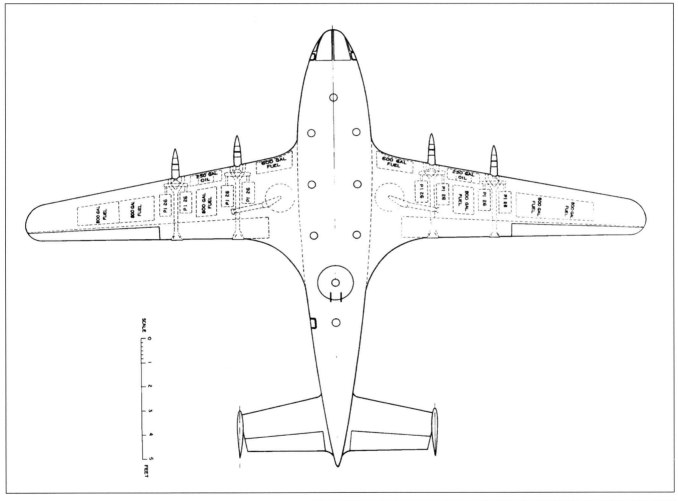

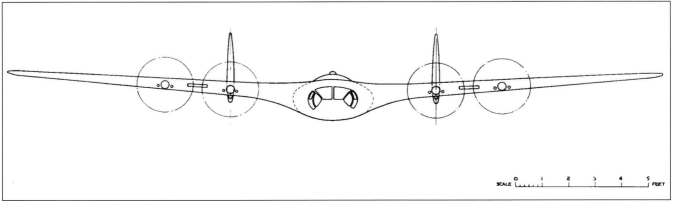

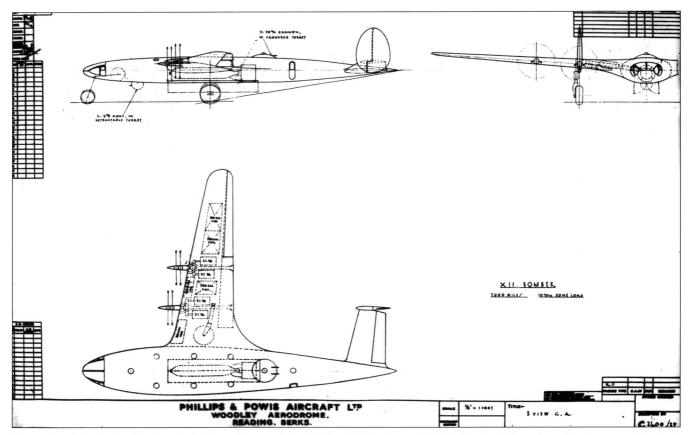

Three-view G.A. drawing No.C2600/19, date unknown, of the M.26L X.11 Bomber, entitled '3 view G.A.' The note on the drawing states: X.11 Bomber 2,000 miles 10 ton bomb load.

The X.11 as a Civil Freighter

The civil freighter version of the X.11 is, like its Service counterpart, also designed for short, medium and long range categories. Apart from its exceptional load carrying capacity, the large unobstructed space available in the fuselage would permit the carriage of large and bulky freight which could not possibly be accommodated in any orthodox aeroplane.

The weight analysis is as follows:-	
	lb
Weight, empty	75,800
Radio and automatic pilot	1,000

Crew (4)	720
Disposable load	87,480
All-up weight	165,000

The payload and range are as follows:-

	Freight lb	
Range against 50 mph headwind		
Long range	28,900	3,450 miles
Medium range	49,800	2,100 miles
Short range	68,000	1,000 miles

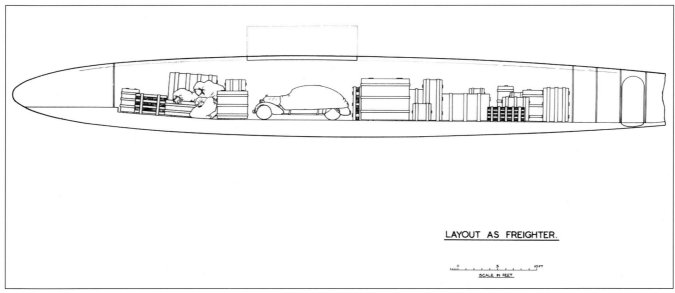

Drawing of X.11 showing layout as Freighter.

Long range version. (3,440 miles against 50 mph headwind)

Alternative Loads – 22,600 lbs

		lb			lb
(i)	85 troops	15,300	(iii)	22 Motor cycles	12,000
	Arms and equipment	7,300		42 troops	7,550
	Arms and equipment	3,050			
(ii)	3 Scout cars	17,500	(iv)	12 Howitzers	21,600
	20 troops	3,600		Equipment	1,000
	Arms and equipment	1,500			
(v)	1 light tank, equipment and crew				

Medium range version. (2,100 miles against 50 mph headwind)

Alternative Loads - 46,700 lbs

		lb			lb
(i)	150 troops	27,000	(iii)	45 motor cycles	22,500
	1 Scout car	5,820		90 troops	16,200
	Arms and equipment	13,880		Arms and equipment	8,000
(ii)	7 Scout cars	40,740	(iv)	18 Howitzers	32,400
	23 troops	4,140		55 troops	9,900
	Arms and equipment	1,820		Arms and equipment	4,400
(v)	3 light tanks				

Alternative Loads - 68,200 lbs

		lb			lb
(i)	8 Scout cars	46,560	(ii)	4 light tanks	
	83 troops	14,940		equipment and crews	
	Arms and equipment	6,700			

The X.11 as a Troop Transport

The troop-carrying version of the X.11 is well adapted for the transportation of a large variety of service equipment ranging from 150 fully armed troops to four light tanks with their crews. In the paratroop version, six exits will be provided: two in each side of the fuselage and two in the floor. Some idea of the alternative loads which may be carried by the three versions is given by the illustrative examples in the table above.

Flying Scale Model

A most important item in the design and development programme is the construction of a representative flying scale model by means of which comprehensive flight trials can be made and data acquired during the actual design and construction of the full scale prototype. As will be seen from the drawings, this machine is a true one-third scale model of the X.11 while the leading particulars given here show that the aerodynamic desiderata in respect of relative weight, power and wing loading are all accurately fulfilled. The machine would be of wooden construction and it is estimated that it would take about nine months to design and build, during which time the design of the full sized machine would be proceeding.

Main particulars

Span	50ft. 0ins.
Length	36ft. 8ins.
Gross wing area	261 sq.ft.
Aspect ratio	9.6
Aerofoil	18 per cent - 15 per cent NACA laminar flow section
All-up weight	6,100 lb.
Wing loading at take-off	23½ lb./sq.ft.

The Ministry's biased attitude towards Miles is best shown by the following:

Appendix 1

Minute to DTD

You asked for a very brief note on the attached statement referring to the Miles X Transport aeroplane. In the time available it is, of course, quite impossible for me to give a complete consideration to the weights, particularly with regard to the very elaborate furnishings and equipment shewn by Phillips & Powis in their illustrations.

To get out a rapid appreciation I have, therefore, used the simple equipment into which we went in great detail when we were dealing with the Airspeed proposal for a transport aircraft.

Actually the whole presentation strikes me as being simply an example of very showy salesmanship. The brochure only mentions Griffon engines without stating what type is intended.

The Griffon RG.20SM. is the only engine giving powers close to those quoted by the firm and I have used this for my estimates.

I cannot agree with the firm on their weights and I am in complete disagreement with them on their cruising ranges. The take off should be satisfactory, being about 1,000 yards to clear 50 ft. but the landing distance will not be very good. In the medium range case the landing loading with 75% of the fuel gone would be something like 46½ lb./sq.ft. and the landing distance to clear 50 ft., 1,150 yards.

I append comparative statement of performance.

(sgd) ADRDT.I.

	FIRM	*MAP*
Structure	*47,650*	*)*
Power Plant	*24,500*	*66,000)*
Tanks and system	*3,880*	*)*
Equipment	*2,450*	*)*
Crew	*900*	*11,000)*
Fuel and Oil	*46,850*	*46,850*
Disposable load	*16,250*	*3,760*
130,000	*130,000*	

(Note: the MAP total is incorrect as the figures quoted total 140,090 lb. - PA)

Range with 5930 galls. of fuel in 50 mph headwind	*3,450 miles*	*1,800 miles*
Max. speed	*425 mph at 16,000 ft.*	*400 mph at 16,000 ft.*
Speed for range	*350 mph at 7,000 ft.*	*300 mph at 7,000 ft.*
Payload	*16,250 lb*	*3,760 lb.*
Still air range at most economical speed	*3,760 miles*	
Range with 3,880 galls.of fuel in 50 mph headwind	*2,100 miles*	*1,160 miles*
Payload	*32,500 lb.*	*20,000 lb.*
Still air range at most economical speed	*2,200 miles*	

In a Minute to the Minister (through CE) re Miles X, N E Rowe (DTD) wrote on 15th April 1943 as follows:

It has been difficult to make a very detailed analysis of this aircraft, but, making reasonable allowances, I find that the aircraft does not carry the load, nor has the range capacity claimed for it by Mr Miles. The main discrepancy is in the empty weight of the aircraft, as a result the load is reduced from 16,250 lb. claimed by the designer to our estimate of 3,670 lb. We cannot follow the firm's estimate for range which is 3,450 miles with 5,930 gallons fuel in a 50 mph headwind: our corresponding estimate is 1,800 miles. I cannot recommend this as a well considered proposition.

In a letter from Mr R N Liptrot of the MAP to George Miles, dated 22th May 1943, he stated:

Dear Miles

Miles "X"

With reference to my visit and to Mr Brown's letter of the 18th May, I am afraid that we cannot substantiate your estimates for the "X", and have the following comments:

1.   Weights

I have made very careful weight estimates for all the components, in the light of the actual design parameters, and on the assumption that the lowest flight factor which we can accept would be 2.0 on accelerations up to 2.25 g. There is no very serious disagreement between us, except as regards the wing, though I have had to increase most components to some extent.

I should point out that, while generalisations are valuable as a guide, in using them we must always remember that the aircraft from which generalised figures are obtained have usually gone through a relatively long period of development during which the operational weight has risen very considerably above the original design weight. Thus, Liberator, on which you base your wing weight, is now flying at 56,000 lb., though designed at 41,000 lb. and its factor, I believe, is just under 4.0. We must also remember that wing weight is also influenced by operating speed, and that it is a far cry from Liberator's normal operating speed of 200 mph to the 350 mph of the "X".

As regards fuselages, we must not forget that transport fuselages are invariably much bigger than the corresponding bomber fuselage, so that these must be heavier, quite apart from the extra flooring etc. with which they have to be provided. Actually on our latest transport fuselage - that for York - the weight is 10% of the take-off weight, as compared with only 8.2% for the bomber fuselage. The latest American transport, the Commando, also has a fuselage percentage weight of 9.6. The figure of 9,900 lb. which I have allowed you in the "X" design is thus, in point of fact, very low, and it would require very good detail design to achieve it.

2.   Performance

We are in substantial agreement as regards drag estimates, and therefore as regards speed performance, but your range is far too high. This appears to be due to your having used .51 pints per crankshaft HP per hour. I think that this figure may have been given to you for the engine as it is now running, i.e. normally aspirated, so that we must remember to take account of the very big blower which will be necessary for it, due to the enormous air requirement of the 2-stroke type. One would expect it to have a specific consumption closely comparable with that of the 2-stage Merlins, and Rolls-Royce have, in fact, quoted me the following figures for cruising conditions at 15,000 ft.

Crankshaft HP	*1200 BHP*
Thrust HP at the jet	*250 Thrust HP*
Consumption .65 pints per BHP/hour at 1200 BHP = 780 gph	

This gives the equivalent specific consumption on gross BHP of .54 pints per BHP/hour.

I enclose a comparison (in the table at the top of page 355) between my estimates and yours, which I have given to the Minister. You will note that, on the specific consumption as now quoted, and even if we accept your weights and your performance, and make no allowances for the fuel used in take-off and climb to operating height, we should only have a range of 3200 miles against a 50 mph headwind if we put the whole available load into fuel and oil.

I am afraid, therefore, that the type falls down hopelessly as an answer to the Brabazon Committee's proposed type for the London-New York route. Indeed, it surely does not need much analysis to show that no aircraft taking off at 130,000lb could possibly have any payload for such a range at a cruising speed of the order of 350 mph. In sending my report to the Minister I have assumed that you will agree this argument on cruising conditions.

With many thanks for the very pleasant and instructive day which I spent with you last Monday. I am keenly interested in your educational experiments.

Yours sincerely, R N Liptrot

Data on the revised P.I.26 engine was given by Mr Wood of Rolls-Royce to George Miles and Don Brown on 26th May 1943, as follows:

Max power for take-off	*2300 bhp*
Max power for WM cruising at 15,000 ft.	*1660 bhp plus 90 thp*
Specific fuel consumption for max. WM cruising	*.48 pints per bhp per hour*

On 12th June 1943, Mr Wood of Rolls-Royce Derby wrote to George Miles further as follows:

We were asked by Major Ross to attend a meeting at MAP to discuss RR.26.P.I. engine ratings in relation to your civil aircraft. Mr Corbitt who attended the meeting had with him the ratings handed to you during your recent visit but the discussion centred round the minimum ratings required to meet the specification. Since that meeting we have had a more detailed estimate of the engine performance to meet these minimum requirements and have pleasure in enclosing herewith this estimate, a copy of which has been forwarded to Major Ross.

Miles "X" Transport Long Range Version
8 Rolls-Royce Two Stroke Engines with Ducted Fan
Exhaust System

	FIRM	RDT.1
Wing	14,500 lb	20,500 lb
Fuselage	9,100	9,900
Tail unit	1,950	2,300
Undercarriage	7,150	7,800
Flying Controls	650	600
Hydraulics	-	300
Structure weight	33,350 lb	41,400 lb
Power unit complete		
with tanks	29,200 lb	29,200 lb
Fixed equipment	1,000	1,000
Crew (5)	900	1,000
Fuel, 5930 galls.	42,620	42,620
Oil, 470 galls.	4,230	4,230
Load available for passengers		
and cabin furnishings	18,700	10,550
Take-off weight	130,000	130,000

Span	150 ft	
Area	2,350 sq.ft	
Wing loading	55.3 lb/sq.ft	
Max speed at 16,000 ft	425 mph	400 mph
Cruising speed at max.weak		
mixture power	350 mph at	347 mph
	7,000 ft	15,000 ft

Range:

(a)	With disposable		
	load	50 passengers.*	32 passengers +
	as above	3450 miles against	2100 miles against
		50 mph headwind	50 mph headwind
(b)	Equipped for		
	and carrying		
	50 passengers	do.	1700 miles +
Take-off to clear 50'		-	1,000 yds

Note:
* No allowances.
+ With usual take-off and climb allowances.

Encl: P.I Engine Ratings with Turbine

The minimum requirements for a certain application of the P.I. Engine have been given as -

Cruising power	-	1300 HP at 15,000'
Take-off power	-	1880 HP

The remainder of the estimate consisted of technical details which are not relevant to this account.

A further letter, dated 23rd June 1943, was sent from Rolls-Royce, Derby (ref Wd.3/AB) to George Miles:

With reference to your letter of the 17th instant, I confirm that the take-off and cruising powers given to you and confirmed to the Air Ministry of the performance to be expected after 4 years development, still hold. I am willing to defer to Major Ross on any case of 4-stroke engine ratings but it is not our practice to give contractors 'wildly optimistic' figures of ratings.

With regard to the figures of 2300 HP for take-off and 1750 for cruising, these are based on engine powers of 1750 and 1250 respectively, the balance being made up by turbine power plus

exhaust jet. We are about to start a 50 hours test at 1250 HP and by the end of the year would have carried out the necessary test work to cover the 1750 HP condition.

In the meantime the turbine design is progressing rapidly and we should expect to have a unit on test by the end of this year and anticipate that little development will be required to make up the balance of the HP to cover the ratings quoted.

Draft minutes of a meeting held in CRD's office on the 16th June 1943. To discuss the proposed Miles "X" Aircraft.

Present: Air Marshal R S Sorley CRD; AVM R O Jones D/CRD; Mr N E Rowe DTD; Captain R N Liptrot ADRDT1; Major A A Ross DD1/RDE; Sqdn Ldr G R M Garratt SO(T) to CRD and for Phillips & Powis; F G Miles, George Miles and Mr Robinson.

1.   CRD said that the meeting had been called to discuss the differences between the estimates of weight and performance submitted by Phillips & Powis, and those considered probable by the Minister's technical advisers.

Structural Weight

2.   As regards structural weight, the main difference in the estimates was in respect of wing structure, the firm's estimate being 14,500 lb, as against ADRD.T1's estimate of 20,500 lbs. The firm stated that their estimate had been arrived at by a comparison with the Liberator, the wing structure of which weighed 11.4% of the present total all-up weight. ADRD.T1. pointed out that the Liberator was originally designed for an all-up weight of 41,000 lbs. at which weight the wing structure amounted to 15.6% of the total weight. As a result of long experience and development, it has been possible to increase the operating weight of the Liberator to its present figure, but it was altogether unjustifiable to base estimates of an entirely new and much larger design on proportions which had only been achieved after lengthy development.

3.   The firm agreed that they had used a strength factor of 4.0 compared with 4.5 which had been used in the official estimates. This would account for a difference in the estimates of the order of 2000 lbs, but it still remained to account for a difference of about 4000 lbs, in the weight of the wing structure.

4.   It was pointed out that the present civil regulations call for a factor of 4.5. There is, however, a possibility that a factor of 4.0 may be adopted in the future and it was agreed that revised estimates might be submitted on this basis.

5.   It was agreed that the firm had probably over-estimated the weight of the power plants by approximately 2000 lbs.

POWER PLANTS.

6.   The firm's representatives agreed that their estimates of performance and range had been originally based upon the use of the Rolls-Royce 2-stroke engine with the ducted fan exhaust system for which a specific consumption of .4 pints per bhp hour had been allowed. CRD pointed out that this engine was a project of the distant future and that performance estimates must be based upon an engine which might reasonably be expected to be available in 3 to 4 year's time - such as the 2-stroke engine with an exhaust-driven turbo supercharger. The firm's representatives agreed and they had now received estimates from Rolls-Royce. They considered, however, that due allowance should be made for improvements likely to be obtained with more prolonged development, say over 5 to 6 years.

7.   DD(1)/RDE stated that the Rolls-Royce provisional estimate for such an engine gave a minimum specific consumption of .457 pints per bhp hour, but allowing for contingencies and differences in ordinary production engines, this would be .48 pints per bhp hour. He pointed out that the engine was not yet running, a great deal of development would be required, and although there was a possibility that a minimum specific consumption of .43 to .44 might eventually be achieved in 4 or 5 years, it was agreed that .465 was the minimum upon which estimates could be based, this figure allowing for variation between individual engines.

8.   As regards take-off power, the firm stated that their estimates had been based upon an expectation of 2,300 hp at 3,000 rpm. DD(1)/RDE considered that these figures were highly optimistic both in the boost required (+ 25 lb/sq.in) and the rpm and stated that Rolls-Royce latest estimates had been reduced to 1,890 hp at 2,600 rpm to be attained in 3 to 4 years' time. DD(1)RDE considered that the attainment of a maximum of 2,000 hp at 2,700 rpm and + 15 lb boost was not unreasonable in 4 to 5 years' time, but he regarded any higher estimate as most unwise. He pointed out that even Rolls-Royce estimate of 1,890 at 2,600 rpm provided for shaft MEP 20% higher than that experienced at the nearest engine speed used for development endurance running over the last two years. Moreover, we were dealing with an entirely new type of engine on the development of which we had very little experience and entirely new problems - for which there was no background - were involved. This warranted a measure of conservation in the initial performance rating.

9.   It was agreed, however, that performance estimates might be based on an expectation of 2,000 hp at 2,700 rpm for take-off, and on 1,500 hp at 2,500 rpm for cruising, although DD(1)RDE would like to see lower rpm for cruising in order to provide the greater reliability demanded for civil aircraft operation.

18.6.43.

Miles' response to these draft minutes was outlined in the letter to Air Marshal R S Sorley, dated 29th June 1943:

Dear Air Marshal,

We would like to have recorded and circulated the following comments on the minutes of the meeting of the 16th June which have been forwarded to us by your Department. Before going into details, the firm's impression on reading the minutes is that the arguments of DTD and DD1/RDE are fully reported, and the arguments used by us in course of discussion are omitted. We feel that either the arguments should be included thereby giving a balanced reason for the findings, or all argument should be omitted and just the findings recorded.

We therefore suggest amendment to the minutes one way or the other and if you agree, leave it to you to choose which you consider the best.

Yours sincerely, F G Miles

The following was attached:

Minutes in which arguments of both sides are included.

1.   CRD said that the meeting had been called to discuss the differences between the estimates of weight and performance submitted by Phillips & Powis, and those considered probable by the Minister's technical advisers.

Structure weight

2.   As regards structure weight, the main difference in the estimates was in respect of wing structure; the firm's estimate being 14,500 lb as against AD/RDT.1.'s estimate of 20,500 lb. The firm said that their estimate had been arrived at by a comparison with other aircraft, in particular the Liberator, the wing structure of which weighed 11.4% of the present total all up weight. AD/RDT.1 pointed out that the Liberator was originally designed for an all up weight of 41,000 lb, at which weight the wing structure amounted to 15.6% of the total weight. He argued that as a result of long experience and development, it had been possible to increase the operating weight of the Liberator to its present figure, but it was

altogether unjustifiable to base estimates of an entirely new and much larger design on proportions which had only been achieved after lengthy development. The firm argued that the reduction of weight from 15.6% to 11.4% was a direct result of the reduction of the factor from 6 to 4, owing to experience showing that a factor of 4 is all that is necessary for this type of aircraft; in starting to design our aeroplane at today's date they were therefore perfectly justified in starting with a factor of 4, particularly as it is understood that this factor is being still further reduced in the case of the Liberator.

The matter was left for discussion between the firm and Capt Liptrot.

It was agreed that the weight of the undercarriage be taken at 5% of the all up weight.

It was agreed not to include the firm's reserve of 2,200 lb in the weight of the power plant.

3.   The firm stated that they had used a strength factor of 4.0 compared with 4.5 which had been used in the official estimates. This would account for a difference in the estimates of the order of 2,000 lb but it still remained to account for a difference of about 4,000 lb in the weight of the wing structure. Certain reserves had been allowed for in the firm's estimates which they suggested could be set off against this difference.

The firm pointed out that they had had reserves of weight in hand both on the structure weight and on the weight of the power plants, in addition to a very large reserve in respect of the take-off: this provided 1,000 yards to clear 50 ft as opposed to 1,400 yards to clear 50 ft which the Ministry would accept, and the differences between the firm's and the official estimates were more than covered by these reserves.

It was agreed that the revised estimates be submitted on the basis of a factor of 4.

4.   It was pointed out that the present civil regulations call for a factor of 4.5. There is, however, a possibility that a factor of 4 may be adopted in the future and it was agreed that revised estimates might be submitted on this basis.

5.   It was agreed that the firm had allowed a reserve in the weight of the power plants of the order of 2,200 lb.

Power plants

6.   The firm's representatives said that their estimates of performance and range had been based upon figures supplied by Rolls-Royce for the two stroke engine with the ducted fan exhaust system for which a specific consumption of .40 pints/bhp/hr had been allowed. CRD pointed out that this engine had now changed in conception to the two stroke engine with an exhaust driven turbo supercharger and the firm stated further that they had now received revised estimates from Rolls-Royce, which they understood had been confirmed to the Ministry.

DD1/RDE stated that the Rolls-Royce provisional estimate for such an engine gave a specific consumption of .457 pints/bhp/hr, but allowing for contingencies and differences in ordinary production engines, in his opinion this would be .48 pints/bhp/hr. The firm argued that Rolls-Royce's figure was .457 and they saw no reason to doubt this.

DD1/RDE stated that the engine was not yet running. A great deal of development work would be required, although there was a possibility that a minimum specific consumption of .43 to .44 might eventually be achieved in four or five years' time. The firm stated that they had seen the engine running eight months previously.

The chairman ruled that a figure of .465 pints/bhp/hr should be used.

As regards take-off power, the firm asked that their revised estimate should be based on the Rolls-Royce figure of 2,300 hp at 3,000 rpm and felt that Rolls-Royce's figures should be accepted as being reasonable.

DD1/RDE considered that these figures were highly optimistic both in boost required (+ 25 lbs/sq.in) and the rpm, and said that Rolls-Royce's latest estimates had been reduced to 1,890 hp at 2,600 rpm to be attained in three to four years' time. DD1/RDE considered that the attainment of a maximum of 2,000 hp at 2,700 rpm and + 15 lbs/sq.in boost was not unreasonable in four or five years' time, but he regarded any higher estimate as most unwise. He pointed out that even Rolls-Royce's estimate of 1,890 hp at 2,600 rpm provided for shaft MEP 20% higher than that experienced at the nearest engine speed used for development endurance running over the last two years. Moreover, he felt we were dealing with an entirely new type of engine on the development of which he again felt we had very little experience, and entirely new problems - for which there was no background - were involved. This warranted a measure of conservatism in the initial performance rating.

The firm argued that Rolls-Royce's figures of 1,890 hp at 2,600 rpm were given to the Ministry by Rolls-Royce as the minimum power required to achieve a certain performance specified by the Ministry and markedly lower than that quoted in their (the firm's) specification. They produced a letter from Rolls-Royce stating this fact. The firm argued that Rolls-Royce's figure of 2,300 bhp should be taken as reliable from a firm of their standing, and again repeated that the estimates were based on the engine which they had running.

The firm further pointed out that reasonably optimistic figures must be used as a basis of estimating, otherwise designers would be producing aircraft not in accordance with the Brabazon Committee's requirements.

As no agreement could be reached on this point, two specifications were to be lodged, one based on the figures under heading (a) and one based on the figures under heading (b):

(a)   A specific consumption figure of .465 pints/bhp/hr and a figure of 2,000 bhp for take-off and 1,500 bhp for maximum wm cruising at 15,000 ft.

(b)   A specific consumption figure of .465 pints/bhp/hr and a figure of 2,300 bhp for take-off and 1,750 bhp for maximum wm cruising at 15,000 ft.

7.   Rolls-Royce's figures for cruising were 1,750 bhp but the Ministry wanted a lower figure assumed, stating that they would like to see a lower rpm for cruising in order to provide greater reliability. The same arguments were put up by the firm in respect of the cruising figures as in the case of the maximum take-off figures, and it was eventually agreed to prepare alternative specifications as stated above.

Minutes in which all discussion at the meeting are eliminated, findings only are set out.

1.   CRD said that the meeting had been called to discuss the differences between the estimates of weight and performance submitted by Phillips & Powis Ltd, and those considered probable by the Minister's Technical Advisers.

Structure weight.

2.   DTD's estimate of wing weight of 15.6% AUW based on a factor of 4½ was not agreed by the firm. The firm's estimate of 11.4% AUW based on a factor of 4 was not agreed by DTD, but a compromise could be reached, and it was left for discussion between the firm and Capt Liptrot.

It was agreed that the weight of the undercarriage be taken at 5% of the all up weight.

It was agreed not to include the firm's reserve of 2,200 lbs. in the weight of the power plant.

It was agreed that the revised estimates of structure weight be submitted on the basis of a factor of 4.

Power plants.

3.   As no agreement could be reached, two revised specifications were to be prepared, one based on the figures under heading (a) and one based on the figures under heading (b):

(a)   A specific consumption figure of .465 pints/bhp/hr and a figure of 2,000 bhp for take-off and 1,500 bhp for maximum w.m. cruising at 15,000 ft.

(b)   A specific consumption figure of .465 pints/bhp/hr and a figure of 2,300 bhp for take-off and 1,750 bhp for maximum w.m. cruising at 15,000 ft.

Conclusion.

4.   It was agreed that the revised specifications would be discussed with Captain Liptrot and then formally submitted to CRD.

The minutes were then finalised as follows:

APPENDIX 9

Minutes of a Meeting held in CRD'S office on the 16th June 1943 to discuss the proposed MILES "X" aircraft.

1.   CRD stated that the meeting had been called to discuss the differences between the estimates of weight and performance submitted by Phillips & Powis Ltd., and those considered probable by the Minister's Technical Advisers.

Structural Weight

2.   As regards structural weight, the main difference in the estimates was in respect of wing structure, the firm's estimate being 14,500 lb., as against ADRDT1's estimate of 20,500 lbs. The firm stated that their estimate had been arrived at by a comparison with other aircraft, in particular the Liberator the wing structure of which weighed 11.4% of the present total all-up weight. ADRDT1 pointed out that the Liberator was originally designed for an all-up weight of 41,000 lbs. at which weight the wing structure amounted to 15.6% of the total weight, with a factor of 6. As a result of long experience and development, it has been possible to increase the operating weight of the Liberator to its present figure, but it was altogether unjustifiable to base estimates of an entirely new and much larger design on proportions which had only been achieved after lengthy development.

3.   The firm stated that they had used a strength factor of 4.0 compared with 4.5 which had been used in the official estimates. This would account for a difference in the estimates of the order of 2000 lbs., but it still remained to account for a difference of about 4000 lbs, in the weight of the wing structure. Certain reserves had been allowed for in the firm's estimates which they suggested could be set off against this difference.

4.   It was pointed out that the present civil regulations call for a factor of 4.5. There is, however, a possibility that a factor of 4.0 may be adopted in the future and it was agreed that revised estimates might be submitted on this basis.

5.   It was agreed that the firm had probably over-estimated the weight of the power plants by approximately 2000 lbs.

Power Plants

6.   The firm's representatives agreed that their estimates of performance and range had been originally based upon figures

supplied by Rolls-Royce for the 2-stroke engine with the ducted fan exhaust system for which a specific consumption of .40 pints per BHP hour had been allowed. CRD pointed out that this engine had now changed in conception to the 2-stroke engine with an exhaust-driven turbo supercharger. The firms representatives agreed, and they had now received revised estimates from Rolls-Royce.

7.   DD1/RDE stated that the Rolls-Royce provisional estimate for such an engine gave a minimum specific consumption of .457 pints per BHP hour, but allowing for contingencies and differences in ordinary production engines, this would be .48 pints per BHP hour. He pointed out that the engine was not yet running and a great deal of development would be required, although there was a possibility that a minimum specific consumption of .43 to .44 might eventually be achieved in 4 or 5 years. It was agreed that .465 was the minimum upon which estimates could be based, this figure allowing for variation between individual engines.

8.   As regards take-off power, the firm stated that their estimates had been based upon an expectation of 2,300 HP at 3,000 rpm. DD1/RDE considered that these figures were highly optimistic both in the boost required (+- 25 lb./sq.in.) and the rpm, and stated that Rolls-Royce latest estimates had been reduced to 1,890 HP at 2,600 rpm to be attained in 3 to 4 years' time. DD1RDE considered that the attainment of a maximum of 2,000 HP at 2,700 rpm and +- 15 lb. boost was not unreasonable in 4 to 5 years' time, but he regarded any higher estimate as most unwise. He pointed out that even Rolls-Royce estimate of 1,890 HP at 2,600 rpm provided for shaft MEP 20% higher than that experienced at the nearest engine speed used for development endurance running over the last two years. Moreover, we were dealing with an entirely new type of engine on the development of which we had very little experience and entirely new problems - for which there was no background - were involved. This warranted a measure of conservatism in the initial performance rating.

9.   It was agreed, however, that performance estimates might be based on an expectations of 2,000 HP at 2,700 rpm for take-off, and on 1,500 HP at 2,500 rpm for cruising, although DD1/RDE would like to see lower rpm for cruising in order to provide the greater reliability demanded for civil aircraft operation.

10.   Conclusion.

It was agreed that the firm would submit a further specification and estimates on the basis of the above discussion. They wished to make it clear however, that the performance estimates submitted to the Ministry with the original proposal had been based upon figures supplied to them by a member of Messrs Rolls-Royce, the validity of which were not accepted by the Ministry.

21.6.43

On 2nd July 1943, F G Miles wrote to Air Marshal R S Sorley at CRD as follows:

Dear Air Marshal,

Since the meeting in your office on the 16th June we have revised our estimates on the 'X' and, as agreed, we have prepared two alternative proposals based respectively on the powers supplied (and since emphatically confirmed) by Rolls-Royce and on those acceptable to DD1/RDE.

The Structure weights have been re-assessed on the lines of previous discussions with AD/RDT1 and I think that they will be acceptable to him. A copy was lodged with him about 10 days ago. The estimate of drag has been carefully checked by comparison with the known performance of the prototype Lancaster and Mosquito and, as a further check, we are endeavouring to obtain some information regarding the performance of two civil types - the Ensign and the Albatross. The speed and range have remained unaltered, namely, 350 mph TAS at 15,000 ft. for 3,450 miles against a 50 mph headwind.

You will note that the payload based on Rolls-Royce figures amounts to 28,900 lb. while that based on DD1/RDE is reduced to 19,710 lb. Even at the latter figure the machine is an outstanding proposition, carrying 60 passengers for the direct Atlantic crossing. In the unlikely event of the P.I.26 engine never coming to fruition, the machine would still be practicable powered with an engine such as the Griffon.

Details of the weight analysis of the two alternatives are given on the accompanying sheet and, in addition, we are examining the possibilities of the same machine but powered with gas turbines, which we understand will be available well within the period of four years envisaged for the project. It was partly with this end in view, as well as that of enhancing the aerodynamic cleanliness, that the power plant has been housed within the wing practically in line with the cg of the machine, thus enabling alternative power plants of widely divergent weights to be used. If we are satisfied as to its feasibility we will forward details of this additional alternative on to you in due course.

We sincerely hope that, after consideration of the accompanying figures, you will be satisfied that this project, so far from being ill-considered, will, by virtue of its exceptionally high cruising speed, be a worthwhile contribution towards meeting and beating the competition with which we shall be faced after the war. I need hardly draw your attention to its potentialities as an exceptionally high speed heavy bomber, should we still unhappily be at war at the end of the period necessary for its construction. A bomb load of nearly 20 tons with a speed of 350 mph and a range of 2,000 miles may, we feel, be claimed as a substantial (and yet perfectly feasible) advance over anything envisaged hitherto.

Yours sincerely, F G Miles

Attached were - Miles X Transport - Alternative revised estimates.

	X Mark III	X Mark IV*
Engines	P.I.26	P.I.26
CPF factor	4	4
BHP available for take-off	18,400	16,000
Max WM Cruising BHP at 15,000 ft.	14,000	12,000
Sp. fuel cons. for WM cruising, pints/bhp/hr.	0.465	0.465
Gross wing area sq.ft.	2,350	2,350
Wing loading at take-off	70.2	63.8
Power loading at take-off	8.96	9.37
Still air range, miles	4,150	4,150
Cruising speed at 15,000 ft. TAS	350	350
Payload lb.	28,900	19,710
Analysis of weight.	lb.	lb.
Wing	22,450	20,650
Fuselage	12,300	12,300
Empennage	2,500	2,300
Controls	900	900
Undercarriage	8,250	7,500
Tanks	2,400	2,300
	48,800	45,950
Power plant	27,000	27,000
	75,800	72,950
Fixed equipment	1,000	1,000
Crew	900	900
Fuel	53,100	50,400
Oil	5,300	5,040
Payload	28,900	19,710
	165,000	150,000

The second column headed X Mark IV is based upon the drag structure weight and HP figures agreed at the Conference on 16th June 1943.

The comparison of the Profile Drag at 100 ft/sec calculated from estimated top speed as between the MAP and Miles was as follows:

| | MAP | P&P |
	lb.	lb.
Wing (4050 sq.ft.)	198	110
Fuselage (3400 sq.ft.)	150	133
Empennage (1648 sq.ft.)	90	80
Prop. shafts	30	7
Cooling drag	40	39
Miscellaneous	90	56
	598	425

F G Miles wrote again to Air Marshall Sorley (CRD) on 16th August 1943; as follows:

Dear Air Marshal,

The discussions between my staff and Liptrot have now gone a stage further and have reached a point where I think we can begin to see light. With regard to structure weights, I think we can now say that there is substantial agreement between us. Actually Liptrot's figure is still, in our opinion, pessimistic but the difference between us is now so small as not to be worth worrying about.

With regard to drag, our estimate remains as before at 425lb at 100ft/sec while Liptrot's estimate has now come down from 600lb to 540lb. We have discussed this latter figure with him at some length and would make the following observations:-

(a) It is derived by taking the theoretical skin friction drag of the various components and adding 25% to the total so obtained.

(b) The corresponding additive factor for the seven-year old Albatross was 23% and that for a Mosquito with guns and aerial mast removed 18%.

(c) It takes no account of the laminar flow wing which is an essential feature of our design and which Liptrot agrees would further reduce the drag.

One even more important point, however, emerged in the course of discussion and really forms, I think, the crux of the whole matter. There is really no argument at all on drag for the simple reason that we are not talking about the same thing.

In all our discussions on the X, I have always made it clear that I was trying to envisage the best aeroplane which could be made in the light of present day knowledge. Liptrot now tells us that his drag estimate is not for one moment intended to represent the drag of the best aeroplane which could be built of the size and shape submitted. It is, he says, an estimate of what the drag will in his opinion be if the aeroplane is ordered and built; that being so, there is really no point at issue between us.

Just why he should consider it impossible (or at least unlikely) that the transport aeroplane of four years hence will be as clean as the old Albatross or as the Mosquito (both with external engine nacelles) is hard to understand. But at least we can, I think, now lay the matter before you to judge whether or not you consider us capable of building a really clean aeroplane.

We would only ask you to bear in mind that we have not yet failed to fulfil a promise either on performance or production and that even in our early days we produced a Falcon which was one of the cleanest aeroplanes ever built (see RAE Report No. BA.1275) and certainly a lot cleaner than the Mosquito and that the prototype Master with a top speed of 295 mph was one of the cleanest aeroplanes of its day.

Yours sincerely F G Miles

On 8th October 1943, Sorley wrote to F G Miles as follows:

Dear Miles,

In order to reach a definite and reasoned conclusion, considerable time and effort has been spent in assessing the value of the "X" project. Performance figures, calculations, data and so on have

already been discussed at length and it is not my intention to go into the relative figures in this letter. I do want to make it clear, however, that although many of the earlier disagreements have been resolved, there are, on the best factual figures available, certain residual differences which I regard as fundamental and of such importance as to prevent us proceeding further with the "X".

In making this assessment we have not been able to go beyond what we believe to be absolutely reliable and what we can confidently expect to be achieved by the aeroplane at the time it is built. In this respect we have assessed the project in exactly the same way as we do all other projects put to us. In this particular instance we are at once faced by the fact that the two-stroke turbo jet driven supercharged engines on which the design is based, are far from being available as reliable units upon which an Air Transport Company would be prepared to rely in five years' time. Indeed, it is questionable whether we can get this type of engine into a sufficiently reliable state as would satisfy Air Line Authorities in less than about seven years.

You will appreciate that there are also other factors to be considered in arriving at a decision on a project of this kind. Bearing in mind RAF requirements, we have to consider available capacity and suitable engineering facilities capable of undertaking an aircraft of this size. Furthermore, we are not in a position to open the door to allow alternative designs to be built around the Brabazon specified types; if this were the case, we should be inundated with requests from all the other major firms to be allowed to enter the market, and clearly it would be most unfair to accept your design without offering free competition.

I fully appreciate and realise your desire to work on this particular aircraft, but after the most careful thought I have come to the conclusion that we cannot consider proceeding with the "X" project and that no further time and effort can be devoted to it. Nevertheless, thank you for putting up the proposal.

I should like to discuss at an early date some work I have in mind for you which will require to be dealt with quickly. I know that DTD is getting into touch with you almost at once and I shall be happy to discuss the matter with you in due course.

Yours sincerely R S Sorley

Note the reference in the last paragraph to *some work I have in mind for you which will require to be dealt with quickly.* This referred to the then highly secret project for a 1,000 mph high-speed research aircraft, to Spec No. E.24/43, ultimately to become the Miles M.52.

In response, F G Miles wrote to Sorley on 13th October 1943 as follows:

Dear Air Marshal,

I am naturally very disappointed at your judgement on the matter of building the X. However, I presume that this only applies to the first 'X' project with the internal engines and the new features and not to the later versions, the X.9 and the X.14, which conform more closely to the Brabazon types and are not quite so advanced.

I am sorry that there remain residual differences that you regard as fundamental and of such importance as to prevent you proceeding further with the X. Of course, anything that looks into the future and tries to jump ahead of the accepted must be a little risky - I have never denied that and have made it clear in everything I have said. I gather from your third paragraph that you consider that the two-stroke turbo engines are too far in the future and unlikely to come to fruition within 5 years. In our later discussion I tried to make it clear that alternative engines still gave the aircraft an opportunity of being something almost as successful and advanced as would these engines. Actually I should say it would be worthwhile to build this aircraft with this type of engine (or for that matter to go a step further and use jet engines) in order to give the airline authorities something they really want in 7, 8 or 9 years. I believe Lord Knollys will agree with me.

With regard to the suitable engineering facilities, I am absolutely confident that we can undertake and make an aircraft of this size. We are as large and as fully equipped as Douglas was when he built the DC-3s and the DC-4. If our youth proves a barrier this might mean that no new firm will ever be given an opportunity to get out of their own particular category. This would surely not be in keeping with national policy?

I may misunderstand your next sentence but surely we shall not be bound to the Brabazon Committee types if any firm can suggest a variation which seems an improvement. I cannot imagine a more stultifying policy. Following from that do you really think it is unfair to accept a very advanced design without offering free competition? I confess I cannot believe that is the present policy. It would spell an absolute end to progress. I am far from having any objection to free competition in getting out designs and thinking out new ideas - in fact, everything I've always thought and written has suggested we do more of that but never that no-one should ever think of a new idea or work out an advanced project until there is a written specification which no firm should step outside with an improvement, in case there should be some sort of advantage.

With regard to the last paragraph of your letter, I have seen DTD and I shall be very glad to have a shot at the research job he discussed with us, in fact we have already started.

Have you seen the X.9 and the X.14 with external Bristol engines?

Yours sincerely, F G Miles

That Miles did not give up the Miles X proposal without a struggle, is shown by his last sentence!. On 29th October 1943, Sorley responded as follows:

Dear Miles,

Thank you for your letter of the 13th October which I am sorry I have not answered before. Taking into account your personal point of view on these questions, it is naturally difficult to make it appear logical when I say that we do not want to curb initiative. If that were the only consideration I would be in favour of allowing the use of a free-hand. But the position is that within the terms of the scheme under which we are told to undertake certain civil types, we are not at liberty to throw them open to the initiative of all designers. In different circumstances this would not apply, but the facts are as I state them. Consequently, I want to thank you for submitting drawings and certain data relating to the X9 and X14 projects, but for these reasons I am afraid I am unable to consider proceeding with either of these two designs.

I know only too well how attractive it is to explore and enter new fields and in view of the disappointment which I know you experienced over the decision which I have had to take, I have brought you in on the next best thing. I am most anxious that you should concentrate your efforts on the research aircraft which you have discussed with DTD recently and I regard this as a project of the utmost importance. I am absolutely certain that in pressing on with this you will be covering new fields and will be doing a really useful job, both for us and for yourself.

Yours sincerely R S Sorley

Never one to give up, F G Miles then wrote to Sir Stafford Cripps, the Minister of Aircraft Production and in his letter of 2nd November 1943, said:

Dear Sir Stafford,

I have delayed writing to you further on the subject of the X until I received a reply to my letter to CRD of the 13th ultimo. This reply informs us that our project has been turned down purely on

grounds of policy and indicates clearly that it has never received serious consideration, at least from the viewpoint that we should build it. In view of our talk I am sure that this was not your intention. I read it that the policy on which the X has been discontinued is that the specified types shall not be awarded to our firm but to certain others.

You will, I hope, forgive me if I put the case before you once more as it appears to me from our previous conversation. On the occasion of our last discussion I approached you with a direct question because I had heard rumours in MAP that our *project was to be turned down in any event and that we had never had a chance against such a decision. My question was 'Has our case already been pre-judged, not on technical but on other grounds?' You replied definitely that it had not and that you rested on CRD's report after the investigation of the design. We then discussed the facilities for building and flight-testing at Reading and you asked for assurance that these were possible. I wrote you on the 10th September giving our suggestions on this score. (Note: this letter has not survived - PA).*

It appeared, therefore, that at that time policy had not determined a decision which rested mainly, as I would wish it, on the merits and possibilities of the project. The case was, by the above evidence, pre-judged. In CRD's words ".....the position is that within the terms of the scheme under which we are told to undertake certain civil types we are not at liberty to throw them open to the initiative of all designers.....".

At the time I discussed the question of pre-judgement with you, however, the protracted investigation into our technical claims was still proceeding and it really is difficult to see the purpose of such a detailed and exhaustive study unless it were to receive serious consideration on technical grounds. For instance, following the first X project we put up others, on yours and MAP suggestions, for lighter types more in accordance with the Brabazon types. These were examined and agreed *by Captain Liptrot. Your own suggestion, if you remember, was that we might build a lighter type of about seventy or eighty thousand pounds weight and I agreed but asked that the larger type should be thoroughly investigated first as we considered that it represented a greater advance over contemporary thought than any smaller aeroplane could offer. In CRD's letter the X.9 and the X.14 were both turned down on the same grounds of policy.*

I saw Lord Brabazon to find out if it were really the policy of his Committee that the specification should be prepared by MAP and only secretly and individually submitted to chosen firms. He showed me the wording of the recommendation, which was to the effect that the types suggested were intended as broad requirements to be submitted to designers and clothed in their own ideas. He was also good enough to say he liked the X design very much. The policy, therefore, did not spring from the Brabazon Committee, nor from you.

Without knowing that policy excluded any possibility whatever of our building a large aircraft of the X type we spent much time and energy on developing it to meet the MAP ideas and it is very puzzling that we were only told at the end of this period, and in spite of assurances to the contrary, that our work was useless. The X was started in 1936, way ahead of contemporary ideas, and was submitted at that time to the Air Ministry who even then considered making a reduced scale prototype. It was recommended by British Airways as a general design. We have worked consistently ever since and are probably a good way ahead of other firms in the concreteness of our ideas on how to build it. It is in no sense a sudden, new, or expedient idea but a well thought out attempt to look forward.

I believe a policy which takes no account of initiative to be a bad one for this country and furthermore I believe myself capable of saying this objectively in spite of my own disappointment. CRD apparently agrees with this sentiment to a large extent, for he says in the same letter ".....it is naturally difficult to make it appear logical when I say we do not want to curb initiative". If you would be good enough to give the question your consideration I should be most grateful for your judgement and advice.

I must refer to the other project which has been allotted to us (the ill-fated Miles M.52 - PA). *It is the most interesting and exciting that any designer would ask. We are devoting ourselves day and night to work on it. But it is irrelevant to the main issue and in no sense a substitute, nor would it be impossible or difficult to proceed efficiently with both.*

Yours sincerely, F G Miles

Meanwhile, Don Brown had been informed, unofficially, that there was no point in all this because the Bristol design had in fact already been accepted and their aeroplane ordered. This was quite incompatible with the assurance given to Miles by the Minister and, as can be seen from the foregoing, the claim for a correct assessment of the project was pursued.

It will also be seen that the Ministry, having refused to accept the estimates from Rolls-Royce in respect of power or specific fuel consumption, decided to prolong the agony by making considerable amendments to their estimates and actually then went so far as to concede that the X.11 would in fact carry 31 passengers at a speed of 270 mph. However, having then suggested that Miles should prepare and submit a design for a large transport aircraft in a different category, the field was left clear for the Bristol Aeroplane design which, it was becoming increasingly clear at the time, had already been chosen.

In this connection, it was interesting to note that the Ministry were beginning to have doubts as to whether their assessment had been correct and, in the final Specification No 2/44, which was issued three years later, the required speed had been reduced to 214 mph at 8,000ft, rising to 250 mph at 25,000ft, a reduction of some 20 mph on the original estimate. Better still, the headwind had also been reduced by 10 mph. The number of passengers specified was 25 - in a 100-ton aeroplane of 18,000 hp - making it hardly a sound economical proposition!

That Miles was obviously very unhappy by the way he had been treated plainly shows in the correspondence both with the Ministry and with the Minister, Sir Stafford Cripps, and even the granting of the contract to design and build the high-speed research aircraft was not considered to be an adequate substitute for not having been granted a contract to build the 'X' Transport aeroplane in the first place. Although perhaps written in a fit of pique, the last sentence in the letter to the Minister, shows that Miles just could not resist having one last 'go' by confirming that he would have been quite happy to undertake both projects together!

Don Brown wrote a 'Case for the Plaintiff' on the merits of the Miles M.26 X.11 and this is reproduced in Appendix 26, on CD.

In the event, Air Ministry Specification 2/44, for a Civil Transport for North Atlantic Service (Brabazon I) was issued on 22nd November 1944, to just one firm, namely the Bristol Aeroplane Company of Filton, Bristol. The requirement was for the:

Design and construction of a prototype aircraft for development purposes of a type basically suitable for the operation of direct non-stop services between London and New York. The aircraft will only be required to operate from prepared runways. The aircraft shall have a normal range of 3,000 nautical miles against a continuous average head wind of 43 knots when carrying a payload of 17,500lb. Accommodation was to be provided for two pilots, one radio officer, one navigator, one engineer, five stewards and 50 sleeping passengers plus luggage (13,500lb). If sleeping accommodation was not required then the aircraft would be suitable for the carriage of at least 100 passengers.

The reason for this Specification being given to only one firm was, apparently; 'to avoid unnecessary dissipation of design effort in

time of war'. However, to make matters worse, the firm chosen to tender for this transport had already prepared and submitted their project design before Miles even learnt of the existence of the specification.

AM Specification 2/44 was later cancelled and replaced by Specification 2/44 Issue II, dated 15th August 1946. This was issued to the Bristol Aeroplane Company, probably also in August 1946, and the result of all this 'conniving' was to be the Bristol 167 Brabazon I. It was originally planned to have the first prototype flying by 1946 or early 1947 and the complete production batch of ten aircraft delivered by the start of 1949. In actual fact, the Brabazon I prototype was not to make its first flight until 4th September 1949, some three years after the planned date. As a civil transport it failed miserably to live up to its expectations. In fact, the Brabazon turned out to be the first, and one of the largest (in more ways than one) of the subsequent post war Ministerial aviation blunders.

It is perhaps appropriate at this point to provide an insight into just how and why the infamous 'Brabazon Committee' came into being in the first instance and the following extract from the *'The Behemoth from Bristol'*, by Bill Gunston, which appeared in *Aeroplane* for September 1999, sums it all up nicely:

By late 1942 Avro, Bristol, Handley Page, Short Brothers and Vickers-Armstrongs (and probably others) had all produced drawings of so called "100-ton bombers". However, by this time the threat of Britain being invaded had receded, and such huge military aircraft were no longer needed. The Air Staff decided just to keep buying Lancasters and Halifaxes.

In July 1941 the Minister of Aircraft Production, Col J T C Moore-Brabazon (who in 1908 had been the second Englishman to fly, and in 1942 became Lord Brabazon of Tara), asked Sir Roy Fedden to be his Special Technical Adviser. Fedden organised a committee which, among other things, studied the prevailing idea for 100-ton bombers. It also increasingly made recommendations about civil aircraft to be built after the war. This led in July 1942 to "Brab" being asked by his successor, Col J J (later Lord) Llewellyn, to form a special committee to study future civil aircraft.

The Brabazon Committee met on December 23, 1942, and drew up a list called Types I to V. Type I was to be a machine able to fly from Britain to New York non-stop against the prevailing winds, summer and winter. This demanded a range of not less than 5,000 miles.

"The objective appeared to be to create an enormous aircraft, without worrying whether it would be commercially viable".

Little over a decade later the Douglas DC-7C and Lockheed L-1649 were to achieve such a range with aircraft of normal size, but from the outset the Brabazon Type I was envisaged as an absolute giant. In true British fashion the objective appeared to be create an enormous aircraft, without worrying too much about such trivia as how many airlines wanted it or whether it would be commercially viable.

It was later decided that, for use until the Type I (Brabazon - PA) *was ready, Avro should build an interim North Atlantic aircraft, the Tudor. Although it was similar in size to the Douglas and Lockheed rivals, it was designed for just 12 passengers! Hence my comment "cloud-cuckoo land".*

One of the foremost "100-ton bomber" firms had been the Bristol Aeroplane Company. Despite this, the Brabazon Committee did not invite anyone from Bristol. (See also the M.52 "Supersonic Committee - PA). *When the company heard about the committee they protested, and on January 14, 1943, L G Frise and Dr D A Russell from Bristol attended the second meeting with the Minister, who by now was Sir Stafford Cripps. Doc Russell told me: "I do not remember any other chief designers being present. Certainly we did not learn anything about other proposals."*

In those days governments seemed to like big and impressive projects, and the Type I took priority over all the other Brabazon proposals. On February 10 (1943 - PA) Lord Sherwood, Under-Secretary of State for Air, announced the existence of the Committee, and its broad recommendations. On March 11, 1943, his boss, Sir Archibald Sinclair, announced that the Type I had been awarded to the Bristol Aeroplane Company. I was later told by Sir Reginald Verdon-Smith that this was mainly because of the depth of work already done at Bristol on the 100-ton bomber. Indeed Capt R N Liptrot, the Committee's secretary appointed by the Ministry (not the Air Ministry but the Ministry of Aircraft Production), ventured the opinion that the Type I "could be based on the Bristol bomber".

Other influences were probably the fact that the company could take responsibility for the aircraft and its engines, and also that, the Buckingham tactical bomber having been cancelled, it had spare design capacity. Surprisingly, I have found no mention of either the February 10 or March 11 announcements in the aviation periodicals of the time.

In passing, the little Miles firm was never afraid to come forward with big or radical ideas, and it brought to the second Brabazon Committee meeting a comprehensive brochure describing the M.26, popularly known as the Miles X. To be powered by eight 3,000 h.p. Rolls-Royce Pennines (Note: There is no record of an engine of that horse-power or name ever being associated with any of the Miles X project studies - PA), it was a beautiful blended-wing/body proposal which on paper was the best of all the Type I submissions. In some ways it resembled ideas Boeing has studied for beating the Airbus A3XX in the next century. As Miles was not part of the clique of big firms, it never had a chance.

Looking back, and with the benefit of hindsight, Don Brown recalled that it still seemed strange that two firms with the eminence and experience of Bristol and Short Bros should have made such a fundamental error in the design of an aircraft to undertake such a specific job. Briefly he felt that the characteristics of the three main competitors' designs may have been summarised as follows:

Bristol:	Large (5,190 sq ft) High powered - slow
Short Bros:	Medium (3,073 sq ft) Low powered - slow
Miles:	Small (2,350 sq ft) High powered - fast

While it is apparent that Bristol were misled by the official specification, it should have been evident, even to them that an aircraft designed in accordance with the specification would just not meet the requirement. It is, therefore, open to conjecture as to

whether it was fear of losing such a unique and challenging contract that prevented Bristol from telling the Ministry frankly that the specification was wrong, and that it would not produce the transport aeroplane that was actually required.

Again, Short Bros, who like Miles had presumably to write their own specification, failed to realise that it was no good producing a slow aeroplane, whether large or small to provide a long-range service on a route on which are encountered headwinds of the magnitude met over the North Atlantic. It is of course possible that they were counting on refuelling stops at either Shannon or Gander when adverse winds were encountered but that was not the object of the exercise, which was to provide a regular non-stop service between London and New York in both directions.

Of the three competing designs, only that of Miles (and 14 years later the Bristol Britannia 300) was capable of providing a non-stop service on the North Atlantic route.

An article by Don L Brown, entitled 'Before the Britannia', appeared in *The Aeroplane* for 19th August 1960, which details the merits (de-merits) of each of the designs put forward to meet the specification for a post war transatlantic civil airliner. It is well worth reproducing and it can be seen as a footnote to this chapter.

It is of interest to note that an undated Phillips & Powis comparative silhouette showed a Miles X (which was almost certainly the X.11), with eight unspecified engines buried in the wings driving four airscrews through gearboxes and extension shafts, a wingspan of 150ft and twin fins and rudders and a weight of 130,000lb. This Miles X variant was shown in two versions, i) 100 passenger transport with a range of 2,000 miles and ii) a 50 passenger transport with a range of 3,400 miles.

Although the X.11 was designed primarily as a civil transport aircraft, two military versions were proposed for the RAF, the X.11 Heavy Bomber (with a 40ft long bomb bay) to carry either one ten ton bomb, four 8,000lb bombs or the equivalent bomb load. Two 20 mm cannon were carried in an armoured gun turret amidships and a retractable ball turret under the nose forward of the bomb bay had two .50 machine guns. The other version was for the X.11 Troop Transport. The dimensions and leading particulars, including power-plants and AUW for both military versions were as for the X.11 Passenger Transport, and it is possible that these two projects were later designated X.12 and X.13 respectively.

To finally close the chapter on the M.26L X.11 it is of interest to show the following undated and unidentified drawings of the X.11, both of which depict fuel and oil tank capacities.

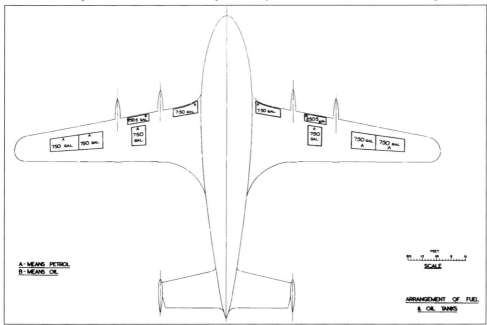

Arrangement of Fuel and Oil Tanks, X.11.

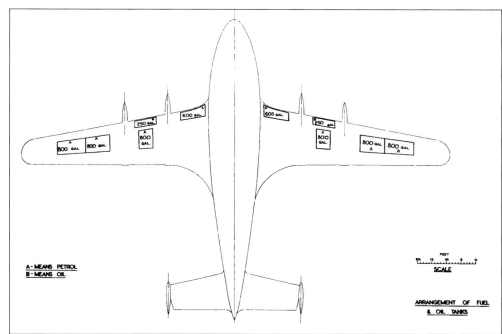

Alternative arrangement of Fuel and Oil Tanks (note different tank capacities).

A - MEANS PETROL
B - MEANS OIL

SCALE

ARRANGEMENT OF FUEL & OIL TANKS

Footnote

In about 1960, an article appeared in the aviation press entitled 'Before the Britannia'. Written by D L Brown, MIMechE, AFRAeS, late of Miles Aircraft, this summarised the situation prevailing as a result of the wartime Brabazon Committee's recommendations for a post war transatlantic airliner. As such, it is of sufficient interest to be reproduced here:

It is not sufficiently widely realised that the Britannia was the first and, for a period, the only aeroplane of any nationality to operate a regular non-stop service in both directions between London and New York.

About 17 years ago, a Government Committee, under the chairmanship of Lord Brabazon, was appointed to make recommendations regarding the types of civil aircraft likely to be required in the immediate post war era. A number of specifications were drawn up, the first of which, named the Brabazon Type I, called for an aeroplane to operate a service non-stop between London and New York. As the war was then at its height, it was necessary to keep the bulk of the industry's design manpower employed exclusively upon military projects and for this reason the specification was issued in secrecy to the Bristol company.

The heaviest aircraft, British, American or German, then in service was the Short Stirling, with an all-up weight of 70,000 lb; whereas the Brabazon specification necessitated a machine of at twice and possibly three times that weight. Even the Douglas Company of America, with considerable experience in the design of large aeroplanes, had failed to make a success of their latest and largest machine, the B-19 bomber. This machine, with a span of 212 ft, had been flying for just over a year and had failed to come up to its makers' expectations.

However, human nature being what it is, rumours soon began to circulate within the industry that a requirement had been issued for a post war transatlantic civil aircraft. And certain firms began to sit up and take a lively, if unauthorised, interest in such an enticing project.

While, however, the rumours continued and gained momentum, it was closely impossible to obtain access to the official specification.

The Bristol 167

The requirements of the Brabazon specification called for an aeroplane to carry a minimum of 25 passengers non-stop between London and New York - a distance of 3,443 statute miles. On this route, headwinds up to 100 mph are occasionally encountered but it was felt that reasonable regularity of service would be achieved if the machine were able to meet the requirements of range and payload against a constant headwind of 60 mph at any height between 8,000 and 25,000 ft. This required a still air range of over 4,500 miles, necessitating an aeroplane very much larger than anything envisaged at that date other than the bomber projects already mentioned and the American Consolidated XC-99 then being designed.

Bristols tendered a design generally similar in size and dimensions to one of their bomber projects (see *The Aeroplane* and *Astronautics*, December 25, 1959 p.666), the main difference being the employment of tractor airscrews instead of the pushers envisaged for the bomber. Judged in the light of the knowledge and experience of 17 years ago - or, indeed, of the present day - the 167 was truly a formidable and courageous design.

Compare the heaviest bomber then in service, having a span of 99 ft, a wing area of 1,464 sq ft and an a.u.w. of 70,000 lb, with the Bristol 167 having a span of 230 ft, a wing area of over 5,000 sq ft and an a.u.w. of over 200,000 lb.

The eight Bristol Centaurus engines were buried in the wings, coupled in pairs through gearboxes to drive through shafting four large contra-rotating propellers. Although these engines were 56 ins in diameter, 31 ft chord of the centre section together with a t/c of 21%, enabled them to be housed comfortably within the wing structure.

Both wing loading and power loading were similar to those of contemporary bombers and the estimated cruising speed was 270 mph at 25,000 ft. The machine was a mid-wing monoplane in which luxurious accommodation was provided for 45 passengers on the upper deck of the 20 ft diameter pressurised fuselage.

In this connection it is interesting to note the modest requirements of the specification with regard to payload. It shows how little was, at that time, realised regarding the number of passengers who, after the war, would desire to cross the Atlantic by air. The Brabazon I was intended as the "Queen Elizabeth" of the air and yet was only required to carry 25 passengers.

Similarly, the specification for the Avro Tudor I, ordered at about the same time as an interim post war type to operate over the North Atlantic via Shannon and Gander, called for accommodation for only 12 passengers.

The "Transatlantic Express"

Unable to obtain access to the official specification, yet nevertheless determined to submit a project design, Shorts had first to compile their own specification. The range was fixed but headwind and passenger accommodation had to be assumed. By luck or otherwise, Shorts allowed for the official headwind of 60 mph; and, in providing for two dozen passengers, they only just fell short of the official requirement.

Their project design, prepared in July 1943, consisted of a low-wing monoplane powered by six Centaurus engines housed in conventional nacelles. It had a span of 184 ft, a wing area of 3,073 sq ft and an a.u.w. of 175,000 lb. The estimated cruising speed was 259 mph at 20,000 ft, giving a ground speed of under 200 mph against the assumed headwind and, therefore, a flight duration, without reserves, of over 17 hrs. The fuselage was 16 ft in diameter and the total wetted area of the aircraft was 11,330 sq ft as compared with 18,935 sq ft for the Bristol 167.

The Miles X.11

Like Shorts, the Miles team had to make their own assumptions regarding headwind and payload. Their design, submitted early in 1943, assumed a continuous headwind of 50 mph and provided accommodation for 50 passengers.

As in the case of the Bristol 167, it envisaged eight buried engines coupled in pairs and driving four tractor airscrews: but beyond this, the Miles design had practically nothing in common with its two competitors, being based on an entirely different approach to the problem. Taking as the dominating requirement the fact that the machine had to provide a very long range against exceptionally strong headwinds, it seemed evident that a high cruising speed was essential if an inordinate eight duration of flight was to be avoided. Instead, therefore, of adopting the low wing loading, high power loading and relatively low speed of contemporary bombers, the Miles design was much smaller than either of its competitors, incorporating what was then a very high wing loading, a low power loading, a thin laminar flow wing and a performance compatible with contemporary fighters.

The span was 150 ft, the wing area 2,350 sq ft - less than that of the Bristol 167 - and the wetted area of fuselage was 3,950 sq ft as compared with 7000 sq ft of the Bristol. With practically the same cruising power as the Bristol, the estimated cruising speed was 350 mph at 25,000 ft giving a flight duration of 11.9 hrs against the "official" headwind. The engines were the Rolls-Royce P.I.26 - a 12- cylinder liquid-cooled two-stroke compression ignition engine with an exhaust driven turbo- supercharger.

This engine, which was already running on the test bed, was designed to provide 2,300 bhp for take- off and have an sfc of 0.42 lb/per bhp/hr.

The Short Tailless

Although not submitted with the three projects already described, it is of interest to note that the following year Shorts, at the suggestion of Prof G T R Hill of Pterodactyl fame, prepared a design study for a tailless aircraft based on the same specification that they had assumed for their Brabazon tender.

On paper the tailless configuration appeared to offer substantial advantages over the orthodox layout both as regards structure weight and drag. As a result, Shorts considered that their tailless project would carry 28,950 lb as compared with 22,450 lb for their orthodox design, while cruising 28 mph faster. The power-plant consisted of five Rolls-Royce 46H24 engines buried in the wing and driving contra-rotating pusher airscrews.

This engine, then in the development stage was a 24-cylinder liquid-cooled engine designed to give 3,300 bhp for take-off and have an sfc of 0.45 lb/bhp/hr.

Of course, at that date, the shortcomings of the tailless layout, especially in respect of low CL max, limited C.G. range and indifferent handling characteristics were not fully appreciated. The seemingly encouraging results obtained by Northrop had not been countered by the experience gained later with the A.W.52 and D.H.108 tailless research aircraft and therefore, on paper at least, the tailless configuration appeared to be an attractive proposition.

After examining the four tenders, the Ministry came to the conclusion that none of them would have the required range at 8,000 feet. They thought, however, that at 25,000 ft the Bristol 167 would carry 33 passengers and that the Miles X.11, if cruised at 270 mph at 25,000 ft, would carry 31 passengers.

In the opinion of the Ministry, no machine of less than 190,000 lb a.u.w. could carry the required crew, equipment and payload, amounting to a total of 20,500 lb for the specified range. This automatically eliminated the Short and Miles designs and confirmed the Ministry in the decision, already made on policy grounds, to order the Bristol 167. Moreover the Miles project was based upon an engine then under development but not yet available; which the Ministry regarded as a gamble they were not prepared to take.

Thus, the decision was made to go ahead, as planned, with the Bristol 167.

The Revised Specification

However, the fact still remained that it would not fulfil the specification requirements. Well, if the mountain will not come to Mohammed ... So the specification was amended, the headwind being reduced - presumably with Divine co-operation!

As the design progressed, it soon became evident that, not only would the machine be unable to meet the range against the headwind originally specified but, in addition, relaxations would have to be made in respect of cruising speed and take-off distance.

Specification 2/44 (Issue II), issued on August 15, 1946, called for accommodation for 50 passengers, a total payload of 17,500 lb with a range of 3,000 nautical miles against a headwind of 43 kts at any height between 8,000 and 25,000 ft. The required cruising speed was 186 kts of 8000 ft increasing to 217 kts at 25,000 ft. This, be it noted, necessitated an endurance, exclusive of reserves, 21 hrs at the lower altitude!

In addition, due to increased tankage and failure to achieve the anticipated structure weight, the a.u.w. had substantially increased and also, therefore the wing loading. However, an extra 100 bhp per engine is now available at take off: but even so W2/SP had increased from 581 to 805, necessitating a relaxation in the take-off requirements. Here it may be observed that, three years previously, the figures of 690 and 630 for the Short and Miles projects, respectively, had been deemed by the Ministry to give an unacceptable figure for take off.

The revised take-off requirement now called for the machine to clear 50 ft against a 4 kt wind in 1,800 yds, as compared with the original figure of 1,500 yds in still air. The machine was, however, required to come to rest within 800 yds of touching down against a 4 kt wind at maximum landing weight and without the use of reverse pitch propellers.

The Bristol 167 Mark II

Meanwhile, the engine division of the Bristol company had been pressing on with the development of the Proteus turboprop engine and by 1946 it was hoped that the enhanced performance obtainable with this type of engine might well prove to be the salvation of the 167. The great increase in cruising power provided by the Proteus would in turn increase the cruising speed to something of the order of 330 mph: and the resultant decrease in the duration required for the flight would more than offset the higher sfc of the developed Proteus turboprop.

This increase in cruising speed was a factor of considerable importance on a route on which such powerful headwinds were not infrequently encountered. In point of fact, the performance now envisaged for the 167 Mark II was approaching that chosen for the Miles X.11 project of some three years earlier.

Such were the anticipated benefits to be gained from the installation of the Proteus engine that the machine was now deemed capable of carrying 68 passengers against headwind of 70 mph. Since this headwind was 10 mph more than that originally specified and, indeed, 20 mph more than the figure quoted in the revised specification, it would appear that the winds to be encountered were in some mysterious way a function of the design of aircraft and of the types of engine available.

When the Mark I first flew in 1949, its bare weight had risen and its cruising speed was decreased so much that it could no longer be regarded as capable of fulfilling the purpose for which it had been designed. Against a 60 mph headwind, the flight time was now to 18.2 hrs, for which there was insufficient fuel.

However, the Mark II - thanks entirely to its turboprop engines - offered a reasonable chance of fulfilling the requirements and it is interesting to note that the fuel and oil amounted to 35.8% of the a.u.w. as compared with 35.3% for the Miles X.11.

Had the Mark II been completed and achieved its estimated performance, the substitution of turboprop engines for piston engines would have resulted in an increase of some 80 mph in the cruising speed, thus reducing the flight time by 4½ hrs and, in addition, would have increased the payload by 3,500 lb. On the other hand, given a high cruising speed, it should not have been necessary to have an aeroplane of anything like 290,000 lb a.u.w. in order to carry a worthwhile payload non-stop between London and New York. This was the philosophy of the Miles project and has since been proven by the Bristol Britannia.

With regard to the Brabazon Mark I, it was surely evident from the start that it could never hope to operate against headwinds of 60 mph. As for the Mark II, while, as already shown, it might have proved to be a useful aeroplane, the fact that it was never completed renders its anticipated performance of little more than academic interest.

The purpose of this article is to give some account of the historical sequence of events which, so many years later, led to Great Britain - and, in fact, to the Bristol company - building the first direct transatlantic airliner.

But first it is worth recording that while all this was going on, yet another uninvited transatlantic design had been submitted to MAP offering a ready staggering performance. This was in May 1945, when the firm of Power Jets, led by Air Cdre Frank (now Sir Frank) Whittle, submitted a project design for a transatlantic civil transport powered by four ducted fan engines and designed for the still-air range of 5,280 miles at a cruising speed of 470 mph at 45,000 ft, carrying a payload of 20,000 lb (see *The Aeroplane and Astronautics* of March 13 1959, p.316).

Characteristically, the Ministry considered that no future civil aircraft would be required to cruise at 470 mph and that it would be virtually impossible to provide a suitable pressurised cabin. The Whittle design was therefore rejected and the Ministry continued to juggle with headwinds and to expend millions of public money upon a machine designed to cruise at exactly half the speed offered by Whittle.

Will now return to the Britannia which, from a very different beginning, was ultimately to develop into the machine to do the job on which so much time, thought and money had already been expended.

The M.R.E. Specification

One of the anticipated requirements of BOAC given to the Brabazon Committee was called the Long Range Empire type. This called for a transport aircraft of about 100,000 lb a.u.w. suitable for operating on stage lengths up to 2,500 statute miles necessitating a still-air range of 3,500 miles. This was agreed by the Brabazon Committee and passed to the Ministry of Aircraft Production in November 1944, under the designation of Brabazon Type III.

Apart from an uninvited tender by Miles, the firm of Avro was selected to tender for the Brabazon III and put forward a project design known as the Avro 693. This was subsequently discussed and modified but various delays occurred and by 1946 BOAC decided that they would prefer to have a machine suitable for economical operation over shorter ranges for which the Brabazon III was unsuitable. They therefore drew up the requirements for an aircraft known as the Medium Range Empire type or M.R.E. and this was passed to MAP who issued it as specification 2/47.

This called for a four engined machine to carry 32 passengers in 2,750 lb of freight over stage lengths up to 1,354 miles at a cruising speed of 320 mph at 20,000 ft. With the necessary fuel reserves, this meant a maximum still-air range of 2,500 miles. The machine was required to unstick in still air in a distance of 950 yds and to land over 50 ft in 850 yds without the use of reverse pitch propellers. It was also required to be controllable with both engines out on one side, even during take-off.

The Britannia

As the war was over, 10 companies were invited to tender and project designs were submitted by Armstrong Whitworth, Blackburn, Bristol, Handley Page and Avro. Of these, the Bristol Type 175 appeared on paper to be the best, though it was not considered by BOAC to meet the specified requirements in every respect. It was to be powered by four Centaurus engines. The subsequent history of the machine which ultimately became the Britannia as we know it today, was given in *The Aeroplane* of February 1 1957. It first flew in August 1952.

By a steady process of enlargement and stretching, the Britannia 300 series was gradually evolved and provided for the first time an aeroplane capable of operating a regular non-stop service between London and New York while carrying a worthwhile payload.

The a.u.w. grew from 94,000 lb for the project design of 1947 to 185,000 for the Britannia 310 of a decade later. Thus the first successful transatlantic transport aircraft was in fact, of substantially the same size, power, weight and performance as that envisaged 14 years earlier by Miles and rejected as inadequate by the then Ministry of Aircraft Production.

	Miles X.11 project of 1943	Bristol Britannia 300 of 1957
AUW lb:	164,000	175,000
Total BHP	17,600 16,480	
Span ft, ins:	150 0	142 3½
Length ft, ins:	110 0	124 3
Wing area sq ft:	2,350	2,075
Aspect ratio	9.6	9.75
Cruising speed mph:	350	345
Fuel capacity galls:	7,400	8,580
Payload corresponding to still-air range of 3,450 miles, lb:	24,000	28,000

This table shows the great similarity between the Miles X.11 project of 1943 and the long-range Britannia of today. It also shows, in terms of performance actually achieved, how completely the Bristol Aeroplane Company have made up for the lack of success of the 167 - a design in which, be it noted, they were whole heartedly supported by the Ministry of Aircraft Production.

It also vindicates beyond doubt the philosophy underlying the design of the Miles project. And, although many years have passed and some millions of pounds have been spent since the original project designs were submitted to those charged with the task of

assessing and judging between them, it is pleasant to reflect that, thanks to the gas turbine, the ultimate success was an all-British product.

But think also of what the Miles X 11, if ordered in 1943, could be doing today powered by four Proteus or Tynes; or, better still, what could have been achieved by the Power Jets design if ordered in 1945.

SPECIFICATION AND PERFORMANCE DATA

Miles M.26L X.11 50 passenger long range (trans-Atlantic) Transport

Engines:	8 x 2,300 hp Rolls-Royce P.I.26, (1,750 THP) driving 4 contra-rotating airscrews (with 6 or 8 blades) through gearboxes and extension shafts
Dimensions:	span 150ft 0in; length 110ft 0in; height 22ft 0in; wing area 2,350 sq ft; cabin 16ft wide x 8ft high giving a volume of over 6,000cu ft; aspect ratio 9.6; thickness/chord ratio, root 0.18c, tip 5C; wing aerofoil section NACA laminar flow
Weights:	tare 71,000lb; overload empty 75,800lb; fuel (6,000 gal normal, wt fuel & oil 46,950lb long range), 7,400 gal overload 53,100lb; oil (589 gal) 5,300lb; disposable load, excluding fuel 59,000lb; normal crew (5) 900lb; equipment 6,000lb; passengers (50) 8,500lb; luggage and freight 15,400lb; AUW normal 130,000lb, overload 165,000lb; wing loading, normal at t/o, 55.2lb/sq ft, overload at t/o 70.2lb/sq ft
Performance:	max speed 425 mph at 16,000ft; cruising speed 350 mph at 16,000ft; run to unstick 2,700ft; distance to 50ft 4,050ft; initial climb 1,500ft/min; range 3,450 miles at 350 mph at 7,000ft against a 50 mph headwind

Miles M.26L X.11 One-third Flying Scale Model

Engines:	not known
Dimensions:	span 50ft 0in; length 36ft 8in; gross wing area 261sq ft; aspect ratio 9.6; thickness/chord ratio, root 0.18c, tip 0.15c; wing aerofoil section NACA laminar flow
Weights:	AUW 6,100lb; wing loading at t/o 23.5lb/sq ft
Performance:	not known

Miles M.26L X.11 Heavy Bomber Project of 1943 to carry one ten ton bomb or an equivalent bomb load; the dimensions and leading particulars as X.11 Passenger Transport but with 40ft long bomb doors.

	Short-range version	Medium-range version	Long-range version
Weights:	77,000lb	80,000lb	84,000lb
Fixed equipment:	4,400lb	4,400lb	4,400lb
Service load:	3,600lb	3,600lb	3,600lb
Fuel:	18,000lb	34,800lb	53,100lb
Oil:	1,800lb	3,500lb	5,300lb
Bomb load:	60,200lb	38,700lb	14,600lb
Performance:	Cruising speed 380 mph at 18,000ft; initial rate of climb 1,500ft/min; range with 25% fuel reserve, short range 1,100 miles, medium range 2,200 miles, long range 3,400 miles		
Armament:	one armoured remote controlled mid-upper turret mounting two 20mm Hispano cannon and a retractable ventral turret with two 0.5in machine guns located behind the nosewheel.		

Miles M.26L X.11 Troop Transport of 1943

Dimensions and leading particulars as X.11 Passenger Transport.

Alternative loads:-

(a)   Long-range version, as X.11 Bomber

1.   85 troops and equipment
2.   3 scout cars, 20 troops and equipment
3.   22 motorcycles, 42 troops and equipment
4.   12 howitzers
5.   1 light tank and crew

(b)   Medium-range version, as X.11 Bomber

1. 150 troops, 1 scout car, 6 tons of arms and equipment
2.   7 scout cars, 23 troops and equipment
3.   45 motorcycles, 90 troops and equipment
4.   18 howitzers, 55 troops and equipment
5.   3 light tanks and crews

(c)   Short-range version, as X.11 Bomber

1.   8 scout cars, 83 troops and equipment
2.   4 light tanks and crews

Miles M.26L X.12 Bomber

This designation was possibly allotted later to cover the X.11 Bomber

Miles M.26L X.13 Troop Transport

This designation was possibly allotted later to cover the X.11 Troop Transport.

An artist's impression of the M.26 X.14.

Chapter 43
Miles M.26 X.14 North Atlantic and
Empire Route Transport

At the height of the dispute between Phillips & Powis and the technical staff of the MAP regarding the estimated performance of the X.11, the Ministry suggested that Miles should perhaps consider a smaller version of the X.11 to be suitable for either the indirect Atlantic crossing (via Shannon or Gander) or for use on the Empire routes. Don Brown thereupon prepared the X.14 project design utilising the same overall dimensions and configuration as the X.11, to carry 64 passengers, but with reduced weight and fuel capacity, twin fins and rudders and a twin wheeled (all units) tricycle undercarriage. Powered by four 2,400 hp Bristol Centaurus CE.125.M radial engines mounted in nacelles on the wings, the X.14 would have had an operational range of 2,500 miles.

Details of the X.14, and also that of the X.9, another smaller proposed version of the X.11, were sent to CRD on 16th August 1943. Detailed structural and aerodynamic data for the X.14 and X.9 designs was supplied to Capt Liptrot's office at the MAP on 21st September 1943 and although this data was agreed by them in practically every detail, the X.11 project was still rejected.

However, in about October 1943, Miles Aircraft Ltd produced a booklet on the Miles X.14, reproduced here:

INTRODUCTION

From time to time in the history of British aviation, an aeroplane has appeared which was a marked advance over any contemporary type. Notable examples have been the Bristol Fighter, the Fairey Fox, the Supermarine Spitfire and the Avro Lancaster. It was with the idea of effecting a worthwhile improvement over the orthodox aeroplane, that the "X" layout was first conceived.

The "X" is no new idea - in fact the general layout was completed in 1936 and an article describing it appeared in *Flight* in April 1938. During the past seven years much painstaking thought and research has been carried out, wind tunnel tests have been made, a flying scale model has been built and flown, from which we received confirmation of our theories and gained much valuable data.

There is still much to be done, but it is felt that our present research can be extended and completed, concurrently with the building of the full sized machine, by the construction of an exact one-third scale model described later. The X.14 is intended primarily as the forerunner of a series of multi-engined airliners which will obviously be needed in the next decade to operate the Commonwealth air routes, linking together the widespread British Commonwealth of Nations. In war it can be used efficiently either as a bomber or as a Service Transport for the carriage of both men and equipment.

Much careful thought has gone into the preliminary layout of the X.14 which will be designed to be representative of the highest degree of aerodynamic efficiency attainable in the light of present day knowledge. Considerable effort has been expended in the preparation of a preliminary plan, whereby it is proposed to finish the whole undertaking within a reasonable time and to design and build the machine in stages so as to allow for revision in the light of any new discovery or knowledge that may become available. In view of its past achievements, this Company has no doubts as to the success of the design as such, while in view of its proud record of maintaining its production programme throughout the war, no apprehension is felt regarding the production of this machine.

The high performance and economy of the X.14 are due in no small measure to the low drag laminar flow aerofoil section employed. In addition, the manner in which the fuselage merges into the wing, which is an essential feature of the "X" layout, not only enhances aerodynamic efficiency by reducing interference drag but also provides a greater space for accommodation of passengers and freight than is possible on any orthodox aircraft of similar size, the volume of the cabin being over 6,000 cubic feet.

The machine will be of all metal construction with special attention to external finish. The flaps are of the Miles patented extensible type. This type of flap has been extensively tested on actual flight trials and by this means it has been found possible to achieve a maximum lift coefficient of more than three, without adverse effects on the longitudinal control. In the layout of the pilot's cabin, the two main objects aimed at have been perfection of view and simplicity of control.

As will be seen from the illustration, the range of view provided is unequalled in any other type of aircraft, British or foreign. In addition the instruments have been limited to the normal blind flying panel, the Beam Approach instruments, two compasses and an outside air thermometer. The engine and fuel controls, instruments and the undercarriage control are all in charge of the Flight Engineer and are conveniently grouped at his station, the pilots being provided with master throttles and the flap control in addition to the normal flying controls and trimming tabs. For details of these see the M.26L X.11.

Leading Particulars of the X.14

Dimensions:	
Span	150 ft
Length	110 ft
Gross wing area	2,350 sq ft
Aspect Ratio	9.6
Aerofoil	18 per cent - 15 per cent
	NACA laminar flow section
Power Plant:	
Engines	4 Bristol Centaurus CE.125.M
Weights:	
Loaded weight	120,000 lb
Wing loading at take-off	51 lb/sq ft
Performance:	
Cruising speed	260 mph at 8,000 ft
270 mph at 22,000 ft	
Run to take-off	900 yards
Distance to clear 50 ft	1,400 yards
Range	2,500 miles against 50 mph wind

The X.14 as a Civil Transport

The X.14 is designed for operation at any height from 8,000 to 22,000 feet and for any range up to 2,500 miles against a headwind of 50 mph. Luxurious accommodation is provided for 60 passengers in the maximum degree of comfort. This will be made possible by the exceptionally large volume available in the cabin and by the attention which will be given to pressurising, sound-proofing, air conditioning and lighting. The cabin is 16 ft wide and 8 ft high and has a volume of over 6,000 cubic feet.

Conditioned air will be admitted at the rate of 17 cubic feet per minute per person. A constant supply of fresh air can be admitted to the freight compartment for the protection of perishable goods.

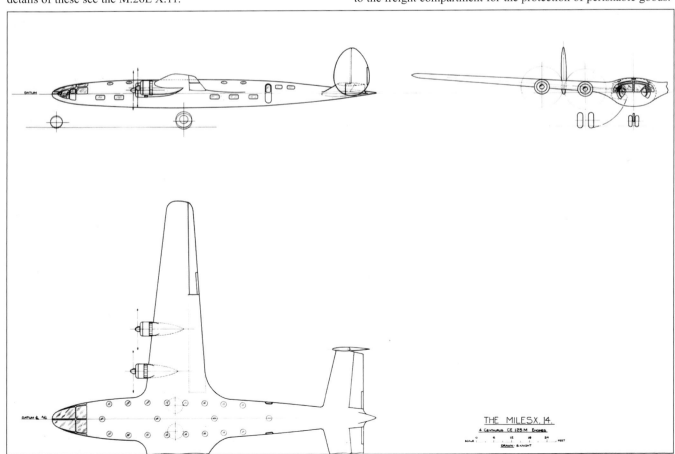

Three-view G.A. drawing of the M.26 X.14.

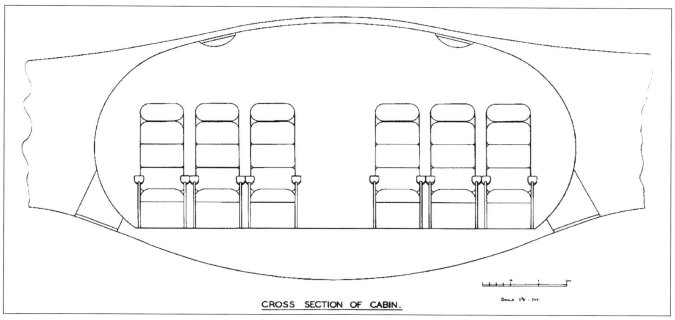

CROSS SECTION OF CABIN.

Drawing showing Cross Section of Cabin.

All fuel will be carried in the wings and smoking can be permitted anywhere in the cabin. A large number of alternative seating arrangements are possible and the cabin may be sub-divided in a variety of ways to suit the requirements of the operator. When operated by night the machine can be arranged as a sleeper, bunks and dressing rooms being provided for 50 passengers. Provision is made for a crew of eight, working in two shifts. Ample lavatory and luggage accommodation is provided.

Analysis of Weight of Civil Transport		
	lb	lb
Weight, empty		58,000
Radio, automatic pilot, cabin furnishing and equipment	8,140	
Crew	1,600	
		9,740
Fuel (4,500 gallons)	32,400	
Oil	2,900	
Passengers (64 at 180 lb)	11,520	
Luggage at 55 lb	3,520	
Food and water 30 lb	1,920	
		52,260
All-up weight		120,000

Imperial Air Routes

Some suggested routes for which the X.14 is suitable are shown below:-

	Distance in miles	Average time in hours
United Kingdom to Newfoundland	2,350	8¾
(Feeder services from Newfoundland to New York and Montreal)		
Montreal to Vancouver	2,290	8¾
United Kingdom to Cairo	2,200	8¼
Cairo to Nairobi	2,200	8¼
Nairobi to Johannesburg	1,810	6¾
Cairo to Karachi	2,310	8¾
Cairo to Berbera	2,000	7½
Berbera to Madras	2,100	8
Madras to Singapore	2,100	8
(Feeder service from Singapore to Hong Kong)		
Singapore to Perth	2,400	9
Perth to Melbourne	1,900	7¼
Melbourne to Wellington	1,700	6½

Operating Costs

A hypothetical case is taken in order to provide the data from which operators can obtain the information relating to their own specific cases. A route of 2,500 miles is assumed with 14 services weekly (a service being one trip in each direction). This gives 728 services pa and if the fleet consists of 8 aircraft, each machine does 91 services pa. If 3 days is allowed for the round trip, it means that each aircraft is on duty 273 days pa. This leaves 3 months pa for major overhaul and for occasional duty as spare aircraft. Each machine does 91 services p.a., i.e. - 455,000 miles p.a.

To be conservative a constant headwind of 10 mph is assumed. The mean still air cruising speed is 265 mph and hence the average ground speed is taken as 255 mph. The total flying hours per aircraft pa will therefore be 1,780.

An approximate estimate of the operating costs of the above service would be as follows:-

	£
Interest on capital 5% on cost of 8 aircraft at 30/- per lb AUW.	72,000
Obsolescence at 20%	288,000
Obsolescence at 40% on spares to the value of 20 % of aircraft	115,000
Insurance at 12½%	180,000
Maintenance:	
Labour at £12 per flying hour	171,000
Materials at £17 per flying hour	242,000
Engineering on cost	120,000
Crews at £12 per flying hour	171,000
Fuel and oil at £38.5/- per flying hour	548,000
	1,907,000
Airport fees, administration costs, advertising etc say 20 per cent of above	381,400
	£2,288,400

On total flying hours of 14,240 p.a.; the operating costs per hour are £161. With total miles of 3,640,000 pa, the operating costs per mile are 12s 6d *(62.5p – PA)*.

While carrying sufficient fuel to allow for encountering a headwind of 50 mph over the whole journey, each machine has accommodation for 64 passengers. The weight per passenger,

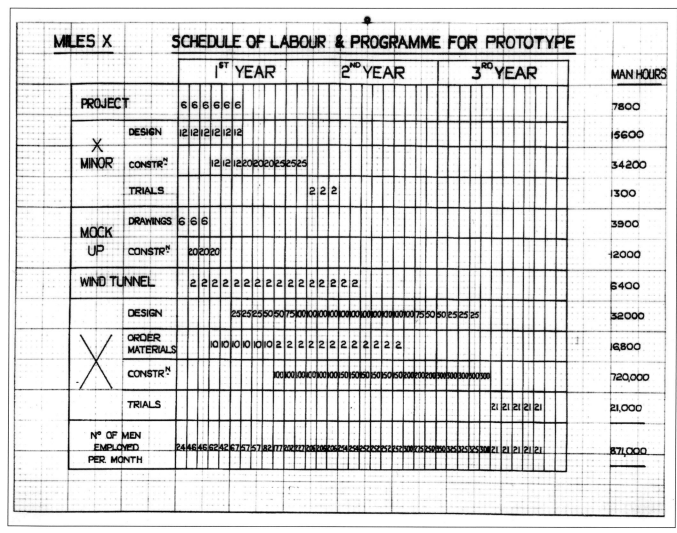

Schedule of Labour and Programme for Prototype.

allowing for luggage and food is taken as 265 lb. A passenger load factor of 70%, or 45 passengers is taken. A total mail movement (both directions) of 2 million lb pa is assumed, the charge being 5/- (25p) per lb.

The remainder of the payload available is assumed as freight at 2/6d per lb. The payload per aircraft per trip is 64 x 265 = 17,000 lb. The total annual payload carried is 24,752,000 lb, made up as follows:-

	lb
65,500 passengers at 265 lb	17,350,000
Mail	2,000,000
Freight	5,402,000
	24,752,000

To meet the operating costs of £2,288,000 pa the revenue from the above sources must be as follows:-

	£
65,500 passengers at £17.1.0	1,138,400
Mail 2,000,000 lb at 5/-	500,000
Freight 5,402,000 lb at 2/6d	650,000
	£2,288,400

Assuming 100 per cent load factors, the total possible alternative annual payloads would be 93,500 passengers - or 14,600 tons of freight. The above figure for freight assumes 350 lb per passenger i.e. - 265 lb plus 85 lb of cabin furnishing. The total possible payload - miles p.a. are therefore 234 million passenger miles pa or 36.5 million ton miles pa.

The operating costs for the range considered and assuming 100 per cent load factors would be, therefore 2.34 pence per passenger mile - or 15 pence per ton mile.

The X.14 as a Bomber

A long range version of the X.14 as a bomber is quoted below. After allowing the usual fuel reserve of 25 per cent the still air range is 2,100 miles, the corresponding bomb load being 17,200 lb. The suggested design includes a mid upper turret mounting two 20 mm Hispano cannon and a retractable mid under turret carrying two .5 in machine guns. The bomb doors are 40 feet in length and it is of interest to note that the machine can accommodate two 8,000 lb bombs or four 4,000 lb bombs.

Analysis of Weight	
lb	
Weight, empty	61,400
Fixed equipment and military load	10,000
Fuel (4,600 gallons)	28,800
Oil	2,600
Bombs	17,200
	120,000

The X.14 as a Civil Freighter

The civil freighter version of the "X", like its transport counterpart, has a range of 2,500 miles against a 50 mph headwind. Apart from its exceptional load carrying capacity, the large unobstructed space available in the fuselage would permit the carriage of large and bulky freight which could not possibly be accommodated in any orthodox aeroplane.

Analysis of Weight	
	lb
Weight, empty	59,000
Fixed equipment	3,000
Crew	1,600
Fuel (4,500 gallons)	32,400
Oil	2,900
Cargo	21,100
All-up weight	120,000

The X.14 as a Troop Transport

The troop carrying version of the X.14 is well adapted for the transportation of a large variety of service equipment ranging from 150 fully armed troops to two light tanks with their crews. In the paratroop version, six exits will be provided two in each side of the fuselage and two in the floor.

A military version of the X.14 with rear loading was also projected and an undated project drawing shows this with an assorted load, including vehicles.

Some idea of the alternative loads which may be carried by the first two versions is given by the illustrative examples in the table below:-

Flying Scale Model

A most important item in the design and development programme is the construction of a representative flying scale model by means of which comprehensive flight trials can be made and data acquired during the actual design and construction of the full scale prototype. This machine is a true one-third scale model of the X.14 while the leading particulars given below show that the aerodynamic desiderata in respect of relative weight, power and wing loading are all accurately fulfilled. The machine would be of wooden construction and it is estimated that it would take about nine months to design and build, during which time the design of the full sized machine would be proceeding.

Main Particulars	
Span	50 ft 0 in
Length	36 ft 8 in
Gross wing area	261 sq ft
Aspect ratio	9.6
Aerofoil	18 per cent – 15 per cent NACA laminar flow section
All-up weight	4,500 lb
Wing loading at take-off	17¼ lb/sq ft

On 8th October 1943, Air Marshal R F Sorley, Controller of Research and Development at the MAP, wrote to Miles and, after expressing doubt as to whether the Rolls-Royce P.I.26 would be available in less than 5 - 7 years, commented:

Furthermore, we are not in a position to open the door to allow alternative designs to be built around the Brabazon specified types.... and clearly it would be most unfair to accept your design without offering free competition.

This excerpt from the letter made it quite clear that, apart from the technical dispute, the 'X' was to be turned down primarily, and finally, on political grounds, despite the assurance that Sir Stafford Cripps had given to the contrary. On 13th October 1943, F G Miles replied to the CRD and said that he presumed the adverse judgement applied to the X.11 only and not to the X.14 or X.9, adding, almost as an afterthought: *Have you seen the X.9 and the X.14 with external Bristol engines?*

In his reply of the 29th October the CRD stated that: *Within the terms of the scheme under which we are told to undertake certain civil types we are not at liberty to throw them open to the initiative of all designers.*

This again made it clear that the X.11 had been turned down primarily on political grounds. CRD went on to say with regard to the X.14 and X.9: *Consequently.... for these reasons I am afraid I am unable to consider proceeding with either of these two designs.*

He had evidently forgotten that it was **at his own suggestion** that these two projects had been prepared and submitted! It was also difficult to see why details of these projects were called for, examined and agreed by Capt Liptrot if no action was to have been taken.

On 2nd November 1943, F G Miles wrote to the Minister, Sir Stafford Cripps and said that it was clear from CRD's two letters that the X.11 had been turned down purely on political grounds and that it was therefore difficult to see the reason for the detailed and exhaustive examination of the technical details. Miles then pointed out that the X.14 and X.9 had also been turned down on political grounds despite the fact that they were submitted at the suggestion of both Sir Stafford Cripps and CRD.

L A Hackett, the Sales Manager and Don Brown visited AVM Strachey, Assistant to the CAS, to discuss the 'X'. They found that AVM Strachey had also been supplied with Capt Liptrot's unfavourable performance estimate and that he had accepted it unconditionally. It was explained how Capt Liptrot had already been forced to reduce his drag figures by 60lb - a factor of tremendous significance in a long range project - and how his drag estimate assumed an aerodynamic cleanness inferior to that attained

Long range version (2,500 miles against 50 mph headwind).
Alternative loads

		lb				lb
(i)	80 troops	14,400		(iii)	30 Motor cycles	13,500
	Arms and equipment	6,400			30 troops	5,400
		20,800			Arms and equipment	2,400
						21,300
(ii)	3 Scout cars	17,460		(iv)	1 light tank and crew	
	14 troops	2,520				
	Arms and equipment	1,120				
		21,100				

Short range version.
Alternative loads

		lb				lb
(i)	150 troops	27,000		(ii)	6 Scout cars	34,920
	Arms and equipment	15,060			27 troops	4,860
		42,060			Arms and equipment	2,280
						42,060
(iii)	2 light tanks and crew					

seven years previously on the DH Albatross. AVM Strachey replied that he had implicit confidence in the accuracy of Capt Liptrot's estimates and it was therefore useless to continue the discussion.

On 29th November, F G Miles wrote to DTD asking for a copy of the performance estimate which had been supplied both to DDOSI and to AVM Strachey and asking also that the official estimate on the X.14 and X.9 should be supplied to them and to the firm. On 3rd December 1943, F G Miles saw Sir Stafford Cripps, who contended that the X.11 had been turned down on technical grounds, saying that he had no alternative than to accept the opinion of his technical advisers. Miles said that he still could not accept their opinion and pointed out that no technical objection had been raised to the X.14 and X.9. Sir Stafford said that these had been turned down on political grounds as had been clearly stated in CRD's letter of 29th October - "Consequently I want to thank you.... etc."

What Sir Stafford did not explain, however, was that:

(a)   CRD's letter of the 8th October made it clear that the X.11 was turned down primarily on political grounds despite his, Sir Stafford's, assurance that it would judged solely on its technical merits.

(b)   Even ignoring completely the firm's claims and taking purely those of Capt Liptrot, the machine would do the direct Atlantic crossing cruising at 270 mph and carrying 31 passengers including sleeping accommodation; or the indirect Atlantic crossing carrying 62 passengers including sleeping accommodation. This clearly showed the aerodynamic superiority of the 'X', in that the proposed Bristol Brabazon I, a machine of 50% greater AUW and also cruising at 270 mph would, according to Capt Liptrot, only carry 33 passengers on the direct Atlantic crossing.

(c)   Why, if the X.14 and X.9 were totally inadmissible on grounds of policy, was their submission initially suggested and approved by himself and by CRD and examined and agreed by Capt Liptrot.

Don Brown concluded his case for the plaintiff thus:

It is submitted that the adverse reports supplied by Capt Liptrot to Mr Rowe and by Mr Rowe to the Minister were ill-considered and misleading in that they were based on the following assumptions:-

(a)   A blind guess at the type of engine envisaged and a manifestly unsuitable engine at that.

(b)   A structure weight greatly in excess of current practice.

(c)   A take-off power 15% lower than figures confirmed by the most well-known and reliable firm of engine manufacturers in the world.

(d)   A specific fuel consumption of 30% higher than the figure supplied by the same firm.

(e)   An estimate of drag which ignored a fundamental and important part of the design, the laminar flow aerofoil section employed and which assumed a degree of cleanness inferior to that obtained on existing and past aircraft.

The effect of any one of these inaccuracies would be seriously misleading - the cumulative effect of them and that on which Mr. Rowe has insisted is such as to give a totally erroneous impression of the capabilities of any project submitted even as, in this case, to the extent of depicting it as quite unfeasible. It is further submitted that, as admitted by CRD in his letter of the 8th October, the project was inadmissible from the first on grounds of policy and that the lengthy technical discussions which have taken place were at no time bona fide but were deliberately concocted in order to give the impression of fulfilling the promise given by the Minister that the design would be judged purely on its technical merits.

From the terms of the policy now revealed, it appears evident that the Minister should never, in fact, have given that promise and, while it was given in all good faith as far as Sir Stafford Cripps was concerned, there was never any intention on the part of the permanent technical staff at MAP that this promise should be implemented

The only alternative, therefore, was to endeavour to turn down the project on every conceivable technical objection and for this reason only, it is submitted, the protracted and deliberately misleading discussions were initiated on a matter which was in fact already pre-judged.

Just three years later, in early 1946, the new Socialist government was forced to spend several million pounds on the purchase of a number of American transport aircraft for British Overseas Airways Corporation. Initially, five Lockheed Constellations were purchased, followed in the summer of 1949 with six Boeing Stratocruisers. This, not unnaturally aroused widespread criticism and *The Aeroplane* for 6th September 1946 was moved to comment:

As we have frequently pointed out in this paper, if, three years ago, when the Brabazon Committee was planning our production, four Bristol Centaurus engines had been taken and a trans-Atlantic aeroplane built around them, we should by now have a British type larger than the Constellation and not much smaller than the Stratocruiser. But the 'Powers That Be' had known better (or had they? - PA), *so what alternative is there to the present policy if we are not to lose most of our Atlantic traffic to the Americans?*

This suggestion precisely fitted the X.14. The frustration felt by all the people in the aviation world in Britain with a modicum of common sense, spilled out in *Air Transport Affairs* in *The Aeroplane* for 9th July 1948, wherein it was stated that:

Two references made in The Aeroplane *this week are of special significance. On page 45 in Don Brown's article, "Some Interesting Projects," it is revealed that, after failing to obtain the Brabazon I contract, Miles submitted a design for a North American and Empire route liner of 120,000 lb. with four Centaurus; still air range 4,000 miles at 270 mph. On page 54 another article describes the new Italian BZ 308 of 101,600 lb. with four Centaurus, the prototype of which is just completed.*

At regular intervals since 1944 The Aeroplane *has urged the Government to specify a liner of this size, using four Centaurus engines. In* The Aeroplane, *page 36, January 5th 1945, a New Year's Resolution said, "Much as we sympathize with the foresight of laying down the 100-ton Bristol 167 for the subsequent period of development, that intermediate gap wants filling mighty badly, and we would rather have heard more at this stage about some further 120,000 lb projects."*

A year later - another New Year's Resolution - The Aeroplane, *January 4th 1946, headed "An appeal to the Minister of Civil Aviation":- "Though a year has passed since we drew attention to the absence of any plans for transport aircraft in the 120,000 lb. category, there is still no indication that Britain is building any trans-Atlantic types. . . This gap between the Tudor I and the Bristol 167 is the weakest spot in Britain's post-War air transport programme."*

My final reference is to a recommendation made 18 months later by the Civil Aviation Requirements Committee, and a subsequent Cabinet Minute dated July 1947, resulting from that recommendation from which sprang the 100,000 lb. project now known as the four-engined Centaurus Bristol 175. It took the committees of "experts" five years to reach a conclusion that had already occurred to many people way back in 1942, and Britain must now suffer for that incomprehensible lack of foresight.

Epilogue

Dennis Bancroft, the chief aerodynamicist of Miles Aircraft Ltd, recently recalled that Miles gave him so many design studies for different 'X' projects to work on that he had had to allocate a full time aerodynamicist to evaluate each of them as they were received! However, despite Miles enthusiasm for the 'X' concept, Dennis Bancroft tells me that he didn't share it!

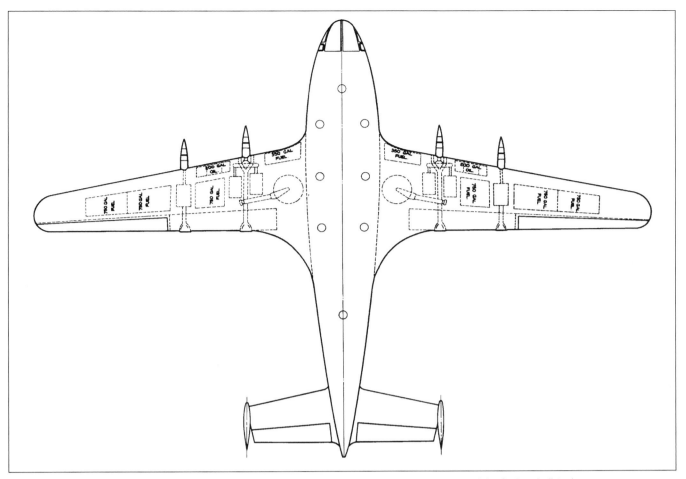

The only drawing to have survived of the M.26 X.15, showing the disposition of the six engines and the fuel and oil tanks.

Chapter 44
Miles M.26 X.15

The X.15 of 1944 was based on the X.11 and was to have been powered by six 2,500hp Napier Sabre engines, the inner four coupled, but all buried in the wings driving contra-rotating airscrews through extension shafts. The X.15 was the last recorded version of the 'X' Transport Aeroplanes.

In September 1944, Miles Aircraft Ltd produced a booklet on the Miles X.15, reproduced here:

From time to time in the history of British aviation an aeroplane has appeared which was a marked advance over any contemporary type. Notable examples have been the Bristol Fighter, the Fairey Fox, the Supermarine Spitfire and the Avro Lancaster. It was with the idea of effecting a worth-while improvement over the orthodox aeroplane that the "X" layout was first conceived.

The "X" is no new idea - in fact the general layout was completed in 1936 and an article describing it appeared in "Flight" in April, 1938. During the past seven years much painstaking research has been carried out, wind tunnel tests have been made, a flying scale model has been built and flown, from which we received confirmation of out theories and gained much valuable data. There is still much to be done, but it is felt that our present research can be extended and completed concurrently with the building of the full sized machine by the construction of an exact one-third scale model described later.

The X.15 is intended primarily as the forerunner of a series of multi-engined airliners which will obviously be needed in the next decade to operate the Commonwealth air routes, linking together the widespread British Commonwealth of Nations. In war it could be used efficiently either as a bomber or as a Service Transport for the carriage of both men and equipment. Much careful thought has gone into the preliminary layout of the X.15 which will be designed to have a performance higher than anything yet attained and to be representative of the highest degree of aerodynamic efficiency attainable in the light of present day knowledge. Considerable effort has been expended in the preparation of a preliminary plane, whereby it is proposed to finish the whole undertaking within a reasonable time and to design and build the machine in stages so as to allow for revision in the light of any new discovery or knowledge that may become available.

In view of its past achievements, this Company has no doubts as to the success of the design as such, while in view of its proud record of maintaining its production programme throughout this war, no apprehension is felt regarding the production of this machine.

The X.15 is designed to have a still air range of 5,100 miles. The manner in which the fuselage merges into the wing is an essential feature of the "X" layout and not only enhances aerodynamic efficiency by reducing interference drag, but also provides a greater space for accommodation of passengers and freight than is possible on any orthodox aircraft of similar size, the volume of the cabin being over 6,000 cubic feet.

The machine will be of all-metal construction with special attention to external finish. Another advanced feature of the design of the

X.15 and one which adds in no small degree to the overall aerodynamic efficiency is the housing of the six engines, gear boxes, radiators and oil coolers, completely within the wing. For servicing purposes, large removable panels are provided over the whole of the power units while for replacement the engines may be lowered through the under surface of the wing, special built-in tackle being provided for the purpose. To ensure that the strength of the wing is not impaired by the presence of these removable panels, a special design of stress-carrying panel will be employed.

The flaps are of the Miles patented extensible type. This type of flap has been extensively tested on actual flight trials and by this means it has been found possible to achieve a maximum lift coefficient of more than three, without adverse effects on the longitudinal control. In the layout of the pilot's cabin, the two main objects aimed at have been perfection of view and simplicity of control. As will be seen from the illustration, the range of view provided is unequalled in any other type of aircraft, British or foreign. In addition, the instruments have been limited to the normal blind-flying panel, the Beam Approach instruments, two compasses and an outside-air thermometer. The engine and fuel controls, instruments and the undercarriage control are all in charge of the Flight Engineer and are conveniently grouped at his station, the pilots being provided with two master throttles and the flap control in addition to the normal flying controls and trimming tabs.

Leading Particulars of the X.15

Dimensions:	
Span	170 ft
Length	120 ft
Gross wing area	2,500 sq ft
Aspect Ratio	11.5
Aerofoil	18 per cent - 15 per cent NACA laminar flow section
Power Plant:	
Engines	6 Napier Sabre
Weights:	
Loaded weight	165,000 lb
Wing loading at take-off	66 lb/sq ft
Performance:	
Cruising speed	300 mph at any height between 8,000 and 22,000 ft
Still air range	5,100 miles
Distance to unstick	1,000 yards
Distance to clear 50 ft	1,500 yards

The X.15 as a Civil Transport

The X.15 is primarily designed as a long range machine with a still air range of 5,100 miles and roomy accommodation for 50 passengers either by day or night, for shorter ranges, however, there is seating capacity for a maximum of 100 passengers. The machine is designed for operation at any height from 8,000 to 22,000 feet.

Luxurious accommodation is provided and the maximum degree of comfort. This will be made possible by the exceptionally large volume available in the cabin and by the attention which will be given to pressurising, sound-proofing, air conditioning and lighting. The cabin is 16 wide and 8 ft high and has a volume of over 6,000 cubic feet. Conditioned air will be admitted at the rate of 17 cubic feet per minute per person. A constant supply of fresh air can be admitted to the freight compartment for the protection of perishable goods.

All fuel will be carried in the wings and smoking can be permitted anywhere in the cabin. A number of alternative seating arrangements are possible, some of which are shown in the illustrations. In the long-range machine the cabin may be sub-divided in a variety of ways to suit the requirements of the operator.

In one arrangement, three cabins are provided, the forward one being the main lounge holding 34 passengers, the mid-ships cabin being the dining and recreation room and the aft cabin being either a ladies room or a smoking room with accommodation for 16 passengers. An alternative arrangement provides for a longitudinal partition in the centre with a ladies room on the one side and a smoking room on the other.

When operated by night the machine can be arranged as a sleeper, bunks and dressing rooms being provided for 50 passengers. In the medium range machine the seats will be arranged in two rows of three on either side of a central gangway over 4 ft wide and some 60 ft long.

Analysis of Weight of Civil Transport

	(a) Long range version lb	(b) Medium range version lb
Weight, empty	80,900	80,000
Radio, automatic pilot, cabin furnishings and equipment	10,500	11,400
Crew (8)	1,600	1,600
Disposable load	8,500	17,000
Disposable load	(50 passengers)	(100 passengers)
Luggage & food/freight	6,700	13,400
Fuel	52,100	38,200
Oil	4,700	3,400
All-up weight	165,000	165,000

Assumptions as to World Air Routes

The main air routes may be conveniently sub-divided into legs, the length of which correspond closely to the ranges available, thus:-

	Miles	Hours
UK to New York	3,450	12
UK to Montreal	3,250	11½
UK to Johannesburg		
UK to Lagos	3,120	11
Lagos to Johannesburg	2,800	10
or UK to Khartoum	3,200	11½
Khartoum to Johannesburg	2,900	10½
UK to Hong Kong		
UK to Cairo	2,200	8
Cairo to Karachi	2,220	8
Karachi to Hong Kong	2,980	10½
UK to Wellington		
UK to Cairo	2.200	8
Cairo to Karachi	2,220	8
Karachi to Singapore	2,950	10½
Singapore to Perth	2,400	8½
Perth to Melbourne	1,900	7
Melbourne to Wellington	1,700	6

Imperial Air Routes:
Some suggested routes for which the X.14 is suitable are shown below:-

UK to Newfoundland	2,350	8¾
(Feeder services from Newfoundland to New York and Montreal)		
Montreal to Vancouver	2,290	8¾
UK to Cairo	2,200	8¼
Cairo to Nairobi	2,200	8¼
Nairobi to Johannesburg	1,810	6¾
Cairo to Karachi	2,310	8¾
Cairo to Berbera	2,000	7½
Berbera to Madras	2,100	8

Madras to Singapore (Feeder service from Singapore to Hong Kong)	2,100	8
Singapore to Perth	2,400	9
Perth to Melbourne	1,900	7¼
Melbourne to Wellington	1,700	6½
UK to Buenos Aires		
UK to Bathurst	2,860	10
Bathurst to Natal	1,800	6½
Natal to Buenos Aires	2,500	9

The X.15 as a Civil Freighter

The civil freighter version of the X.15 is, like its passenger counterpart, also designed for either short or long range categories. Apart from its exceptional load carrying capacity, the large unobstructed space available in the fuselage would permit the carriage of large and bulky freight which could not possibly be accommodated in any orthodox aeroplane.

The weight analysis is as follows:-

	lb
Weight, empty	80,900
Radio and automatic pilot	4,500
Crew	1,600
Disposable load	78,000
All-up weight	165,000

It will be noted that the disposable load amounts to 35 tons.

Flying Scale Model

A most important item in the design and development programme is the construction of a representative flying scale model by means of which comprehensive flight trials can be made and data acquired during the actual design and construction of the full scale prototype. As will be seen from the drawings, this machine is a true one-third scale model of the X.15 while the leading particulars given below show that the aerodynamic desiderata in respect of relative weight, power and wing loading are all accurately fulfilled.

The machine would be of wooden construction and it is estimated that it would take about nine months to design and build, during which time the design of the full sized machine would be proceeding.

Main particulars:

Span	56 ft 8 in
Length	40 ft 0 in
Gross wing area	278 sq ft
Aspect ratio	11.5
Aerofoil	18 per cent – 15 per cent NACA laminar flow section
All-up weight	6,100 lb
Wing loading at take-off	21.9 lb/sq ft

Unfortunately, like all the other 'X' projects before it, the X.15 was not ordered and with this version, the advanced 'X' blended wing design concept reached its conclusion, or did it?

Advance the clock forward to October 2010, when I happened to ask Mike Hirst if he had heard anything more on Boeing's plans for a similar concept and he kindly wrote this to complete the story of the Miles 'X':

The Miles 'X' projects were no longer high on the company's priority list when the remnants of the firm were absorbed into Handley Page, but the latter was possibly influenced by them, and enthusiastic throughout the 1950s to develop a tail-less jet airliner (essentially 'all-wing' aircraft) that had passengers in a wing-body blended section akin to the 'X' series of projects. The company's designs were destined to remain paper projects, but an 'all-wing' concept has been revived time and again, and revitalised by the emergence of the Northrop B-2 'stealth' bomber.

An airliner variant does need more space for payload, and the concept that has emerged from more recent research is the blended-wing body (BWB) concept.

In 2001 Boeing did toy with the idea of a tandem-wing airliner that was almost the M.63B updated, and whose mainplane was very much the planform of a BWB. The 'Sonic Cruiser' was offered as an alternative to the A380, being smaller and faster. It had a relatively thin wing, and a conventional fuselage, with the foreplane essential for stability. Airline interest was muted, as the 20% increased cruise speed had little advantage over conventional Mach 0.82 cruise speed airliners.

Boeing decided to develop the wholly conventional, in terms of planform, Boeing 787 Dreamliner, and concentrated risk in the choice of material, by using carbon-fibre reinforced plastics (CFRP) throughout.

This project is seen as spearheading the problems in developing large-scale CFRP aircraft components, and to be a major stepping stone toward having a large-capacity long-range BWB airliner ready for service entry in the period 2020 to 2030. The company has already committed to fly-by-wire (FBW) flight controls.

The most visible evidence of the commitment towards a 21st Century equivalent of the 'X' projects is the Boeing X-48B demonstrator, which flew on 20th July, 2007 (photograph on page 376), and that was one of two examples built by Cranfield Aerospace Ltd, a technology-transfer off-shoot from Cranfield University in Bedfordshire.

The UK University's academic department have researched the BWB concept extensively for over a decade, and their choice as the site at which the scale-demonstrators of the airliners of the future would be built remains testimony to the strength of UK aerospace industry research and commitment.

UK innovation has sadly been backed by too little political support to be able to nurture a world-ranking home-based industry, built on the legacy of its once most progressive raft of companies, but aviation businesses worldwide still knows to turn to Britain for the very essence of innovative and good design.

The Miles effect lives on.

Regarding the future - the attached images are of the Boeing X-48B research aircraft, in the wind tunnel and over the Desert. It is a radio-controlled scale demonstrator and it was built at Cranfield in 2006, by a team lead by Dave Dyer; an absolutely first-rate engineer. The sub-structure is aluminium, the surfaces in most cases are composite.

- *Wingspan: 20 ft 5 in (6.22 m)*
- *Wing area: 100.5 sq ft (9.34 m2)*
- *Aspect ratio: 4.1*
- *Gross weight: 500 lb (227 kg)*
- *Powerplant: 3 × turbojet, 52 lbf (0.23 kN) thrust each*

There are two diagrams of the proposed airliner version too. These were researched at Cranfield in the late-90s and I was a supervisor of research projects that delved into many aspects - structures, power-plant integration, flight controls and stability, landing gear, FBW, internal configuration and evacuation - to name just a few. I am still very proud of what they do at Cranfield, and what they can achieve. What a pity that we don't have a home industry to support the place. **Mike Hirst**

With reference to Mike's last statement, it is indeed a great pity . . .

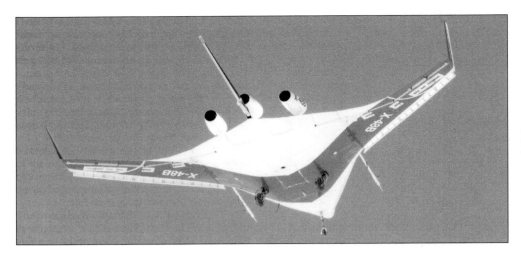

The Boeing X-48B Blended Wing Body aircraft during its first flight on 20th July 2007.

Chapter 45
Summary of Miles 'X' Transport, Bomber and Troop Transports

The following is a summary of all known Miles "X" Transport design studies. It is of interest to note that project letters were also allocated to the early "X" design studies, a practice which apparently continued even after they had been given the designation M.26, following the initial X.7 proposal but this finished with the M.26L X.11.

Miles X.1   A   nothing known

Miles X.2   B   1936 design study for 18 passenger trans-Atlantic transport aeroplane; 38 passenger short range, i.e. London-Paris flights or 32 passenger long range, i.e. on London-Moscow flights. Four 900 hp engines developed from the Rolls-Royce Kestrel buried in wings, driving airscrews through extension shafts. Metal construction with flush riveting where applicable on external surfaces. Twin fins and rudders; tricycle undercarriage; span 99ft 0in; overall length 78.8ft; max AUW 61,928lb. Project submitted to the Air Ministry in early 1938, together with two 'Diagrams of arcs of fire' for the armament of 4 x 27 mm cannon and 14 Browning machine guns of the proposed Miles X.2 Bomber, a very heavily armed bomber version of the Miles X.2.

Miles X.3   C   1940 development of the X.2 with six 900 hp developed Rolls-Royce Kestrel engines probably partially housed in the wings. Twin fins and rudders; twin wheeled tricycle undercarriage.

Miles X.4   D   Design not completed and no details recorded

Miles X.5   E   Design not completed and no details recorded

Miles X.6   F   Design not completed and no details recorded

Miles X.7   G   1941 project for a 50-100 passenger transport with eight 2,300 hp Rolls-Royce Merlin engines buried in the wings, driving four contra-rotating airscrews through gearboxes and extension shafts. The X.7, X.7 Mod and the later X.8 were the only X variants to have a single fin and rudder; single large wheeled tricycle undercarriage; span 150ft; length 110ft; AUW 165,000lb. The X.7 was projected in three different versions: 1) 50 passenger long range, 3,450 miles; 2) 100 passenger medium range, 2,000-2,500 miles, and 3) 100 passenger short range, 1,100 miles.

M.26H X.7 Mod   1942 project for a 550-seat Troop Transport project based on the X.7, to carry 290 men on the lower Deck 'A' and 260 men on the upper Deck 'B'. Single fin and rudder, twin nose and main wheeled tricycle undercarriage.

M.26I X.8   The X.8 was probably the designation for the unspecified 'Scheme X' freighter version of the X.7. Powered by four engines of unspecified type (but probably Rolls-Royce Griffon II) mounted in nacelles on the wings. The fuselage had no windows and the pilots sat in a 'bug eye' teardrop cockpit mounted centrally on the top of the forward fuselage. The 'Scheme X' had a single fin and rudder and a large single-wheeled tricycle undercarriage.

M.26J X.9   Autumn 1942 project for a development of the X.2 for use in the Far East. Four 1,740 hp 'Miles' engines buried in the wings driving three blade airscrews through extension shafts. Twin fins and rudders; large single-wheeled tricycle undercarriage; span 116ft; length 80ft;

AUW 76,000lb. A project drawing dated 31.3.43 shows four alternative military loads and a rear loading ramp. It was proposed to build a ½ scale flying model of the X.9 Scheme BX to verify the flying qualities and performance of the design and this would have been the M.26A.

M.26A X.9 — A project drawing dated 6.2.43 shows the M.26A, a ½ scale flying model of the M.26 X.9 Scheme BX. Powered by four 175 hp Lycoming 0-435 engines mounted in nacelles on the wings. Twin fins and rudders; single wheel tricycle undercarriage; span 58ft; length 40ft; AUW (normal) 8,250lb, (overload) 10,000lb; provision for the pilot seated under a teardrop canopy and 7-8 passengers.

M.26 X.9 Scheme BX — A project drawing dated 2.1.43 shows the alternative 74 passenger transport, with 3 crew and a similar specification to the X.9 but powered by four x 1,740 hp Rolls-Royce Griffon II engines mounted in nacelles on the wings and driving 3 blade constant speed airscrews. Twin fins and rudders; large single wheeled tricycle undercarriage; span 116ft; length 80ft; AUW (normal) 66,000lb, (overload) 80,000lb. The Scheme BX was also projected as a military freighter with a rear loading ramp, and a note on the project drawing makes reference to a tankage of 2,150 gallons to allow for its use as a long-range glider tug.

M.26 X.9 Scheme CX — A project drawing dated 26.1.43 shows that the Scheme CX was similar to the X.9, being powered by 4 x 1,740 hp 'Miles' engines buried in the wings driving 4 x 3 blade airscrews through extension shafts. The 'Miles' engines were to produce the same hp as the Rolls-Royce Griffon. Twin fins and rudders; large single wheeled undercarriage; span 116ft; length 80ft; AUW (normal) 66,000lb, (overload) 80,000lb. The Scheme CX was also projected as a military freighter with a rear loading ramp and a note on the project drawing makes reference to a tankage of 2,150 gallons to allow for its use as a long-range glider tug.

M.26 X.9 Mod — An undated Phillips & Powis comparative silhouette also shows the Miles X Junior, a 50 passenger transport with a 2,000 mile range which appears to have been a scaled down version of the X.9 and was probably the X.9 Mod. Four unspecified (but probably Rolls-Royce Griffon) engines buried in the wings driving two airscrews through gearboxes and extension shafts. Twin fins and rudders; span 106ft; AUW 65,000lb.

M.26K X.10 — 1942 project for a 30 passenger twin-engined version of the Miles X.9 with a 1,000 mile range. In-line engines were to be mounted either in nacelles or buried in the wings? Twin fins and rudders; span 75ft, AUW 32,500lb. An undated Phillips & Powis comparative silhouette also shows the X.10 with the same specification but with twin-engines buried in the wings driving airscrews through extension shafts.

M.26L X.11 — 1943 development of the X.7 for a 50 passenger post war long range (trans-Atlantic) transport to meet the later Brabazon 1 Spec. 2/44. Eight 2,300 hp Rolls-Royce P.I.26 engines buried in the wings coupled in pairs driving four contra-rotating airscrews through gearboxes and extension shafts. Twin fins and rudders; single wheel tricycle undercarriage; span 150ft; length 110ft; AUW 165,000lb. The X.11 project design was rejected by the MAP in October 1943.

M.26 X.11 Bomber — A project drawing, date unreadable but it was in 1943, shows the X.11 Bomber with the same dimensions and leading particulars as the X.11 but with a 10-ton bomb or the equivalent bomb load; two 20 mm Hispano cannon in an armoured, remote control dorsal gun turret and two 0.5in m/g's in a retractable ventral turret located behind the nose-wheel.

M.26 X.11 Transport — The X.11 Troop Transport had the same dimensions and leading particulars as the X.11 but with the facility for carrying troops and an assortment of military equipment.

Miles X — An undated Phillips & Powis comparative silhouette shows the Miles 'X' (which closely resembled the X.11) with eight engines buried in the wings driving four airscrews through gearboxes and extension shafts. Span 150ft; twin fins and rudders; weight 130,000lb. The Miles 'X' was projected in two versions i) 100 passenger transport, 2,000 miles range and ii) 50 passenger transport, 3,400 mile range.

M.26 X.12 — Nothing is known of the X.12 Bomber project but it could possibly have been a revised designation for the X.11 Heavy Bomber.

M.26 X.13 — Nothing is known of the X.13 Troop Transport project but it could possibly have been a revised designation for the X.11 Troop Transport.

M.26 X.14 — 1943 project for a passenger transport for Empire routes based on the X.11 but with four external 2,400 hp Bristol Centaurus C.E.125 M radial engines; twin fins and rudders; twin nose and main wheeled tricycle undercarriage. The X.14 was also proposed as a military freighter.

M.26 X.15 — 1944 project for a civil transport or freighter based on the X.11 but with six 2,500 hp Napier Sabre engines buried in the wings driving airscrews through extension shafts. Span increased to 170ft; AUW 165,000lb.

The M.26 X.15 was the last known design study for the "X" series of transport aeroplanes to be undertaken by Miles Aircraft Ltd.

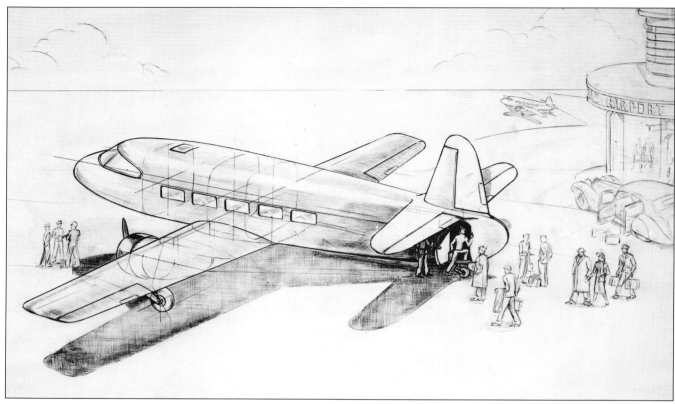

An artist's impression of the Miles BOAC Transport. The photograph print date of 11th August 1943 was stamped on the back and this gives the only clue as to when the project was first proposed.

Chapter 46
Miles BOAC Transport Aircraft

Before the chance discovery of an undated Phillips & Powis Aircraft Ltd brochure, nothing was known about this project, which was not given a Miles type number.

The brochure, entitled 'The Miles BOAC Transport Aircraft', provided a very detailed insight into the design philosophy behind this eight passenger projected transport and is reproduced here:

Introduction

This project is to fulfil the need for an eight-seater aircraft basically designed for safe flying in its most economical form. Consideration has been given for operation in any part of the world. The design submitted is influenced by the following features incorporated for the specific purpose of:

1. Increasing the safety.
2. Reducing the structural weight.
3. Providing a high degree of comfort and view for both passengers and crew.
4. Economy in manufacturing and operating costs.
5. Good control at all speeds.
6. Improving the serviceability.

1. Safety

A low wing was partly chosen to increase safety in the event of a crash, as the relatively high weight of the wing, power units and fuel help directly to absorb the crash landing loads instead of having to be transmitted by the fuselage to the part in contact with the ground, as in the case of the high wing. The possibility of collapse of the fuselage and wing, etc. onto the occupants is, therefore, greatly minimised. *(In a recent crash of a Bristol*

Freighter, the fuselage collapsed and the wing fell onto the passengers in that area, with dramatic results - PA). The fuel tanks are carried inboard of the engine nacelles and are crash-proofed. At each nacelle an emergency fuel cock (pilot controlled) is fitted in the fuel pipe for operation in case of fire or pending crash landing.

It should be noted that the entrance door has been placed behind the tailplane for structural reasons - this will ensure that the passengers' entrance is as far away from the airscrews as possible and easy entry and exit obtained without the use of steps or ladders. The means for operating chassis and flaps may be either electrical or hydraulic. If the latter the hydraulic circuit would be completely isolated from the fuselage and housed in the wing. Electrical push button controls in the cockpit operates solenoid controlled valves in the hydraulic control unit fixed in the wing.

2. Reducing the Structural Weight

The following arrangements assist in weight saving:-

a) Entrance door at rear and in unstressed part of the fuselage structure, avoids concentrated loads and heavy local structure which is the case when positioned normally just aft of the passengers' compartment.
b) Toilet compartment positioned between the two strong frames carrying the wing attachment points, thus avoiding additional bulkheads as is the case when this is placed further aft.
c) Wing in one piece with detachable wing tips save considerable weight by the elimination of costly spar continuity joints, carrying high loads, which require maintenance and frequent inspection.
d) The low wing enables relatively short undercarriage legs to be used.

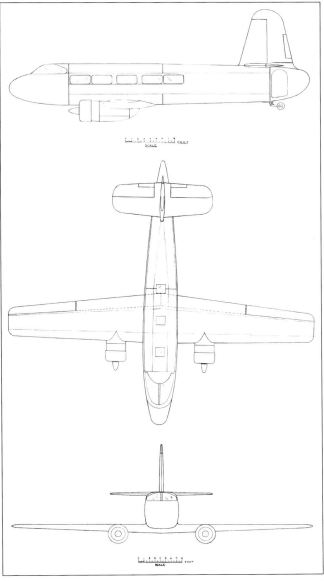

Three-view G.A. drawing, undated, showing the original version of Miles BOAC Transport.

3. Comfort and View

The crew are positioned well forward of the area of airscrew and engine noise and as a result are provided with excellent view. The passengers disposed above the surface of the low wing are not so advantageously placed with regard to view as would be the case in a high wing arrangement.

This, however, is offset to a considerable extent by the high aspect ratio wing which results in a chord of small dimensions and the fact that the toilet compartment is positioned between the spars where the view would be bad. Moreover, the reduction of noise and the elimination of the "shut in" effect, which two engine nacelles on either side of a high wing produce, is a further compensation. From a study of a drawing it will be seen that an excellent view is provided for the forward four passengers, whilst the rear four are only affected in the forward direction, the direct view downwards being entirely unrestricted.

4. Economy in Costs

Manufacturing economy is closely allied with those arguments related to weight saving by producing a simple and straight-forward design; the one-piece wing, the form of fuselage construction, the short chassis, all contributing to a low initial cost. Operating costs have also been carefully considered in the original layout and good aerodynamic efficiency has been sought. The low wing loading chosen will reduce power required for cruising conditions, and greatly benefit engine maintenance and reliability as a consequence. The good aerodynamic shape of the fuselage and surfaces and the underslung engine nacelles have all received careful attention to improve efficiency. With the exception of the wing the whole structure may be of metal construction.

5. Control

It is considered essential that an aircraft of this type should be provided with first class control at all conditions of flight. Accordingly, large control surfaces have been indicated and all surface volumes kept high to ensure good stability and handling qualities. The power loading of 11.4 lb per BHP with a wing loading at take off of 24.0 lb/sq.ft high aspect ratio and large flaps should ensure good take-off, climb and ceiling performance, and low landing speed. Good single engined performance should also be obtained. The toilet being placed roughly over the cg will eliminate large changes in trim which will be a considerable help to the pilot.

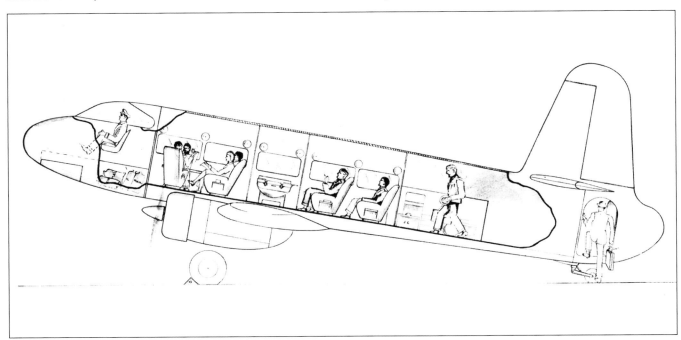

Cut-away drawing showing the passenger and crew arrangement. Note the rear entry.

6. Serviceability, Maintenance and Repair

By producing the fuselage in sections it is possible to replace portions in the event of damage. This is particularly applicable to the case of a wheels-up landing, when the fuselage bottom may become damaged to the extent that replacement is necessary. As manufacture will utilise this sectional build up, it will be possible to obtain a section forming the bottom of the fuselage from stock with a consequent reduction in the time that the aircraft will be unserviceable. We have embodied this feature for the same reasons on a type which is now going into series production for the Ministry of Aircraft Production. By utilising a low wing combination the servicing, inspection and refuelling aspects are improved, especially under conditions when expensive trestles and gantries are not available.

General Description

Pilot's Cockpit

This station will be furnished in order that the pilot and co-pilot will have the maximum comfort and convenience in carrying out their duties. The crew will be seated side by side behind a windscreen which will have as wide a view as possible, with the framing reduced to a minimum. A side panel will be provided which will give direct view opening, while the screen will be fitted with a de-icing spray in conjunction with a windscreen wiper.

Dual flying controls will be provided and all others duplicated which are not accessible from either seat. A panel incorporating all instruments with automatic pilot controls will be flexibly mounted and removable from the aircraft as a unit. All connections to the aircraft services from the panel being provided by quickly detachable electrical and mechanical junction boxes of standard design.

All engine, landing gear, flap controls and fuel tank selector valves are placed on a built-up structure beneath the instrument panel and between the two seats. All control runs will be made readily accessible by removable covers. The complete compartment will be insulated against wide temperature variations and noise and provided with heating and air conditioning systems. The cabin top will be jettisonable to provide emergency exit for the crew and to suit the fitment of alternative designs for operating under various conditions.

Passengers' Compartment

The demand for comfort and roominess for the passengers must be assessed against the requirements of performance and is always a difficult decision to make. In this aircraft, the layout has been developed to provide ample room for seats of large proportions, leg room and height. Entry is straightforward with a wide level floor throughout the whole length of the fuselage. The passengers do not have to step over awkwardly placed spars or avoid other obstructions when entering or leaving the aircraft. The internal height available varies from 5' 3" under the tailplane to 6' 2" throughout the whole length of the passengers' compartment. The total accommodation for the eight passengers is divided by the toilet compartment situated above the wing for the reasons previously quoted. Adequate emergency exits are provided in the roof.

At each seat is a large fixed window, ashtray, pilot's call button and individual reading lamp. Provision is made for two folding tables. General illumination of the cabin is furnished by ceiling lights and wireless is installed with speakers in both passengers' compartments under separate control. Directly over the windows on each side is a fresh air duct with individually operated openings at each passenger seat. A cabin heating system is installed, controlled from the pilot's cockpit. The whole cabin, including the windows, is sound-proofed which, with the underslung engines, should result in a cabin with a uniform and low sound level.

Toilet Compartment

The toilet compartment is lighted, ventilated and heated. Communication from this compartment may be had with the pilot by means of a call button. Equipment of this compartment includes wash basin with hot and cold water supply, large mirror, towel rack, paper holder and a stool which closes and is vented separately to the outside air. The covered floor will curve upwards at the edges so that it can be cleaned easily. No corners are left for the collection of dirt.

Baggage Compartment

Two compartments are provided for the stowage of mail or baggage so disposed that it can affect the cg position and thus obtain the necessary balance with the various load combinations. One compartment is provided in the nose while the other is aft of the passengers' compartment. Lashing points will be provided in the structure to prevent movement of the various articles.

Equipment

The aircraft will be provided with the following equipment. In the Pilot's Station will be the flying, engine and navigational instruments; electrical control panel; windscreen wiper and de-icing spray; brake system; hydraulic or electric controls; engine controls; cabin heating controls; tab controls; undercarriage controls; cockpit and instrument lighting; radio; automatic pilot (if necessary); a hand flash lamp and fire extinguisher.

In the Passengers' Compartment will be radio loudspeakers; cabin lamps; reading lamps; folding tables; ashtrays; safety belts; foot rests; individual pilot's call buttons; first aid kit; illuminated signs - "Fasten belt for take-off and landing"; wireless and fire extinguishers. In the Cloakroom will be a chemical closet; a toilet paper holder; wash-water tank; washbasin; mirror; handrail; a liquid soap dispenser and a wastepaper container.

General equipment will include navigation lights; landing lamps and a static vent for ASI. The Power Plant Accessories comprise starters; hydraulic pump; generator; vacuum pump; fire extinguisher; booster coil; hand turning gear and a fuel primer.

Leading Particulars

A Twin-Engined low wing transport monoplane.
Power Plant: Cheetah XV – 7-cylinder, single row, air-cooled, geared and moderately supercharged.

BHP take-off	420 hp at 2,550 rpm
Fuel Consumption at take-off	.82 pts/BHP/hr
BHP Cruising	260 hp at 2,100 rpm
Fuel Consumption at cruising	.51 pts/BHP/hr
Capacity of fuel tanks	160 gallons
Capacity of oil tanks	17 gallons

Overall Dimensions:

Span	55 ft
Length	49.3 ft
Height over propeller tip (tailwheel on ground)	9.8 ft
Height over fin and rudder	22.3 ft
(fuselage datum horizontal)	

Wing

Aerofoil Section - Root	NACA 23019
Aerofoil Section - Tip	NACA 2412
Gross Wing Area	400 sq.ft
Chord at Root	8.9 ft
Chord at Tip	5.38 ft
Tip - Root ratio	0.605:1
Aspect ratio	7.56
Mean Geometric Chord	7.28 ft
Dihedral on bottom surface	3°

Horizontal Tail Surfaces

Span	17.0 ft
Gross Area	91.0 sq.ft
Chord Root	6.5 ft
Chord extended tip	5.0 ft
Mean Geometric Chord	5.35 ft
Aerofoil Section	NACA 0012
Dihedral on datum line	0°

Vertical Tail Surfaces

Height	9 ft
Gross Area	57 sq.ft
Aerofoil Section	NACA 0012

Fuselage

Width (maximum)	6.8 ft
Height (maximum outside)	8.0 ft
Height (maximum inside)	6.2 ft
Length of accommodation for crew, passengers, toilet and baggage	31.5 ft

Undercarriage

Mainwheel units - type	Two retractable single wheel units
Track	16 ft
Tailwheel unit - type	Fixed-lever suspension type
Ground angle of datum at u/c static deflection	10°

Area and Ratios

Gross Wing Area	400 sq.ft
Aileron Area	32 sq.ft
Flap Area	60 sq.ft
HTS Gross Area	91 sq.ft
Elevator Area	32 sq.ft
VTS Gross Area	57 sq.ft
Fin Area	26.3 sq.ft
Rudder Area	30.7 sq.ft
Aileron Area/Gross Wing Area	8.0%
Flap Area/Gross Wing Area	15.0%
HTS Area/Gross Wing Area	22.75%
Elevator Area/Gross HTS Area	35.1%
VTS Area/Gross Wing Area	14.25%
Rudder Area/Gross VTS Area	54.0%
HTS Volume	.710
VTS Volume	.118
Aileron Volume	.045

Miscellaneous Data

Tare Weight	6,260 lbs
Payload	1,600 lbs
(passengers 1,360 lbs; luggage 240 lbs)	
Disposable load	3,340 lbs
(passengers 1,360 lbs; luggage 240 lbs; crew 360 lbs; fuel (160 gal) 1,230 lbs; oil (17 gal) 150 lbs)	
Max. Take-off weight	9,600 lbs
Payload % Max. Take-off weight	16.7%
Disposable load % Max. Take-off weight	34.8%
Wing loading	24.0 lb./sq.ft
Power loading at take-off	11.4 lb./sq.ft

Performance

Maximum Speed at sea-level	185 mph
Maximum Speed at 7,000 ft	204 mph
Cruising speed at Max. Economic BHP at 7,000 ft	172 mph
Landing speed at sea-level with flaps	65 mph
Normal ideal range	670 miles
Range 30 mph headwind and 45 mins to spare	450 miles

A further set of three-view drawings and an artist's impression, stapled to 'Issues' cards, entitled 'Spec. GA BOAC', were dated 10th September 1943. These show that this, the original design concept differed slightly from the one which appeared in the brochure, insofar as the top of the pilot's cabin formed a continuous line with that of the top of the fuselage, but this was raised in the later drawings shown in the brochure.

Four other photographs showing a three-view G.A. of the Miles BOAC Transport, but with a raised roof to the pilot's cabin, with the print date 23rd September 1943 stamped on the back, are shown here:

The Miles BOAC Transport Project was presumably submitted to British Overseas Airways Corporation but nothing further was heard and there the matter rested.

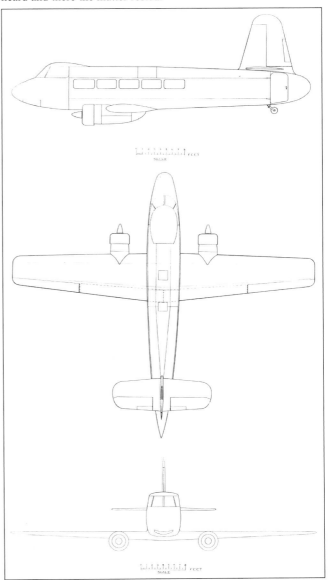

Three-view G.A. drawing of the Miles BOAC Transport with revised pilot's cabin roof and side windows.

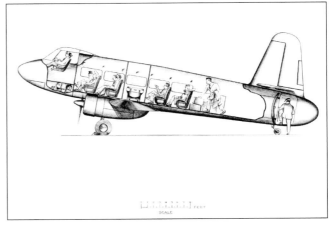

A cut-away drawing showing passengers and crew arrangements.

A fine photograph of an anonymous M.50 Queen Martinet.   *[MAP RTP Photographic Section]*

Chapter 47
Miles M.50 Queen Martinet Pilotless Aircraft to Spec. Q.10/43

In mid 1940, the Airspeed Queen Wasp was cancelled and for two years no real effort had been made towards producing a new full-sized pilotless target aircraft. The DH Queen Bee was still in active service but its performance had become increasingly unrealistic in terms of speed alone. However, in mid 1942, the quest for a Queen Bee successor was seriously discussed and the result was the issue of a combined Naval and Air Staff Requirement OR.119. This called for a high-speed, twin-engined target-towing aircraft with a provision for the towing of target gliders. OR.119 led directly to Specification Q.9/42, against which Miles Aircraft submitted the design which ultimately became the M.33 Monitor. However, the introduction into service of this new type was likely to be a lengthy process.

The Admiralty in the meantime had also begun to consider operating target aircraft in a manner already tried, tested and adopted by the Americans. This involved, what the Americans termed, a 'Shepherd' and a 'Sheep' aircraft. The 'Shepherd' aircraft being a manned airborne control post that controlled the 'Sheep', an unmanned aircraft, in mid-air and at a safe distance from it. Hitherto, Queen Bees and other target aircraft had been controlled in flight by a ground-based station operated by a pilot.

Another view of the same aircraft.

The US Navy had proven the two-aircraft target system using a Beechcraft JRB-1 (a naval version of the Beechcraft 18) as an airborne drone director - a controlling 'Shepherd' aircraft and such was the interest being shown by their Lordships in the Admiralty, that a Royal Naval party was formed and sent out to the USA for training in drone equipment and procedures. The party's other task was to arrange for the supply of necessary control equipment and bring it back to Britain.

Meanwhile, the Admiralty had drawn up a list of suitable types for conversion to target drone 'Sheep' aircraft and these included the Gloster Gladiator II, Westland Lysander III/IIIA and even the Miles Master. The Admiralty then suggested the Fairey Fulmar and the Boulton Paul Defiant for the 'Shepherd' aircraft. The Lysander was soon ruled out on the grounds that it was not available in sufficient numbers, if at all and similarly, only a limited number of Gladiator IIs could be obtained. But the lack of availability of any other suitable types prompted the Admiralty to re-consider the Gladiator II and, by using the American drone equipment (when it arrived in the UK) to convert up to 25 of these into 'Sheep' aircraft. Four Fairey Fulmars would fulfil the 'Shepherd' role.

As a direct result of these deliberations, the Air Ministry drew up a fresh Specification, Q.10/43. This called for a high-performance, radio-controlled pilotless aircraft but no mention of 'Sheep' and 'Shepherd' aircraft appeared in the specification and the Admiralty then eventually agreed to adopt Q.10/43 as an ultimate staff requirement. However, as a short-term measure, the Admiralty sought to acquire a number of Queen Bees, currently on order for the Army.

It would appear however, that the specification was never actually prepared and instead the Air Ministry officially approached Phillips & Powis towards the end of 1942 with a view to the firm producing an aircraft that would meet the Admiralty's short-term need pending the design of a high-speed target aircraft. George Miles decided to submit two proposals, one based on rapid availability and the other, to appear later, with enhanced performance, the M.47/M.47A and the M.49 and details of these can be found in the appropriate chapters.

It was eventually decided not to pursue these designs but to modify the M.25 Martinet to radio-controlled target drone configuration. A number of Martinets were in storage and new-build examples were being put straight into storage, so design of what was to become the M.50 Queen Martinet proceeded apace.

We now have to move forward in time to the 2nd July 1945 as a document, prepared by J Park with that date, addressed to Don Brown, obviously in preparation for the Investigation at Miles Aircraft Ltd by the Industrial Advisory Panel on 4th and 5th July 1945, throws new light on the background to what was ultimately to become the Miles M.50 Queen Martinet.

Nothing was known about this document until May 2012, when an anonymous donor deposited a packet of Phillips & Powis/Miles Aircraft correspondence and documents with The Museum of Berkshire Aviation, Woodley. Thanks to Jean Fostekew I am now able to reproduce this noteworthy document in its entirety here:

Queen Martinet

Pilotless Controlled Aircraft.
Prototypes LR244, EM500 and PW979.

Production and Conversion Aircraft.

23rd April 1943. First discussions took place on the 23.4.43, when we had a visit from Sqdn Ldr Bennett, RDLI(c) together with Mr Dunn and other representatives from RAE to discuss the possibility of installing automatic controls in a Martinet aeroplane.

11th May 1943. Letter from RDLI(c) stating that installation should be done in two in accordance with and to the satisfaction of RAE Instrument Department who would supply space models and the relevant information.

10th July 1943. Nothing further transpired until this date when authority to proceed with the job was received. Space models not available, but were delivered towards the end of the month.

Aircraft LR244 was allotted for trial installation of space models. Some doubt existed on the possibility of being able to embody all equipment necessary for a suitable installation for operation of the systems. However, design work could only proceed in stages being entirely at the discretion of RAE based on the results of their investigations. Rapid information never available.

12th August 1943. Godfrey and Partners undertook to design Compound Hand Control Box in conjunction with and to the satisfaction of RAE instrument Department.

15th September 1943. Meeting convened with MAP and RAE to discuss the position of and repositioning items of Pilotless Control Equipment, and also to urge for further information on details and other aspects of the installation to enable us to proceed more fully with the job in hand.

29th November and 3rd December 1943. RTO's letter containing a mock-up conference to inspect proposed installation of control equipment in the aircraft and to consider certain deletions from the pilotless version.

16th December 1943. Following a further visit and discussions by MAP and RAE, I found it necessary and advisable to inform Mr G H Miles and Mr Parsons of my impression that the whole project for the LR244 would be eventually dropped in favour of an American installation, the reason being that it was stated the prospects of production deliveries of British and RAE units could not be met for some considerable time, RAE units being still in the development stage.

18th January 1944. The meeting held at this date confirmed our impressions and instructions were given to complete the LR244 as arranged, but not to proceed with any further work on the 2nd prototype EM500, which would have been the basis for the production version.

LR244 was completed - given design clearance - inspected and flight tested here. Delivered to RAE at the end of the month.

24th January 1944. RTO's letter to Mr G H Miles concerning fitment of Drone equipment to subsequent aircraft when information etc became available.

22nd February 1944. EM 500 inspected by RAE with a view of a 12 Volt Drone installation being fitted. There were delays in receiving equipment and information required was not in the country. Design requirements proceeded steadily with many changes as the relevant information trickled through during the following months.

This aircraft was finally inspected, received design clearance - flight tested here and delivered to RAE in November 1944.

1st August 1944. It was decided at the conference held at this date to layout the 3rd Prototype for a 24 Volt Drone System and which would be the version for Production and Conversion aeroplanes. No positive information was available at this date for details of the 24 Volt American Drone installation as sets had not yet arrived in this country. RAE supplied information to the firm as and when it became available. This also became applicable to items of equipment until the full installation was obtained.

Modifications became necessary as units and items of equipment eventually became available as it was found that they differed from the provisional sketches supplied.

This aircraft PW979 is 95% complete. Tests are being carried out for operation of the various systems. Extra parts etc are being called for in the installation by RAE from time to time as their investigations progress.

NOTE:

We find that equipment supplied for production and conversion sets differs from that installed on the prototype PW979. This has necessitated modification action for production requirements.

The routing of information and equipment has not been very satisfactory. This, however, we believe is due to the fact that information and equipment was not available at the time and that plans were far in advance of facilities at that date

(Signed) J Park

So it was, in 1943, that Miles commenced work on the modification of the Martinet to Spec. Q.10/43. This called for a ground operated radio-controlled pilotless version of the M.25 Martinet TT Mk.I which became the M.50 Queen Martinet. On 7th April 1943, the Admiralty also finally agreed to accept the Queen Martinet but to fulfil the role of a pilotless 'Sheep' aircraft to be controlled by a Naval 'Shepherd' aircraft, such as the Fairey Fulmar. The aircraft remained unchanged externally as the modification was confined to structural items to take the additional equipment but all equipment associated with the target towing role was removed. The all-up weight was increased to 6,780 lb.

Details of the modifications required to convert the Martinet into the Queen Martinet were outlined in RAE Tech. Note No.I AP.971 (N.A. Ref: AVIA 15/1749), as follows:

The Queen Martinet aircraft was operated by equipment designed for similar purposes in the USA, which had undergone considerable modification during adaptation to British technique. Two types of signal were used. The 'Fixed Attitude' series produced preset flight conditions, each signal controlling a number of aircraft components. The 'Beep' series provided continuous control of single units (with one exception) and were used to obtain intermediate flight conditions. The American scheme made no provision for fixed attitudes. The control gear was installed in an Anson ('Shepherd') aircraft for flight tests and landing approach, and in a ground vehicle for take-off and landing. The gyroscopes were a suction driven directional gyroscope and an artificial horizon, fitted with a photo-electric pick off to reduce pick off reaction to a minimum. Angular disturbances caused relative movement between a beam of light and a stabilised interrupter blade. The signal was amplified electronically, and then electrically through a relay to a hydraulic transfer valve.

For turning flight, an electric motor could rotate the roll datum of the aileron control, thus applying bank, and at the same time a variable speed gear box was used to rotate the azimuth datum at a rate proportional to the bank datum shift. The attitude was fixed by producing pitch datum displacements through a reversible electric motor, which was controlled by a commutator with adjustable brushes suitably positioned.

Selection of undercarriage flaps and brakes was made by hydraulic servo motors, controlled by valves similar to those used for the aircraft controls. Small geared DC electric motors with dynamic armature braking were used to operate the throttle and propeller pitch levers. Air speed indicators, an altimeter and an engine speed indicator were used to provide safeguards and assist control. The most important results obtained from the trials were the need for rapid datum changes when landing, and a high rudder gearing during the landing run. A historical account of target development follows.

The Queen Bee radio-controlled aircraft was developed to provide realistic targets for anti-aircraft gunfire. The speed of the Queen Bee was only 95 mph, yet the need for such targets was proved immediately, and the rapidly increasing performance of military aircraft necessitated corresponding target development. A prototype Queen Wasp (top speed 170 mph) was flown, before the effort was diverted to more urgent requirements in 1940.

The project was re-considered in 1942-43 and the Martinet Mk.I aircraft (highest speed 220 mph) was chosen to provide an interim solution, pending the design of equipment suitable for high speed aircraft. Flight trials of Queen Martinet **LR244** *(the modified 2nd prototype M.25 Martinet which then became the first prototype M.50 Queen Martinet - PA)* indicated the possibilities of the Queen Wasp equipment, but stocks were insufficient to cover the Queen Martinet Programme, and further production was impossible. No other suitable equipment was available in the UK. A mission to USA examined the air pick-off systems, successfully operated by the USAAF and USNAF, and a sufficient number of units were ordered to cover the Queen Martinet Programme. Auto-pilots of later design were delivered, which embodied a photo-electric pick-off, and these were not operated successfully in the USA.

The flight trials included considerable development of the auto-pilot as such, and the pilotless programme was correspondingly delayed. These were performed in the second and third prototype *(M.50 Queen Martinet - PA)* aircraft **EM500** and **PW979**. Further production installations were completed at RNAS Brawdy, but the project was cancelled before these were flown pilotless.

The equipment with suitable modifications was installed in a Spitfire V aircraft (top level speed 300 mph). Ground tests on the first prototype were completed when the project was cancelled. Reference Numbers of the equipment are given in Appendix III, and a list of Associated Publications in Appendix IV. The project has been carried through jointly by IAP Dept. and Radio Dept. The latter department was responsible for the radio equipment, control boxes and relay sets. IAP Dept. was responsible for the automatic pilot, instrumentation, control operation and the conduct of the trials.

Differences between Queen Martinet and Martinet Mk.I Aircraft:

The Martinet Mk.I is powered with a Mercury 25 or 30 engine. The Queen Martinet has the Mercury 26 or 32, which differ from the corresponding Mercury 25 or 30 in two respects:-

    (a)   There is no manual mixture adjustment.
    (b)   An extra ancillary drive is provided, to operate the auto control hydraulic system.

The Martinet Mk.I 12 volt two pole DC supply is replaced by a 24 volt DC supply, with the auto pilot and communications equipment negatively earthed to the aircraft frame. There are no fuel cocks in the fuel system of the Queen Martinet. Fuel is drawn continuously from the inner tanks. The fuel in the outer tanks is pressurised from the Pesco Pump, and feeds the inner tanks through float valves. Flights of 3½ hours are possible under normal operational conditions. A suction venture is fitted to operate the pilot's instruments. The Pesco Pump supplies the auto pilot, but for piloted flight a manual cock permits change over of the supplies.

Provision is made for automatic action of the undercarriage, flaps, brakes, throttle and propeller pitch selector mechanisms, and involves in some cases very considerable changes from the Mk.I systems. Clutches are provided in the above five linkages, and between the auto pilot servo motors and the controls. Any faulty unit may be immediately declutched. At a late stage in the trials the tail wheel and brake relay valve, which gives differential braking with rudder, were modified.

Description of Equipment installed in the Queen Martinet:

The Auto Control Hydraulic System - Hydraulic fluid is contained in, and nearly fills, an oil sump. The engine driven hydraulic pump draws fluid from the sump, and delivers it to a pressure regulator mounted on the sump. The regulator maintains a pressure of 150 psi, feeds the auto pilot system, and returns excess fluid to the sump. The fluid to the automatic pilot system passes through a wire wound filter, and the pipes are connected to a hydraulic pressure gauge in the cockpit, and an expansion tank. The latter is an air filled cavity, in which air is compressed, and which assists in the maintenance of pressure when undue demands are made on the supply.

The supply then reaches the Servo Block, which contains five transfer valves and their corresponding hydraulic servo motors. Two motors are locked and the supply is taken to external motors. Fluid displaced by operation of a motor is returned to the top of the sump. Oil which leaks past the transfer valve glands, is gravity fed to the Sperry Drain Trap, which is vented to atmosphere and contains a float valve. At a definite oil level the valve opens and allows oil to pass into a pipe, from which a suction venture reintroduces the fluid into the main hydraulic circuits. An additional filter (Vokes E29L) was later fitted before the servo block to provide further protection for the valves. The filtering element consists of a felt stitched to gauze, corrugated and arranged in cylindrical form, the whole contained in an additional silk element.

The Servo Block (Hydraulic Servo Unit):

Elevator, rudder and ailerons are operated by three servo motors on the block, through linkages to the main controls. Each servo motor consists of two cylinders and pistons, the latter being joined by a piston shaft. To the centre of each piston shaft is attached a crosshead connector, which provides location for the shaft, and which is connected to an output link. This rod carries the follow up cable bracket, and at the far end links with the emergency clutch before joining the main control run.

A main hydraulic valve connects the corresponding cylinders of all servo motors when the gear is 'out', thus permitting manual control operation by displacement of hydraulic fluid from one side to the other. An external pulley is cable linked to the 'cut in' lever in the cockpit. The cable is spring loaded towards the 'in' position, and the lever has a locking notch in the 'out' position. A lever on the pulley operates a micro-switch in the 'out' position, releases it when 'in', and thus effects important changes in the control circuits. When the main hydraulic valve is in, the controls are locked, and operation is only possible through the transfer valves.

The transfer valves are spring loaded to a central position, in which both cylinders of a servo motor are isolated. Valves may be displaced in either direction by solenoids energised by 24 volt D.C. supply. When displaced the high pressure line is connected to one cylinder, and the opposing cylinder is connected through the valve to the sump. Electrical supplies reach the unit through a junction box mounted on the block. The remaining servo motors are locked in a central position, but are connected to external motors. One transfer valve controls the undercarriage selector, the other the flaps selector and brakes motor. To permit the normal 'throw out' operation of undercarriage and flaps the valves are modified so that in the central position both sides of the motors are connected to the sump.

The statement that 'Further production installations were completed at RNAS Brawdy, but the project was cancelled before these were flown pilotless', is interesting as it implies that there was no requirement for the Queen Martinet but in fact many more were built/modified after that.

The M.25 Martinet, EM500, was allotted to Miles Aircraft Ltd on 16th December 1943 (for 6 months) for 'fitment as 2nd prototype pilotless aircraft', i.e. the M.50 Queen Martinet Radio-Controlled Target Aircraft. On 27th January 1944, EM500 was recorded as being 'retained by firm for trial installation and test of drone equipment' and then became the second prototype M.50, being delivered to RAE Farnborough for flight trials on 29th November 1944.

Martinet PW979 was allotted to Miles Aircraft Ltd on 7th July 1944 'for trial installation of Drone equipment on 6 month loan (later extended to 20th July 1945)', to become the third prototype M.50 Queen Martinet. On 9th August 1945, PW979 was delivered to PAU Manorbier 'for investigation by the Pilotless Aircraft Unit' and from there it went to RAE Farnborough on 14th December 1945 'for flight trials re pilotless aircraft development programme'.

These trials indicated the possibility of using equipment intended for the cancelled Airspeed Queen Wasp programme but, unfortunately, stocks of these were insufficient to cover the Queen Martinet programme and further production was not possible. No other suitable equipment was available in the UK and therefore a mission was sent to the USA to examine the air pick-off systems, which had been successfully operated by the USAAF and US Navy. A sufficient number of these units were apparently ordered,

but the units that were finally delivered were of a later design of auto-pilot, which embodied an electric pick-off and which had not proved wholly satisfactory in American service.

An order was placed for 193 M.50 Queen Martinets, but this requirement was later reduced to 58, with the final 135 being cancelled. However, at least 24 M.25 Martinets were modified to M.50 Queen Martinets by Miles Aircraft Ltd at Woodley in 1945.

The M.50 Queen Martinet radio controlled pilotless aircraft was kept on the 'Secret' list until after the war had ended with its existence not being officially announced until March 1946. Although the original order had been reduced, the Ministry then ordered a further 34 M.50s in 1946 but, although there is no record of the first 4 being built, it has been confirmed that the next 7 <u>were</u> built, being delivered to the RAF between April and June 1946, with the remaining 23 being cancelled.

773 Squadron RNAS Brawdy were issued with M.50 Queen Martinets during 1945-46 and Mike Draper writes of the naval use of the Queen Martinet in his book '*Sitting' Ducks*' as follows:

Virtually the entire Queen Martinet output (production and conversions) was placed into long-term storage at 12 MU Kirkbride; others were temporarily stored at 113 Sub-Storage Site at RAF Market Harborough, Leicestershire (the Site being an offshoot of 273 MU at Polebrook, Northamptonshire). Four examples (RH123, RH125-RH127) were released to the Pilotless Aircraft Unit at Manorbier but they were for evaluation purposes rather than for issue as 'live' targets. Four others (RH169, RH182, RH185 & RH186) were transferred to Royal Navy charge in May 1946 and allocated to 773 Naval Air Squadron.

773 Squadron PAU reformed at Lee-on-Solent during August 1945 as a Service Trials Unit but was designated to become a Pilotless Aircraft Unit under the command of Lt Cdr(E) Peter Richmond. Only a handful of pilots were posted to 773 and there was little flying activity at first. One of those pilots was Sub Lt(A) Douglas Harley, RNVR, who was waiting to be deployed to the Far East, hostilities having ceased in Europe. But with the sudden surrender of Japanese forces he was quickly re-posted to 773, a posting, which Harley queried by demanding to know why a pilotless aircraft squadron should have a need for pilots!

There is little doubt that the role of 773 Squadron would be to operate a fleet of 'Shepherd' and 'Sheep' aircraft. A small number of Mosquito B.25s (including KA930, KA940 and KB670) were taken on charge at Lee-on-Solent to operate in a 'shepherd' role, in other words, to take over control of the Queens once they had become airborne. It is also just possible, considering that 773's pilots had earlier spent a brief period at Manorbier on a Queen Bee familiarisation course, that 773 was due to operate

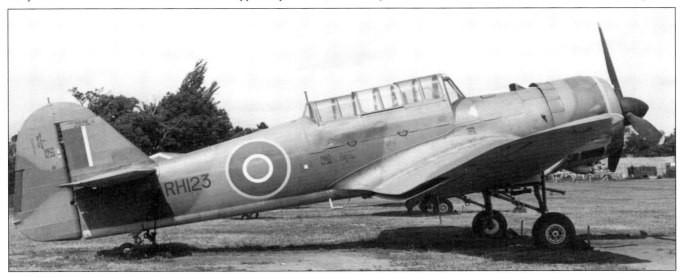

RH123, the second production M.50 Queen Martinet, at Woodley before delivery.

Queen Bees as 'Sheep' drones. What did become clear, however, is that Lee-on-Solent was not the wisest choice of locations for the base for a pilot-less operation. The precise role of 773 Squadron was never widely publicised, but word soon got out, needless to say eventually reaching the Station Commander, RNAS Lee-on-Solent, and to say that he was not impressed by the choice of his station to host this operation was but to put it mildly! In fact he apparently was heard to say that: "There'll be no bloody unmanned aircraft let loose around my Station", and as nobody on the Squadron was prepared to risk countering the word of the Station Commander, 773 was promptly transferred to RNAS Brawdy - the (as yet unused) "remotest and wildest" outstation in Pembrokeshire, Wales!

The actual movement from Lee-on-Solent to Brawdy took place on 27 March 1946. By then it was known that 773 Squadron's drone aircraft would be the Miles Queen Martinet but it was not until mid-May 1946 that the first of four aircraft (RH185) was delivered in from Woodley. It must be assumed that 773's aircraft were delivered with drone equipment already installed; they were certainly fully painted in the adopted Queen Martinet scheme - an overall drab yellow.

The Squadron immediately began establishing operational procedures with the Mosquito and Queen Martinet. Much of the work out of Brawdy involved formation flying, radio range testing and general handling of the Queen Martinet which, once airborne, was flown under radio control but with a pilot on board in a 'no hands' manner. 773 Squadron PAU did not fly any of its Queen Martinets in pilotless mode. Sub Lt D Harley RNVR, a former 773 Squadron pilot recalled that, because of the aircraft's over-bearing torque and swing on take-off, fully unmanned radio-controlled flights - while certainly contemplated - were never attempted. In the event, and with Britain no longer at war, plans for a Fleet Air Arm drone Squadron were shelved and the unit was disbanded at RNAS Brawdy on 30th September 1946.

No evidence has come to light that suggests any of the 89 Queen Martinet conversions ever performed their intended role as pilotless target drones. It seems hardly credible that such an amount of time, effort and funding should have been expended on a fleet that was condemned to permanent storage. The final chapter closed on 7 August 1947 when all Queen Martinets were struck off charge, and scrapped.

However, because the auto-pilot system required much development, the Queen Martinet programme was never straightforward and became dogged by complex and lengthy flight trials. All the flight-testing took place at Farnborough and was carried out jointly by the RAE's IAP and Radio Departments. The latter was responsible for radio equipment, control boxes and relay sets, while IAP Department was responsible for developing the automatic pilot, instrumentation, control operation and conducting the flight trials. In the end, just 69 M.50 Queen Martinets were built from scratch.

The end of the M.50 Queen Martinet finally came in the mid 1950s, when a gang were told to demolish an old asbestos shed on Woodley aerodrome. The contents of this shed were found to comprise some 7-8 partly completed Queen Martinet fuselages, probably left over from the last cancelled contract. These were later taken to the Miles Aircraft Sports Ground (on the Sonning side of the A4), where they were stacked on a bonfire, probably in readiness for the 5th November Guy Fawkes night celebrations! Fortunately, they were seen and photographed by David Kynaston before the end came.

For a summary of M.50 Queen Martinet production and individual aircraft histories see Appendix 30 on the CD.

Above and below: The partially completed M.50 Queen Martinets on the Miles Aircraft Sports Ground in readiness for the bonfire.

[David Kynaston]

SPECIFICATION AND PERFORMANCE DATA

Engine:	870 hp Bristol Mercury 26 or 32 (Note: These engined differed from the Mercury 25 or 30 engine of the Martinet in two respects; i) the Queen Martinet had no manual mixture adjustment but was provided with an auxilliary drive to operate the auto-control hydraulic system and ii) the Martinet's 12-volt (with two pole DC) supply was replaced by a 24-volt DC supply, with the autopilot and communications equipment negatively earthed to the aircraft frame.
Dimensions:	span 39ft 0in; length 30ft 11in; height 11ft 7in; wing area 242sq ft; aspect ratio 6.3; wing section root NACA 23024, tip NACA 23009
Weights:	empty 4,640lb; fuel (130 gal) 975lb; oil (8.5 gal) 76lb; crew 400lb; useful load 659lb; AUW 6,750lb; wing loading 27.9lb/sq ft
Performance:	max speed 221 mph at sea level, 240 mph at 5,800ft, 238 mph at 10,000ft; max cruising speed 199 mph at 5,000ft; max design diving speed 330 mph IAS; stalling speed 83 mph with flaps up, 62 mph with flaps down; run to unstick 780ft; distance to 50ft, 1,380ft; landing run 1,275ft; landing from 50ft, 1,614ft; time to 5,000ft, 3.5 min and to 10,000ft, 8.0 min; range 694 miles; duration 5.0 hrs.

III.   Application of Do. Gerate *(Dornier Ramjet - PA)* to Projectiles.

DSR stated that a Ministry of Supply Committee was considering this subject in the light of this and other information available on German rocket projectile development.

IV.   Boundary Layer Control and Wing Profiles for Subsonic and Supersonic flight.

The section of the report on boundary layer control was agreed to obtain no new information, and it was evident that the prisoner had little knowledge on this subject. On supersonic flight the information was also not new, but it was interesting to note that the prisoner had some knowledge of the special problems involved.

V.   A New Fuel.

Prof Garner stated that the low density quoted would indicate hydro-carbon compound, but that the heat of combustion was some ten times higher than for known compounds. W/Cdr Whittle suggested that the high value might be obtained largely from the heat of decomposition and pointed out that the conditions obtaining in the synthetic fuel processes were favourable to the discovery of new compounds which could not normally exist at room temperature.

It was agreed to record that no compounds were known that could give means of combustion approaching the 52,000 kilocalories per kilogram ****ed, and that if such compounds existed their manufacture was entirely outside present knowledge. It was further agreed to submit this section of the report to the HEI and the ICI Research Department, Billingham, for comment.

The Second Meeting was held on 4th June 1943 to further discuss AI(K) Report No 184A/1943 and two additional Reports Nos.227A/1943 and 264B/1943. Chaired by Ben Lockspeiser, it was attended by Messrs Jones, Taylor, Relf, H M Garner, Roxbee-Cox, Whittle, Constant, Smelt and Vessey from the First Meeting but with the addition of Dr Knight and Dr Fereday (both from the Ministry of Supply), Mr I Bowen (DDRD Inst) and W/Cdr Felkin (from AI(K)). The Minutes read as follows:

Report AI(K) No.227A/1943 had been circulated to the members of the Committee but the most recent Report 246B/1943 had been received immediately prior to the meeting and few of the members had seen it. Copies were distributed and the Chairman proceeded to run through the main points explaining that this report was in the main a summary of the two previous ones.

The paragraphs on the projectile were briefly considered and the Ministry of Supply representatives agreed that the performance quoted was possible even with present fuels. The Chairman pointed out the importance of this statement, as it meant that confirmation of the existence of the projectile was not necessarily confirmation of a new fuel with the extraordinarily high calorific value claimed in the reports. It was agreed that the projectile as described was not athodyd-propelled, but was a simple rocket. Professor GI Taylor pointed out the value of a rocket for testing athodyd performance at supersonic speeds and after discussion it was agreed that the Ministry of Supply should be asked to develop a rocket to which athodyds might be fitted to investigate their behaviour at high speeds.

The portion of the report dealing with aircraft was then considered and it was agreed that the aircraft described in paragraphs 36-41 was probably not athodyd-propelled but appeared to be a large aircraft with turbine-driven jet propulsion engines using rocket-assisted take-off. The comparatively low take-off thrust of gas turbines made the use of rocket-assisted take-off likely and the description was consistent with our knowledge.

A short discussion on the value of rockets for accelerating a supersonic aircraft to speeds at which athodyds were of value

followed, and Mr Vessey stated that the present rockets, as used for assisted take-off did not appear suitable for this purpose, as their duration was short. For endurances exceeding say 3 minutes the jet turbine was preferable due to its much lower fuel consumption. The fuel consumption of the known cordite and bifuel rocket motors was 5.6 lbs per 1000 lb sec. impulse.

The other aircraft described in the report were claimed to have supersonic speeds and athodyds might then be appropriate. It was agreed that it was clear from this and other sources that the Germans were building jet-propelled aircraft, and that possibly some of these were capable of supersonic speeds. We, in this country, had not studied the problems of aircraft flight at supersonic speeds, but it was clear that there were many difficult problems and if Germany had, in fact, solved them then that country was years ahead of Great Britain or the USA.

A general discussion then followed on the characteristics of a supersonic aircraft. A considerable amount of data was available from wind tunnel tests and this appeared to agree closely with theory. It was agreed that there appeared to be little difficulty in maintaining supersonic flight for short periods if the difficulties of the transition from subsonic to supersonic flight could be solved, and W/Cdr Whittle expressed the opinion that the power units involved no serious problems. The various stages of flight, take-off (and landing), flight at subsonic speeds, flight at speeds near the speed of sound and then at supersonic speeds required different characteristics which it appeared difficult to reconcile in a single aircraft. Mr Relf suggested that some information might be obtained by testing a model of a supersonic aircraft in a normal wind tunnel, as this would allow the behaviour at take-off and subsonic speeds to be investigated. The difficulty lay in deciding on the design. It was agreed that Mr Relf should discuss with RAE with a view to deciding the general lay-out of a model and then testing it in one of the NPL tunnels.

Methods of investigating the transition from subsonic to supersonic speeds were discussed, and it was agreed that RAE should consider the tests required on, say, a rocket propelled model.

The RAE letter dated 31.5.43 was then read and a discussion followed on the RAE proposals for work on athodyd propulsion. It was agreed that, in general, athodyd propulsion was not an advantage for aircraft of present design. The tests, therefore, would not serve to improve the present F.9/40. They would, however, serve to test the performance of athodyds at speeds in the immediate subsonic region. It was agreed that the proposals should be considered later when the investigations at RAE had gone further.

The RAE representatives stated that two notes were in preparation, one dealing with supersonic flight and the other with propulsive ducts. The latter would include a note on the athodyd-driven airscrew. It was agreed that the two notes should be circulated to the members of the Committee as soon as possible.

The reported new explosive was briefly discussed, and in view of recent German propaganda claims to have caused extensive damage in South Coast towns by the use of a new bomb, it was agreed to consult the Ministry of Home Security on the available evidence of recent bomb damage. Wg Cdr Felkin said he knew of nothing to substantiate these claims. It was further agreed that a discussion was desirable between the Scientist who had assisted in the interrogation and authorities on molecular-physics, fuels and explosives. Wg Cdr Felkin stated that this could probably be arranged.

Subsequent to the meeting, a suggestion by Sir Henry Tizard that at supersonic speeds it might be impossible to keep the aircraft and pilot cool enough was discussed and it was agreed that RAE should investigate the problem.

The Third Meeting was held on Friday 23rd July 1943 and a document, probably written soon after by the Special Projects

Development Panel, gave probably the first indications of the future requirement for a very high speed aircraft (N.A. Ref: AVIA 15/1930). The document, entitled *Planning for Jet Propelled and Gas Turbine Aircraft* is reproduced here:

The objectives are as follows:

- To get as many gas turbine aeroplanes based on engines at present under development into operation as quickly as possible. Inter alia, to aim at an operational flight by March 1st 1944.

- To produce gas turbine aeroplanes of high performance as rapidly as possible, in particular developing a high speed aircraft for bombing or mail carrying and a large high speed aircraft for bombing or air transport.

- To develop aircraft capable of supersonic speed.

With reference to 1.3, the relevant extract read:

Athodyds - The possibility of very high and conceivably supersonic speeds by the use of aero-thermodynamic ducts, referred to as athodyds, has recently been appreciated. The possibility of achievement of such speeds is sufficiently great to warrant an intensive experimental effort. Work with which the RAE is associated has begun at Power Jets Ltd. It is early to say what additional facilities will be required on the laboratory side, but it is certain that some extra provision will have to be made.

Full Scale Experiment - We shall need capacity for the modification of existing aircraft to do full scale experiments with high speed devices. Not only will it be necessary to do experiments in the air with athodyds, but the possibilities of ammonia injection must also be tried as a means of obtaining the very high speeds necessary for experimenting adequately with the athodyds. This work will need the services of a test pilot of unusual accomplishment.

Very High Speed Aircraft - It is also necessary to investigate with RAE and NPL the aerodynamic design of aircraft suitable for travelling up to supersonic speeds. Some design and construction capacity will be required later for this, but it is not possible at present to define the needs precisely. **It is considered that the help of an enthusiastic constructor like Mr Miles should be enlisted** *(the significance of this last sentence should not be lost - PA).*

Recommendations relating to Objective 1.3:

Intensive laboratory experimental work at Power Jets Ltd and RAE.
Full scale experiment with high speed devices on existing aircraft.
Investigation of aerodynamic design for very high speed, sub-sonic and supersonic.

Facilities required for Recommendations.
Further workshop and test facilities (not yet defined) at Power Jets Ltd.
Design and constructional capacity for adapting high speed devices to existing aircraft.
Design and constructional capacity for model and full scale very high speed aircraft.
An exceptional pilot with wide experience of aerodynamic test work. Wing Commander Wilson is wanted back from USA.

An extract from a minute referring to a meeting held on 25th September 1943 (N.A. Ref: AVIA 15/1968) stated under the heading of DTD:

I attach hereto my notes on the meeting we held on 25th September (1943) on future gas turbine engines and aeroplanes. This meeting was general in character, and the object of my minute is to agree with you if possible a more definite engine-cum-aeroplane plan

than is provided by paragraph 7. From the engine point of view, three conditions I would like fulfilled are:
to find an outlet for the F.2 class engine.
to design a double-compound engine in parallel with a large aeroplane.
to design a duct fuel burning turbine engine in parallel with a high speed aeroplane.

The sort of plan which would be the most satisfactory from my point of view is the following, in which I have selected the names of aircraft firms on the strength of our informal discussion on 25th September:-
The Westland fighter bomber project to go forward, engined with F.2 class units.
A design contract to be given to (say) Armstrong Whitworth for a large bomber in parallel with which Power Jets to design the appropriate double compound engine, this work taking priority of outstanding W.4/100 work.
To order from (say) Phillips & Powis a very high speed experimental aeroplane in parallel with which Power Jets would design a supercharged duct fuel burning turbine engine, adapted from one of their current types *(another very significant statement - PA).*

The first is of course dependent upon Westland's finding the most advanced F.2 design at least as suitable as the W.4/100, which they have so far contemplated for it, for their design. I suggest the two firms are immediately brought together.

So, by October 1943, the MAP, having failed in their very determined attempt to find technical grounds for rejecting the projected M.26L X.11 Transport Aeroplane, had then to find an excuse as to why the Miles 'X' should not be ordered. This was despite the fact that, as one of the staff in the department concerned admitted, the X.11 was by far the most promising of the three paper projects considered.

The fact of the matter was, in reality, that the Ministry had, for reasons best known to themselves, already taken the decision to award the contract to build the post war transport aeroplane to Bristol Aeroplane Company and had anticipated no difficulty in finding technical grounds for rejecting the X.11 proposal. In the event, far from proving a relatively easy paper exercise, the Ministry found itself in the position of being unable to reject on technical grounds, a project which they had undertaken to assess fairly on its technical merits; a project, moreover, that challenged the one to which they were already committed.

Therefore, when Air Marshal Ralph Sorley, Controller of Research and Development (CRD) at the MAP since April 1943, was forced into the position of telling Miles that, whether he liked it or not, the X.11 would not be ordered regardless of the assurances given by Sir Stafford Cripps, he realised that this decision would be fought on the basis of the Minister's promise, which clearly had not been fulfilled.

It was in a letter from CRD dated 8th October 1943, (see the chapter on the M.26 X.11), which stated that the Miles 'X' project was to be rejected that CRD finished his letter:

I should like to discuss at an early date some work I have in mind for you which will require to be dealt with quickly. I know that DTD is getting into touch with you almost at once and I shall be happy to discuss the matter with you in due course.

This was to be the first hint that CRD gave Miles on the Supersonic project and on 9th October 1943, Miles was invited to a meeting at MAP in London to initiate action on a very high speed experimental aeroplane, to explain what was wanted and ask if his firm would accept a contract to design and make such an aircraft. He was handed a six-line outline specification. Miles replied to CRD on 13th October 1943 characteristically: *With regard to the last paragraph of your letter, I have seen DTD and I shall be very glad to have a shot at the research job he discussed with us, in fact we have already started.*

The fact that Miles had 'already started' on the project by that time showed the degree of enthusiasm which he felt for the challenge. This was to be the most ambitious and advanced research project to be attempted in the history of aviation in the world up to that time, calling as it did for the design and construction of a high-speed research aircraft, capable of a speed of 1,000 mph.

The incredibly high speed of 1,000 mph, which the aircraft was required to be capable of, probably came about as the result of the interrogation of the German tank engineer since he had implied that an aircraft capable of attaining a cruising speed of 800 mph and a maximum speed of 1,000 mph at a height of 59,000 feet, was under development in Germany. The German engineer had gone on to describe some of the means taken to deal with the special problems of flight above the speed of sound.

Some years later, Don Brown wrote of the projected Miles high speed research aircraft thus:

All these problems and many others were described to F G Miles when, following the final letter from the Controller of Research and Development, he was invited to visit the Director of Scientific Research, then Mr (later Sir) Benjamin Lockspeiser. In a flash the M.26 X.11 controversy was forgotten (although Miles was of the opinion that he could in fact undertake both projects at once!), the tremendous new challenge was accepted with alacrity. Lockspeiser went on to say that the design and production of the power-plant would be undertaken by Group Captain (later Air Commodore Sir Frank) Whittle at Power Jets Ltd and therefore the closest co-operation between the airframe and the power-plant teams would be necessary.

Finally, the magnitude of the challenge was revealed, Specification E.24/43 dated 14th August 1944, issued to Miles Aircraft Ltd on 26th August 1944 was for a High Speed Single-Engine Experimental Aircraft capable of a speed of 1,000 mph at 36,000 ft and that at a date when no aircraft had yet achieved 500 mph in level flight.

The project bristled with problems and was one moreover on which practically no data was available, since entirely fresh ground was to be broken. Needless to say, the project, designated M.52 was categorised 'Top Secret' and the greatest care had to be exercised to ensure that at any moment only the minimum number of people would even know of the existence of the project let alone any details. Just six people were initially to be aware of the project and they were F G and G H Miles, Dennis S Bancroft, the chief aerodynamicist, Henry Stock Wilkinson, chief stressman, Lionel Charles 'Toby' Heal, the project engineer and Don Brown.

From the first it was clear that with the low thrust engines then available, sonic speed would only be attainable with a very small aircraft, with a wing of either double wedge or biconvex section and thinner than any wing ever built and flown to date. No full scale flight data was available on such an aerofoil and before the

necessary wing area for the M.52 could be determined, it was necessary to know, reasonably accurately, the coefficient of lift of such a wing.

In fact, in an attempt to keep abreast with current jet engine developments, on 5th November 1942 George Miles and Don Brown had made a visit to Power Jets Ltd at Rugby and Don's report on this visit follows:

At the suggestion of Flt Lt W E P Johnson, Messrs G H Miles and D L Brown called to inspect and discuss the latest developments of the Whittle jet propulsion unit, with a view to possible future co-operation. The unit in its latest form consists of a series of 10 cylinders arranged axially. The fuel used is crude paraffin, which is fed into the cylinders by an axial compressor. The fuel is burnt in the cylinders and the products of combustion pass forward into the turbine unit which exhausts from its centre into an exhaust pipe of about 12" diameter which runs back through the centre of the nest of cylinders to the tail of the aircraft. The temperature of the exhaust gases is of the order of 600° C. The starter, consisting of a small electric motor driving the compressor and turbine, is attached to the front of the unit.

It is proposed to utilise the considerable heat in the exhaust gases by a method of augmentation on somewhat similar lines to that proposed for the Rolls-Royce P.1.26 two stroke engine. By this means it is anticipated that an increase in thrust of approximately 100% will be obtained. It is also proposed to obtain a further large augmentation of thrust for a short period by introducing ammonia into the fuel. This may be employed for facilitating take-off at heavy load and also for momentarily out-climbing the enemy in combat. When used in conjunction with the normal exhaust augmentation, an increase in thrust of the order of 180% over the un-augmented thrust is temporarily obtainable.

The dimensions of the unit in its present form are as follows:-

> Overall diameter - 42"
> Overall length from front of starter to rear of cylinders - 67".

The weight of the unit is - without exhaust augmenter 800 lb and with exhaust augmenter – 990 lb. The weight of the RAE Metropolitan Vickers F.3 unit is 1,800 lb. The thrust of the unit is:-

> Rated augmented static thrust at sea level - 1,600 lb;
> Max augmented static thrust at sea level - 1,800 lb;
> Augmented static thrust - 3,200 lb

The RAE F.3 unit gives a static thrust at sea level of 2,300 lb. Its thrust/weight ratio appears to be inferior to the Whittle unit. The variation of thrust with height may be taken as proportional to the (Density) o.7.

The comparative figures in the table below are interesting and are based on a climbing speed of 150 mph, IAS.

Power Plant:	Merlin XX F.3 lb	RAE Whittle lb	Un-augmented Whittle lb	Augmented lb
Weight of installation.	2,560	1,800	800	990
Thrust at sea-level	1,280	1,430	1,120	1,990
Thrust at 5,000 ft	1,340	1,290	1,010	1,800
Thrust at 10,000 ft	1,400	1,150	900	1,600
Thrust at 15,000 ft	1,260	960	750	1,340
Thrust at 20,000 ft	900	840	660	1,170
Thrust at 25,000 ft	760	600	1,060	

The variation of thrust with speed is illustrated by the following comparative figures, all relating to sea-level conditions:-

Static thrust	3,200	2,375	1,800	3,200
Thrust at 100 mph	2,200	1,940	1,470	2,620
Thrust at 300 mph	740	1,400	1,060	1,890
Thrust at 500 mph	440	1,190	900	1,600

The fuel consumption of the Whittle was given as averaging about 1.15 to 1.20 lb per lb of thrust, the best figure obtained so far being 1.06. The figure claimed for the RAE F.3.unit is 0.96 lb per lb of thrust. From the thrust figures quoted above, the consumption at any speed or height can readily be calculated. The consumption of air is of the order of 40 lb/sec.

With regard to the test flying done so far, the Gloster E.28 powered by a single unit has been flying now for nearly 2 years at Cranwell and Newmarket and is shortly being sent to the RAE. It has, so far, only been flown by one pilot, the late P E G Sayers, and has altogether done about 12 hours flying. On one occasion it reached a height of 30,000 feet at which point icing trouble occurred and necessitated a forced landing. It is proposed to overcome this trouble in future by carrying a small quantity of ammonia, the injection of which causes a temporary large increase in power with a corresponding increase in temperature.

One of the advantages of this type of power unit, particularly for interceptor fighters, is the quick start obtainable with no necessity to warm up. Full power is available within 8 seconds of starting.

With regard to future production the position is this. Over a year ago the F.9/40 specification was issued, catering for a high altitude twin-engined fighter. Three designs were considered, two being orthodox aeroplanes by Westland and Vickers and powered by two Merlin 61 engines, the third design was the Gloster Meteor powered by two Whittle units. The Westland Welkin and the Gloster Meteor were ordered in quantity and the prototype Welkin has just flown and will be in production in six months' time.

The Meteor is being produced at the rate of 20 week at the Gloster factory at Brockworth. Due to the fact that the type was ordered while the power unit was still in the very early experimental stage, the production of the airframe has out-stripped the production of the power units and two Meteors are now actually at Newmarket

awaiting power plants. The estimated initial climb of the Meteor is as follows:-

| With normal Whittle unit - 2,000 ft/min |
| With augmented Whittle unit - 4,500 ft/min |
| With ammonia augmentation - 6,200 ft/min |

Flt Lt Johnson stated that Major Bulman, DDGEDP was arranging to put the Halford jet unit into immediate large-scale production in spite of the fact that Major Halford had not reached nearly as advanced stage of development yet as they, Power Jets, had. In fact he stated that the decision to proceed with the production of the Halford unit was, in fact, based on a demonstration run in which the momentary maximum static thrust developed was 1,300 lb from a unit whose designed output was 3,000 lb.

Flt Lt Johnson was most anxious to effect a working agreement with us and he proposed to approach MAP for permission to do so. In the meantime he stressed the fact that we must regard the visit as strictly unofficial and confidential in that he had to obtain official permission before he was allowed to disclose any information whatever.

We showed him the Libellula specification and pointed out its particular suitability in that it overcomes the CG difficulty which is encountered in an orthodox aeroplane if more than one jet unit is envisaged. Flt Lt Johnson was particularly interested in this point which strengthened and confirmed his desire to form a liaison with us. He asked to be allowed to keep the Libellula specification and also that of the M.39 which he visualised as a potential flying test-bed.

He mentioned that an odd number of power units was preferred, i.e. 1, 3, 5, and so on. Since the visit, the M.39 has been examined with this end in view and it has been found suitable for the incorporation of either one or three units. With the former a very light wing

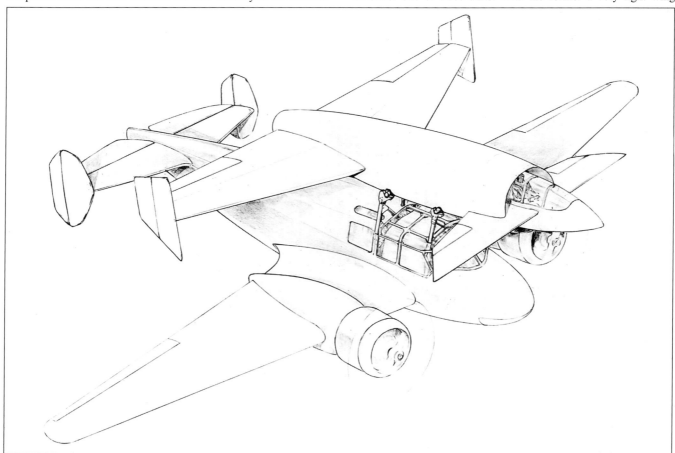

An undated sketch of a jet propelled high speed Libellula layout, mounted on a twin-engined project based on the M.36 Montrose, was recently discovered in the archives of the late Don Hannah, which probably originated from Don Brown. Note the angle of cut-off for the front wing, a scheme later suggested for the M.52.

loading is obtained together with a reasonable power loading and the machine should be very suitable for conducting the initial trials. On the completion of these, two more units could be added with no structural alteration other than the repositioning of the single unit in the fuselage and the machine would still have a reasonable wing loading together with an extremely low power loading, which should give a very high performance.

A Miles Aircraft Internal Memo dated 8th November 1943, written by F G Miles, is one of the earliest pieces of correspondence on the problems which Miles expected to be associated with the new design for a very high speed aircraft:

Herewith a list of the promises made at Saturday's meeting:

1.   It was agreed that we should go over to Farnborough early next week to see Messrs Morgan & Gardner to get all the information we can regarding structure, aerodynamics and electric control of aircraft including undercarriages.

2.   See if there is any way possible of getting Mr Brown over to America without upsetting things.

3.   Send to Mr Rowe on Monday all the drawings that we have done on the machine and also a rough schedule of the number of draughtsmen and men we shall require to replace those who are working on this job.

4.   Apply for a contract with priorities, internal and external, especially for such things as landing wheels and special forgings which may have to be made up for us.

5.   Write to Mr Garner about the Falcon asking to borrow it with the original Falcon wings and also for a flight programme of tests for the new section - Action Mr G H Miles.

6.   See the people at Farnborough about the tunnel programme the special project and find out from them the size of the models they are likely to require.

7.   In the drawings going up to Mr Rowe we might put up one or two alternative tailplane arrangements, one with a considerably lower aspect ratio.

8.   Generally speaking it was agreed that we should go ahead with two aircraft firstly but obtain material for at least three machines.

9.   We should try to carry out all tests, such as structural tests and experimental work within the factory, but we should get in touch with Farnborough about any outside assistance such as borrowing the Falcon and Spitfire at the same time notifying Mr Rowe.

It was at the meeting of the Supersonic Committee held on 9th November 1943, where the first proposal for a piloted aircraft to fly faster than the speed of sound was considered. By this time the Committee was fully established and were holding regular monthly meetings to consider methods of achieving speeds equal to or greater than that of sound. A very relevant extract from the minutes of this meeting read:

4.1   E.24/43 - DTD remarked that it was appropriate here to mention the Miles high speed aircraft which had been proposed. A brief description of the aircraft was then given. DSP stated that RAE were considering the power plant proposals in a more general manner, but had not yet looked into this particular design. In connection with this DDSR1 suggested that an analysis should be made, on a thrust minus drag basis, of the relative merits of different types of engine combinations. It was agreed that the RAE should prepare a note on the subject.

Soon after the war had ended the MAP instructed all aircraft manufacturers to provide a report on their wartime activities. A description of the M.52, to Spec. E.24/43, was duly prepared by L C 'Toby' Heal, the chief project engineer on the M.52 and was published in the Scientific War Records, dated October 1947.

A description of the M.52, dated 8th November 1945, by L C Heal, is reproduced here:

Description of Aircraft

When we were first asked to investigate a suitable layout for a high-speed aircraft it was realised that whilst the main consideration should be aerodynamic cleanliness, which would afford the pilot some possibility of escape from the aircraft should it become uncontrollable, he should also be provided with the best possible view. Apart from the shape of the fuselage, which is almost entirely dictated by engine requirements, it was considered undesirable that any supporting or stabilising surface should have a thickness chord ratio in excess of 7½%.

It was realised that the question of directional stability would be one which would have to be very carefully considered, and our early ideas were associated with the pilot positioned in a cockpit which formed part of the rearward fin area

Whilst this position had various advantages in relation to the safety of the pilot in the event of a crash landing, it was found that owing to the high position of the pilot due to the tailpipe, it was difficult to fair this at a t/c of less than about 12%, which we considered to be much too high. In addition, this area represented some addition to the frontal area, therefore another location for the cockpit had to be considered.

One of the difficulties of putting the pilot forward was allowing him some means of escape in all conditions of flight.

It is suggested in the present scheme that this can be overcome by fitting stabilising fins to the aft part of the cockpit and arranging accommodation for a suitable number of UP rockets to create sufficient thrust to accelerate the cockpit assembly away from the aircraft whilst in flight. The resulting aft movement of the cg of the aircraft would probably result in the aircraft leaving the straight line of flight which the cabin would maintain for a few seconds. The normal attachments of the cabin to the frame would be severed by some quick-release mechanism, which must be released before it is possible to fire the rockets. The cabin would be fitted with its own special parachute, which would open at a pre-determined speed of about 200 mph. The pilot will be able to subsequently make his own parachute exit from the cabin at a suitable altitude under good conditions.

A further advantage with this scheme may lie in the fact that the automatic observer which will be carried in the pilot's cockpit should stand a good chance of being undamaged. Thus valuable records can be available.

With the pilot in this forward position the view was considered to be the best possible. Since it has been agreed that the design submitted should form the basis of further design work, the following is a brief description of the project:-

The fuselage is of circular construction throughout its length, which will considerably simplify the design and construction and avoid concentrated loads. The construction will be monocoque throughout with rigidly built-up frames at the major attachments, i.e. engine and augmenter, wings and undercarriage and empennage. Between the skin and the inner duct the fuel tanks are situated, which will be of flexible crash-proof type. The tanks will be interconnected and pressurised if required.

Our ideas regarding servicing the engine installation have undergone a change since this was last discussed, with the result that we are now able to completely rivet up the whole fuselage structure and extract the complete power plant as illustrated.

The wing is of single spar construction using very thick duralumin sheet. In the first instance this will be of the curved aerofoil type and will have fixed incidences. The root rib will be of very strong construction and will have the torque attachment near the leading edge to a strong frame in the fuselage.

Ailerons are of ordinary unbalanced type and the flaps are of a simple split type form.

The undercarriage will use the high pressure Dunlop tyres and the complete undercarriage will retract into the fuselage.

EMPENNAGE - The rudder will be built into the fin in orthodox fashion. No elevators will be provided, the complete tailplane being under the control of the pilot.

Control Operation. It is proposed to operate these electrically by means of ac motors operating irreversible jacks. Some form of electronic converter will be necessary to supply power to the ac motors. Coupled with this will be a device giving proportionate control through the speed range. It is suggested feeding the electronic converter from batteries, the design of which is not yet decided.

Strength. It was agreed to stress the aircraft with a factor of 2 for all accelerations from 0 - 5G at all speeds from 0 - 1,000 mph.

Work to be undertaken by other firms who should be informed of priority:

1. Dunlop's - high pressure, double braked main u/c tyres and wheels. Also unbraked nose wheel and tyre.
2. Hand forgings for spars and main frame rings.
3. Instruments (ASI)
4. Automatic observer.
5. Radio ASI.
6. Electric motors, etc for controls and wind tunnel test for subsonic.
7. Pressure gyro instruments partially developed by Power Jets Ltd.
8. Special parachute for cabin.
9. Altitude compressor.

Special Equipment Required:

1. Contract for service equipment, i.e. engine removal trolley.
2. Engine starting and servicing trolley.

Work at NPL, RAE, etc.

Due to unusual relative size of the fuselage, wings etc and the necessity for obtaining practically neutral longitudinal stability etc, extended wind tunnel tests are required. Those marked with an asterisk are very urgently required:

(a) Subsonic Tests

* Longitudinal stability with nose
* Longitudinal stability without nose
* Directional stability with nose
* Directional stability without nose
  Control effectiveness prior to full scale tests
  Tip stalling characteristics
  Drag, if possible
  Stability tests and drag on nose portion
  Pressure plotting over nose in straight and yawed flight
* Body C_{MO}
* Wing characteristics
  Pressure distribution over undercarriage doors
  Effect of power on stability
  Span loading
  Lateral stability

(b) Supersonic Tests

* Wing pitching moment
* Body pitching moment
* Tailplane moment
  Forces on nose
  Pressure distribution on undercarriage doors
  Any information regarding stability

Note:- A powered model will be required for the majority of the subsonic tests.

Other requirements

1. Use of high speed aircraft for control and handling tests.
2. Allocation of labour particularly urgently aerodynamic and stressing personnel.

LCH/MHW 8.11.43.

Having extracted the relevant sections appertaining to the E.24/43 project from the minutes of the Committee Meetings on the Problems of Supersonic Flight from 1943 to 1946 and interspersing these with equally relevant correspondence from the RAE, NPL and many other interested parties in the MAP, Power Jets and Miles Aircraft, it has been possible to chart the progress of the design and development of the Miles E.24/43 with some degree of accuracy.

From this mass of information (reproduced in Appendix 34), a picture emerges of Miles Aircraft Ltd trying to design a new and revolutionary supersonic jet propelled aircraft with the 'help' (or hindrance?) of a Committee, whose members mostly comprised representatives from just about every MAP department and whose numbers appeared to increase proportionately as time went by. However, and for reasons as yet unexplained, Miles Aircraft Ltd, the firm contracted to design and build this research aircraft, were not invited to join the Committee.

In 1996, Josh Spoor and I travelled to Cornwall to meet Dennis Bancroft, who was responsible for the aerodynamics of the M.52, to discuss the M.52 with him and to get his views on the project. Dennis, and Derek Ruben, his assistant, are the only surviving members of the original M.52 design team but when we spoke to them regarding the Committee to *discuss the Problems of Supersonic Flight*, they agreed that neither of them, nor for that matter, anyone else in Miles Aircraft, had known anything of the existence of such a committee.

An Internal Memo by Don Brown, written following a visit to MAP on 21st October 1943 stated that Mr R McKinnon Wood (formerly chief of BA Dept., RAE Farnborough and then on the staff of Mr Garner, DD/SR1) who was then examining the proposals for research equipment in general and high speed wind tunnels in particular, had told Don that he was a member of a Committee which had been formed by DSR for the consideration of very high speeds. I suspect however, that the true significance of this committee (which was to have such far reaching consequences in the future) was not fully appreciated by Don at that time.

Even in retrospect, I find it very difficult to comprehend why the firm who had been contracted to design and build the high speed aeroplane to the MAP's requirements were not invited to join this committee. Therefore, it will be seen that, almost from the outset, the Committee was, in effect, trying to direct the design of the aeroplane without any reference to the manufacturers - a very strange situation indeed.

In fact the committee, having initially decided that it should take just nine months from conception to completion of such an advanced project, continuously interfered in the proposed design which did nothing to speed up its progress. Indeed, considering that this project was by its very nature to be such a revolutionary aircraft, it seems quite remarkable that the 'boffins' at the Ministry should have decreed that it should be completed in nine months from the placing of the contract - a totally impracticable undertaking, even by Miles' standards.

The trouble with all 'new things' in this country is that no sooner have they nearly reached completion then someone comes along with what they consider to be a 'better idea', and interest in the original project wanes. This, I fear, is almost certainly what happened to the most promising M.52, designed to meet Specification E.24/43 for a High Speed Research Aircraft. If only Miles Aircraft had been left to get on with the design and construction of the M.52 without the Committee continuously trying to interfere in its 're-design', I consider that it would not only have been completed in a reasonable space of time at a reasonable price but it would also certainly have achieved its original purpose.

Mr A E Rowe, DTD, met with Miles at Reading on 6th November 1943, and a letter from him to CRD dated 11th November 1943 gives details of this meeting:

I gave you a brief verbal account of my meeting with Miles at Reading on 6/11/43, when we discussed his designs for the high speed aircraft with his staff, DSP, DDSR1, DD/RDA and representatives of Power Jets. The firm have evolved a very attractive layout shown in the folder immediately behind this file. You will note the very large body and the small wing. This is necessary to induct all the air required for the W.2/700 engine with after-burning behind a ducted fan. DDSR1 has asked that the question of the optimum power plant be critically examined from the standpoint of thrust, less drag, and the RAE will do this as quickly as possible. It may turn out that there is a better balance of thrust over drag with a smaller diameter engine without after-burning, and hence, with a much smaller diameter body.

You will note the implications of the high priority Miles expects when applied to a project of this sort. It affects not only materials and labour but runs over to other firms already deeply committed and to extensive wind tunnel tests at NPL and RAE, as set out in the separate sheet within the attached folder. I think the project merits very high priority, but we shall have to watch the situation very carefully to ensure that other urgent things more directly related to war activities are not prejudiced.

I think the firm has shown, by the way they have tackled the initial stages, that we could safely entrust this project to them, and I would like your agreement to the placing of the contract for two prototypes and parts for a third, and also your concurrence in the high priority Miles asks for.

On 15th November 1943, R Sorley (CRD) responded:

I agree to the placing of a contract for two prototypes and parts for a third for this experimental aircraft. Clearly Miles is keen on the job, but he must not expect super priorities which cannot be given. Each priority will require to be related to effect upon war effort, but wherever it is possible to give the work preference we must do so. You will have to weigh up each priority as it arises and decide at the time as I cannot give an over-riding ruling at this stage of the war. When this design has gone a little further I shall be interested to see how the various novel features which must be adopted are working out.

On 17th November 1943, Rowe wrote to DD/RDT Thro' DD/RDA, DDSR1 & DD/RDQ.

Please take action to place the contract as agreed by CRD in the first para of Minute 3. I should like this done as a matter of urgency. A copy of my letter to Miles informing him of the intention to place a contract is at Enclosure 4A. I also want RDT1 to report on the design with special reference to the structural problems and the estimated weight. Referring to the priorities, will DD/RDA please have a fairly early meeting with the firm and DDSR1 and others concerned, to settle the various priorities as far as is practicable at this stage, taking into account the general policy laid down in para 2 of Minute 3.

I want DDRDQ to exercise their usual function regarding the layout of the aircraft, bearing in mind that the aircraft is experimental, and hence, consulting DDSR1, DSP and RAE as representing the user interests.

On 24th November 1943, Mr H M Garner (DDSR1) wrote to DDRDT:

With reference to Min. 2 Para 2 I am discussing the net thrust of the engine unit tomorrow with RAE. Until we have a clear idea of this

I do not see how the design can be finally settled. The wind tunnel programme called for is very extensive and some of the tests (those under supersonic conditions) cannot be done with our existing equipment.

On 3rd December 1943, DD/RDQ wrote to DD/RDA:

Reference minute 4, is it your intention to call a small meeting to discuss the relative merits of the alternative proposals in the attached folders and to decide upon the most promising layout. Possibly such a meeting would be premature at this stage but I trust that you will advise me as soon as the stage is reached when RDQ can co-operate actively.

Mr H M Garner wrote on 3rd January 1944 to DTD (Thro' DSR and DDRDA):

As a result of discussions at DSR's Supersonic Committee on 14th December and with Miles Aircraft on 20th December (enc.16A), there is some change in the proposals laid down in my letter of 1st December. The committee decided that as for wings of 7½% thick or less the behaviour at low speeds was, according to wind tunnel tests, hardly affected by the shape of the section and in view of the advantage of a sharp leading edge at high speeds a wing with this feature was desirable. This brings back the importance of tests of wings on the Falcon and these are being arranged. Tests on all-moving power-operated tailplane on the Spitfire are also being arranged.

Mr J E Serby (DDRDA) responded to DTD - *Further to above. I am holding a preliminary specification meeting within 8 days.*

Mr Garner's memo of 3rd January 1944 referred to *Tests on all-moving power-operated tailplane on the Spitfire are also being arranged.* This needs to be expounded upon here as Captain Eric Brown RN has recently referred to this and ML Aviation Ltd's involvement with the design and manufacture of a 'large tailplane' in relation to its use on later marks of Rolls-Royce Griffon engined Spitfires. To clarify the situation, the work to modify a Spitfire with a power-operated all-moving tailplane was entrusted to Miles Aircraft Ltd under a Ministry contract and assistance with the rear fuselage stressing was to be provided by Joe Smith, chief designer of Supermarine's at Hursley Park, Winchester.

At the Meeting of the Supersonic Committee held on 11th January 1944 the proposal to fit a Spitfire with an all-moving tailplane for power operation tests in connection with the M.52 was referred to as follows:

DDSR1 recalled the full discussion that took place at the last meeting of the Supersonic Committee, and summarised by saying that the speed would not be greater than 600 mph TAS in level flight and the aircraft must therefore dive to obtain a speed in excess of the velocity of sound. Thus, there were the conflicting requirements of a thin wing for low drag properties, and a thicker wing for the higher CL necessary for landing. It had been agreed at the last meeting that as far as wind tunnel tests showed no serious problems should be encountered by using supersonic wings at low speeds.

A week later, at a discussion with the firm, they were worried by the high take-off and landing speeds particularly during the early flights. Finally it had been agreed to increase the wing area, thus reducing the nett wing loading to 46 lb/sq ft for the preliminary tests, which could be done with a reduced amount of fuel. The wings were now contemplated, one of nett area 130 sq ft, aspect ratio of 5, and thickness/chord ratio of 7½%, and one of nett wing area about 100 sq ft, and thickness/chord ratio of 5%. The wing loading for the final tests would be about 65 lb/sq ft. It was proposed to make both the 7½% and 5% thick wings of supersonic section, adding a fairing or blister over the leading edge for the first flights. Preliminary experiments on the 7½% thick type of wing with the blister would be made on the Falcon, which Miles already had, and DDSR1 stated that he was awaiting their proposals for

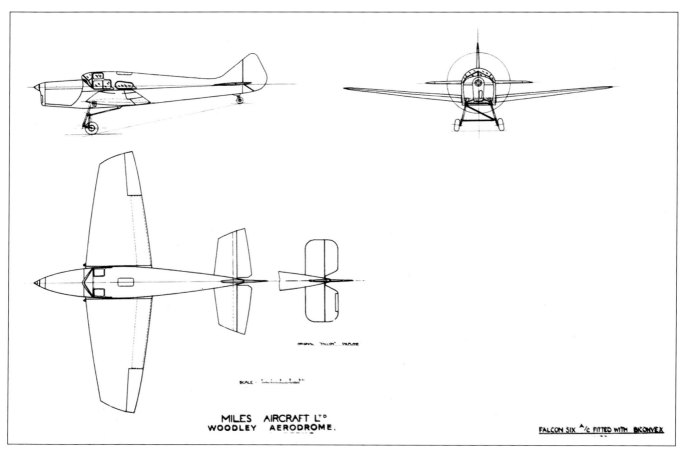

An undated three-view drawing, No.C5264004, of the Falcon Six Aircraft fitted with Biconvex wings and also showing the first two stages of tailplane, both with elevators.

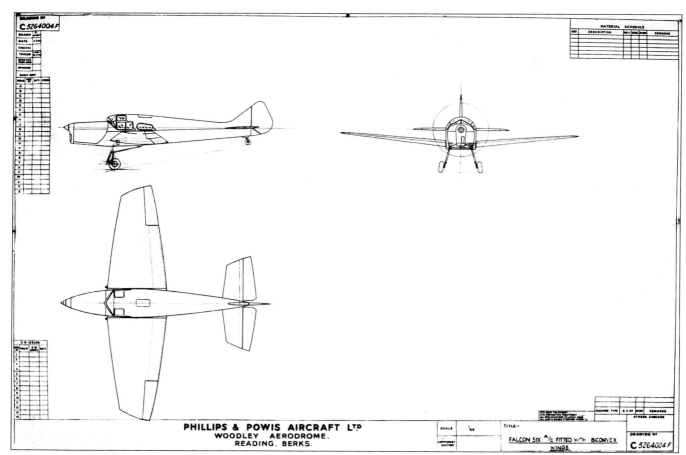

Three-view drawing, No.C5264004F, dated 4.2.44, of the Falcon Six Aircraft fitted with Biconvex wings. Note: Drawing shows Falcon with biconvex tailplane with elevators, denoting the second stage of testing, but also note that the undercarriage does not have an axle or lateral cross-bracing struts as shown on the previous drawing.

these tests. The aircraft will have a power-operated all-moving tailplane for longitudinal control, and all-moving tailplane tests are to be made on a Spitfire.

The last paragraph of a letter, dated 28th January 1944, from F G Miles to J E Serby, MAP, in connection with the cancellation orders for the M.38 Messenger, he mentioned the M.52 and the other work associated with its development as follows:

I am sorry that I have not been able to let you have a statement of the work involved in connection with the special Falcon wing and Spitfire modification associated with the E.24/43 but as I explained before, our clerical staff has been severely overloaded with the work involved in the M.38 cancellation and I have not been able to press them for the other estimate. However,........... (unfortunately, the next page is missing - PA).

Then, at the Meeting on 7th March 1944:

Spitfire with all-moving tailplane - Miles Aircraft representatives agreed to send detailed arrangements of the power-operated tailplane for the Spitfire. In view of the decision to operate the tailplane of the E.24/43 hydraulically, this method will be employed on the Spitfire. Subject to MAP agreement and the provision of an estimate of cost, a third contract would be placed. Early notification of the date when an aircraft will be required is necessary in order to allocate a Spitfire.

At the Meeting on 14th March 1944:

DDSR1 said that the specification for the aircraft had been discussed recently and was now settled in general terms. The design should not now change appreciably. The wing would be 7½% thick at the root and 4.9% at the tip, and preliminary tests would be made with a plaster on the wing to ensure safety in the early trials. Both types of wing were to be tested on the Falcon, the difficulty being that the Falcon wing would be 5.5% thick at the tip instead of 4.9% thick. The Chairman remarked that he had spoken to Mr Miles recently and had been impressed by the firm's enthusiasm, and felt that they were making extremely good progress (another significant observation - PA).

At the Meeting held on 11th April 1944:

DDSR1 reported that a discussion on radio equipment had been held at which it had been decided that the pilot must have some means of returning to base. The design work at Miles was proceeding quickly. DSP stated that in a matter of only a few months, work was required on the engine (W.2/700 with No.4 Augmenter) and if the aircraft was not built very quickly, other aircraft would be built which would compete in speed with the E.24/43 (*see note below). Very high speeds had been reached in level flight already on aircraft fitted with engines capable of 2,300 lb thrust. It was pointed out that the engine in the E.24/43 should be capable of 4,000 lb thrust at 500 mph at 3,000 ft; and would have a relatively big margin of speed over other types, Mr Smelt pointed out that an additional 50 mph was extremely difficult to obtain, and extremely important in the range from 500 - 600 mph.

*Note: When such an advanced aircraft as the Miles M.52 is being built 'by committee' and the manufacturer of that aircraft was not even invited to sit on that aforementioned committee, I think that this was indeed a most foolish and ill-informed statement to have made by such a body. The M.52 was the only aircraft being constructed to explore the supersonic region and no other British manufacturer could have possibly taken on such a challenging project at that time as they were all engaged in mass production of existing types - or for some considerable time afterwards as it turned out - PA).

The Meeting on 27th July 1944 considered the Power-Operated Controls:

DDSR1 explained that it was hoped to test on a Whitley a power system capable of operating the tailplane of the E.24/43. This test would admittedly not represent the complete conditions but as it

would be applied to the rudder it would be a safe test and would provide information on air functioning. The firm did not agree and explained that they had examined the Lockheed system and found it unsatisfactory in some respects. They had developed a unit of their own and asked that they be allowed to continue work on it with a view to installation in a Spitfire for the movable tailplane investigation. DDSR1 agreed to this subject to RAE agreement that the design was promising. After discussion it was agreed that it was desirable that first flight tests be made on the E.24/43 with a normal tailplane and elevator. At a later stage this would be made adjustable with power operation of its incidence before the final tailplane of supersonic section without elevator was fitted.

Contract action was required on the following:-
    Half wing and tailplane for firms strength tests (para.3)
    Special wind tunnel models.
    Special wing for Falcon and flight tests.
    Moveable tailplane for Spitfire and flight tests.

For the record, the Meeting on 12th December 1944 further referred to the Spitfire:

Mr Vessey stated that the work on the Falcon with bi-convex wings was proceeding rapidly and that the aircraft was now fitted with bi-convex wings and tailplane. Flight tests had been made successfully and it had been found necessary to reduce the tailplane incidence, (for details of Falcon tests see Appendix 33 - PA). It was now proposed to fit an all-moving bi-convex tail to the Falcon, and to dispense with the proposed tests on a power-operated bi-convex* tailplane for the Spitfire. The power-operation would now be cleared elsewhere, and the tests on the all-moving tail made only on the Falcon.

* (This statement must have been made in error, as it was never intended to fit the Spitfire with a bi-convex tailplane, as to do so would have been pointless. The sole purpose of fitting an all-moving tailplane to a Spitfire was to test the power-operation - PA). This then, was the end of the proposed tests of a power operated all-moving tailplane on a Spitfire.

However, to return to the commitment to meet the requirement for the high-speed research aircraft, which was to break into hitherto unknown territory, the M.52 had to meet some completely new challenges. Unfortunately, it was these same challenges which were ultimately, according to the Ministry of Supply and Aircraft Production (and others not even associated with the said Ministry, or Miles Aircraft Ltd), to lead to its later undoing.

For the record, the M.52 Contract was No. SB.27157/C 23c, Requisition No.4352/D/RDT1, 'to design and construct an aircraft to Spec. E.24/43, covering the supply of prototype aircraft to Specification E.24/43 and additional bare airframes etc'. It was placed with Miles Aircraft on 13th December 1943 'as a matter of urgency', although it was actually dated 29th December 1943 and was for the supply of three prototypes.

The preliminary brief specification for the E.24/43 was dated 1.3.44 but as Dennis Bancroft recalled in March 2004:

I well remember a visit I made - almost exactly 60 years ago to the day - with F G Miles to a Ministry of Aircraft Production meeting in London on 7.3.44, to discuss and modify where necessary this draft specification paragraph by paragraph. About 20 of us sat round a table for a very long afternoon's discussion. That draft specification of 1.3.44 was thus only applicable for seven days. Almost every paragraph was discussed, and most altered. For example, paragraph 2.08 of the Minutes of the Meeting of 7.3.44 refers to the requirement for a 1,500-watt generator, and the fact that as this could not be provided on the engine, the maximum 500-watt generator was acceptable. This 1,500-watt requirement gives the possible date for the spec. reproduced later.

It is difficult to state briefly a true fact, as so much misleading data has been circulated. Take for example just the thrust and drag of the M.52 at 1,000 mph at 36,000 ft. By the spring of 1944 this thrust at 1,000 mph had been given by Power Jets as 4,100 lb. with a 3.28 sq ft nozzle and a maximum temperature of 1,500° C at 16,750 rpm. But in the RAE Report Aero 1470 of July 1944, they had used a thrust of 4,000 lb. The same report gave their estimate of the drag of the M.52 as 7,750 lb. at 1,000 mph, compared to Miles' drag estimate of 5,620 lb. - i.e. 38% more.

It should be noted that Professor Brian Brinkworth comments on the above thus:

Incidentally, in 1948 the one and only successful launch of Barnes Wallis' rocket propelled model of the M.52 (of which more later - PA) gave an actual, measured, supersonic drag as 14.6% LESS than the Miles estimate for the M.52, showing that the correct M.52 drag at 1,000 mph at 36,000 ft. would have been 4,800 lb. This measured figure of drag means that the RAE estimate of 7,750 lb. was 2,950 lb or 61.5% more than the correct drag.

Therefore, it was not until 26th August 1944 that the full Specification 24/43, dated 14th August 1944 [File No.SB.54720/RDT2(d)], incorporating the actual work already done by Miles since October 1943, was issued to Miles Aircraft Ltd. Although the official specification had not been drawn up until long after work had commenced, it was very gratifying to recently discover in the National Archives, a copy of the very first schematic 3-view GA Drawing, titled: 'Miles E.24-43 [M.52] with Large Wing constant T/C 7½%'. It was drawn by W B Barnes and dated 7.1.44. At that time, Mr Barnes was the only draughtsman engaged on the project.

Considering that the design team had only been engaged on the project for a couple of months, the drawing shows the initial scheme of the M.52 to be remarkably close to the final configuration, with the exception of the following features:

- straight leading and trailing edges to the wing
- leading edge of wing longer than trailing edge
- nose cone shape *(Note: later shape pencilled in)*
- un-swept tailplane

The tables of data shown on the drawing are reproduced in the following table:

Component	lbs	ft	Moment
Power Plant complete	1,770	13.55	24,000
Equipment	340	6.30	2,315
Wing	650	14.25	9,260
Fuselage	750	15.25	11,420
Empennage	150	26.00	3,900
Chassis	150	15.20	2,300
Nose wheel	80	8.00	640
Controls	120	151.50	1,818
Cabin & Structure	280	6.00	1,680
Pilot & Parachute	200	5.80	1,160
Fuel	2,000	13.35	26,700
Oil	10	10.70	107
Max AUW	6,500	13.10	85,300
28% SMC			
Normal take-off			
AUW 150 gals	5,700	13.08	74,610
AUW Fuel Gone	4,500	13.00	58,600
Normal take-off			
AUW less Auy?	5,260	13.05	68,670

(Note: The abbreviation 'Auy' was probably a miss-spell for Augmenter).

Particulars:

Wing

Area Gross	139 sq ft
Area Net	106 sq ft
Span	26.5 ft
Aspect Ratio	5.05
Dihedral	5°
T/C	7½%
Sweepback	Nil 50% chord
Incidence	2°
Root chord	80"
Tip. 12' 5½" from C/L	42"
Section	Biconvex

Fuselage

Max diameter	5.00 ft
Length c/w cabin	28.25 ft

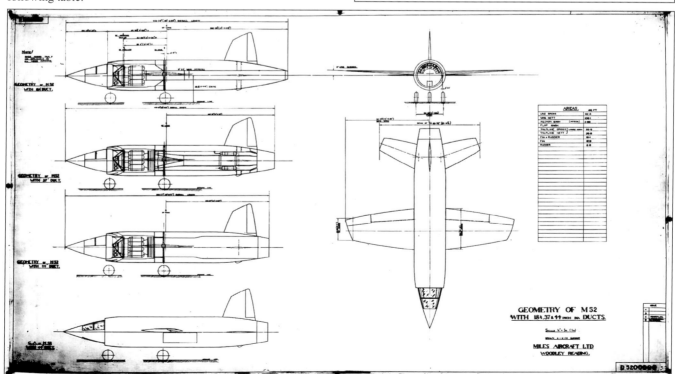

Geometry of M.52 with 18½, 37 and 44 inch diameter Ducts. Drawn 6.9.44 by B Knight.

Tail-Plane		
Area Gross	42.50 sq ft	
Area Net	28.40 sq ft	
Span	12.75 ft	
Rudder - Area	6.00 sq ft	
Fin – Area	18.00 sq ft	
Outside duct dia	50.70"	52.00"
Area	13.90 sq ft	14.70 sq ft
Inside duct area	46.00"	28.00"
Area	11.50 sq ft	4.80 sq ft
Duct area open	9.90 sq ft	
Duct area closed	2.40 sq ft	

Details of the design and construction of the M.52 were given in a MAP Scientific War Records Report, entitled Development of Supersonic Aircraft, written by Lionel Charles 'Toby' Heal, M.52 Project Engineer and dated 21st September 1945. The full report may be seen in Appendix 32, together with its constructional details. Extracts from the report have been used in the Specification and Performance Data at the end of this chapter.

Returning to the various letters being written in 1944, it will be seen that the RAE were not entirely blameless in the events which, ultimately, were to lead to the cancellation of the M.52:

On 2nd August 1944, Mr J E Serby (DD/RDA) wrote to DDSR1.

If Tech Note Aero 1470 is correct then more importance attaches than before to the conventional wings. We were previously thinking of making these by building fairings on to the biconvex wings, but they should now be built as proper wings to the conventional profile as it may be that we shall do most of our work with them. You may have plans in hand for this.

On 4th August 1944, Mr H M Garner (DDSR1) responds:

We had a long discussion on this at our meeting on 28th July and decided to go ahead with the supersonic wings but to have wings with rounded leading edges as a second string. Miles and RAE are to discuss the latter and I am not sure whether they will be modified supersonic wings or conventional. I am not sure what weight should be attached to Aero 1470 in view of the low Reynolds number.

At the 23rd Meeting of the Supersonic Committee held on 10th April 1945, it was stated in relation to the Miles E.24/43:

DDSR1 reported that no reply had yet been received from the firm on the draughtsmen and labour positions. The Chairman asked that this be urged.

The Meeting went on to consider the Miles E.24/43 Replacement:

After some discussion it was agreed that both the jet-propelled and rocket-propelled aircraft should be proceeded with, and the discussion that followed dealt with the rocket propelled version. The Chairman was of the opinion that the proposed rocket aircraft should be piloted, but Mr McKinnon Wood considered that the aircraft should be radio-controlled for safety considerations. Mr Smelt pointed out that it was impossible to investigate the control characteristics without a pilot, and this was necessary in the transition period near Mach=1.0. If an automatic pilot was used the problem would be complicated by stability.

Mr Smelt suggested that scale models be used for investigation of the transition period as far as was possible, with a full scale aircraft with a pilot to be flown later. The Committee agreed that this was a good suggestion, and DDSR1 called attention to the lack of design facilities in the country. The Chairman understood that the Martin Baker Company had no work at the moment and asked that this be investigated. In addition Mr B N Wallis of Vickers-

Armstrong could probably be of assistance in the design of the models. The Chairman stated that he would approach Mr Wallis.

It is of interest to note that the question of models to run concurrent with full scale aircraft flight testing was mooted so early in the programme, albeit for the 'E.24/43 Replacement aircraft' and that it was Mr Lockspeiser, a friend of Barnes Wallis, who suggested that Mr Wallis 'could probably be of assistance in the design of the models'.

A small Secret memorandum, probably to the RAE, dated 23rd April 1945 and written by Ben Lockspeiser regarding 'Rocket Development for Aircraft Propulsion' also makes for interesting reading:

Minute of my Supersonic Committee Meeting held on 10/4/45 will reach you shortly. It is now proposed to build a rocket-propelled aircraft, and a scale model of it for preliminary pilotless tests, to investigate flight at supersonic speeds. We shall probably be asking you to develop the required rocket motors but at the present time it is impossible to lay down a specification of requirements. This is therefore intended only as advanced information.

Unfortunately, it has not been possible to find a copy of the official specification for the E.24/43, nor the Power Jets W.2/700 engine, and the original six-line specification given to F G Miles on 9th October 1943 is all that appears to remain. The date at which the two specifications were initially issued is important to this narrative as, from 1943 to 1946, both the aircraft and engine were being continually updated. The engine thrusts expected were also increasing very materially owing to continuing improvements as new materials became available and other design improvements were incorporated.

The following specification details are reproduced from Air-Britain's '*The British Aircraft Specifications File*' by K J Meekcoms and E B Morgan and it should be noted that this data probably relates to that prevailing at the Spring of 1944, and NOT the aircraft and engine as finally produced:

Specification E.24/43 High Speed Single-Engine Experimental Aircraft

Design and construction of a high speed single-engine, single-seat, jet propelled aircraft, suitable for high speed research work and having no military role. Power plant: W.2/700 engine with No.4 design thrust augmenter (as being designed by Power Jets Ltd). The following thrusts may be used:-

a)   With a by-pass exhaust nozzle area of 3.28 sq.ft.
Static take-off thrust =
        3,200 lb (dropping to 2,650 lb at 175 mph).

At an altitude of 36,000 ft the following thrusts may be assumed:-
    1,000 mph (TAS) thrust =
        4,100 lb. 900 mph (TAS) thrust = 3,450 lb.
    800 mph (TAS) thrust =
        2,830 lb. 700 mph (TAS) thrust = 2,300 lb.
    600 mph (TAS) thrust =
        1,900 lb. 500 mph (TAS) thrust = 1,620 lb.

The rpm of the basic engine is 16,750 and the maximum temperature 1,500° C

b)   With a by-pass exhaust nozzle area of 3.9 sq.ft.
Static take-off thrust =
        3,300 lb (dropping to 2,800 lb at 150/175 mph).

At an altitude of 36,000 ft the following thrusts may be assumed:-

700 mph (TAS) thrust =
        2,700 lb. 600 mph (TAS) thrust = 2,200 lb.
500 mph (TAS) thrust =
        1,850 lb. 400 mph (TAS) thrust = 1,580 lb.
300 mph (TAS) thrust = 1,400 lb.

It shall be possible to remove the prime mover, augmenter and jet pipe from the aircraft when it is in the vertical position; suitable strong points for slinging purposes shall be fitted to the fuselage. Provision shall be made for determining the thrust in flight. A 1,500 watt, HX type electrical generator shall be fitted. The pilot's compartment shall be situated in the nose of the aircraft and provision shall be made for escape of the pilot at high speeds in an emergency. The compartment shall be pressurised with H1 = 60,000 ft, H2 = 25,000 ft and p = 2.5 lb. Oxygen shall be provided.

The mainplanes shall have a gross wing area of 143 sq ft, a thickness/chord ratio of 7.5% at root dropping to 4.09 at tip. The first mainplane shall be bi-convex, of constant curvature with a single centrally placed spar. Split flaps shall be provided *(see below – PA)*. The tailplane thickness shall be 6% at root and it shall be of bi-convex section having a constant radius of curvature giving a thickness at the tip of 4.28%. It shall be all moving and controllable by the pilot through a hydraulic power operated system.

Fixed tankage for 200 gallons of fuel shall be provided, with provision for 120 gallon drop tank. The whole structure shall have an ultimate factor of safety of at least 1.5 under normal accelerations. Radio: TR.1464.

Serial numbers RT133 and RT136 were allotted to two 'high speed single engine experimental aircraft' under Contract No. SB.27157/C.23(c) dated 15.12.43 *(although the correct date the contract was placed was, in fact, the 29.12.43 - PA).*

Regarding the statement that 'Split flaps shall be provided', Dennis Bancroft points out that:

Actually, it was considered essential to test the bi-convex wing in practical flight as soon as possible, as the initial jet engine power and potentially high drag expected made it very important to see, as early as possible, if the supersonically-desirable bi-convex section was practicable in real flight conditions. A wing as near as possible to our M.52 wing was therefore designed and made for the Falcon. The Falcon and similar aircraft had split flaps at that time, and so split flaps were used in the interest of speed and convenience in the use of an existing aircraft. The detailed design of the actual M.52 wing was, of course, not seriously started until the initial flight tests on the Falcon had been made.

When then considering the flaps, it was soon obvious that a simple split flap was just not suitable. Calculations showed that the best climbing speed was an amazing 600 mph, and to make a split flap strong enough would be exceedingly difficult. A normal, but usually more complicated, PLAIN flap would be easier to make and lighter, as well as being much better from an aerodynamic point of view. On slow, low wing loaded machines, the high lift and drag of a split flap enabled a desirable, steep approach to landing and, once having touched down, did not "float" off again. For a fast, very high wing loaded aircraft with a relatively poor lift/drag ratio, the opposite was true, and a high lift flap with the minimum drag was desired. Therefore, a plain flap was chosen for the M.52 at an early stage.

However, the statement that 'Split flaps shall be provided' was to lead to much misinformation being published later.

Meanwhile the construction of an extremely accurate, full scale, wooden mock-up of the M.52 was progressing rapidly as the following photographs, dated 26th August 1944, show:

Rear fuselage with biconvex all-moving tailplane.

Above: Nose wheel in retracted position.

Above: Cabin and forward fuselage.

Above: A wooden mock-up of the Power Jets W.2/700 engine.

Above: A selection of components.

Above: The M.3/52 Falcon Six with bi-convex wings and standard Falcon tailplane. Note unidentified structure on narrow-track undercarriage cross bracing struts.

Above: Front view of the 'Gillette' Falcon showing the narrow-track undercarriage positioned on the fuselage to be clear of the bi-convex wings.

Above: The fuselage jig with a circular frame in position.

Above: Photograph showing the port side of the partially completed mock-up of the M.52 fuselage, September 1944. Note the cut-outs for the variable intake for the supersonic version; the small circular hole in the mid fuselage frame for the wing attachment spigot and the mock-up engine, with jet-pipe, installed.

In August 1944 the Supersonic Committee's membership was, on average, 19 members (from 15 different Ministry departments/private companies), together with a further 11 new members, from the NPL, Vickers-Armstrong and various Ministry departments, who joined later. However, no representatives from Miles Aircraft Ltd were ever invited to join the committee at any time.

The first flight of the M.3/52 Falcon Six. L9705, with the bi-convex wings (but with straight leading and trailing edges to the wings), or the 'Gillette' Falcon as it soon became known at Woodley, was a 10 min 'Local', made by Flt Lt Hugh Kennedy on 11th August 1944.

At the 16th Meeting of The Supersonic Committee, on 12th September 1944, DDSR1 stated that the Falcon with the bi-convex wings had now flown successfully. No stalling speed had yet been measured but it was believed that this would be lower than had been expected. The large drag increase with incidence was evident in the take-off, as if the stick was eased back the aircraft sank back on to the ground. A point of interest was that the lateral control was stated to be exceptionally good.

Further photographs of the M.52 mock-up and jigs, dated 29th September 1944, are shown top right.

Further photographs of the M.52 mock-up and jigs, dated 11th November 1944, are shown below.

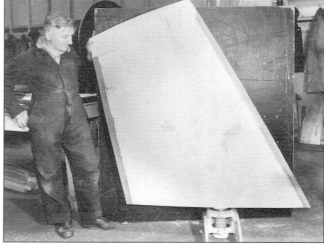

Above: A mock-up tailplane with spigot shown assembled in the tailplane mounting bracket.

Above: The M.52 fuselage mock-up showing the circular attachment hole for the wing mounted spigot (above worker's right arm).

Above: The fin and rudder.

Further photographs of the M.52 mock-up and components, dated 17th November 1944, show:

Above and below: Two views of the rear fuselage showing the tailplane and operating linkage in different positions.

Above: Front view of engine installation with lower half of intake and capsule attachment bolts visible.

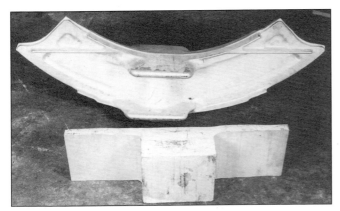

Above and below: Two views of the wing attachment forgings.

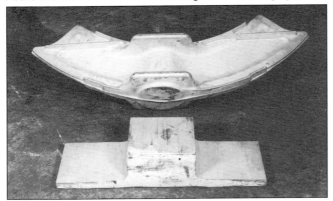

A fuselage frame being rolled to shape.   [Via Bert Clarke]

Above: A fuselage frame jig being checked for concentricity.

On 21st November 1944, Hugh Kennedy made a 25 min 'Local' flight, which was probably its first flight with the bi-convex tailplane (with elevators) and this was made from Farnborough. Then, on 21st February 1945, a 10 min 'Test' flight was made by Hugh Kennedy, and this was possibly its first flight (from Woodley?) with the bi-convex all-moving tailplane (Note; this was confirmed at the 22nd Meeting of The Supersonic Committee on 13th March 1945, where it was stated that; *the Falcon with the all-moving tailplane had been flown successfully*).

As mentioned previously, the Supersonic Committee eventually decided not to proceed with the fitment of a hydraulically

A view of the M.3/52 'Gillette' Falcon in its final form, clearly showing the knife-edge wing section and the equally knife edged all-moving bi-convex tailplane.

A close up view of the biconvex wing showing the sharp leading and trailing edges to the bi-convex wing.

Above: Another view of the M.3/52 in its final form.   [GS Collection]

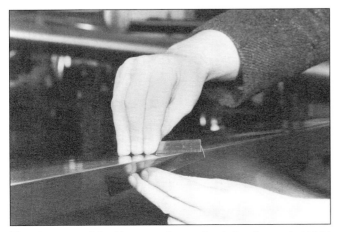

The sharpness of the biconvex wing section being demonstrated on the 'Gillette' Falcon being with the aid of two steel rules.

controlled, all-moving tailplane on a Spitfire and the requirement was duly cancelled, following its success on the Miles 'Gillette' Falcon. On 12th December 1944, although nothing was minuted in subsequent meetings, Miles received Contracts Aircraft/5123/ CB.9(a) 'Research Work on Power Operation of Flying Controls' and, presumably some time in 1945, Aircraft/5498/ CB.9(a) 'Flight Tests on Power Operated Control Systems on Master Aircraft'.

For the record, the M.19 Master GT Mk.II, DL429 was allotted to Miles Aircraft Ltd Woodley for fitment of booster jacks to rudder and elevator on 2nd October 1945 and it arrived at Woodley on 12th October 1945, from General Aircraft at Hanworth, where it had been used for glider towing trials. The first, and only recorded 'Test' flight of this modified Master, was made by Hugh Kendall on 16th March 1946, the month of the cancellation of the M.52 (about which much more later). No details of the tests have come to light, but these were almost certainly made in connection with the M.52 programme. Fred Lynn visited Woodley on 14th June 1946 and saw a Miles M.19 Master GT Mk.II, carrying no serial but he noted that it was 'fitted with hydraulic controls' and this aircraft was subsequently found to be DL429

An Internal Memo, dated 2nd July 1945, was written by Mr H S Wilkinson (Chief Stressman), to Don Brown, obviously in preparation for the Investigation at Miles Aircraft Ltd by the Industrial Advisory Panel on 4th and 5th July 1945, and this gives details appertaining to the M.52 - Design Delays and Design History, which is very relevant to this part of the story. Nothing was known about this document until May 2012, just before the completion of this volume, when an anonymous donor deposited a packet of Phillips & Powis/Miles Aircraft correspondence and documents with The Museum of Berkshire Aviation, Woodley. This memo is therefore reproduced in full here:

I am attaching hereto a short summary of the technical points which have caused us some delay in the completion of this project. Obviously they do not include all the changes that have been made, since we have made quite a number ourselves, and we have made some at RAE and MAP's suggestions, though they have not caused us any undue delay. The ones shown on the attached you will agree are fundamental in the design of the aircraft, particularly the overall value of the pitching moment coefficient, which you will see has been a point of contention for nineteen months.

Note that had the final value given to us on the 2nd July 1945 been of the order of -.02, as was suggested some time ago, this would have involved complete redesign of the tailplane and fuselage, with the consequent delay in the completion of the aircraft.

The overall stability of the aircraft is still a matter of conjecture and as you know we have recently been asked to increase the size of the tailplane to provide a greater measure of stability in the supersonic threshold region. I feel we are justified in complaining about this change, since RAE first promised to investigate the stability on the 12th November 1943.

The Labour position has always been acute, both in the Drawing Office and Stress Office, and I presume Mr Heal has supplied you with all the relevant information.

I am attaching, however, some correspondence between Mr Capley and the Ministry and I would draw your attention to the telephone message from Mr Vessey in January of this year, in which he says "the position was cleared up".

M.52 - DESIGN

1)   Project was started on 9th October 1943.

2)   First Design Meeting held at Woodley in November 1943 - DTD in the Chair - No minutes available.

3)   Meeting at RAE on <u>12th November 1943</u> with Dr G P Douglas in the chair. The following action was promised by RAE:

a)   <u>Size and Aspect Ratio of Tailplane:</u> This was settled by Miles in absence of any other information and RAE have requested increase in area on 18th June 1945.

b)   <u>Size of Fin & Rudder & Stability:</u> Stability tests in May 1944 indicated 15% reduction in Fin area and restriction of C.G.to 26%, and increase of Fin and Rudder arm of 12". This involved moving engine, cabin and front fuselage forward (13½") and repositioning wing - virtually redesign of aircraft.

June 1945 - New tunnel tests indicate increase in tailplane area (12%) and restriction of C.G. to 23% for initial flights. This condition is impossible to achieve with final version of aircraft.

4)   Meeting held at RAE on 10th February 1944 - W G Perring in the Chair. The following action was promised:

a)   Wind tunnel tests to assess Pitching Moments: Spec originally called for $C_{mo} = 0$.
From L.S. tunnel results - Altered on 16th May 1944, to $C_{mo} = -.022$.

This was attributed to wing angle of 2° which was reduced to ½° and C_{mo} taken as -.005 (Spec altered 14th August 1944).

H.S. tunnel tests on 5th May 1945 on this body (½° wing angle) and flow gave $C_{mo} = -.023$. This obviously conflicts with previous ideas and on 15th June 1945 $C_{mo} = -.015$ was given by RAE (Re-plot of results).

On 2nd July 1945, Preliminary L.S. results from RAE give $C_{mo} = -.003$.

What is the value???

We are working to Spec $C_{mo} = -.005$. These changes have involved considerable time for investigation.

b)   <u>Data on Dive Recovery Flaps:</u> Still awaiting results. Mr Relf, NPL, further promised 18th June 1945 to investigate this.

c)   <u>Spitfire to be dived with feathered propeller to see if this affects change of rudder hinge moment.</u>

No information to date.

Sgd HS Wilkinson

The actual 1/6.154 scale model with the author (seen under the port wing!) in 1990, on the occasion of my first talk on the Miles M.52 that I gave to the Royal Berkshire Aviation Society at Woodley. Note; the model now has flaps and the tailplane fairing has been deleted, being replaced with a moveable addition to the tailplane root.

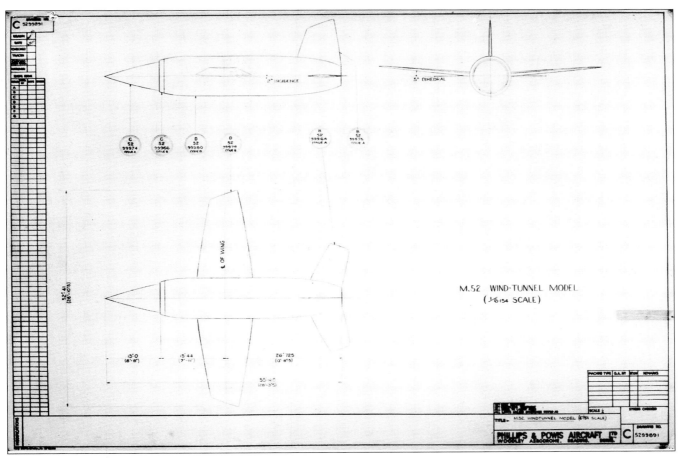

M.52 WIND-TUNNEL MODEL
(1/6.154 SCALE)

Above: Three-view G.A. drawing, dated 3.9.44, of the M.52 Wind Tunnel Model (1/6.154 scale). Note, no ailerons or flaps shown.

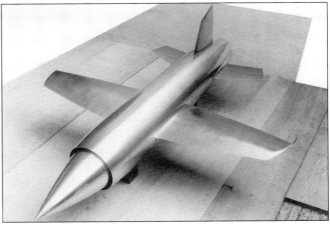

Above and right: Two views of the 1/6.154 scale metal wind tunnel model. Note the all-moving, variable incidence tailplane and the fairing between the tailplane and rear fuselage, later deleted. This model is all that survives of the M.52 project and it is now on display in The Museum of Berkshire Aviation, Woodley. Note the model has no ailerons.

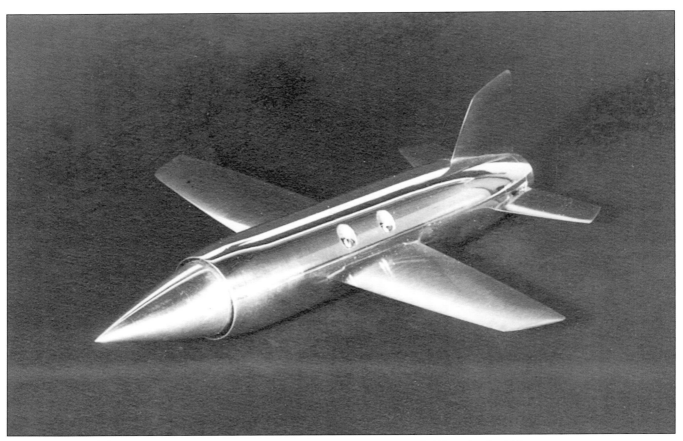

Above: The 9 inch wingspan wind tunnel model of the M.52 tested in the Supersonic Wind Tunnel at the NPL.

Below: The 9 inch model in the Supersonic Wind Tunnel at the NPL.

Above: The M.52 nose cone in the Miles Wind Tunnel at Davis Farm, Woodley 1945.   *[Via Jim Pratt]*

A colour photograph of the completed M.52 mock-up, taken on 27th November 1945 by Matthew Nathan of Power Jets Ltd, confirms that the mock-up only had a starboard wing, with the port side being up against the wall. This photograph, together with a montage of colour photographs, entitled 'Supersonic Flight - Power Jets Ltd and the Miles M.52', also by Matthew Nathan, appears with the other colour photographs at the end of this book.

The story of the M.52 will conclude in the next volume.

SPECIFICATION AND PERFORMANCE DATA

Engine:	1st Flights - With 18½" Duct Prime Mover Only: Power Jets W.2/700 - 2,000lb basic static thrust Final Flights - With 37" Duct Prime Mover Augmentation & After Burning: Power Jets W.2/700 with No.4 Augmenter and afterburning, which was expected to increase the thrust to 5,000lb at 1,000 mph at 36,000ft
Dimensions:	The dimensions shown below were taken from an undated Miles Aircraft Ltd three-view general arrangement drawing (possibly that by Barnes which was drawn in September 1944 - PA). A report prepared by Miles Aircraft Ltd for 'MAP Scientific War Records', gave slightly different dimensions and these are shown in brackets where they differ (see Appendix 32): span 26' 10.5"; mean chord 5.26; aspect ratio 5.09; root chord 6' 8"; tip chord 3' 7"; root section 7½% Biconvex, tip section 4.02% Biconvex, both constant radius; gross wing area 141.4 sq ft, net wing area 108.1 sq ft; overall fuselage length 1st Flights 35' 6.59" (35ft 7.22in), overall fuselage length Final Flights 33' 6.22"; max diameter 5ft; u/c track 4' 6.16"; thickness ratio 0.140; wetted area 443 sq ft
Weight	wing 1,162lb; fuselage 1,134lb; tail unit 426lb; undercarriage 455lb; controls 150lb; analysis: fuel tank 175lb; power-plant 1,940lb; fuel (200 gal) 1,600lb; pilot 200lb; equipment 468lb; AUW 7,710lb; wing loading 52 lb/sq ft
Performance:	max speed without augmenter 585 mph at 30,000ft; max speed with augmenter 705 mph at sea level; max speed at 36,000ft after dive from 50,000ft, 1,000 mph; best climbing speed 600 mph; distance to 50ft - 4,560ft.

Abbreviations

AACU	Anti-aircraft Co-operation Unit		CinC	Commander-in-Chief
A&AEE	Aeroplane & Armament Experimental Establishment		Cld	Cancelled
			CLN	Clifton L Nash (Phillips & Powis keeper of aircraft production records)
AAPC	Anti-aircraft Practice Camp			
AAS	Air Armament School		c/n	Constructor's Number
AASF	Advanced Air Striking Force		CO	Commanding Officer
ACM	Air Chief Marshal		Col	Colonel (army)
ACRS	Air Crew Refresher School		CofA	Certificate of Airworthiness
ADGB	Air Defence of Great Britain		Comm	Communications
AFDU	Air Fighting Development Unit		CofR	Certificate of Registration (registration number/date)
AFDU	Air Fighting Development Unit			
AFE	Airborne Forces Establishment		CRD	Controller of Research and Development (MAP)
AFEE	Airborne Forces Experimental Establishment		CRO	Civilian Repair Organisation
AFS	Advanced Flying School		CRU	Civilian Repair Unit
AFTDU	Advanced Forces Tactical Development Unit		CS(A)	Controller of Supplies (Air)
AFTS	Advanced Flying Training School (ATA)			
AGBS	Air Gunnery & Bombing School		DARD	Director Armament Research and Development
AGS	Air Gunners School		DBF	Destroyed by fire
AID	Aeronautical Inspection Directorate		DBR	Damaged beyond repair
ALG	Advanced Landing Ground		DD	Deputy Director (of a Directorate)
AM	Air Ministry		Deld	Delivered
AMDP	Air Member for Development & Production		Dely	Delivery
AMO	Air Ministry Order		Dett	Detachment
ANS	Air Navigation School		DBF	Destroyed by fire
AOC	Air Officer Commanding		DBR	Damaged beyond repair
AOC in C	Air Officer Commander in Chief		DFC	Distinguisehed Flying Cross
AONS	Air Observers Navigator School		DFLS	Day Fighter Leaders School
AOP	Air Observation Post		DDOR	Deputy Director Operational Requirements
AOS	Air Observers School		DGRD	Director General of Research & Development
APC	Armament Practice Camp		DGSR	Director General of Scientific Research
APS	Armament Practise Station		DH	de Havilland
ARDE	Armament Research and Development Establishment		DTD	Director of Technical Development (Air Ministry)
ARU	Aircraft Repair Unit		EAAS	Empire Air Armament School
ASR	Air Sea Rescue		EANS	Empire Air Navigation School
AS&RU	Aircraft Salvage & Repair Unit		ECFS	Empire Central Flying School
AST	Air Service Training		EFTS	Elementary Flying Training School
ASU	Aircraft Storage Unit		ERFTS	Elementary & Reserve Flying Training School
ATA	Air Transport Auxiliary		ERS	Empire Radio School
ATC	Armament Training Camp		E&WS	Electrical & Wireless School
ATC	Air Training Corps		ETPS	Empire Test Pilot School
ATDU	Air Transport Development Unit			
ATDU	Air Torpedo Development Unit		FA	Flying accident
ATS	Armament Training Station		FAA	Fleet Air Arm
AVM	Air Vice Marshal		FATU	Fighter Affiliation Training Unit
AUW	All-up Weight		F-BFTS	Franco-Belgian Flying Training School
			FC	Fighter Command
BADU	Blind (later Beam) Approach Development Unit		FIS	Flying Instructors School
BAFO	British Air Forces of Occupation		FIU	Fighter Interception Unit
BBOC	Brought back on charge		Flt	Flight
BC	Bomber Command		F/Lt	Flight Lieutenant
BCBS	Bomber Command Bombing School		F/M	Field Marshal (army)
B&GS	Bombing & Gunnery School		F/O	Flying Officer
BER	Beyond Economical Repair		FP	Ferry Pool
BLEU	Blind Landing Experimental Unit		FPP	Ferry Pilot Pool
BOS	Board of Survey (SAAF)		FRU	Fleet Requirements Unit
BU	Broken up		FTC	Flying Training Command
			FTS	Flying Training School
CA	Controller, Aircraft (Air Ministry)		FU	Ferry Unit
C&M	Care & Maintenance			
Capt	Captain		GA	Ground accident
Cat	Category of accident damage (see below)		Gen	General (army)
CCDU	Coastal Command Development Unit		GEU	Glider Exercise Unit
Cdr	Commander (RN)		GI	Ground Instruction
CF	Communications Flight		Grp	Group
CFE	Central Fighter Establishment		G/Capt	Group Captain
CFI	Chief Flying Instructor		GPEU	Glider Pilot Exercise Unit
CFS	Central Flying School		GSU	Group Support Unit
c.g.	Centre of Gravity		GTS	Glider Training School

HCU	Heavy Conversion Unit
HGCU	Heavy Glider Conversion Unit
HQBC	Headquarters Bomber Command
IFTS	Initial Flying Training School (ATA)
ITP	Instruction to Proceed
Lt Cdr	Lieutenant Commander (RN)
Lt	Lieutenant (RN)
Lt Col	Lieutenant Colonel (army)
MAAF	Mediterranean Allied Air Force
Maj	Major (army)
MAP	Ministry of Aircraft Production
ME	Middle East
MEAF	Middle East Air Force
MED/ME	Mediterranean and Middle East Air Force
MI	Major inspection
Mk	Mark
MoS	Ministry of Supply
MR	Major repair
MU	Maintenance Unit
NAFDU	Naval Air Fighting Development Unit
NAFS	Naval Air Fighter School
NFD	No further data
NFT	No further trace
NTU	Not taken up
(O)AFU	(Observers) Advanced Flying Unit
OADF/U	Overseas Aircraft Despatch Flight/Unit
OCU	Operational Conversion Unit
OR	Operational Requirement
OTU	Operational Training Unit
PA	Peter Amos (Author)
(P)AFU	(Pilots) Advanced Flying Unit
PAS/U	Pilotless Aircraft Section/Unit
PFTS	Polish Flying Training School
P/O	Pilot Officer
P&P	Phillips & Powis
PRU	Photographic Reconnaissance Unit
RAAF	Royal Australian Air Force
RAE	Royal Aircraft Establishment
RAFC	Royal Air Force College
RCAF	Royal Canadian Air Force
Regd	Registered
Regn	Registration
R&D	Research & Development
RIW	Repair in works
RN	Royal Navy
RNAS	Royal Naval Air Station
RNDA	Royal Navy Deposit Account
RNR	Royal Naval Reserve
RNVR	Royal Naval Volunteer Reserve
RNZAF	Royal New Zealand Air Force
ROS	Repair on site
RP	Rocket projectile
RRE	Radar Research Establishment
RS	Radio School
R&SU	Repair & Salvage Unit
RTO	Resident Technical Officer
RTP	Reduce to produce
RTS	Reduced to spares
RU	Repair Unit
S&H	Short Bros & Harland
SofAC	School of Army Co-operation

SAAF	South African Air Force
SAS	Servicing Aircraft Section
Scr	Scrap
SFP	Service Ferry Pool
(S)FPP	(Service) Ferry Pilots Pool
SFTS	Service Flying Training School
SOC	Struck off charge
SofAN	School of Air Navigation
SofP	School of Photography
SofTT	School of Technical Training
Sqdn	Squadron
SS	Signals School
SS	Salvage Section
SS	Storage Section (RN)
SS	Steamship
Stn Flt	Station Flight
Sub Lt	Sub Lieutenant
TAG	Telegraphist Air Gunner (RN)
TEU	Tactical Exercise Unit
TFPP	Training Ferry Pilots Pool (ATA)
TFP	Training Ferry Pool (ATA)
TFU	Telecommunications Flying Unit
TI	Trial installation
TOC	Taken on charge
TRE	Telecommunications Research Establishment
TSCU	Transport Support Conversion Unit
TSTU	Transport Support Training Unit
TT	Target Tower
TTC	Technical Training Command
TTF	Target Towing Flight/Towed Target Flight
TU&RP	Training Unit & Reserve Pool
u/c	Undercarriage
UP	Universal Projectile (rocket)
USAAC	United States Army Air Corps
USAAF	United States Army Air Force
WDCF/U	Western Desert Communication Flight/Unit
Wef	With effect from
WFU	Withdrawn from use
Wg	Wing
W/Cdr	Wing Commander
WO	Warrant Officer
2nd TAF	2nd Tactical Air Force

RAF - Damage Categories

Pre-1941

Cat.U	Undamaged
Cat.M(u)	Repairable on site by unit
Cat.M(c)	Repair beyond unit capacity
Cat. R(b)	Beyond repair on site
Cat.W	Write-off

1941-1952

Cat. U	Undamaged
Cat.A	Repairable on site by unit
Cat.Ac	Repair beyond unit capacity
Cat.B	Beyond repair on site
Cat.C	Ground Instructional Airframe
Cat. E	Write-off
Cat.E1	Components (R.T.S.)
Cat.E2	Scrap
Cat.Em	Missing on sortie (after 28 days)

Registration & Serial or C/n Cross-Reference

RAF/RN Serials

N7408-N8081	M.9B/C Master I	
N9003-N9017	M.9C Master I	
R1810-R1984	M.14A Magister	
T8268-T8885	M.9C Master I	
T8886-T9037	M.19 Master II	
T9669-T9982	M.14A Magister	
V1003-V1102	M.14A Magister	
W8437-W9003	M.27 Master III	
W9004-W9099	M.19 Master II	
AX834	M.20/2	
AZ104-AZ856	M.19 Master II	
DK798-DK994	M.19 Master II	
DL111-DL546	M.19 Master II	
DL552-DL793	M.27 Master III	
DL794-DL983	M.19 Master II	
DM108-DM454	M.19 Master II	
DM455-DM581	M.19 Master II [Cancelled]	
DR616	M.20/4	
EM258-EM409	M.19 Master II	
EM410-EM716	M.25 Martinet TT.1	
HM583	M.28 Mk.II	
HN861-HN984	M.25 Martinet TT.1	
HP114-HP528	M.25 Martinet TT.1	
JN273-JN682	M.25 Martinet TT.1	
LR241 & LR244	M.25 Martinet TT.1	
MS499-MS931	M.25 Martinet TT.1	
NF900 & NF904	M.33 Monitor TT.1	
NP406-NP425	M.33 Monitor TT.1	
NP426-NP660	M.33 Monitor TT.1 [Cancelled]	
NR293-NR666	M.25 Martinet TT.1	
PW937	M.28 Mk.III	
PW947-PW988	M.25 Martinet TT.1	
PX101-PX198	M.25 Martinet TT.1	
RG327 & RG333	M.38 Messenger I	
RG882-RG997	M.25 Martinet TT.1	
RH113-RH121	M.25 Martinet TT.1	
RH122-RH192	M.50 Queen Martinet	
RH193-RH365	M.50 Queen Martinet [Cancelled]	
RH368-RH378	M.38 Messenger I	
RH379-RH409	M.38 Messenger I [Cancelled]	
RH420--RH429	M.38 Messenger I	
RH430-RH680	M.38 Messenger I [Cancelled]	
SR392	M.39B	
SV739-SV999	M.33 Monitor TT.II [Cancelled]	
SW113-SW240	M.33 Monitor TT.II [Cancelled]	
VF100-VF110	M.50 Queen Martinet	
VF111-VF133	M.50 Queen Martinet [Cancelled]	

Civil Registrations

G-AGEK	M.27	DL670
G-AGEO	M.14A	2022
G-AGOY	M.38	4690
G-AGPX	M.38	6266
G-AGUW	M.38	6267
G-AGVX	M.28	4685
G-AHAA	M.28	6268
G-AHKP	M.14A	1832
G-AHNE	M.14A	2170
G-AHNU	M.14A	2033
G-AHNV	M.14A	1949
G-AHNW	M.14A	1921
G-AHOB	M.19	T8886 (6434)
G-AHUJ	M.14A	1900
G-AHUK	M.14A	1959
G-AHYL	M.14A	2071
G-AHYM	M.14A	2085
G-AICE	M.14A	2049
G-AIOJ	M.14A	2105
G-AIOK	M.14A	2148
G-AISH	M.28	4684
G-AITN	M.14A	1826
G-AITO	M.14A	1842
G-AITS	M.14A	1997
G-AITW	M.14A	1884
G-AITX	M.14A	1843
G-AIUA	M.14A	2035
G-AIYB	M.14A	1840
G-AIYC	M.14A	2087
G-AIYD	M.14A	2132
G-AIZM	M.19	EM300
G-AIZN	M.19	DM442
G-AJCM	M.14A	1934
G-AJDF	M.38	RH370
G-AJDR	M.14A	2169
G-AJFE	M.28	6697
G-AJGK	M.14A	1941
G-AJGL	M.14A	1933
G-AJGP	M.14A	1979
G-AJHA	M.14A	1972
G-AJHF	M.14A	2081
G-AJHG	M.14A	1984
G-AJJI	M.14A	1985
G-AJJK	M.25	HP145
G-AJJL	M.25	EM646
G-AJJO	M.25	HN913
G-AJSF	M.14A	1932
G-AJVX	M.28	HM583
G-AJZB	M.25	MS836
G-AJZC	M.25	MS871
G-AKAS	M.14A	1971
G-AKAT	M.14A	2005
G-AKAU	M.14A	1947
G-AKGR	M.14A	1982
G-AKKR	M.14A	1995
G-AKKX	M.14A	2039
G-AKKY	M.14A	2078
G-AKKZ	M.14A	2227
G-AKMR	M.14A	1820
G-AKMY	M.14A	2191
G-AKOS	M.37	JN668
G-AKPF	M.14A	2228
G-AKRJ	M.14A	1862
G-AKRK	M.14A	1860
G-AKRL	M.14A	2042
G-AKRM	M.14A	2104
G-AKRT	M.14A	2100
G-AKRU	M.14A	1874
G-AKRV	M.14A	2113
G-AKVZ	M.38	RH427
G-AKZC	M.38	RH372
G-AKZU	M.38	RH369
G-AKZX	M.38	RH424
G-ALAC	M.38	RH420
G-ALAE	M.38	RH421
G-ALAF	M.38	RH425
G-ALAG	M.38	RH422
G-ALAH	M.38	RH377
G-ALAI	M.38	RH423
G-ALAJ	M.38	RH429
G-ALAP	M.38	RH368
G-ALAR	M.38	RH371
G-ALAV	M.38	RH428
G-ALAW	M.38	RH426
G-ALBE	M.38	RG327
G-ALBP	M.38	RH376
G-ALBR	M.38	RH378
G-ALFE	M.14A	2239
G-ALFH	M.14A	2063
G-ALFI	M.14A	2110
G-ALGJ	M.14A	2106
G-ALGZ	M.14A	2150
G-ALHA	M.14A	1879
G-ALIN	M.14A	2027
G-ALIP	M.14A	1825
G-ALOH	M.14A	2025
G-AMBO	M.14A	1956
CS-AFI	M.14A	2052
D-EHAB	M.28	6268
EI-AGE	M.38	4690
F-AZOR	M.14A	2005
F-BDPI	M.14A	2041
F-BDPN	M.14A	1848
F-BGOM	M.38	RH369
F-BGQZ	M.38	RH422
F-OAPJ	M.14A	2049
HB-EED	M.28	4685
HB-EEF	M.28	6697
HB-EIP	M.38	4690
LV-XMD	M.14A	2061
LV-XMG	M.14A	1981
LV-XMJ	M.14A	1834
LV-XML	M.14A	2075
LV-XMX	M.14A	1958
LV-XOX	M.14A	2056
LV-XOZ	M.14A	2127
LV-XPE	M.14A	2008
LV-XPF	M.14A	2084
LV-XPJ	M.14A	1881
LV-XPQ	M.14A	1977
LV-XPY	M.14A	2077
LV-XPZ	M.14A	1816
LV-XQG	M.14A	1991
LV-XQM	M.14A	1999
LV-XQR	M.14A	1889
LV-XQS	M.14A	1811
LV-XQW	M.14A	2036
LV-XQZ	M.14A	1829
LV-XRH	M.14A	2065
LV-XRJ	M.14A	1962
LV-XRM	M.14A	2047
LV-XRN	M.14A	2062
LV-XRS	M.14A	1847
LV-XRV	M.14A	1957
LV-XRW	M.14A	1953
LV-XRY	M.14A	2128
LV-XSL	M.14A	2059
LV-XSN	M.14A	1929
LV-XSO	M.14A	1822
LV-XSQ	M.14A	1858
LV-XST	M.14A	1882
LV-XSU	M.14A	1961
OO-CCM	M.38	6267
OO-NIC	M.14A	2037
OO-PAB	M.14A	2042
OY-ABI	M.14A	2026
OY-ALW	M.28	6268
OY-DNI	M.14A	1946
SE-AZC	M.25	EM546
SE-AZD	M.25	NR471
SE-AZE	M.25	NR469
SE-AZF	M.25	EM629
SE-AZG	M.25	EM592
SE-BCI	M.25	EM640
SE-BCN	M.25	HN913
SE-BCO	M.25	EM646
SE-BCP	M.25	HP145
SE-CGF	M.14A	2026
TF-REX	M.14A	1979
TF-SHC	M.25	MS902
VH-AKC	M.28	4685
VH-AKH	M.28	4685
VH-BBK	M.28	HM583
VH-KCH	M.28	HM583
VH-PMG	M.28	HM583
VH-WYN	M.38	RH376
VP-KJL	M.38	RH371
VP-KNW	M.14A	2113
ZK-ATE	M.14A	2105
ZK-BBA	M.14A	2170
ZK-BED	M.38	RH425

Chile

M.14A	2057; 2125; 2188	

B Conditions Identities

U-0223	M.28/38	unknown
U-0228	M.20/4	DR616
U-0232	M.28	unknown
U-0233	M.30	unknown
U-0235	M.35	unknown
U-0237	M.28	HM583
U-0242	M.28	4684
U-0243	M.28	4685
U-0244	M.39B	unknown
U-0245	M.38	RH368
U-0246	M.19	T8886
U-0247	M.38	4690
U-0254	M.14A	2061
U-0255	M.14A	2125
U-0256	M.14A	2057
U-0257	M.14A	1836
U-0258	M.14A	1818
U-0269	M.14A	2188
U-0273	M.38	6266
U-0274	M.38	6267
U5	M.19	T8886 (6434)
U9	M.20/2	AX834
G-2-1	M.38	RH420

Foreign Military Sales

Belgian Air Force

DMT-50	M.14A	2037
TMR-50	M.14A	2037
G.1	M.14A	2037
R.1	M.25	MS856
R.2	M.25	MS815
R.3	M.25	EM521
R.4	M.25	EM683
R.5	M.25	HP415
R.6	M.25	MS773
R.7	M.25	NR441
R.8	M.25	NR422
R.9	M.25	NR297
R.10	M.25	JN539
R.11	M.25	NR650

Egyptian Air Force
M.14As – 1843; 1884; 1933; 1941
M.19s – see Appendix

France (Armée de l'Air)
M.19s – AZ520; AZ529; AZ642;
    AZ696; AZ774; AZ778; AZ813;
    DK804; DK956; DL187;
    DL289; DL339; DL411; DL455;
    DL861; Dl895; DL980; DM110;
    DM178; DM185; DM189;
    DM194; DM201; DM230;
    DM263; DM338; DM355;
    DM429; DM451; EM404
M.25s: EM474; EM553; EM630;
    EM648; EM661; EM679;
    EM712; EM713; HN975;
    HP316; HP440; HP471; MS797;
    MS798; MS799; MS800;
    MS851; MS907; MS909;
    MS926; NR316; NR321;
    NR322; NR324; NR356;
    NR357; NR367; NR368;
    NR369; NR386; NR417;
    NR420; NR439; NR468;
    NR470; NR484; NR487;
    NR528; NR583; NR586

Irish Air Corps

97	M.19	DM260
98	M.19	W9028
99	M.19	DM258
100	M.19	DL352
101	M.19	AZ741
102	M.19	DM261
121	M.19	DL194
122	M.19	DK835
123	M.19	DK934
124	M.19	DM220
125	M.19	DL408
126	M.19	AZ250
128	M.14A	1827
129	M.14A	2000
132	M.14A	2044
133	M.14A	2242
134	M.14A	2189
135	M.14A	2040
136	MS.14A	2247
138	M.14A	1835

Portugal

195	M.14A	2086
196	M.14A	2038
197	M.14A	2052
1206	M.14A	2086
1207	M.14A	2038
1208	M.14A	2052

M.19s – see Appendix
M.25s – see Appendix
M.27s – see Appendix

Siam (Thai) Air Force
M.14As – 1854; 1887; 1899; 1908;
    1954; 1973; 1976; 2011; 2028;
    2046

South Africa
M.19s – see Appendix

Turkey
M.19s – see Appendix

Ground Instruction Airframes

2517M	M.14A	R1843
2551M	M.9B	N7410
2791M	M.9B	N7569
2878M	M.9C	T8462
3127M	M.19	AZ104
3160M	M.9C	N8051
3301M	M.9C	N7994
3460M	M.9C	N7815
3643M	M.9C	T8271
3644M	M.9C	T8495
3646M	M.9C	N7938
3648M	M.9B	N7603
3661M	M.9C	N8012
3662M	M.9C	T8549
3663M	M.25	HP381
3670M	M.9C	T8433
3671M	M.9C	T8567
3673M	M.9C	T8319
3675M	M.9C	T8842
3755M	M.9B	N7455
3756M	M.9C	N7751
3757M	M.9B	N7499
3765M	M.9B	N7573
3811M	M.9C	N7701
3818M	M.9B	N7478
3819M	M.9C	N9005
3820M	M.9B	N7541
3821M	M.9C	N7687
3822M	M.9B	N7623
3823M	M.9C	N7503
3831M	M.9C	N9004
3836M	M.9C	T8276
3837M	M.9C	T8279
3868M	M.9B	N7534
3869M	M.9B	N7682
3870M	M.9B	N7599
3991M	M.27	W8905
4079M	M.19	DL372
4080M	M.19	DL462
4089M	M.9B	N7536
4091M	M.27	W8774
4096M	M.14A	R1849
4117M	M.9C	N7817
4123M	M.14A	V1017
4128M	M.9C	N7781
4156M	M.9C	N7820
4157M	M.9C	N7814
4158M	M.9C	N7803
4159M	M.9C	N7804
4160M	M.9C	N7810
4161M	M.9C	N7811
4162M	M.9C	N7821
4163M	M.9C	T8544
4164M	M.9C	N7809
4254M	M.19	DL542
4255M	M.19	DL461
		(DL483)
4318M	M.14A	R1980
4334M	M.9C	N7768
4335M	M.9C	N7829
4357M	M.27	W8449
4358M	M.27	W8532
4367M	M.14A	V1087
4463M	M.9C	T8462
4475M	M.14A	T9836
4482M	M.9C	T8601
4483M	M.14A	R1855
4491M	M.27	W8653
4492M	M.27	W8955
4493M	M.27	W8946
4512M	M.14A	T9894
4514M	M.14A	R1823
4542M	M.27	W8884
4543M	M.27	DL614
4544M	M.27	W8956
4545M	M.27	W8654
4549M	M.14A	T9681
4556M	M.14A	V1092
4601M	M.9B	N7605
4658M	M.27	DL617
4676M	M.14A	R1908
4769M	M.14A	T9913
4897M	M.27	W8928
5365M	M.14A	V1099
5437M	M.19	DM215
5438M	M.19	DK967
5474M	M.19	DL842
5475M	M.19	W9088
5476M	M.19	DM401
5547M	M.19	DL409
5548M	M.19	AZ847
5549M	M.19	AZ853
5550M	M.19	DL526
5587M	M.19	AZ499
5672M	M.19	DL222
5673M	M.19	DK969
5715M	M.19	DL421
5772M	M.19	DM387
5775M	M.25	JN489
5776M	M.25	EM545
5777M	M.25	HP255
5796M	M.25	HP249
5822M	M.25	EM530
5944M	M.25	EM389
6009M	M.25	HP495
6181M	M.19	EM331
6194M	M.19	DM395
6238M	M.19	DM449
6239M	M.19	DM353
6240M	M.19	AZ785
6543M	M.14A	T9979
6912M	M.25	NR465
6925M	M.25	JN543
6926M	M.25	HP218
6927M	M.25	NR636
6941M	M.25	EM444
6942M	M.25	MS908
8378M	M.14A	T9708

A Selected Bibliography

Aeronaves Militares Portuguesas no Seculo XX	Adelino Cardoso (Essencial 2000)
Aviation in Doncaster 1909-1992	Geoffrey Oakes (GH Oakes 1995)
Blossom – Biography of Mrs F G Miles	Jean M Fostekew (Cirrus Associates 1998)
Book of Miles Aircraft (The)	A H Lukins (Harborough 1946)
British Aircraft (vols 1 & 2)	R A Savile-Sneath (Penguin 1944)
British Aircraft Specifications File	Ken Meekcoms & Eric Morgan (Air-Britain 1994)
British Secret Projects – Fighters & Bombers 1935-1950	Tony Buttler (Midland Publishing 2004)
Fleet Air Arm Aircraft 1939 to 1945	Ray Sturtivant & Mick Burrow (Air-Britain 1995)
History of Britain's Military Training Aircraft (The)	Ray Sturtivant (Haynes 1987)
Les Avions Britanniques aux Couleurs Francaises	Jean-Jacques Petit (Avia Editions 2003)
Long Drag (The) – History of British Target Towing	Don Evans (Flight Recorder 2004)
Miles Aircraft – The Early Years	Peter Amos (Air-Britain 2009)
Miles Aircraft since 1925	Don L Brown (Putnam 1970)
Miles Magister	Graham H R Johnson (Newark Museum 1975)
Milestones (3 volumes)	Don L Brown (Miles Aircraft 1944-46)
RAF Flying Training & Support Units since 1912	Ray Sturtivant & John Hamlin (Air-Britain 2007)
Secret Years (The) – Flight Testing at Boscombe Down 1939-45	Tim Mason (Hikoki 2010)
Spitfires e Hurricanes em Portugal	Mario Canongia Lopes (Dinalivro 1992)
Squadrons of the RAF & Commonwealth 1918-1988	James J Halley (Air-Britain 1988)
Testing for Combat	Capt Eric Brown (Airlife 1994)
UK Flight Testing Accidents 1940-71	Derek Collier Webb (Air-Britain 2002)
Wings over Woodley	Julian C Temple (Aston Publications 1987)
Yellow Wings – Joint Air Training Scheme	Dave Becker (SAAF Museum 1989)

Index

(Due to space constraints, this index focuses on named individuals, important references and key contents & events)

Chapter 1 (below)

Bert Clarke recalled that Harry Hull regularly used to escape the pressures of work for a few minutes by cycling to the canteen, which Bert's mother and father ran, for a well-earned cup of tea, whilst also using his 'ladies' bicycle to travel at great speed around the works so as to keep up with everything! This is that canteen, which was at Woodley from the early 1930s and which Bert later rescued for use as his garden shed, in his home at Caversham. This photograph was taken shortly after Bert's death in 2006. [Peter Amos]

Chapter 4 (right and below)

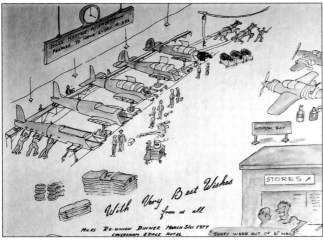

A cartoon depicting Miles Masters on the moving assembly line at Woodley, presented at the Miles Re-union Dinner, held on March 31st 1977, at the Caversham Bridge Hotel, Berkshire.

[via Jim Pratt]

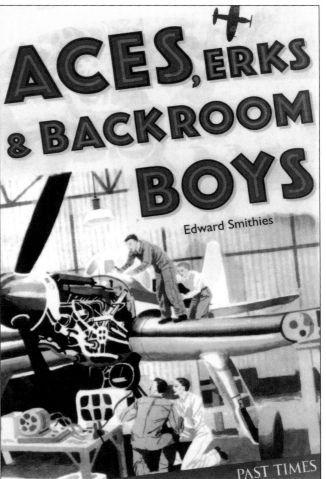

The front cover from the book 'Aces, Erks & Backroom Boys', by Edward Smithies (Past Times), depicting a Miles Master Mk.I on the final assembly line at Woodley in 1940.

Chapter 4 (continued, below)

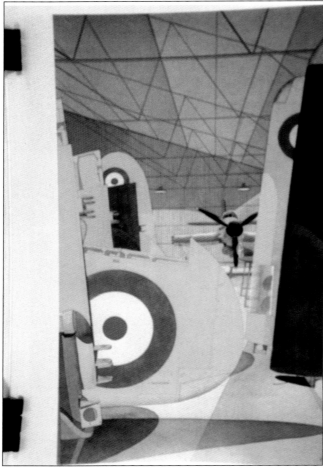

A print from a watercolour painting, by Raymond McGrath, entitled 'Hangar 1940' (from 'Colours of war' (Jonathan Cape 1983), showing Master Mk.Is on the assembly line at Woodley.

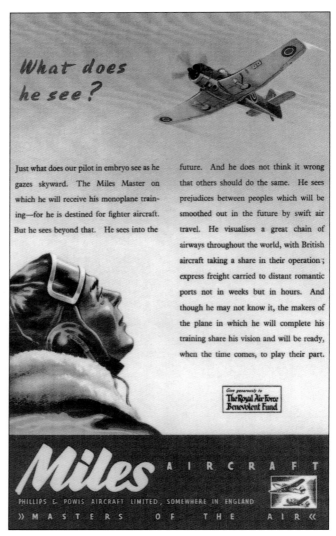

What does he see?

Just what does our pilot in embryo see as he gazes skyward. The Miles Master on which he will receive his monoplane training—for he is destined for fighter aircraft. But he sees beyond that. He sees into the future. And he does not think it wrong that others should do the same. He sees prejudices between peoples which will be smoothed out in the future by swift air travel. He visualises a great chain of airways throughout the world, with British aircraft taking a share in their operation; express freight carried to distant romantic ports not in weeks but in hours. And though he may not know it, the makers of the plane in which he will complete his training share his vision and will be ready, when the time comes, to play their part.

Give generously to
The Royal Air Force Benevolent Fund

Miles AIRCRAFT
PHILLIPS & POWIS AIRCRAFT LIMITED, SOMEWHERE IN ENGLAND
» MASTERS OF THE AIR «

An advertisement from 'Country Life' magazine for 30th April 1943, cleverly foreseeing the future.

Chapter 6 (above right and below)

Miles Master Mk.III, W8667, '3' of 5 FTS Ternhill. Note: it still retains the original full span wings. Delivered to 5 FTS 1.10.41, SOC Cat.E1 (MR) 6.3.42.

Chapter 24

Above: This superb photograph, taken from a 16 mm colour cine film, probably depicts the first engine run on the prototype Miles M.33 Monitor, NF900.

These two, photographs taken from a 16 mm colour cine film, probably depict the prototype Monitor, NF900, taxying out to take-off on its first flight.

Chapter 24 (continued)

Continuing the sequence from page III, this photograph, also taken from a 16 mm colour cine film, probably shows prototype Monitor, NF900, taking off on its first flight.

Chapter 29

Above: A painting, by Les Vowles, depicting U-0245, the prototype Miles Messenger, in June 1944, soon after D-day, being flown by F/O Trevor Martin, Gen B Montgomery's personal pilot, with the General sitting alongside him.

Left: General Bernard Montgomery standing alongside RH326 (previously U-0245), his first Messenger.

Right: The badge of the 21st Army Corps which was painted on the cowling of Montgomery's Messengers.

Chapter 29 (continued)

Left: The cover of the book 'identification FRIEND OR FOE', by Tim Hamilton, showing an Oddentification, by Wren, of Montgomery's Messenger.

Below: Montgomery's personal pilot, Trevor Martin, signing copies of Les Vowles' painting at the Air-Britain Fly-in at Wellesbourne Mountford on 23rd June 1996.

Chapter 49

The very realistic, complete, mock-up of the Miles M.52 in the Experimental Department at Woodley on 27th November 1945.

[Matthew Nathan]

Chapter 49 (continued)

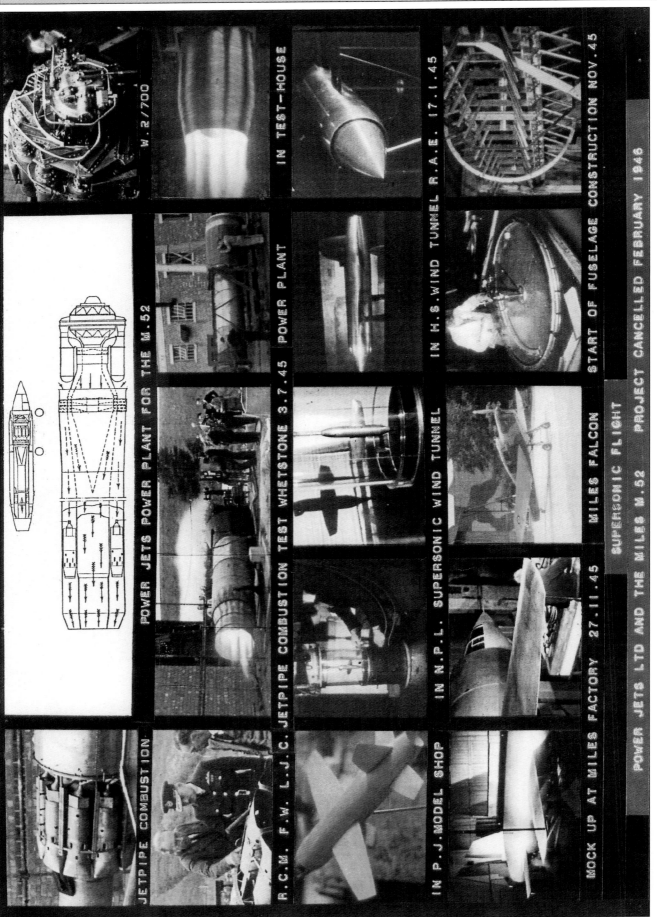

Supersonic Flight - Power Jets Ltd and the Miles M.52. A montage of photographs taken by Matthew Nathan of Power Jets Ltd.

Appendix 9

The Miles M.14A Hawk Trainer Mk.III G-AKAT 'Skylark' (previously Magister T9738), with the Wolverhampton Flying Club.   *[Dave Welch]*

Appendix 11

Magister TC-KAY of the Hürkanatlar Civilian Flying Club in 1969. It is now in the Air Force Museum.   *[Ole Nikolajsen Archive]*

The 'pattern' Magister seen here after modification to a single-seat sprayer.   *[Ole Nikolajsen Archive]*

Appendix 11 (continued)

TC-KAI (previously TC-UGUR), the Ugur prototype, with Hürkanatlar Flying Club.   *[Ole Nikolajsen Archive]*

TC-KAI Ugur prototype survived until about 1970, to probably make it the longest-lived Ugur/Magister variant.   *[Ole Nikolajsen Archive]*

Believed to be one of only two colour photographs of a Turkish Air Force Ugur to have survived.   *[Ole Nikolajsen Archive]*

Appendix 11 (continued)

The second colour photograph shows the last batch of Ugurs in front of the MKEK (ex THK) factory at Etimesgut, awaiting handover to the Turkish Air Force.   *[Ole Nikolajsen Archive]*

Appendix 17

Miles Master Mk.II, 2636, of the SAAF, being cleaned at Waterkloof (Zwartkop) in 1.43.   *[IWM 24GP]*

MILES AIRCRAFT – THE WARTIME YEARS – 1939-1945

Appendix 18

■MILES MASTER NA ARMA DE AERONÁUTICA DO EXÉRCITO

MILES MASTER
NA ARMA DE AERONÁUTICA DO EXÉRCITO

TEXTO: Dr. José Manuel Correia

O aspirante Jorge Brochado de Miranda preparado para mais uma saída em Master II, durante o tirocínio na BA1 em Julho de 1948

No final dos anos 30, com as suas esquadrilhas de caça equipadas com Gloster Gladiator, o Ministério da Guerra – na altura titulado por Oliveira Salazar, em acumulação com a Presidência dos Conselho de Ministros – procurava com denodo reforçar a defesa aérea da Nação face ao avolumar de perspectivas de um conflito militar que poderia saldar-se por um ataque ao território continental.

As visitas efectuadas a Inglaterra por missões militares lusas saldaram-se pelo fornecimento, no último trimestre de 1940, não dos desejados Spitfire Mk I, mas de uma esquadrilha de Curtiss Mohawk IV. Na altura em que Portugal formalizava o seu interesse pêlos Spitfire, o Air Ministry encarava a possibilidade de fornecer pelo menos um Miles Master para treino avançado em caças monoplanos.

Assim, não é de estranhar que, em Outubro de 1941, a Grã-Bretanha concretizasse a sua promessa, entregando os dois primeiros

The front cover from Portuguese Aviation Magazine Mais Alto (the magazine of the FAP) for July/August 2006, which carried an article on the Miles Master, by Dr José Manuel Carreia. [via Luis Tavares]

Appendix 24

HN862, the second production Martinet, being test flown by chief test pilot Tommy Rose in July 1942.   *[Charles E Brown]*

Appendix 29

Messenger G-ALAI (previously RH423) at Lasham in 1963.   *[Dave Welch]*

Messenger G-ALAW (previously RH426) at an unrecorded location.   *[via Peter Amos]*

Appendix 29 (continued)

Messenger G-AKVZ (previously RH427) at Henstridge.

Appendix 42

The remains of TF-SHC being recovered from the farm on 7.7.79.   *[Jon Karl Snorrason via Douglas A Rough]*

Appendix 42 (continued)

The remains of TF-SHC on the flat-rack container on the quayside at Reykjavik docks awaiting loading.   *[Douglas A Rough]*

Appendix 42 (continued)

Left: EIMSKIP's container ship MV Bruarfoss alongside at Reykjavik docks on 20.3.96 prior to her departure for Immingham, Lincs later the same day.
[Ragnar Ragnarsson via Douglas A Rough]

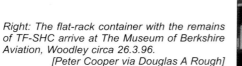

Right: The flat-rack container with the remains of TF-SHC arrive at The Museum of Berkshire Aviation, Woodley circa 26.3.96.
[Peter Cooper via Douglas A Rough]

In early April 1996 the assorted remains of TF-SHC were arrayed against the hangar wall of The Museum of Berkshire Aviation. Note the wing from a Master Mk.II against the wall and the Icelandic flag on the hangar door.
[Douglas A Rough]

Appendix 42 (continued)

Above: Great progress had been made on the Martinet's reconstruction by 24.5.03, when this photograph was taken, including a fully functioning undercarriage. At this stage the cockpit internals and instruments have been mostly installed as per the original. The newly built tailplane can be seen on the left and the new rudder is propped against the hangar door.   *[Douglas A Rough]*

The photograph above shows the Martinet TF-SHC nearly complete but awaiting engine and outer wings in The Museum of Berkshire Aviation in 2012.   *[Douglas A Rough]*

Appendix 46 (below)

Pygmy Power - the Miles Electric Actuator.

Appendix 43

On this page are four photographs of the Whittle W.2/700 jet engine which was to have powered the Miles M.52.   [Jim Pratt]